THE 101 WORLD'S CLASSICS

Edited by

CHARLES GRAY SHAW, Ph.D.

HEAD OF THE GRADUATE SCHOOL
PROFESSOR OF PHILOSOPHY
NEW YORK UNIVERSITY

THE LITERARY GUILD OF AMERICA, INC.

New York   *1937*

PRINTED AT THE *Country Life Press*, GARDEN CITY, N. Y., U. S. A.

CONTENTS

I. NOVELS

[v]

CONTENTS

II. TALES

[vi]

CONTENTS

IV. SCIENCE AND CIVILIZATION

V. PLAYS

CONTENTS

VI. BELLES LETTRES

VII. PHILOSOPHY AND RELIGION

CONTENTS

ACKNOWLEDGMENT

The editor wishes to make grateful acknowledgment for permission to use copyrighted material, as follows:

To Harper & Brothers, New York and London, for *The Adventures of Tom Sawyer,* by Mark Twain.

To Charles Scribner's Sons, for *Peer Gynt* by Ibsen.

To The Macmillan Company, for *La Gioconda,* from *The Renaissance,* by Walter Pater.

To D. C. Heath and Company, for *How We Think,* by John Dewey.

To Henry Holt and Company, for *Creative Evolution,* by Bergson, translated by Mitchell.

To Brandt and Brandt, and Alfred A. Knopf, for *Decline of the West,* by Oswald Spengler.

TO THE READER

HAVE YOU ever asked yourself what kind of books you really like? Have you cultivated such a taste for literature that when you recommend a work your friends know that such a book is worth reading? Or do you feel that your sense of taste needs some cultivation as your form in golf or tennis needs practice? Are you so sure of your literary opinions that you know just what works should be placed on the ideal "five-foot shelf?"

You read your newspaper morning and evening to get the spot-news, foreign cables, market-quotations, editorials and columns. You have your favorite magazines with their news-digests, short stories and essays. You know the best sellers, fiction and non-fiction, and may have helped swell the number of sales by your purchases. Then in the persistent literature of the past, you may have your pet novelist, poet or philosopher, Dickens, Tennyson, Montaigne.

But it is possible that your stock of literature stands in need of revision and reorganization. In it there may be gaps to be filled, replacements to be made and appraisals to be re-valued. Your books are supposed to be a part of you. They are meant to do more than fill the present hour; they are intended to relate you to life and your present to the past in that long historical continuum of which you are a part.

It is possible that at times you may have felt embarrassed by your lack of adequate, well-ordered knowledge of the world's literature. Perhaps in talking with a clever person whose graces you would cultivate you could not follow him in his references to classic works. He may have likened some disgruntled person to Achilles sulking in his tent, or in a joking mood have exclaimed, "O that this too too solid ice would melt," or expressed the wish to be "far from the madding crowd," or said, "O that my enemy would write a book," or made some reference to "the eternally feminine," *laissez faire* and the class-struggle. Expressions of this sort are likely to come up when you are talking to superior people or reading clever writers. What are you to do?

You do not need to possess this present volume to be a capable, cultured person, but you do need to be in possession of what this volume contains. One may be well informed and, like the mythical "man about town," know what is going on in the world, but to be a person whom people will take seriously one must be familiar with the books that have been talked about and referred to for centuries. Easy familiarity with the classics is calculated to bring out charm, and the person who has that can command attention without resorting to the abominable "say, listen" of cheap conversation. Now this doesn't mean that you must embellish your conversation with phrases like, "as Shakespeare has well said," or "as Browning puts it," or "as the Latin expression has it." Such things are banal and boresome. Yet the person who is at home in the classics will reveal that august fact by his choice of words and the way he turns a phrase. Although his conversation will be "plain English" it will be just as plain that he is talking by note and not by ear.

To converse well one must be conversant with the best that has been said in the past, and this past must be brought up to date. The intellectual demands made upon us today are different from those made in the previous century, or even before the World War. In the earlier period, it was sufficient to be familiar with polite literature, the conventional novel of manners and characters and the science in which things were given once for all. That was the closed season of literature, or what might be called the "horse-and-buggy" period of letters. Life moved languidly and the range of one's reading was correspondingly limited. The world of that era was a settled one in which everything that could happen had happened so that everything could be taken for granted. Nobody had glands or complexes; if they did have, these psychophysical things did not make their presence obtrusive. The present work would not for a moment ignore that tranquil period nor fail "to cast one longing, lingering look behind" toward the Victorian scene. It would simply extend the idea that English island-literature and that of New England which imitated it is about all the cultured person needs to know. The age of the "gentle reader" is gone and that of the robust reader come. Now what is the thing called literature?

Literature is the verbal expression of life as it is lived by human beings; it is life in so many words. As our mode of existence changes our manner of expression changes with it. This is now the open season of the human race so that whatever is said, however grim, and whatever is done, however ghastly, in the uttermost parts of the earth is bound to be part if not parcel of our own mental lives. The newspapers will have it so. They ransack the whole earth, aye, the whole galaxy in which we live and peep into giant nebulas beyond our ken to tell us what's really going on in the universe. Their startling reports are echoed over the radio and reviewed in the weekly magazines, those trailers of the daily papers. Should not our minds have the same range as our eyes and ears? Should we not consider what we see and hear and thus get in solid volumes what is flashed on flimsy news-print paper and flung out on the thin air? There may be some permanent ideas in all these fleeting impressions. Are you able to grasp them?

In keeping up with the times in this stream-lined age, the thoughtful reader is helped by various "digests" which the public has come to require as first aids to its knowledge. The public is persuaded that it should know a little something about almost everything, hence it seizes upon the paper-covered things that give much in little. Our range of interests is wide and we are well served by these little hand-books of contemporary fiction and drama. But we may take what we call a "deep interest" in literature and thus may need something that will go into the third or even the fourth dimension of life. Sometimes we are satisfied merely to scratch the surface of life; occasionally we want to go into it to the very hilt. The flower of contemporary civilization is at least interesting to observe; its fruit, while sometimes bitter, appeals to our robust sense of taste. But where shall we find the tangled roots, where the gnarled trunk of that which we call history, or human life as it was and as it has become?

The trunks of literature are to be found in the classics; out of these our best sellers and most successful plays branch. We demand something more than that which rustles in the present, for we cannot go on living merely by reading the newspapers or listening in on the radio. Unless they have depth of earth our minds soon wither. It is our tendency, is it not? to expect a quick turn-over in our mental merchandise. We want to see at a glance and learn without delay. Give us but an inkling of an idea and we are likely to call it "all right." Let us look into some plan or project and we conclude that "it will do." But just how much that is said is really all right, and just how much that is being done will really do? If we are to escape superficiality in thought and deed, we must have some historical knowledge; then when an idea is put forth we shall know whether to believe it or not and when some exigency arises we shall know whether it can or cannot happen here. How can we know?

We must give life and its literature a "knowing look." Now some conception of the past can be gathered from the literature of the ages, for every age has at least one spokesman and even in the wilderness a voice may be heard crying out. It is for us to discover these prophets and learn what they had to say for themselves and their age. How is this to be done? We might get a history of literature and survey the whole field, and in many ways this would prove fruitful. But after all that would amount to little more than looking over the map of the country we wish to visit and the results might be rather scant and skeletal. It is wiser to take a typical work of a typical author and get a definite amount of knowledge in the form of nucleus or nugget, just as it is better to visit famous cities than to have a general idea of the world at large. What does such selective, intensive reading require; vast erudition?

Selective, intensive reading requires taste. You may be more inclined to think it requires "brains" and may imagine that to pore over a classic story is like solving a mathematical problem or a cross-word puzzle. Taste is just as superior but not so severe; it is rational emotion. Like the true poet, as described by Wordsworth, the person with taste is one who "surveys the spectacle of life with appropriate emotions." The office of taste is to keep you from going by fits of feeling and starts of sentiment. You may imagine that you know what you like but that is quite improbable, since we know as little about our likes and dislikes as we know about our dreams and nightmares. We are required to study our

TO THE READER

hearts as well as our minds and train our emotions as well as our thoughts in order that we may come to an understanding with ourselves. Then we can tell what we like to read. The "reading matter" sold at the railway news-stand or peddled on the train may be a more acceptable means of killing time en route than anything to be found in the present volume, but you throw it away when you reach your destination. Now a classic work is one which the men of the past refused to throw away.

You cannot decide for your sense of taste; your sense of taste decides for you. A vigorous, independent person may insist that he has as much right to choose the "snappy story" in place of Dickens, the daily journalistic jingle rather than Keats' *Ode on a Grecian Urn*. He does indeed have that "right" and the court might uphold him in it, but the present question is not a juristic one; it is an aesthetic question of tastes, not of rights. The same self-asserting individual may further claim that he likes what he likes in matters of both reading matter and food, and may suspect that like spinach a classic work is nourishing but unpalatable. But we know that even in such arbitrary matters as those of the palate it is necessary to have the tea-taster and other experts to determine the proper blend, and what one really does like is that which the chef has prepared according to the most approved culinary standard. Such experts know that you will like the kind of dish or beverage they set before you. Is not something of this sort true in connection with approved works of literature?

"A word fitly spoken," said the wise man, "is as apples of gold in pictures of silver." In a classic work you have just such apples of gold in the silver picture of the fitly spoken word. It is this that really appeals to you. Perhaps you are not aware of it, but you like Homer and Sophocles, Dante and Milton, Shakespeare and Cervantes, Wordsworth and Goethe, Ibsen and Nietzsche. You may think your mind is satisfied with the daily philosophy of the newspaper-Socrates whose ideas are featured in your favorite evening paper, but your real longing is for Plato and Kant, for Schopenhauer and Bergson. You may think that you prefer to loiter in the lowlands of literature when you feel in your bones the desire to ascend the mountains of classic works whose summits, often sharp and icy, shine in a sunlight of their own.

[xvii]

Here as well as anywhere we might consider the business of getting substantial results from a classic work. We go at it impelled by personal interest, as though it were a treatise on Contract Bridge or a pamphlet on the Income Tax. Our desire is to play a better game, to get greater exemptions. You want to make some immortal work your own so that when reference is made to it you will not have to say, "I have read it but it was a long time ago." Instead of letting your mind down in that way you can say, if only to your most intimate friend or to yourself, "I know my *Hamlet,* my *Copperfield,* my *Vanity Fair,* my *Faust."* Your aim is to appreciate the work as though it were a painting or a symphony. You know that it is foolish to rejoice in mere familiarity with the titles of books, for that is little more than playing the old-fashioned Game of Authors. You will select something that appeals to you as worth while and dig into it. Then, book after book, you will read into the world's literature as though you were digging artesian wells deep down into the very sources of the literary streams.

Suppose we take *Hamlet* as an example. It is short, generally well known and of supreme interest. The scholar's interest will be in the sources of the dramatic story, and he will tell you that in some form or other it must have appeared in the gay nineties of the XVIth century, if not somewhat earlier. He would have you consider the famous First Quarto of 1603 to determine, if you can, whether it was from Shakespeare's own quill, or was a pirated work made up of short-hand notes taken down by some spy in the audience, or obtained by gaining access to the script used by the actors in the old Globe Theatre. But the historical facts in the case are not the same as the literary values and to ascertain the very, very source of *Hamlet* would be to satisfy historical curiosity, not to enhance aesthetic appreciation. You will realize that if you look into that First Quarto, which was by no means the original *Hamlet,* and read certain lines spoken by the hero—

> *To be, or not to be, I there's the point,*
> *To die, to sleepe, is that all? I all:*
> *No, to sleepe, to dreame, I mary there it goes,*
> *For in that dreame of death when wee awake,*

TO THE READER

And borne before an euerlasting Judge
From whence no passenger ever return'd,
The undiscouered country at whose sight
The happy smile, and the accursed damn'd.

Is this Hamlet, is this Shakespeare or this the famous soliloquy?

The professional Shakespearean would have you go in still deeper. He would bid you look into the *Hystorie of Hamblet* taken and translated from Belleforest's *Histories Tragiques* of 1570, but that would only take you back to the *Historia Danica* of the XIIth century, whence you would have to move backwards to Icelandic sagas and Roman myths. Then at least one special question of higher criticism would come up and, small as it is, it cannot escape the attention of the scholar. It comes up in this way—when the story went from French into English, the translator departed from the text he was following and made the English Hamlet, as he thrusts his sword through the arras at Polonius, cry, "A rat, a rat!" Where did that rat come from? If we knew, our curiosity on that point would be satisfied better than our literary appreciation of the world-drama.

To get his *Hamlet* one must read the play to the point of familiarizing himself with it so that he will recognize most of the lines when he hears them read on the stage or over the radio. There are certain doubtful passages which the actor wisely omits and over which we need not ponder; we will save our strength for those parts in which beauty and intelligibility unite to produce a supreme effect. Not so the professional scholar; he would consider the many, many possible interpretations of the following line—

The dram of eale
Doth all the noble substance of a doubt
To his own scandal.

Hamlet himself recites this line but that may have been for him only a matter of "words, words, words." Let it go with the "rat" that appears in Act III and center your attention on lines that sound more like the hero who, we will suppose, speaks for himself and what Ophelia was to him—

TO THE READER

What is he whose grief
Bears such an emphasis? Whose phrase of sorrow
Conjures the wandering stars, and makes them stand
Like wonder-wounded hearers? This is I,
Hamlet the Dane!

To read *Hamlet* means more than running over the lines as though the play were a short story. It means less than working over it as though it had to be translated from a foreign language. You are to get your *Hamlet* as so much soul-stuff realizing that there is somewhat of the stage-character in your own soul, that of man or woman, as there is not that of Ophelia or King Claudius, still less of the nondescript Guildenstern and Rosencrantz. You are privileged to believe with the older critics that Hamlet's problem was the *subjective* one of overcoming certain impediments within his own mind. Or with later scholars you may conclude that the difficulty experienced by the temperamental prince was something *objective,* an obstacle presented by the very situation in Denmark. But in either case it is a matter of human nature of which you have your own supply. You have your problem to solve even if it is only getting the right job or the right mate. You have your part to play even if it isn't as bloody as young Hamlet's, and if Marcellus could say "something is rotten in the state of Denmark," you may have to admit that there may be something rotten in the United States of America.

What you do with *Hamlet,* and there is something you must *do,* you can do with other characters in other stories. You feel the difference between Don Quixote and Sancho Panza and may have classified your friends or customers on the basis of such theoretical and practical souls, dividing them into groups of the scatter-brained and the hen-minded. You can appreciate the turpitude of Becky Sharp, Anna Karenina and Emma Bovary and then wonder if the ambiguous creature you took out to dinner was of that sort. You can enter into the mind of David Copperfield and, if you're a woman, wonder whether the men of this day and generation expect you to be a silly Dora or an unselfish Agnes. Life as you live it is to be your guide in the book as you read it.

The essence of all literature, of all art is expression. It is two-edged, for it *puts forth* the ideas, emotions and strivings of the artist and *brings forth* corresponding states of mind in the reader or beholder. The manner of expression is style, but this is not "the man himself," as has been said; it is a man to man affair, writer and reader. The author is the steel, your mind the flint, the book the flash. The writer who talks of and for himself is as much a nuisance as the man who talks to himself. Great authors never mumble. They themselves speak—Shakespeare in *Hamlet,* Cervantes in *Don Quixote,* Dickens in his *Copperfield,* Charlotte Brontë in her *Jane Eyre,* but they speak to you. They inform you of what they have observed and let you know how it affected them as much as to say, "haven't you seen such things and felt this way?" This is the reason that they have become the favorite authors of the world. Good taste selects them from among the millions of books the way a magnet finds a needle in a hay-stack.

"Beauty," as the Italian critic, Benedetto Croce, informs us, "is successful expression." Like business enterprise, artistic expression may fail or succeed. Some two thousand plays were written in Shakespeare's day but how many are now rated as examples of successful expression? The Bard of Avon himself, busy theatrical man that he was, turned out thirty-seven plays, but how many of them are now worth producing, worth reading? You behold Shakespearean successes in such plays as *Hamlet, Lear, Othello, Macbeth, Romeo and Juliet, Caesar, Cleopatra* and a few others. If you have time you might consider Shakespeare's failures in such flimsy productions as *Love's Labour's Lost, Timon of Athens, Two Gentlemen of Verona, Troilus and Cressida, Titus Andronicus, Pericles* and the like. If Shakespeare hadn't produced the first list, those on the second would have gone to the scrap-heap or the British Museum, or they might never have been printed at all. In the great XVIIth century the French produced a great array of plays, but professional scholars aside, no one can name more than a few by Corneille, Racine and Molière. A vast number of French novels, as we call them, were brought out in the talkative XVIIIth century, but how many of them are still read? You read *David Copperfield* and *Eugénie Grandet* and a few others by Dickens and Balzac, but who can stand all of dickensia and balzacia without being bored to death? Time will tell and time has told the works that have enduring merit. It is silent about those that have "gone with the wind."

As the author expresses himself in what he writes, you express yourself in what you read, in the books upon your table, the pictures on your walls, the people with whom you associate. Full self-expression demands that you shall be both up and down to date. You should not overlook Ulysses even if his exploits have not been filmed in Hollywood. You cannot ignore Antigone even if she was so unlike the modern flapper. In like manner, the Beatrice of Dante's ghastly poem is inescapable and in spite of her supercilious piety and scholastic theology she is still a woman who will "increase our loves," and one for whom a king might reasonably sacrifice his crown. Don Quixote is still with us, although in our day he has ceased to tilt at wind-mills and seems to be aiming at "economic royalists" and such other supposed giants of our civilization.

The present work is intended to supply you with so many examples of successful expression. By reading them you should succeed in expressing yourself. Time has no power over them for they speak as though they lived in "the perfect day."

The method employed in condensing the novels, as well as the dramas, is different from that used with the scientific and philosophical works. In those the main ideas have been put in condensed form as much compressed thought. The method used with the novels is that of sampling the plot and dialogue of the author's story. Thus it will be observed that where the first person singular is introduced, the "I" refers to Charles Dickens or Emily Brontë or Oliver Goldsmith, as the case may be. In this manner the autobiographical touch of the original work has been preserved.

CHARLES GRAY SHAW, PH.D.

I

NOVELS

TOM JONES

By

Henry Fielding

HENRY FIELDING (*1707–1754*) was an English novelist and
dramatist. His first comedy was produced at Drury Lane when
he was 21 years old. When he was 33 he became a lawyer and
traveled the western circuit, meanwhile continuing with literature. He published his first novel in 1742 and three years later
drifted into journalism. In 1748 he became a magistrate for
Westminster and the following year he published his second
novel, his famous *Tom Jones*. He wrote one more novel,
Amelia. His further literary efforts were confined to pamphlets
and periodicals.

LATELY there lived in Somersetshire a gentleman named Allworthy
and his sister Bridget, somewhat past thirty, who was all his
family, since his wife was dead. He was at one time obliged to be
absent in London on business, for he had much property. On the
night of his return home, as he prepared to retire, he was
astounded to discover a sleeping infant in his bed. Hastily he sent
for Mrs. Wilkins, a servant, and bade her care for the child.
Bridget, when presented with the babe the next morning, was
pleased to be kind to the illegitimate brat, since her brother
wished, though she was a lady of the strictest virtue. The mother
proved to be Jenny Jones, a good girl, envied by the villagers for
her learning. She had often been at Mr. Allworthy's house; indeed,
only recently she had nursed Bridget through a violent illness.
Because of her former good reputation, Mr. Allworthy was lenient
with her, and arranged to send her away to a place where her misfortune was not known.

There was living in Mr. Allworthy's house at this time Dr. Blifil,
a learned man. He longed to court Bridget, since she was her

brother's heir, but having a wife, he could not, and so introduced his brother, a former captain of dragoons, into the house. Captain Blifil and Miss Bridget were soon married, and eight months after a son was born to them.

Captain Blifil was very jealous of the affection Mr. Allworthy showed for the young foundling, Tom Jones, whom he was having brought up in his own home. Therefore the Captain was glad to be able to tell Mr. Allworthy that the child's father had been discovered. He was supposed to be Mr. Partridge, the village schoolmaster. There was really no truth in the story, which had originated from Mrs. Partridge's jealousy of Jenny Jones, who had been one of her husband's pupils. Nevertheless the poor man was not able to clear himself, and was found guilty and deprived of an annuity which Mr. Allworthy had formerly given him. Soon after, his wife dying, he left the town, where he was in danger of starving. The Captain had gained nothing by his part in the affair. While planning what he would do when his wife inherited her brother's estates, he was stricken with an apoplexy, and died.

We shall now pass to the time when our hero had reached the age of fourteen. Master Blifil had grown into a sober, pious youth, but Tom was light-hearted and thoughtless, often getting into scrapes. Needless to say, Blifil was the favorite of Mr. Thwackum, their schoolmaster, and Mr. Square, a philosopher of sorts, who lived at the house. But the lad was detested by his own mother, who seemed very fond of Tom, with the result that Mr. Allworthy, who tried to see justice done, began to look most compassionately on the neglected Blifil. Tom had other friends than Mrs. Blifil, however; Squire Western and his daughter Sophia, about Tom's age, were very fond of him. Sophia had enough sense to see that Tom was no one's enemy but his own, while Blifil was friend to no one but himself. She was glad, at Tom's instigation, to get her father to help Black George, a poacher, who had been dismissed by Mr. Allworthy for a scrape Tom had got him into. In fact, she would have done anything for Tom, since she was falling in love with him, but at the moment his affections were settled on Molly, Black George's daughter. It was discovered that Molly was pregnant, and she was taken before Mr. Allworthy, as justice, to be sentenced. But Tom acknowledged that he was the child's

[4]

father, and asked mercy for her. When Sophia heard this, she resolved to love Tom no more, but her mind was changed when she was thrown from her horse and miraculously caught by Tom, at the expense of a broken arm. In the weeks while he lay recovering at Squire Western's, Tom came to learn that he loved Sophia. For long he was torn by what he thought was his duty to Molly, but when he learned that both Square, the philosopher, and Will Barnes, a country gallant, had been her followers, and that Barnes was probably the father of her child, he felt that he owed her nothing.

Tom was suddenly called back home by news of Mr. Allworthy's serious illness. It was expected he would die, and the good man bade farewell to those about him. As the crisis of his illness approached, news was brought that Mrs. Blifil, who was away from home, had died suddenly. In spite of this news, Mr. Allworthy rallied and grew better. Tom, in tremendous excitement at the good news, got drunk with liquor and joy. After dinner he went out for a walk, and, still under the influence of liquor, met Molly. After they had talked a bit, they retired to the depths of a thicket. Blifil and Mr. Thwackum, happening to walk by, and espying a young couple, tried to ascertain their identity. Tom flew toward them to hide Molly, and a battle royal ensued that ended only when Squire Western, passing by with a party, came to his defense.

Seeing Tom all bloody, Sophia fainted. Mrs. Western, the Squire's sister, with true feminine perception, saw that Sophia loved—but decided that she loved Blifil, whom Tom had knocked flat on the ground. The next day Mrs. Western took pains to tell the Squire that Sophia was in love. At first, being an irascible man, he flew into a rage, but when Mrs. Western mentioned Blifil, he was pleased at the idea of joining the two estates. He proposed the match to Mr. Allworthy, who approved if it was pleasing to the principals, and spoke of it to Blifil. That young man, though having no tender thoughts for Sophia, did have tender thoughts for her inheritance, and went off straightway to spend an afternoon courting. Sophia, apprized of his approach by her aunt, almost fell into hysterics, and disclosed the true object of her passion. Her aunt learned with horror of her affection for

[5]

the baseborn youth, and threatened she would do all in her power to hasten the marriage with Blifil. Mrs. Western was a town woman, wise in the ways of the world, and saw no wrong in marrying a man one disliked. She made Sophia promise to be kind to Blifil. The two had a very stiff meeting. When Sophia met her father afterwards, seeing that he was in a happy mood, she told him of her hatred of Blifil and her love for Jones. Thereat her father flew into a rage and promised to disinherit her. Blifil, angry that Jones had won Sophia's affection, sought to turn Mr. Allsworthy against Tom by telling him, among other things, that while he had been seriously ill, Tom had got drunk and had then gone a-wenching. When Mr. Allworthy asked Tom for an explanation, the boy could make no reasonable reply. His foster-father, tired of forgiving the boy's thoughtless offenses, gave him five hundred pounds and expelled him from the house forever.

Most unfortunately, before Tom had gone very far he lost the money, which was picked up by none other than Black George, who was too greedy to return it to its owner. Tom sent a message to Sophia through Mrs. Honour, her maid, bidding her farewell. Sophia answered with a letter and sixteen guineas, all her available money, and with this in his pocket Tom set out to seek his fortunes.

Sophia was now left to the tender mercies of her father, who wished to subdue her by force, and her aunt, who tried to subdue her by reason. The Squire, an irascible fox-hunting Tory, and his sister, a self-possessed town-loving Whig, were opposed in all things but their desire to see Sophia married. Mr. Allworthy, who would have been kind to her, had been told she cared for Blifil, so he helped to push the match forward. But when Mrs. Honour told Sophia that her father had fixed on the next morning for the wedding, Sophia resolved to flee.

Tom intended to go to Bristol, but being misled by his guide, was forced to spend the night at an inn about thirty miles from home. The landlord, being told by the guide that Tom was a cast-off bastard son, would not give him a room, and he had to sleep in a chair in front of the fire. A band of soldiers on their way to fight the Pretender stopping at the inn, Tom resolved to join them. As he dined with the officers that night, he was

[6]

provoked into an argument by one of them, and finally knocked unconscious by him. His head was wounded severely, and in his illness he was tended by a barber-surgeon called Benjamin. After he had told all his story to the latter, he learned that he was none other than Partridge, who was supposed to be his father. Partridge assured him that this story was false. The two became friendly, and Partridge vowed to accompany Tom to the wars. He did not really believe Tom's story, but thought he had run away from Mr. Allworthy. If he could reconcile the two, Partridge thought to profit from Mr. Allworthy's pleasure at having the boy back. He therefore resolved to accompany Tom.

The next evening, when darkness fell, they found themselves far from any inn. Applying for shelter at a secluded cottage, they arrived just in time to save the old gentleman of the house from robbers. The following morning Tom went for a walk with the old gentleman. Near a wood they heard screams. Tom rushed forward and found a woman struggling in the grasp of a ruffian. He escaped, and Tom decided the best thing to do was to take the woman to a nearby town, where she might find clothes to replace the ones torn in the struggle. The landlady of the inn to which they repaired, thinking the woman a whore, attacked her, but learning from a group of soldiers who came in that the woman was the wife of one Captain Waters, she became civil.

At midnight, a gentleman rode up to the inn seeking his wife. Susan, the servant, thought Mrs. Waters must be the lady, and escorted him to her chamber. Walking in, he was greeted by Tom; he attempted to approach the bed, but Tom prevented him. Mrs. Waters (it was she in the bed) screamed with fear at the ensuing fray. An Irish gentleman next door, hearing the noise, rushed in, and recognizing Mr. Fitzpatrick (the attacker), called to his attention that the woman in the bed was not his wife. The landlady now rushed in, and Mrs. Waters, to hide her own shame, swore that the gentlemen had broken into her room, and that Tom had run in to defend her. Finally all became quiet.

The landlady had retired to her kitchen, when a lady and her maid arrived. The lady went to her room to lie down for a few hours. The maid sat in the kitchen, and there learned that Tom was in the house. She went at once to her mistress, who indeed was no other than our Sophia, and told her the news. But when Honour went to ask Partridge to call his master, Partridge said Tom was in bed with a wench. This was only one of the many times that Partridge foolishly harmed Tom, either by telling the truth at the wrong time or by concocting lies about him. Needless to say, Sophia was greatly disturbed, and resolved to leave at once, especially because she was anxious to evade pursuit by her father. She gave the maid her muff, and told her to leave it in Tom's empty bed. Tom's grief on recognizing it may be imagined.

At about the time Sophia departed, there also left Mr. Fitzpatrick's wife, who had been in the inn all the time. Squire Western arrived too late to find either his daughter or his niece, for such was the wife of Mr. Fitzpatrick, who had run away with her five years before, out of the custody of Mrs. Western. Since then he had spent all her money save a pittance, and had so cruelly tried to gain that, that she had run away from him.

As Sophia jogged on her way, she was joined by another lady on horseback, and to her joy discovered her to be her cousin, Mrs. Harriet Fitzpatrick. Harriet told Sophia all her sad story, concluding with the statement that, when her husband had locked her up in her room until she should sign her property over to him, she had escaped, with the help of a neighboring nobleman, and made her way to England. Soon she and Sophia arrived at an inn for a short rest, and there that very nobleman waited upon them, and offered them his protection on the journey to London.

When they arrived in town, Sophia was very glad to leave Harriet, for she perceived that her cousin's relations with the peer were somewhat dubious. She made her way to the home of Lady Bellaston, a friend who had long before invited her to visit her. There she was safe for the time being. Her father had given up hope of finding her and returned home.

In the meantime, Tom had taken to the road again with Partridge. As they went along, they met a beggar who showed them a pocket-book he had found. It was Sophia's, and in it was a hundred-pound note which her father had given her for her trousseau. The night drew dark and rainy and they lost their way. They found shelter for a while with some gypsies in a barn, and then went on to Coventry and thence to St. Albans. As they dined, a quarrel arose. Partridge was annoyed that Tom would not use the money which he had found, and could not understand when Tom told him that to do so would be dishonesty. At length they made their peace, and started on to London. On the road a gentleman asked leave to accompany them, and as he looked genteel, though shabby, Tom consented. Near Highgate, the man demanded the bank-note of Tom. Tom offered him all the money he had in his pocket, but refused to give him the note belonging to Sophia. The man threatened Tom with a pistol, but Tom jumped on him and overcame him. He then discovered that the fellow had taken to crime because his wife and children were starving. Tom felt that the man was honest, and gave him money before continuing into London.

At the Irish peer's house (at one of the country inns he had learned that this gentleman was guarding the ladies) he discovered Mrs. Fitzpatrick's address, and visited her. But since Sophia had never spoken to her of Jones, she thought him the man from whom Sophia was fleeing, and would not give away her address. Her maid, who had learned the tale from Honour, telling her of Jones' history, she straightway communicated it to Lady Bellaston. Jones had gone to live with a gentlewoman, Mrs. Miller, whom he had heard Mr. Allworthy mention, and at whose house he used to stay when he came to town. He became friendly with her, her two daughters, Nancy and Betty, and their lodger, Mr. Nightingale, a young man-about-town. A few days after he moved there, he was surprised to receive a package containing a mask, a domino, and a masquerade ticket. At the masquerade, he was accosted by a woman who told him that anyone in his situation should not pursue Sophia. He assured her that he meant Sophia no harm. When the lady left, he followed her to a house, and discovered she was none other than Lady Bellaston. She hid from him the news that Sophia was staying with her, and promised that she would try to find the girl for him. Lady Bellaston had conceived a fondness for Tom, and gave him fifty pounds, which he sorely needed, having spent his last shilling.

Ten guineas of this Tom gave Mrs. Miller when she told him the sad tale of the dire poverty of a cousin of hers; he would have given her the whole purse, but she would not take it. A few days later he met this cousin, Mr. Anderson, and was astounded to discover it was no other than the would-be highwayman whom he had aided on his way into London. He now owed other obligations to Lady Bellaston, who still refused to tell him where Sophia was, saying that the girl did not wish to see him. One night, when Sophia was absent at the play, Lady Bellaston received Tom at her own home. The lady being delayed, and Sophia arriving home early, by great good chance the two lovers met. Tom begged her pardon for his behaviour, and she kindly forgave him. But Lady Bellaston could not forgive them, when she came upon them. She even followed Tom to his lodgings, much to the disapproval of Mrs. Miller.

Tom felt that he must leave Mrs. Miller's house, because of this, but he found out that Nightingale was leaving too. He was sorry, for he knew the youth had engaged Nancy's affections. He liked her, in return, but his father had chosen for him a woman he had never seen, and he must obey. He left the house, much to the consternation of the family when it was discovered, for Nancy was pregnant by him. Jones went to his friend, finding him brooding over his own actions, and told him of the violent grief which Nancy was suffering. Tom went to reconcile the elder Nightingale to the match, but found him recalcitrant. When the young man's uncle discovered him set upon the match, he too attempted to dissuade him, but in spite of all opposition, the pair were married. Meanwhile Sophia was in great trouble. Young Lord Fellamar had fallen in love with her, and Lady Bellaston, from spite, had encouraged his suit. But first he must get a rival suitor out of the way. Sophia was told that Tom had been killed in a duel. As she sat weeping for him, Lord Fellamar came in. He seized her violently, and was about to dishonor her, when the door flew open and Squire Western stormed in. He packed Sophia into his coach and took her off to his lodgings. Squire Western had found his daughter through the kind offices of Mrs. Fitzpatrick, who had thought to reconcile herself to her uncle and aunt by giving them this information. All this news was taken to Tom by Honour. He managed to convey a letter to Sophia in her prison, to her joy, and she was able to respond.

The Squire had sent word to Blifil that he had found Sophia,

and Blifil persuaded Mr. Allworthy to go with him to London.
Meanwhile Mrs. Fitzpatrick had sent for Tom, to give him news
of Sophia, for Mrs. Western and the Squire had refused to see
her, and she wanted revenge on them. As Tom was leaving, he
was accosted by Mr. Fitzgerald, who had been notified by the
angry Mrs. Western of his wife's dwelling. A fight ensued, which
ended when Tom sheathed his sword in Mr. Fitzgerald's body.
He was seized by a gang of men who were most opportunely
present. Indeed, they had been sent by Lord Fellamar to make
away with Tom, but now they dragged him to a magistrate. In
prison he was doubly tormented, for he received a letter from
Sophia saying farewell forever. In order to break off his affair with
Lady Bellaston, he had written to her proposing marriage (as he
had been told this device had proved successful before); she had
furiously refused him, but had kept his letter and shown it to
Sophia. He was aided by Mrs. Miller, however, who took a letter
from him to Sophia, and told that young lady how kind Tom
had been to her family, so that Sophia's anger melted somewhat.
Mrs. Miller also took pains to tell the same story to Mr. Allworthy, who with Blifil was staying at her house.

Mrs. Waters, who had been living with Mr. Fitzgerald, visited
Tom in prison to tell him that his opponent was recovering.
Partridge, seeing her, and perceiving that she was the former Jenny
Jones, and the woman with whom Tom had lain at the inn,
horrified him by telling him he had lain with his own mother.
Black George, who was now a servant in the house where Squire
Western was staying, brought news that Sophia, who had been
staying with her aunt, had refused definitely to marry Lord
Fellamar, in spite of her aunt's desire, and had been returned to
her father, with whom she was now on good terms.

Mr. Allworthy now visited young Nightingale's father, and persuaded him to forgive his son's marriage. From him he learned
that Black George was investing £500 in a mortgage, and soon
found out that this was the money he himself had given Tom.
Mr. Allworthy's feeling toward Tom was further softened when
he learned that Fitzpatrick had sufficiently recovered to state that
he had set upon Tom first. At this time he received a letter from
Square, who was dying, telling him that Tom had been injured

by others. Mrs. Waters called upon him to tell him that Tom was the child of Mr. Allworthy's own sister Bridget and a Mr. Summer, who had once lived in his house. He also found out that Blifil had been trying to obtain evidence that Tom had murdered Fitzpatrick. Mr. Allworthy, angered by Blifil's secret treachery toward Tom, disinherited him, and made Tom his heir. Tom was released from prison and perfectly reconciled to his uncle and Sophia. He and Sophia were married at once, as Squire Western no longer objected to the match now that Tom was his uncle's heir.

THE VICAR OF WAKEFIELD

By

Oliver Goldsmith

OLIVER GOLDSMITH (*1728–1774*) was a British author who was born in Longford, Ireland. He entered Trinity College in Dublin. A poor scholar, he became involved in a college riot and he ran away. Later he studied for the ministry, for the law, for medicine and after a tour of the continent became an author-of-all-work on the Monthly Review. His first definitive work, a two volume translation, appeared when he was 30 years old. Then came a series of editorships, essays, letters and books. The *Vicar of Wakefield* appeared in 1766 and his reputation as a novelist was secured. Following this he produced two plays at Covent Garden and in 1770 he wrote *The Deserted Village*. This was followed three years later by the successful *She Stoops to Conquer*. He died a year later.

IT WAS ever of opinion, that the honest man who married and brought up a large family did more service than he who continued single, and only talked of population. From this motive, I had scarce taken orders a year before I began to think seriously of matrimony, and chose my wife, as she did her wedding gown, not for a fine glossy surface, but for such qualities as would wear well. To do her justice, she was a good-natured notable woman; and, as for breeding, there were few country ladies who could show more. She could read any English book without much spelling; but for pickling, preserving, and cookery, none could excel her. She prided herself also upon being an excellent contriver in housekeeping; though I could never find that we grew richer with all her contrivances.

However, we loved each other tenderly, and our fondness increased as we grew old. There was, in fact, nothing that could make us angry with the world or each other. We had an elegant house situated in a fine country, and a good neighborhood. The year was spent in a moral or rural amusement, in visiting our rich neighbors, and relieving such as were poor. All our adventures were by the fireside, and all our migrations from the blue bed to the brown.

As we lived near the road, we often had the traveller visit us to taste our gooseberry wine, for which we had great reputation. Our cousins, too, came very frequently to visit us. Thus we lived several years in a state of much happiness, our troubles confined to minor rubs, such as the schoolboys' robbing my orchard, the cats' or children's plundering my wife's custards and the Squire's falling asleep in the most pathetic parts of my sermon.

My children, the offspring of temperance, were well-formed and healthy; my sons hardy and active, my daughters beautiful and blooming. Our eldest son was named George, after his uncle, who had left us ten thousand pounds. Our second child, a girl, was called Olivia after the heroine in a romantic novel. Our third, less than a year later, was Sophia. Then came Moses, and after an interval of twelve years, we had two sons more. I rejoiced when I saw them about me.

My son George was educated at Oxford and just upon leaving college, fixed his affections upon the daughter of a neighboring clergyman, a great dignitary in the church and also possessed of a large fortune. Miss Arabella Wilmot was allowed by all (except my two daughters) to be completely pretty. The lovers were very happy, but just before the wedding, misfortune assailed us. I became involved with Mr. Wilmot in an argument about monogamy. He was courting his fourth wife, of which I strongly disapproved and this angered him. The merchant in town, in whose hands my money was lodged, betook himself off to avoid a statute of bankruptcy, and was thought not to have left a shilling in the pound. When I explained this to Mr. Wilmot, he determined to break off the match: one virtue, prudence, he had in perfection, too often the only one that is left us at seventy-two.

I sent George to London where I hoped his abilities might contribute to our support and his own. I myself was offered a small cure of fifteen pounds a year in a neighborhood seventy miles distant and within a few days with my family set out for the place.

The first day's journey brought us within thirty miles of our future retreat, and we put up for the night at an obscure inn in a village by the way. When we were shown a room, I desired the landlord to join us there. He knew the whole neighborhood to which I was removing, particularly Squire Thornhill, our future landlord, who was remarkable for his attachment for the fair sex. No virtue was able to resist his arts, scarce a farmer's daughter within ten miles round but what had found him successful and faithless. This news grieved me, but seemed to please my wife and daughters. Just then the hostess burst into the room to inform her husband that a gentleman was about to depart without paying his bill. When I learned that he was a worthy, charitable fellow who only two days before had given three guineas to the beadle to spare an old broken soldier, I asked that he join us for supper and later offered him my own purse.

The next morning this new companion, Mr. Burchell, joined us as he was going in the same direction. We lightened the fatigues of the road with philosophical disputes. En route he told me that young Squire Thornhill was entirely dependent upon the will of his uncle, Sir William, a whimsical, benevolent gentleman. While crossing a rapid stream, my youngest daughter was thrown from her horse and would have drowned, had not my new-found friend rescued her. When he finally left us, we begged him to visit us in our new home.

This we soon found was situated at the foot of a sloping hill. Our neighbors were all farmers who not only welcomed us with a feast, but when we were settled, frequently came to visit us. Most welcome were the talkative Flamborough and the blind piper who loved to play soothing ballads like the Cruelty of Barbara Allen.

One autumn afternoon Squire Thornhill rode across our land with his hounds and huntsmen. My wife was delighted when he seemed to favor Olivia, who indeed secretly admired him.

"Disproportionate friendships ever terminate in disgust," cried I. "Let us keep to companions of our own rank."

A few days later our friend, Mr. Burchell, visited us and partook of the venison sent by the Squire. He loved children and amused them by singing them ballads and telling them stories. My wife was not sparing of her gooseberry wine. One day he helped us at saving an aftergrowth of hay and I could not avoid observing how assiduous he was in assisting Sophia in her part of the task. We learned that he visited in the neighborhood once a year. All the farmers welcomed the poor man, for he helped them at their labors, provided whistles and gingerbread for the children and was always good company.

The morning after his departure Mr. Thornhill with a couple of friends, his chaplain and feeder, came to dinner. He politely ordered his numerous servants to the next alehouse; but my wife insisted on entertaining them all; for which, by the by, our family was pinched for three weeks after. He stoutly denied that he was making some proposals of marriage to Miss Wilmot, my son George's former mistress, and directed his looks and conversation to Olivia. My wife was delighted, but I felt misgivings. I could have been better pleased with one that was poor and honest, than this fine gentleman with his fortune and infidelity. Besides he was a freethinker. My wife argued, however, that that was no reason for his not being a good husband and she knew some sensible girls that had had skill enough to make converts of their spouses.

Mr. Burchell again visited us the next morning and I noticed his attachment to Sophia whom he called his little mistress. We dined in the field and enjoyed the companionship of two blackbirds and a familiar redbreast that pecked crumbs from our hands. Our visitor read us a ballad but our tranquillity was interrupted by the report of a gun close by. Sophia threw herself into Mr. Burchell's arms for protection. The sportsman, the Squire's chaplain, then appeared to take up the blackbird he had killed and offered it to Sophia. He informed us that that very night Mr. Thornhill intended giving the young ladies a ball by moonlight on the grass plot before our door. The music and refreshments had already been provided. Mr. Burchell refused to stay in spite of my youngest's urgent invitation. I marvelled how she could prefer a man of such broken fortunes, but as men are most capable of distinguishing merit in women, so the ladies often form the truest judgments of us. The two sexes seem placed as spies upon each other, and are furnished with different abilities, adapted for mutual inspection.

Our landlord soon arrived with a couple of under gentlemen and two young ladies richly dressed whom he introduced as women of very great distinction and fashion from town. Since there were not enough ladies to make up a set of country dances, the two gentlemen with Moses went in quest of my neighbor Flamborough's rosy daughters who presently arrived flaunting with red top-knots. The neighbors, hearing what was going forward, came flocking about us. All noticed that the Squire favored Olivia who far surpassed the fine ladies at dancing. At supper, though, they threw my girls into the shade; for they would talk of nothing but high life, and high-lived company; with other fashionable topics, such as pictures, taste, Shakespeare, and the musical glasses. They suggested a winter in town would benefit both my girls who seemed quite taken with them. They proposed, too, that my daughters accompany them home, but this I refused to permit and had nothing but sullen looks and short answers the whole day ensuing.

My daughters now began to aspire toward high life. They cast off the poor Miss Flamboroughs as mean acquaintance, concocted washes for neck and face, avoided the sun as an enemy to the skin, new-modelled their old gauzes instead of finishing George's shirts and insisted that their hands were whitest when they did nothing. A fortune-telling gypsy told one of them that she would be married to a Squire in less than a twelve-month, to the other that she would marry a Lord. My wife's lucky dreams about this time served to encourage the delusion.

Michaelmas Eve was spent at neighbor Flamborough's where we had a happy time burning nuts, playing tricks and engaging in country games. In the midst of the revelry our two great acquaintances from town appeared. They had been at our house to see us, and finding us absent had sought us hither. They talked of the grand affairs in town and mentioned that they were in need of companions, to whom each was willing to pay thirty pounds a year, to read, write and behave well in public. My wife informed them that our two daughters could fulfill the requirements and they agreed to accept them upon their cousin Thornhill's recommendation. All this time, Mr. Burchell sat with his face toward the fire and at the conclusion of every sentence would cry out fudge, an expression which displeased us all.

Fortune now seemed resolved to humble us, for a series of mortifications often more painful than real calamities now overtook us. My wife, feeling that we should have a better horse than the Colt which was grown old, induced me to sell him at the neighboring fair and buy us one that would make a pretty appearance at church, or upon a visit. I had intended going myself, but as I had a cold, was persuaded to let Moses, a prudent lad, go in my stead. His sisters decked him out in fine style and he set forth upon his errand. He returned some hours later, not with the new horse but with a box full of green spectacles with silver rims and shagreen cases that a prowling sharper had sold him. Mr. Flamborough had been deceived in the same manner.

The two ladies had received such favorable recommendations from Mr. Thornhill that they were willing to take our two daughters. Mr. Burchell who was visiting us failed to be impressed. He had secret reasons, he said, and parted from us in anger. We needed money, however, to fit out the girls for their journey to London, so it was decided that I go to the fair to sell our remaining horse that was utterly useless for the plough without his companion, and equally unfit for the road, as wanting an eye. No one would buy it, so I accepted an old friend's invitation to repair to a neighboring tavern. At a table near us sat a venerable old man who was bent over a book. When my friend left me, we became engaged in philosophical conversation. He desired to know, at length, what had brought me to the fair and when I told him, offered to buy my horse. When I was unable to change a thirty pound note, he gave me a draft, payable at sight, upon my neighbor, Solomon Flamborough, who, he assured me, was a warm friend of his. When later I presented it to my honest neighbor, that worthy gentleman informed me that I had been cheated by the very rogue who had sold him the spectacles. I dreaded to face my family, but they bore my disappointment with great resignation, as it was eclipsed in the greatness of their own. The two ladies, having heard reports of us from some malicious person, had decided to seek elsewhere for companions.

Our enemy proved to be Mr. Burchell. Our little boys found a letter-case belonging to him on the green. In it was a sealed note, superscribed, the copy of a letter to be sent to the ladies at Thornhill Castle. We discovered upon reading it that he was responsible for our daughters' failure to secure the positions. When I confronted him with the news, and in anger, bade him begone from our house forever, he merely took up his pocketbook with a smile and left us.

Our landlord's visits now became more frequent. While my son and I were in the fields, he sat at home entertaining my family. He taught my daughters piquet and sometimes set my little ones to box, to make them sharp as he called it. My wife laid a thousand schemes to entrap him. She praised Olivia's virtues to the skies, even went so far as to have a limner include him in a portrait he was painting of the family. When in spite of everything he failed to ask her hand in marriage, it was decided to bring a rival upon the scene. Farmer Williams' son now sat across from him in the evenings, and Olivia played the coquette to perfection. She even went so far as to inform him that that day month was fixed upon for her nuptials with his rival. He made no effort to restrain them and soon discontinued his visits entirely. Olivia seemed resigned and four days before the wedding went out for a walk with her little brother, Dick.

The child soon afterwards came running in crying, "O papa, pa, she is gone from us. She is gone off with two gentlemen in a post-chaise, and one of them kissed her, and said he would die for her: and she cried very much, and was for coming back; but he persuaded her to go with him."

My suspicions fell entirely upon our young landlord, so I sought him at Thornhill Castle. He seemed amazed at my daughter's elopement, but a later witness insisted that he and my daughter were actually gone towards Wells, about thirty miles off, where there was a great deal of company. For three weeks I languished in an alehouse seventy miles from home. A philanthropic bookseller loaned me a few pieces to defray my expenses at the inn and I set out for home by easy journeys of ten miles a day. En route I met some strolling players who invited me to join them. We put up one night at a magnificent mansion where we discussed politics. In the midst of the harangue, Miss Arabella Wilmot entered the room and flew to my arms with the utmost joy. My host proved to be her uncle who desired me to stay for several days.

One of the players was my son George from whom I had not heard in three years. He told us he had met with misfortune in London, had written essays there, had met Ned Thornhill one day in St. James Park, had worked for him for a while, had even fought a duel for him with a gentleman, whose sister it was pretended he had used ill. The lady it turned out was only a woman of the town, and the fellow her bully and a sharper. My son had then been sent to Sir William but that worthy gentleman would do nothing for him. He then went to Amsterdam to teach the Dutch English. Knowing no Dutch, he was unable to make a living this way, so strolled about the continent playing his flute. At length he had returned to England.

Next day Mr. Thornhill arrived and seemed embarrassed upon seeing my son and me. He thought it prudent that I had not told George about Livy's misfortune. He himself was seeking Miss Wilmot's hand. Perhaps for that reason he procured George an ensign's commission in one of the regiments that was going to the West Indies. My boy was delighted to go.

The next morning I myself took leave of the good family, and returned towards home, despairing of ever finding my daughter more, but sending a sign to Heaven to spare and forgive her. Night coming on, I put up at a little public-house by the roadside where to my great delight I found my beloved child. She told me Mr. Thornhill had seduced her, that Mr. Burchell in reality was their warmest friend as he had warned her against the young landlord. A popish priest had privately performed the marriage ceremony but it was in no way binding, as he had been married in the same manner to six or eight wives more, whom he had likewise deceived and abandoned. Some of them were contented to be prostitutes, but my daughter would not submit to such treatment. Neither would she agree to marry a young baronet of his acquaintance. She had refused his offer of money and boarding a stage coach, had been set down here.

The next morning, taking my daughter behind me, I set out for home. As we travelled along, I strove, by every persuasion, to calm her sorrows and fears, and to arm her with resolution to bear the presence of her offended mother. I determined to leave her that night at an inn about five miles from home, while I went ahead to prepare the family for her reception.

It was near midnight when I reached my door: all was still, but suddenly to my amazement, I saw the house bursting out in a blaze of fire. I gave a loud convulsive outcry which waked my son, and he instantly called his mother and sister, but in the confusion forgot the two little ones. Soon hearing them cry I rushed through the flames and brought them out safely but in so doing scorched my arm to the shoulder in a most terrible manner. Everything except a box with some papers that stood in the kitchen had been consumed. Kind neighbors, however, brought us clothes, and furnished one of our outhouses with kitchen utensils; so that by daylight we had another, though a wretched dwelling to retire to. Since my arm pained me too much to go for Livy my son and daughter went in my stead and soon returned leading the poor delinquent. Her mother was inclined to be cruel, but I reproved her for it, reminding her that the real hardships of life had descended upon us and we should not increase them by dissension among ourselves.

My poor Livy continued to be unhappy. Every tender epithet bestowed on her sister brought a pang to her heart, and a tear to her eye. In company she dreaded contempt; and in solitude she only found anxiety. The news that Mr. Thornhill was going to be married to Miss Wilmot merely increased her misery.

One morning we agreed to breakfast on the honeysuckle bank where my poor Olivia first met her seducer. As we were enjoying ourselves his equipage appeared in the distance. My daughters fled to the house, but I told him what a reptile I considered him. Insulted by my speech, next day he sent his steward to demand my annual rent, which I was unable to pay. Our cattle were then driven off and sold for half their value and we ourselves were despatched to prison.

My family lodged at a nearby inn but I myself was imprisoned. The prisoners seemed all employed in one common design, that of forgetting thought in merriment or clamour. One of them,

Mr. Jenkinson the sharper who had cheated me at Wellbridge fair, offered me part of his bed clothes as only straw was provided by the authorities. For this I thanked him and offered to endeavor to soften or totally suppress Mr. Flamborough's evidence, the only prosecutor he feared at the next assizes. I learned next day that my eldest daughter was ill of a fever and therefore could not come to visit me. I attempted to reform my fellow-prisoners by conducting services. At first they laughed but later became more respectful. Mr. Jenkinson continued to be my fast friend. He told me of his past iniquities and asked me how I had come to such misfortune. When I told him, he slapped his forehead, as if he had hit upon something material, and took his leave, saying, he would try what could be done.

My daughter's health steadily declined and at length I learned she was dead. My little ones, who were staying with me, did their best to comfort me, and Mr. Jenkinson advised that since my daughter was no more, I should approve my landlord's marriage to Miss Wilmot and thus restore my family to better conditions. I also appealed to his uncle, but news reached me that both efforts were fruitless. Disheartened I felt that my own end was near at hand. My wife informed me of further misfortune, that Sophia had been carried off by ruffians. A letter from George added a ray of comfort but scarcely had we finished reading it when he himself entered bloody, wounded, and fettered with the heaviest irons. He had come to this plight by seeking to avenge his sister's honor.

That night my dear Sophia visited me in company with Mr. Burchell who had rescued her from the ruffians. I offered her to him in marriage since she dearly loved him, but he feared he could not support her as she deserved. He ordered refreshments sent from the next inn. I requested that my son and Mr. Jenkinson be invited to the feast.

We learned to our amazement that Mr. Burchell was none other than the celebrated Sir William Thornhill, to whose virtues and singularities scarce any were strangers. He freed George from his bonds, and rebuked his nephew who arrived at that moment for his villainy. Miss Wilmot was apprized of it and although under the law she could not retrieve her dowry that had been signed over to the Squire she gave her hand to George.

"And that, Madam," cried her real lover, "was indeed all that you ever had to give; at least all that I ever thought worth the acceptance."

Mr. Jenkinson then informed us that the Squire, unknowingly, had legally married my daughter. He produced the license to prove it and also Olivia whom I believed dead. Sir William gave her a third part of that fortune that once was his and made him entirely dependent upon her tenderness for any extraordinary supplies for the future.

Sir William, after teasing Sophia by pretending that he desired her to marry Jenkinson to reward him for his favors to us all, caught her to his breast with ardour saying, "My loveliest, most sensible of girls, for some years I have sought for a woman, who, a stranger to my fortune, could think that I had merit as a man. How great is my rapture to have made a conquest over such sense and such heavenly beauty."

The generous Baronet then ordered forty pounds to be distributed among the prisoners, and Mr. Wilmot, induced by his example, gave half that sum. Mr. Jenkinson was to receive five hundred pounds from his Lordship's steward as a reward for his services. I and my family were taken to the inn.

Next morning my eldest son brought further good news. My merchant, who had failed in town, was arrested at Antwerp, and there had given up effects to a much greater amount than what was due to his creditors. Later that morning the two marriages were solemnized. Mr. Jenkinson married the elder Miss Flamborough, and my son Moses, the younger. Mr. Thornhill was sent to reside at a relation's house where he employs his time in learning to blow the French horn. When he completely reforms, my eldest daughter is willing to relent. A feast was then served, and when it was over we assembled once more by a cheerful fireside. My two little ones sat upon each knee, the rest of the company by their partners. I had nothing now on this side of the grave to wish for: all my cares were over; my pleasure was unspeakable. It now only remained that my gratitude in good fortune should exceed my former submission in adversity.

IVANHOE

By

Sir Walter Scott

SIR WALTER SCOTT (*1771–1832*) was a Scottish novelist and poet. As a student he was a bold, high-spirited boy with an odd turn for story-telling. Upon graduation from the University of Edinburgh he studied law and had fair success at the bar. When he was 31 he published the first two volumes of his *Border Minstrelsy* and another the next year which won for him a prominence among the literary men of his time. For the next twenty years he averaged better than a book a year. When he attained the heights of his fame and prosperity, he entertained princely at his estate in the border country which he loved. In 1820 he was created Baronet. He joined a publishing venture which presently failed to the extent of almost $500,000. Scott regarded the debt as personal and he set himself to liquidate it by his pen. His novels earned huge sums but under the severe labor he broke down. The Admiralty placed a warship at his disposal for a health cruise but he pined for his home to which he returned only to die. By the sale of copyrights all Scott's debts were liquidated in 1847. Scott "discovered" and gave to literature the historical novel.

IN THAT PART OF ENGLAND which lies between the present towns of Sheffield and Doncaster, formerly lay a large forest. This forest, in the days of Richard I, is the chief scene of our story. At the time of which we write, Richard had long been in captivity abroad, and his absence was mourned by his subjects, who were suffering under the oppression of the nobles. These Normans never hesitated to show the native Anglo-Saxons the superiority of Norman language and civilization.

As our story begins, the sun was setting over that forest which we have mentioned, and in the fading light two figures were walking along. One was a stern, savage man dressed in rough clothing, and wearing around his neck a brass ring bearing the words: "Gurth is the born thrall of Cedric of Rotherwood." The other, dressed in the fantastic dress of a fool, wore a similar collar with the inscription: "Wamba is the thrall of Cedric of Rotherwood." As they talked in the Anglo-Saxon of the inferior classes, Gurth the swineherd cursed his swine, who showed no inclination to take the homeward way. He feared lest they be captured by the Normans and turned from Saxon swine into Norman pork ere morning. Presently the sound of hoofs broke upon their ear, and a small band of horsemen overtook them. One of the two foremost was obviously an ecclesiastic of high rank; his dress was that of a Cistercian monk, but composed of rich materials, and the plumpness of his person and the sly epicurean twinkle of his eye showed also that the Prior of Jervaulx was no ascetic. His companion, the Templar Brian de Bois-Guilbert, was a tall, athletic man burned almost black by the tropical sun; his fierce eye and stern brow impressed the beholder with awe, if not fear. In the *lingua Franca,* the mixed language in which Saxons and Normans conversed, Prior Aymer asked the Saxons the direction of the house of Cedric the Saxon. The Saxons were loath to disclose the dwelling of their master, for they feared these Normans, and they gave them wrong directions. Their fear would have been greater had they known the Templar was especially anxious to see Rowena, the ward of the noble Saxon, and of even nobler blood. The Normans would never have found Rotherwood that night had it not been for a palmer, just returned from the Holy Land, whom they met at a cross-roads, and who seemed to know perfectly the way to their destination.

Within the hall, Cedric the Saxon awaited dinner. He was a man of about sixty, with a face expressive of both good humor and sudden temper. The temper was uppermost now, for he wanted his dinner, and he was anxious about Gurth and Wamba and the swine they were herding. The blast of a horn broke in upon his mutterings, and the Prior and the Templar sought entrance. They were followed by the palmer, who withdrew to the shelter of the hearth. Cedric's temper cleared with the news that his serfs and swine were safe, but became somewhat uncertain again with the appearance of the beautiful Lady Rowena, for he saw the Templar cast an over-bold glance upon her. As the meal progressed, another wanderer sought admission, the Jew, Isaac of York, a thin, stooped old man beaten by the storm without. He was received with scorn by the attendants, but with pity by the Pilgrim, who helped to warm and feed him. Meanwhile the Templar was boasting of the unequalled prowess of his order in the Holy Land. The Pilgrim arose to defend the English chivalry who had accompanied Richard; in a tournament, some of these had defeated a group of Knights of the Temple, among whom had been Brian de Bois-Guilbert. One of the victorious party had been the Knight of Ivanhoe. At the mention of his name, Rowena's face lighted, for she loved him. But mingled pride and resentment occupied Cedric's face; Ivanhoe was his son, whom he had banished because the youth loved Rowena, and because Rowena, of the highest Saxon blood, should, he thought, marry one of her equal in rank that the Saxon race might be restored to power. Sir Brian grew angry at the name, and challenged the absent Ivanhoe to combat in England.

When the party broke up for the night, the Pilgrim was lodged near the Jew. On his way to bed, he was led to Rowena's apartments, where she questioned him further about the absent Ivanhoe. The Pilgrim awoke early in the morning, and went into Isaac's cell. There he warned him that the Templar had ordered his Mussulman slaves to seize the Jew when he was some distance from the mansion. The Jew was overcome with terror, and the Pilgrim promised to help him. Whispering in Gurth's ear a few words which made him marvellously obedient, the Pilgrim led Isaac out of the house and across the moat, where Gurth brought the mules. The Pilgrim escorted Isaac as far as Sheffield, where he might find companions to safeguard him to Ashby-de-la-Zouche, the scene of a forthcoming tournament. Protesting that he was only a poor old man, Isaac offered to reward the Pilgrim for his kindness. He said he could tell that the other wanted a horse and armour—had he not seen the glint of metal within the palmer's gown?—and that he might obtain them from the Jew's kinsman in Leicester.

We now turn to the passage of arms at Ashby. Among the

spectators were Isaac and his beautiful daughter Rebecca. Isaac was somewhat roughly trying to find a place, and was rebuked by a stout yeoman archer in Lincoln green. At that moment Prince John entered, accompanied by the Prior of Jorvaulx and various other attendants, among whom were several Knights Templar and Knights of St. John, who, since they were hostile to King Richard, John was glad to have about him. They, as little as John, desired the return of Richard to England. As much as he liked these knights, John hated the Saxons, who hated him in return for his violation of their liberties. Thus it was that when John saw Isaac the center of a commotion, being temporarily friendly to the Jew because he wished to borrow money from him, he commanded that the Jew be given a seat among the Saxon churls in the gallery. Since these "churls" were Cedric and his family with that of his kinsman Athelstane of Coningsburgh, they were not ready to comply. Trouble might have arisen had it not been for the foolery of Wamba, who tumbled the Jew head over heels down the steps, at which John laughed and commanded that he be given a position in the lower ring.

Thereupon the tournament began. Suffice it to say that after four encounters, the Normans Bois-Guilbert, Front-de-Boeuf and Malvoisin of the challengers were still unconquered. This displeased Cedric, who detested all things Norman, and would never forgive his own son for following Richard. He tried to stir Athelstane to enter the combat, but the latter was too lazy. At this point an unknown, called the Disinherited Knight, entered the lists and opposed himself to Bois-Guilbert. At the second encounter, the Norman was thrown to the ground, to his rage and despair. The stranger vanquished the other Norman challengers as easily, and was announced the winner of that day's honors. Still refusing to raise his visor, he received the noble horse awarded as prize and left at Rowena's feet the coronet of the Queen of Love and Beauty. That night, according to the laws of chivalry, the squires of the knights he had vanquished brought him the horses and armour of their masters; for these he accepted ransom, giving gifts to the squires, but from Bois-Guilbert he refused to accept either arms or ransom. The Knight then gave his attendant, Gurth, a bag of gold to carry to Isaac in repayment for the horse and armor he had obtained through him; thus we discover that the Knight and the Pilgrim are one. As Gurth was about to leave Isaac's house, he was stopped by Rebecca, who gave him a purse of gold, telling him to repay his master the sum he had sent to her father, and to take what was over for himself. On his way to his master, Gurth was attacked by a band of robbers. He was, however, freed when he demonstrated that he could wield a staff better than their champion, and the gold was returned when he told of the generosity of the Jew who he said had given it to him.

The next day there was a general tournament in which all the knights, divided into two parties, jousted. One party was led by Bois-Guilbert, and this Athelstane joined; the other was led by the Disinherited Knight. At one time in the fray the Knight was in great danger, for the Templar, Front-de-Boeuf and Athelstane had attacked him simultaneously. Death seemed certain for him, when he was saved by the sudden appearance of a tall knight in black armour. Together, they won the field. But when Prince John rose to award the prize of the day to the Black Knight, he was gone. Reluctantly, he was forced to give it to the Disinherited Knight. As the Knight knelt at the feet of Rowena to be crowned with the chaplet of honour, he was seen to sway; the attendants removed his helm, and his countenance was as pale as death. The knight was Ivanhoe! He swooned, and lay prostrate at her feet. In the confusion that ensued, Ivanhoe was removed by friends.

It was now time for the archery contest. This was won by the astonishing skill of Locksley, the archer in Lincoln green whom we have mentioned earlier. That night Prince John held high festival. He had invited Saxons as well as Normans to the feast; he desired to conciliate them that they might help him hold the throne against his brother, whom he expected to return soon. But he could never long continue his civility, and the Saxons had no love for him. After the banquet, De Bracy, one of John's followers, hatched an infamous plan. Having fallen in love with Rowena's self and lands, he resolved to capture her. Bois-Guilbert and his men were to impersonate outlaws and seize the lady, taking her to Front-de-Boeuf's castle; De Bracy then was to appear and rescue her.

The next day Cedric and his company reached the dangerous wooded country on their journey home. With them was the bound and unhappy Gurth, who had been discovered looking for his vanished master on the field of Ashby. As the party travelled through the woods, they heard cries, and discovered Isaac and Rebecca, with a horse-litter. They had been abandoned by their body-guard, who were afraid of the outlaws who frequented the wood. Cedric consented that they join his party. In the confusion which followed, Wamba helped Gurth free himself, and he disappeared into the woods. No sooner had the party started on than it was overpowered by a masked band which burst out of ambush. None escaped but Wamba. When he and Gurth happened to meet, they resolved to seek aid for Cedric. In the forest they came upon the yeoman Locksley; he had learned the destination of the marauding band, and offered to help them. At a cell in the forest they found the Jolly Clerk of Copmanhurst, and with him the Black Knight; then they all set off for the rendezvous with the rest of Locksley's band.

In the meantime, the captives had been taken to the castle of Torquilstone, where they had been locked up in several different apartments. There Cedric and Athelstane were left in comparative peace. Unhappy was the fate of Isaac, however. He was thrust into a dungeon-vault where he was soon visited by Front-de-Boeuf and two Saracen slaves. The Norman demanded of his victim one thousand pounds of silver as ransom. When Isaac protested that he could not pay, Front-de-Boeuf commanded the slaves to light a fire under the grate in a corner of the room. He then bade them strip the Jew, but Isaac's courage gave way at this, and he promised to pay, providing Rebecca be allowed to go free. When he heard that Rebecca had been given to Bois-Guilbert, he swore not to pay a single penny. Front-de-Boeuf was about to put him to the torture, when a horn blown outside the castle walls made him leave the dungeon.

Rowena was meanwhile being forced to listen to the suit of De Bracy. He had changed his original plan of appearing as rescuer, and admitted that he had caused her capture. Rowena would not listen to his protestations of love, despising her captor. He forced her to listen, however, when he told her that the occupant of the litter which had been taken also by the band was Wilfred of Ivanhoe, and that he was in danger from Front-de-Boeuf, who had been given by John the barony of Ivanhoe which had been bestowed on Wilfred by Richard. He was forced to leave her by the horn without the battlements. All this while Rebecca had been in an even more ignoble predicament. She was sought out by the Templar, who told her that he intended to make her his mistress. Disdaining him, she leaped to the parapet of the castle, and threatened to plunge from the precipice if he persisted in his design. Admiring her spirit, promising her great power if she would yield to him, the Templar left her at the sound of the bugle without.

The bugle heralded a messenger with a challenge signed by Wamba, Gurth, the Black Knight and Locksley. With them were at least two hundred men. Front-de-Boeuf and his companions sent back answer that they proposed to execute their captives, but that those without might send a priest to reconcile the doomed ones to God. Wamba was disguised as a friar that he might penetrate the castle and discover what state it was in. When Wamba had gained access to his master, he insisted that Cedric don his robes and so escape from the castle. As Cedric left his chamber, he was met by an old hag, Urfried, or Ulrica, who told him that she was the daughter of his former friend, the Saxon owner of the castle, who had been killed long years before. She had been kept as the mistress of Front-de-Boeuf's father, and because of her years of suffering longed for revenge upon her oppressors. She told him to lead the attack on the castle, and when he saw a red flag wave from one of the turrets, to press hard. Their conference was interrupted by Front-de-Boeuf, who told the supposed friar that he wanted him to carry a message to the castle of Philip de Malvoisin, asking him to send it on to York; the message sought aid for the besieged and needless to say, it was never delivered.

When Ivanhoe's guards were withdrawn to help defend the castle, Rebecca was given the task of tending him. This she was glad to do, as she had long felt love for him; had she not rescued him and tended him when he had swooned after the tournament? From his chamber window she viewed the assault on the castle and kept him informed of its progress. As the besiegers battled to enter the castle, they spied Ulrica's red flag upon the battlement, and saw flames rising from the castle. Front-de-Boeuf was already dead; De Bracy was defeated by the Black Champion. The Templar fled with Rebecca, tearing her from the side of Ivanhoe. Rushing into the flaming castle, Cedric rescued Rowena and the Black Knight, Ivanhoe. Of the chiefs of the besiegers, Athelstane alone was hurt; he was felled to the ground by the Templar when he attempted to rescue Rebecca.

The besiegers had won the day. As a reward for his help, Cedric gave the serf Gurth his freedom; Cedric also promised the Black Knight whatever reward he wished for his aid in the fray. Locksley gave the Black Knight a bugle and told him to blow it whenever he was in danger in the forest. As the outlaws divided the spoil from the castle, a loud shout announced the arrival of the jolly Friar of Copmanhurst, who had taken part in the fray and whom they had thought lost. He dragged with him the unhappy Isaac, whom he had found cowering in one of the dungeons. Soon afterwards some of the yeomen brought forward the Abbot of Jorvaulx, who had unhappily been captured as he travelled through the forest. The outlaws, in high good humor, allowed Isaac and the Friar to set each other's ransom. Then Locksley in pity reduced Isaac's, telling him that without treasure he could not hope to redeem Rebecca from the clutches of the Templar. Through Locksley's intercession, the Prior wrote a letter to Bois-Guilbert asking him to release the Jew's daughter.

At the preceptory of Templestowe, Lucas Beaumanoir, head of the order, bewailed the way in which the Templars had fallen away from the ideals of the founders. Therefore he was suspicious when he heard a Jew wanted to see Bois-Guilbert, and enraged when, having forced Isaac to give him the letter intended for another, he found that the Templar had secreted the Jewess in the monastery. Taking the view that only a witch could have made the Knight so lose his senses, he condemned the girl to death as a sorceress. He gave her one chance of life: if a champion could be found to fight for her against the champion of the order, Bois-Guilbert, and if he was successful, her innocence would be proved. When the news was carried to Isaac, he set off in anguish for Ivanhoe's help.

Meanwhile the Black Knight, with Wamba, had started for Coningsburgh, where the funeral-rites of Athelstane were to be held. He told Ivanhoe, who had been taken to a priory near the forest, to follow him when he had somewhat recovered. As the Black Knight continued on his journey, he was suddenly attacked from ambush, and if Wamba had not blown Locksley's horn, summoning the aid of the outlaws, would have been overcome. As it was, the attackers were defeated, and the Knight removed the helmet of their chief to discover Waldemar Fitzure, one of John's chief friends, who had been sent to dispose of the lawful king. For the Black Knight was revealed as none other than Richard. Locksley, who had aided him, proved to be the outlaw Robin Hood, who was gladly forgiven by his king.

The King, joined by Ivanhoe, made his way to Coningsburgh, where, revealing himself to Cedric, he reclaimed his promise, and reconciled father and son. The funeral guests were startled out of their wits when Athelstane suddenly appeared, claiming to have recovered and been imprisoned by the monks who were supposed to pray for his soul, since they did not want to lose their fees. When the King learned that Ivanhoe had been suddenly called away from the castle by a Jew, he followed him, fearing some trouble, and arrived at Templestowe to find that Ivanhoe, though still weak from his wound, had defeated Bois-Guilbert in the lists. Yet it was really God who had slain the Templar. Still desiring Rebecca above all things, unharmed by his enemy's lance, he had fallen a victim to his own contending passions.

Ivanhoe then learned that on his way to the lists Richard had met some of his own followers, and with their help had peacefully turned aside John and his band, whom he had come across shortly after. Richard was now restored to his throne. Cedric agreed to the marriage of his son and Rowena, especially when Athelstane, whom he had always wanted to marry her, refused the honor. Rowena saw Rebecca once again. The Jewess, about to leave England, brought to the wife of the man she loved a parting gift of jewels of great value.

VANITY FAIR

By

Wm. Makepeace Thackeray

WILLIAM MAKEPEACE THACKERAY (*1811–1863*), one of the great-est of English novelists, was born in Calcutta, India. After two years of study at Cambridge he traveled for two years and indulged his passion for drawing and literary composition. When he was 22 he became a magazine contributor, then editor and subsequently proprietor. Art was Thackeray's real ambi-tion. After studying painting in Paris he returned to London to make his famous application to illustrate *Pickwick*. Financial reverses and domestic misfortunes caused him to become a literary hack but by the time he was 30 his genius was assert-ing itself. The publication of *Vanity Fair* began in monthly numbers early in 1847. By the time it was finished it had made the author's reputation. This was followed by his *Pendennis* and in turn by *Esmond*. The three volumes were published together in 1852. He then sailed for the first of his American lecture tours. In 1860 he became editor of the Cornhill Maga-zine and resigned after two years because he disliked refusing manuscripts. He continued as a contributor, and died a year later.

REBECCA SHARP'S poverty-stricken but gay and Bohemian childhood, spent in the society of her artist father's men friends rather than of women, was guaranteed to make her apprenticeship as a French instructor at Miss Pinkerton's an unhappy one. She hated the place. Soon there developed a feud between her and the head-mistress, who, having no strength or will like that of her little apprentice—that pale, sandy-haired thing who looked like a child, not a nineteen-year-old young lady—felt she could not maintain discipline with this rebel present, and so, hearing that Sir Pitt Crawley's family was in need of a governess, she recommended Miss Sharp for the position.

At this same time, Miss Amelia Sedley, being seventeen years old, was about to leave school, and asked permission for Miss Sharp to pass a week at her home before entering upon her new duties. There was no one else who cared tuppence whether Miss Sharp came or went. And in truth, one can hardly be too sorry for her, for in her two years at the school she was never known to have done a good action in behalf of anybody. Amelia Sedley liked her, but Amelia was so guileless and good-natured she liked everybody.

The Sedleys, prosperous Londoners, had home with them their son, a great, fat, overdressed dandy, with a lucrative position in India. Becky Sharp made the acquaintance of this big beau on her first evening at the Sedleys', and set her cap for him. In fact, she had decided to do this before she saw him. How is a young girl without a mother to get her a husband going to succeed in life, unless she acts for herself?

The Sedleys saw through her plans that very evening. But since Mr. Sedley rather despised his son, and was relieved at his not bringing home a black wife from India, he said, "Jos might do worse," and let the little upstart of a governess play her hand. Jos walked into the snare. He would undoubtedly have proposed to her on a certain evening had it not been for a bowl of rack punch—a bowl which, emptied wholly by himself, sent Jos to his quarters maudlin drunk, and gave Amelia's fiancé, who had social ambitions and did not approve of having a Becky in the family, a chance to make him change his mind.

The Osbornes and the Sedleys, old friends, had long hoped their children would marry, and now it had come out as they wished. George Osborne was entered on a military career, and the marriage was to take place as soon as he got himself a proper advancement. Amelia was tenderly, madly in love with him; and he was much in love with her as a conceited, spoiled, and hand-some young man is likely to be.

Now George had a friend, one Captain Wm. Dobbin, a tall, gawky, generous and reliable person who in their school days had adored George as some sort of superior being, and who, thor-oughly liked by the younger boy, had at the same time frequently been "used for a good thing" by him. Captain Dobbin was brought to the Sedley house on the evening of the punchbowl affair, and

there he fell in love at first sight with Amelia. What ensued, we
shall learn later. At present Rebecca has the stage.

Her first adventure having ended ignominiously, Becky kept her
engagement and entered the service of Sir Pitt Crawley, Bart. of
whom she wrote to her dear Amelia that he was "an old, stumpy,
short, vulgar, and very dirty man, in old clothes and shabby old
gaiters"—a man perpetually at law preventing his neighbors from
collecting their debts and using their rightful property, with a
poor beaten second wife who says not a word for herself, and two
sets of children. The sons by the first wife were Mr. Pitt Crawley,
a pious and conventional prig, and Rawdon, a great hulk of a
dragoon; a simple, stupid man, always in debt through gambling,
to whom Miss Becky seemed a heavenly kind of being, and whom
he lost no time in waylaying in hall-way or bridle-path. Brother Pitt
was pale, thin, ugly, silent; a student and a pious prig.

Lady Crawley had been a tradesman's daughter, half-engaged to
a young farmer. Upon her marriage to a man of higher rank she
of necessity lost her old friends; and the women of her new rank
would have none of her not even her own sister-in-law, Mrs. Bute
Crawley. Sir Pitt got drunk every night, and sometimes beat
her; away at Parliament, he forgot her. She grew apathetic, pale,
dull. She that—O Vanity Fair!—but for you might have been a
cheery lass: Peter Butt and Rose, a happy man and wife, in a
snug farm, with a hearty family; and an honest portion of pleasures,
cares, hopes and struggles. But a title and a coach and four are
toys more precious than happiness in Vanity Fair.

In this household it was soon Rebecca who held the real reins.
It was she who read, with indefatigable patience, all those law
papers of Sir Pitt, and copied his letters, and kept his accounts,
and took his after-breakfast walks through the estate with him. It
was with her (not, as in the old days, with Horrocks the butler)
that he conversed at the dinner-table. But Rebecca acted very
prudently. She was modest and affable with the authorities of the
kitchen and the stable; she offended no one and acted haughtily
toward none.

Like the rest of the family, she made special efforts to please
their most distinguished visitor, a wealthy and rakish old half-
sister of Sir Pitt's, who had practically adopted Rawdon, and

meant to leave him half of her money. Enchanted by Becky's wit and conversation, what must she do but borrow her for a fortnight, and establish her in London as nurse, intimate, companion, and errand girl. Here Rawdon came conscientiously, to inquire after his dear Aunt's health. One day mourning crepe appeared on the Park Lane house of Sir Pitt Crawley: Poor Lady Crawley had died at last of her ailments.

It was before the burial that Sir Pitt called at Miss Crawley's and getting Rebecca alone, proposed to her—on his knees, and leering like a satyr, till that young girl, weeping and choking with emotion, blurted out, "Oh, Sir Pitt—oh, sir—I—I'm married already."

For a whole day Miss—no, Mrs.—Rebecca was blue with regret that so marvelous a piece of good fortune had come her way and she be actually obliged to refuse it. To be Lady Crawley,—the mistress of that hall and that estate! But being a woman of resolution and energy she soon wisely turned her eyes to the future, and after discussing the matter with Rawdon, departed secretly from Miss Crawley's, leaving behind her a note of tearful explanation.

She also, unknowingly, left behind all hope of a fortune through Rawdon. For Miss Crawley had hysterics, gave him 200 pounds, and cut him off.

But Becky and Rawdon are not to be the only disinherited couple in this story. For sunny as Amelia's prospects have seemed, they did not include the possibility that Napoleon Bonaparte would leave his island of Elba and plunge Europe into financial panic, ruining Mr. Sedley's stock-market business forever; or that such misfortune would turn Mr. Sedley's sometime beneficiary and friend Mr. Osborne, now his creditor, into a bitter enemy, who maligned his character and forbade George to marry his daughter; the son of the great Mr. Osborne must marry a wealthy girl —the one picked was a mulatto millionairess from St. Kitts, who had been at school with Amelia and Rebecca—or that George himself would forget and neglect Amelia till she nearly died of a broken heart.

It was Dobbin who brought Lt. Osborne round. By what maneuvers we need not go into detail, but the fact remains that on a dreary rainy April day in the year 1815, Amelia Sedley was married to Lieutenant George Osborne in the presence of her mother, her brother Joseph, and Captain Wm. Dobbin.

A queer person, Captain Dobbin. Here he loved Amelia as though she were the only woman in the world, and never told her so. He only strove for her happiness.

At the other house in Russell Square, the news of George's marriage led to the crossing out of a name in the family Bible. Mr. Osborne was through with his son forever.

The young couple honeymooned at Brighton, Amelia deliriously happy and George, for the nonce, proud of his new role and of her. There settled a fly on the ointment, however. For who should also be in Brighton but Rawdon and Rebecca, and it was but the shortest while before Amelia sensed that her school friend was far more interesting to George than she herself was, and not averse to his attentions.

The affairs of Napoleon, which had ruined her family, cut short Amelia's honeymoon. The army was ordered to Belgium, and in a few short weeks after her marriage, Amelia found herself in Brussels with hundreds of other officers' wives engaging in the gay social life which preceded Waterloo. The war seemed unreal and far away. Young Lt. Osborne was in his element. He wormed his way into the higher levels of society with his good looks, his charm, and his money; if the little mouse Amelia was too simple to appreciate sophisticated company, why, so much the worse for her.

But the greatest hardship for Amelia was the presence of Becky —Becky riding with General Tufto in the park and shining at great parties, Becky inviting George but not Amelia to dine, Becky laughing and sneering at her expense behind her back— something which George knew and which did not make him angry. The fifteenth of June came, and with it the hysterically famous ball which a certain Duchess gave on that evening.

All our friends, invited because of certain connections they had made, were there. It was the debut of both Amelia and Rebecca into society, and for Rebecca, it was a brilliant one. As always, her appearance was distinguished; her face was radiant, her dress perfection. People took her word for it that she was a relation of the Montmorency family, the men paid her court.

Amelia, though she had spent a large sum for her clothes, and though she had a good figure, had somehow managed to buy the wrong things, and did not look attractive. George left her sitting on a bench, where Mrs. Rebecca spied her, and in the particularly enraging affectionate tone with which some women know how to patronize, greeted her as a sister, and forthwith found fault with her dress and figure and vowed she would send her own *corsetière* the next morning. She vowed it was a delightful ball; that there was everyone that everyone knew, and only a *very* few nobodies in the whole room. It is a fact that in a fortnight, and after three dinners in genteel society, this young woman had got up the genteel jargon so well that a native could not speak it better.

George very soon found his way to Amelia's bench when he saw Mrs. Becky there, and that young woman greeted him gaily. "Where have you been, wretch? Here is Emmy crying her eyes out for you. Are you coming to fetch me for the quadrille?" and she left her bouquet and shawl by Amelia's side, and tripped off with George to dance.

At last George came back for Rebecca's shawl and flowers, not bothering to speak to Amelia. When he gave the bouquet to its owner, there lay a note, coiled like a snake among the flowers. Amelia went to Dobbin, who was near her. "William," she said, unconsciously calling him by his Christian name, "you've always been kind to me—I'm—I'm not well. Take me home."

Much later, Dobbin found George at a gambling table, and imparted news: they were in three hours to march against Napoleon. George, hurrying homeward, thought of his wife, the child, perhaps, from whom unseen he might be about to part. Oh, how he wished that night's work undone, that he might with a clear conscience say farewell!

"I am awake, George," her soft voice whispered. Awake, poor soul, to what? At that moment a bugle from the Place of Arms began sounding clearly, and was taken up through the town; and amidst the drums of the infantry, and the shrill pipes of the Scotch, the whole city awoke.

Three days later, no more firing was heard at Brussels—the English pursuit of Napoleon's fleeing guard rolled miles away. Darkness came down on the field and city; and Amelia was praying for George, who was lying on his face, dead, with a bullet through his heart.

The doctors who attended Amelia in the following months would promise nothing about the safety either of her life or her mind till after the birth of her child. When the boy was laid in her arms, they saw she would live—she had a new love. William Dobbin saw that she was cared for in Flanders and at length escorted her and the child to her parents' home. When he was certain she had no place in her heart for any but little George, and the memories of his hero father, he arranged affairs so that she would think her husband had left her an income, gave her his blessing, and joined a regiment in India.

For awhile Amelia was peacefully happy. Then her parents became ill, and all the income went for debts. Old Osborne yearned for his grandson, and when Amelia's position was intolerable, she gave him the boy. The grandfather lavished money and toys on him, and in a year he was a thoroughly conceited little snob. Amelia wept and went through her duties as one dead.

But hearing all this, and other things, Major Dobbin took ship and came home. He enlightened fat Jos as to the true state of affairs, and diplomatically enticed him into setting up a splendid London establishment for the family. Then the elder Sedley died, and soon as though the passing of his enemy had drawn strength from him, old Osborne followed. Now Amelia had her boy. But it was Dobbin who took him off his high horse and made a man—and a gentleman—of him.

The four of them—Amelia, Georgey, Jos, and William—set off together for a continental tour.

In all Amelia's life there had been no time so happy as this. The German women liked her and she entered a little into society. Best of all, she discovered music—she, who could sing and play the popular things so well, having spent all her days domineered over by vulgar intellects, had had to wait till her thirties to be introduced—by Dobbin—to Mozart and Cimarosa and Beethoven.

One day a small, blonde lady at a gambling table, alongside which Georgey happened to be wandering asked him to bring her luck by choosing her number. Georgey's men folk, coming for him, recognized Mrs. Rebecca.

What has she been doing these ten years? From Flanders she and Rawdon went to Paris, where Rawdon Jr. was born, and where his mother climbed very high on the social ladder. Her husband was terribly bored—he was a dragoon, not a gentleman —but he loved Becky, nay, he adored her. He helped her pull wires and they lived high in Paris, on no money, till their debts were such that there was nothing to do but run for it. They escaped to England leaving tradesmen, maids, tutors unpaid and in several cases ruined.

A clever person can always start again. Mrs. Becky spoke here and smiled there. She rented a fine house from old Miss Crawley's former butler. That lady, long dead, had finally left all her money to Pitt Crawley, because she had taken a fancy to his wife—who really was a good dear person, much better than the old lady knew. Old Sir Pitt had died, and now young Sir Pitt had money, the estate, and seats in Parliament.

Becky hunted up Arabella Briggs, Miss Crawley's old "companion" and made her her own "sheepdog". Now she could go where she pleased without Rawdon. Her child she disliked and neglected. And though as a small boy he had adored the vision he called mother, he had turned more and more to his father, who did love him, gave him long hours of his company. Colonel Crawley had been in a curious way regenerated by this boy. He wanted to be decent—for the boy to have reason to like him. There was no turning back from their way of life—but if only, in some ways——.

Mrs. Becky had acquired a friend—the elderly Marquess of Steyne, Earl of Gaunt, Viscount Hellborough, Knight of the Most Noble Order of the Garter, etc. etc. etc. And my Lord Steyne saw that Becky rose in the world. Sir Pitt Crawley also saw to it, for he had come to think of Becky as an admirable little woman—in fact, his wife Lady Jane, had good reason for the heartache she felt on knowing Sir Pitt to be a frequent visitor at the Crawleys. Becky was very kind and attentive to Sir Pitt. And the reward was exceedingly great.

If Mrs. Crawley did not wish to lead a virtuous life, at least she wished to enjoy a character for virtue, and we know that no lady in the genteel world can possess this desideratum until she has put on a train of feathers, and has been presented to her Sovereign at Court. From that august interview she comes out stamped as an honest woman. The Lord Chamberlain gives her a certificate of virtue—whatever her reputation might otherwise have been, she issues from the wholesome ordeal of the Royal presence free from all taint.

Thus, through Sir Pitt and the unwilling offices of his lady, who acted as her godmother, Rebecca Crawley reached as high an English society as a woman not of the nobility might. She was presented to King George.

In the carriage, on the way to the Court, her husband looked at the new jewels sparkling in profusion in her ears and on her neck, and asked "Where the deuce did you get the diamonds, Becky? Sir Pitt Crawley blushed. He had given her only the diamond clasp which confined her pearl necklace, but he had a guilty conscience.

Becky answered, "You silly man, I hired them."

Later, the diamonds did not go back to Mr. Polonius, the jeweler, but retired into a little private repository in an old desk, where also reposed a number of other useful, and perhaps valuable, things that her husband knew nothing about.

For instance, a certain thousand pound note. Lord Steyne had given it to her to pay back a loan she owed Briggs. It was really a five hundred pound debt. Becky had doubled the supposed sum, and not paid Briggs, either.

After the presentation, where the great and prominent Lord Steyne made much of Mrs. Crawley and thereby won her plenty of flattery from others, he made his own hostile but eventually obedient women-folk leave their cards for Mrs. Crawley and invite her to dinner. The women all snubbed her there but the men besieged her—as usual.

Becky moved among the very greatest circles of London fashion that year. Her success excited, elated, then bored her. Lord Steyne got wise to her trick of getting money for legitimate purposes and spending it otherwise (he didn't know she *kept* it), for which, being a villain, a roué and a rascal himself, he admired her all the more.

Becky's final triumph of the season was at a party given by Lord Steyne at her request, in which charade-tableaus were the main feature, and Mrs. Crawley the main participant. Becky acted

[41]

—Becky sang—Becky had the world at her feet. Lord Steyne was frantic with delight.

Rawdon Crawley was scared at these triumphs. They seemed to separate his wife farther than ever from him somehow. He thought with a feeling very like pain how immeasurably she was his superior. He wasn't afraid for her virtue. After all, a woman in Becky's position is never alone with a gentleman—there is always a maid or a chaperon of some kind.

The night of the charades Rawdon put his wife into her carriage, which drove off. Mr. Wenham, Lord Steyne's confidential friend, offered him a cigar and suggested they walk home. A few paces down Gaunt Square they were accosted by several men. Crawley knew at once what had happened. He was in the hands of the Bailiffs. One hundred and sixty pounds he must pay, or be haled bodily to prison till he did. Wenham could lend him nothing—he was carried off.

In the morning he sent to Becky by messenger asking for the funds at once. And Becky in a tender letter wrote back that no one could be found to give her the money till the morrow. She would be there early—to rescue her dear darling.

Then Rawdon grew savage—Who had put him in prison? Wenham had walked home with him . . . Was there . . . ? He could not bear it. Hurriedly he addressed another message, "To Sir Pitt or Lady Crawley."

It was Lady Jane who came, kindly toward him as always. She guessed later why he fairly sobbed on her sisterly shoulder. Rawdon walked home rapidly. As he entered the door he heard laughter and singing—Becky was singing a fragment of her song of the night before; a hoarse voice shouted "Bravo! Bravo!"—it was Lord Steyne's.

Becky sat on a sofa in brilliant full toilette, Steyne's diamonds sparkling on her breast and fingers—his Lordship was bending over her.

There was no one else in the house.

Rawdon walked in.

At once, Becky was on her knees. "I am innocent, Rawdon, before God I am innocent. Say I am innocent," she cried to Lord Steyne.

That lord thought a trap had been laid for him and was as furious with the wife as with the husband. "You innocent!" he screamed, "why, I've given you thousands of pounds which this fellow has spent and for which he has sold you . . . Make way and let me pass."

But Rawdon sprang and seized him by the neck cloth until Steyne, almost strangled, writhed and bent. "You lie, you dog!" said Rawdon. And he struck the Peer twice over the face with his open hand, and flung him bleeding to the ground. Rebecca stood there trembling before her husband. She admired him, strong, brave, and victorious.

He tore the diamond ornament out of her breast and flung it at Lord Steyne. It cut him on his bald forehead. Steyne wore the scar to his dying day.

Rawdon ordered his wife upstairs—he tore open her desk, found the bank notes. Some of these were dated ten years back and one—for a thousand pounds—was of recent date. Rawdon sent it to Lord Steyne, and awaited his pleasure for a duel.

The remainder of this story can be told in a few words. The servants, realizing the end was come, seized the valuables in lieu of pay. Becky fled. Lord Steyne neatly evaded the duel. Rawdon accepted a governorship—instrumented by Lord Steyne who both before and after that fatal night had been anxious to get him out of the country—in one of the hot fever-stricken colonies, where he died a few years later.

His boy he had entrusted to his brother Pitt and Lady Jane, who already loved him. Circumstances paved the way for this Rawdon to become, while he was still a young man, the next Lord Crawley.

Rebecca wandered over Europe. Nobody "knew" her, but they "knew of" her, and many a time were the cause of a landlord's suddenly asking her to leave. She gambled, she sang a little, she used skillfully the annuity Rawdon sent her and was never in want. But she was alone.

And thus, after four or five years we meet her again in a little town on the Rhine. Kind-hearted Amelia was nice to her, old Jos became infatuated again, and though she led him a dog's life, he stayed in her company several years, and left her a good sum at his death.

It was over Rebecca that Amelia and Major Dobbin quarreled. The Major saw through her, sized up her friends, forbade her the house. Amelia scornfully told him he had no authority. So he packed and sailed for England—he who had wasted his youth for one woman, who dreamed of some one dead.

Several months later Amelia read that he had joined the —th regiment, sailing soon for India. Then at last she realized her loss. She sat down and wrote him a letter.

It was Mrs. Becky who, not knowing of the letter, but having decided Amelia must marry Dobbin, cleared her heart of the past: she told her that she was pining for a selfish humbug, a low-bred cockney dandy, who would not have married her had not Dobbin forced him to keep his word; who made love to Rebecca a week after the marriage. Did Amelia doubt it? Before her face Rebecca, with provoking good humor, held the letter George had put into the bouquet at the Duchess of Richmond's ball: it begged her to fly with him.

Amelia's head sank, and she wept. For her fallen idol? Or because the barrier was down that had stood so long between her and a real affection? Now at last the tender little parasite could put forth leaves and grow green again, clinging rightfully to her rugged old oak.

Becky kissed her—and went away. They never spoke again. Years after, Colonel Dobbin, carrying his little daughter, and Mrs. Dobbin, escorted by her tall son, came upon Rebecca acting as patroness of a stall at a charitable fair in London, and hurried quickly away. But Mrs. Crawley had a good reputation now. She went weekly to church, always attended by a footman. And she was famous for her gifts to charity.

As for Colonel Dobbin he lives with his family in the country estate, and is fonder of his little daughter than of anything in the world—fonder even than of his "History of the Punjaub", which he will complete soon.

"Fonder than he is of me," Amelia thinks, with a sigh. But he never said a word to Amelia that was not kind and gentle; or thought of a want of hers that he did not try to gratify.

Ah! *Vanitas Vanitatum!* which of us is happy in this world? Which of us has his desire? or, having it, is satisfied?

MADAME BOVARY

By

Gustave Flaubert

GUSTAVE FLAUBERT (*1821–1880*) was a French novelist whose works are deeply tinged with somber horror. Although he had published some fragments earlier, he published his first complete book, his masterpiece *Madame Bovary* when he was 36 years old. He was decorated with the Legion of Honor when he was 45. In the following 10 years he produced numerous books and plays including *Trois Contes* which represents most of his best manners. In his later years he was a member of a small set of distinguished French writers. Flaubert was a pure romanticist.

CHARLES BOVARY was the son of a good for nothing father and an ambitious disillusioned mother. He was sent to medicine school because of his mother's persistence. He failed the first examinations because of indifference, but passed the second time by dint of hard labor. His mother found him a practice, and that not being enough, also gave him a wife, a widow of forty five with an income of twelve thousand francs. She was ugly, complaining and the master of the house.

One night Charles was called from his bed to Bertaux, a good eighteen miles from his home, to set a broken leg. The fracture was simple and Monsieur Rouault was soon resting comfortably. Charles was much impressed with Mademoiselle Rouault so instead of returning in three days as he had promised, he went back the very next day, and continued to go even after Monsieur Rouault had recovered. Finally Madame Bovary forced him to discontinue. One day, not long after, she died suddenly and Charles, after all was over, spent an evening in sorrowful reverie. She had loved him after all.

One day old Rouault brought Charles the money for setting his leg and invited him to his home. Charles soon fell in love with Emma Rouault and promised himself to ask her hand in marriage. Monsieur Rouault thought Charles a little meager but he was economical, learned, and probably wouldn't be too difficult about the dowry so he consented to the union.

The wedding was attended by all the relatives of both families and there was much merrymaking. Two days after, the couple returned to Tostes, Charles' home, as he could not leave his patients any longer.

Charles was very happy with his new wife whom he loved and thought very beautiful, as indeed she was. Emma, before her marriage had thought herself in love; but the happiness that should have followed this love, not having come, she must she thought have been mistaken. And Emma tried to find out what one meant exactly in life by the words felicity, passion, rapture, that seemed to her so beautiful in books.

Emma had been educated in a convent and had loved and dreamed the romantic literature she had come in contact with there. The uneasiness that Charles' presence caused her had led her to believe that at last she felt that wondrous passion which, till then, like a great bird with rose-colored wings, lived in the splendor of the skies of poesy, and now who could not think that the calm in which she lived was the happiness she had dreamed.

Charles' commonplace talk bored her and as their intimacy became deeper, greater became the gulf that separated them. Charles' position in the community rose because of his wife as she could manage the house well and always had a tasty dish for company. Charles finished by rising in his own esteem for possessing such a wife. Emma wanted to make herself in love with her husband but could not as his love was too commonplace. Moreover, Charles' outbursts of passion became regular, he embraced her at certain fixed times. It was merely one habit among others. Emma wondered why she had married.

In September of the first year, something extraordinary fell upon Emma's life; she was invited by the Marquis d'Andervilliers to Vaubyessard. He was preparing his candidature to the Chamber of Deputies long beforehand. Having seen Madame Bovary's pretty figure and that she did not bow like a peasant, he thought he was not going beyond the bounds of condescension, nor on the other hand, making a mistake in inviting the young couple.

Emma was much impressed by the château, the ladies and their grand manners, the dancing, and the champagne. Charles was bored and heavy and Emma was ashamed of him. When they returned home, the memory of the ball became an occupation for Emma. For a year she dreamed of it. Charles went about his tasks, and always returned home to a well-cooked meal, a charming and well-dressed wife, and was very happy. Emma grew bored finally and began to neglect the house, letting things run themselves. When Madame Bovary senior visited them, she was much surprised at the change. Emma complained about Tostes so much that Charles decided they should move. He chose Yonville-d'Abbaye. When they left Tostes in March, Madame Bovary was pregnant.

The most important landmarks at Yonville were the Lion d'Or, the inn of the town, and opposite that, the chemist's shop of Monsieur Homais. His house from top to bottom was placarded with inscriptions written in large hand, round hand, printed hand. "Vichey, Seltzer, Barege waters, blood purifiers, Raspail patent medicine, Arabian racahout, Durcet lozenges, Regnault paste, trusses, baths, hygienic chocolate" etc. . . . Homais was also one of the leading citizens of the town.

On their arrival, Monsieur and Madame Bovary stopped at the inn. Emma talked for two and one half hours with Leon, a clerk who lodged at the chemist's. It was one of those conversations where the hazard of all that is said brings you back to the fixed center of a common sympathy.

Charles was dull as business was slow in coming to him. He was distracted by the pregnancy of his wife. Emma hoped for a boy. When the time came and she heard that the child was a girl, she turned her head away and fainted. She named the child Berthe and had her sent out to nurse.

When she went to visit the child, Emma met Leon and they talked together. Leon was very much bored in Yonville. The people of the village were unbearable companions. From the general background of all these human faces, Emma's stood out isolated and yet farthest off; for between her and him he seemed to see a vague abyss. In the beginning he had called on her several times along with the druggist. Charles had not appeared particularly anxious to see him again, and Leon did not know what to do between his fear of being indiscreet and the desire for an intimacy that seemed almost impossible.

It was the custom for a group to gather at the chemist's in the evenings to talk and play dominoes. Leon was always there and he watched Emma play écarté with Monsieur Homais. When the card games were over, Emma and Leon would talk of books and music. When Emma gave Leon a rug for his room, everyone decided she must be his mistress. Emma did not ask herself whether she loved. She thought that love must come suddenly with great outbursts of lightning.

One Sunday afternoon, Emma, Charles, Leon, and Homais went to see a yarn mill that was being built in the vicinity of Yonville. While walking Emma compared the peasant appearance of her husband with that of Leon. She thought Leon charming and her husband countrified. Leon often made excuses to visit Madame Bovary in the afternoon. He was madly in love with her but because he believed her the perfect wife, devoted to her husband and child, dared not declare himself. Emma finally discovered that she loved Leon but this discovery made her appear all the more the perfect wife, for she took pains to conceal it from everyone. This great longing for Leon, nursed privately, made her so nervous that she became quite ill, particularly as she believed that he did not return her love. She had fits of sobbing which left her weak and nerveracked.

One evening Madame Bovary heard the angelus ringing. She set out for a walk to church thinking that a talk with the village priest might do her good. He was just about to give the village boys their lesson to prepare them for their first communion and could not give Emma much of his time. Receiving no help from him, Emma returned home slowly. She found her little girl, trying to walk in her knitted shoes. Berthe was anxious to reach her mother, but Emma impatiently pushed her aside. Berthe's foot slipped and she fell against the brass handle and cut her cheek which began to bleed. Just at that moment Charles came in and put a piece of sticking plaster on the cut, making light of it. Emma felt very much frightened and guilty.

Meanwhile, Leon, believing that Emma did not return his love, became more and more bored with Yonville and decided to go to Paris where he could enjoy himself and also get ready for an examination. He wrote to his mother who finally gave her consent. After a month's preparation, he finally left Yonville. His farewell to Emma was very formal, neither one displaying in any way their secret desires. When he had gone, Monsieur Homais, the doctor, and Emma talked for a time of the dangers that threatened Leon in Paris, the dangers of contracting disease and that of meeting the wrong women. Of course this talk was agonizing to Emma who feared the worst for Leon. Just before Homais left, he told Emma and Charles that the agricultural meeting of the Semi-Inférieure would be held at Yonville that year and would be of great importance to the town.

After Leon left, Emma reproached herself for not having succumbed to Leon while he was there. She tortured herself with longings and regrets and became very ill. She took more care with her appearance and bought a Gothic prie-dieu, and in a month spent fourteen francs on lemons for polishing her nails. She took up philosophy and studied Italian. This lasted only a short time however. Finally she became so ill that she spat blood. Charles was so upset that he wrote his mother and begged her to visit them. His mother stayed three weeks and then returned home. Her visit did not help at all.

The day after Charles' mother left, Emma was leaning out of the window watching the crowd, when she saw a gentleman in a green velvet coat. He had on yellow gloves and heavy gaiters and was walking toward the doctor's house. He announced himself as Monsieur Rudolphe Boulanger of La Huchette. He wished to be bled because he felt a tingling all over. As soon as the blood spurted out, the man fainted. Emma was called in and moistened his temples with vinegar. A little later he revived and after a short conversation with Charles and Emma, put three francs on the table, bowed negligently, and went out.

While walking under the poplars, Monsieur Boulanger thought about Emma, wondering how she, with a figure like a Parisienne happened to marry the fat doctor. She probably was bored with him as his nails were dirty and his face unshaven. Then he thought about his mistress, an actress at Rouen and decided he was tired of her and would discard her for Emma. It would be a nuisance with her husband and child, hardly worth the bother. He thought of her pale complexion, the kind he adored, and finally decided that when the opportunity offered, he would have her. He would call at the house occasionally, and send venison and poultry. Then he remembered the agricultural show and realized that he would see her there and would then begin his pursuit.

At last the agricultural show was on. Emma decided to go and later met Monsieur Boulanger, who walked with her around the show. They went to the hall where the speeches were to be given and sat together apparently listening. The speeches were mostly about agriculture, soils, manures, farm animals, and even government, none of which interested either of them; but all of which served to permit them to sit together and secretly admire and desire each other. Monsieur Boulanger was so bold as to tell Emma of his infatuation for which she did not repulse him. After the show was over, Monsieur Boulanger saw her home.

Rudolphe did not see Emma again until six weeks later, when he called at her home. While he was there, Charles came in and told him of his anxieties over Emma's health. Rudolphe offered Emma a horse but she refused. Later Charles prevailed upon her to accept. Finally she did when Charles told her to order a riding habit.

The next day Rudolphe appeared with two saddle horses. Emma was delighted and they rode for several hours. At last, becoming tired, they sat down on a log to rest. It was here that Rudolphe obtained his desire. That evening, Emma was in ecstasies because she felt that now she would experience that grand passion of which she had so often read. She was not disappointed and rode with Rudolphe every day, becoming more and more entranced with him. She even visited Rudolphe at his château whenever Charles went out early. After a while she stopped this practice at Rudolphe's request because he pointed out that she was compromising herself.

All through the winter, three or four times a week, Rudolphe came to see her. He came in the dead of night to the garden. Emma was not at all ashamed at her infidelity to her husband, but rather rejoiced in her affair with Rudolphe.

Some time later, Emma felt a little conscience stricken and decided to try to love Charles a little. But she had no opportunity to lavish her affection on him, as the druggist called with an idea to have Charles perform an operation for club-foot upon the stable boy, Hippolyte. Charles was very skeptical at first but finally consented urged on by Emma. The operation at first seemed successful but poisoning soon set in and the leg had to be amputated. Charles heard the agonized cries of the boy as the city doctor who had been called in, completed the operation. Emma could not sympathize with Charles in his failure and now could not bear the sight of him. That night Emma met Rudolphe in the garden where they threw their arms around one another, and all their rancor melted like snow beneath the warmth of their kiss.

As Emma's hatred for Charles grew more intense, her love for Rudolphe increased. She began to beg him to take her away. Rudolphe began to think her an encumbrance especially as she proposed to take Berthe with her. To satisfy her Rudolphe promised to go away and allowed her to make all preparations for the flight.

The next morning as Emma was about to leave, a box of fruit came from the château. Among the pieces of fruit was a letter from Rudolphe, telling her that they were making a great mistake and that he was going away alone but would sometime return at which time they would talk together very coldly of this old love.

Emma rushed to the attic where she could read the letter alone. She did so again and again with angry sneers. She wished that the earth might crumble to pieces. She thought of suicide. As she lost herself in her agony she felt her maid Félicité touch her arm and she collected herself and went downstairs. She could not eat but tried to compose herself while Charles ate his meal. When a blue tilbury passed over the square at a rapid trot, Emma fell rigid to the ground.

She was put to bed where she lay dangerously ill with brain fever for many weeks. Late in October, Emma recovered enough to be taken to the garden, but had only been there a short time when she was seized with giddiness and became more alarmingly ill than before. Charles was terribly concerned now for he feared cancer, and besides this he was worried over money matters.

Emma suffered terribly for many more weeks and finally thought she was about to die. The priest was sent for and made arrangements for her to be given the last sacrament. This was done, but Emma did not die. She improved gradually and finally began to receive visitors. When she was strong enough to get around, Charles suggested going to the opera by way of diversion. The opera was at Rouen. Emma bought a new dress for the occasion and looked very lovely in it.

They arrived at the opera before the doors opened. When the show began, Emma was very much absorbed by the performance. She recognized all the intoxication and the anguish that had almost killed her. After the first act Charles went to get her some water, for he was afraid she would faint in the suffocating air. He brought none other than Monsieur Leon back with him. It was settled between them that Emma would stay in Rouen to see other operas while Charles, who could no longer absent himself from Yonville, would return.

Monsieur Leon's passion for Emma reawakened on seeing her again. When they got together in Rouen, the next day, they talked of their past love and how it was wasted. Leon wanted to begin again but Emma claimed they were too old.

The next day they met in the cathedral. After they turned away a persistent guide, they took a cab around the city, merely rode and rode much to the despair of the coachman who cast longing eyes at the public-houses. The folk of the country were wonder struck at the sight of a cab with blinds drawn and which appeared more closely shut than a tomb. Once in the middle of the day, a bared hand passed beneath the small blind of yellow canvas and threw out scraps of paper that scattered in the wind. About six o'clock the carriage stopped in a back street and a woman got out who walked with veil down and without turning her head.

When Emma returned to Yonville she was greeted with the news that her father-in-law was dead. Madame Bovary senior arrived and she and Charles wept together.

Monsieur Lheureux was the linendraper of the town and it was his custom to make loans to the villagers. Madame Bovary had bought things from him from time to time. She had purchased the traveling trunks from him when she had planned to flee with Rudolphe. Now he was here again and Emma bought some cloth. Monsieur Lheureux never mentioned money.

Emma decided that affairs of her father-in-law needed the advice of an attorney for settlement. She claimed she didn't trust the town notary and it would be wise to consult Monsieur Leon. Charles agreed, so she went to Rouen and stayed there three days. These days were a true honeymoon for Emma and Leon. They took a room together in an obscure hotel and had a merry time together.

Madame Bovary began to call on Monsieur Lheureux constantly for silks and other things and he was always ready and obliging. Emma had to devise a means for seeing Leon more frequently, so decided she needed piano lessons. She went to Rouen on Thursdays. She and Leon had a room in a hotel which they grew to love and think of as their own.

Emma was always very impatient for Thursdays and could hardly contain herself until they arrived.

One day Charles mentioned that he had seen Mademoiselle Lempereur, supposedly Emma's piano teacher but the good lady had never heard of Madame Bovary. Emma received a momentary fright but passed it up lightly with several possible reasons for the teacher's lack of memory. She made sure that a receipted bill was found by Charles for the lessons.

Monsieur Lheureux soon approached Emma for money. When she didn't have any, he suggested that she sell her father-in-law's estate and then she could pay her debts and have some left over. She had obtained the power of attorney from Leon and so she could do this. Emma grew confused about the figuring. She bought things extravagantly as she seemed to have money.

One Thursday night Emma didn't return to Yonville. Charles, frightened, went to Rouen but could not find Emma anywhere. He was just about to go to Mademoiselle's, the music teacher's, when he saw Emma coming down the street. Emma pretended to be angry at Charles' concern, saying she couldn't feel free if he went looking for her if she were a little late. By this she gained even more freedom and went to see Leon on any pretext. Leon's master complained at the slackening of his work.

Monsieur Lheureux became more demanding. Emma did all she could to get money. She tried unsuccessfully to gain some from her father-in-law's estate. She began selling old gloves, hats, and odds and ends. She bargained rapaciously. She collected from some of her husband's patients. And then she ran up more bills. She became very temperamental and Charles thought her old nervous ailment was returning.

Leon was growing tired of Emma's excesses which all the time became more extravagant. Emma was sick of them herself. She found again in adultery all the platitudes of marriage. She longed for some catastrophe that would bring about their separation, since she had not the courage to make up her mind to effect it herself.

One day she received a judgment against her from the court. By dint of buying and not paying, of borrowing, signing bills and renewing these bills, that grew at each new falling in, she had ended by preparing a capital for Monsieur Lheureux which he was impatiently awaiting for his speculation.

All her pleadings for time availed nothing. She tried to get money from the brokers in Rouen whom she knew. She tried Leon and made him ask his friends but he was unsuccessful. When she returned from Rouen on her scouting trip, she discovered a public notice that her furniture was for sale. She went to Monsieur Guillaumin, the notary, and told her story to him with many recriminations against Lheureux. Monsieur Guillaumin already knew the situation for he was secretly connected with Lheureux. However he was a vain man and had always admired Madame Bovary and coveted her, so he began to make love to her. Emma was much disgusted with the man and left with the words, "I am to be pitied—not to be sold."

She tried everywhere for help. All of a sudden she thought of Rudolphe. She went to see him at La Huchette. Rudolphe appeared glad to see her but could not give her any help for he spoke the truth when he said he didn't have the money she was asking for.

Emma then went to the chemist. She was by this time completely frantic. She went to the shelf on which she knew arsenic was kept and began eating it. The chemist's assistant, a young lad, was very much frightened but couldn't stop her.

Charles had been looking all over for Emma for he had returned home and discovered how things were for them. He finally set out on the road towards Rouen. When he finally returned he found Emma home and quite ill as the poison had begun to work. She writhed in agony. Charles saw a letter she had written and was frantic at learning about the poison. He called other doctors in. Berthe was frightened at her mother's appearance. The doctor from the city, sorrowfully declared that there was nothing that could be done. The priest came and ministered the last rites of extreme unction. First, upon the eyes, that had so coveted all worldly pomp; then upon the nostrils that had been greedy of the warm breezes and amorous odors; then upon the mouth that had uttered lies, that had curled with pride and cried out in lewdness; then upon the hands that had delighted in sensual touches; and finally upon the soles of the feet, so swift of yore, when she was running to satisfy her desires, and that would walk no more. She died shortly, while the priest was there praying.

Charles was exhausted and weak. He had Emma buried in her wedding dress and placed in three cabinets. Homais cut some of her beautiful hair for Charles to keep. Old Rouault arrived at Yonville and fainted when he saw the blank cloth as he wasn't sure as to why he had been called.

After the funeral, piles of Emma's bills came in to Charles. He paid all he could and with each one thought he had seen the last but there were always more, and he often had to apologize.

One day, wandering aimlessly about the house, he came upon one of Rudolphe's letters. He saw only part and not being a person to go to the bottom of things he passed it up thinking that perhaps they had loved platonically.

Then Emma began to corrupt him from the grave. He began to spend lavishly on his own appearance and to sign bills of hand the way she had. He sold furniture and silver piece by piece. He was indulgent towards Berthe and did not like to see her looking so badly.

Homais, the chemist, was prospering. He aided Charles in his plans for Emma's tomb. From respect or from a sort of sensuality that made him carry on his investigation slowly, Charles had not yet opened the secret drawer which Emma had generally used. One day he did however. All Leon's letters were there. There could be no doubt this time. He found Rudolphe's portrait and his letters.

People wondered at his despondency. He appeared wild. He never went out and saw no one, even his patients.

One day when he went to market to sell his horse, his last resource, he met Rudolphe. Rudolphe at first turned pale but then grew bold and invited Charles to the public house for some beer. As he talked Charles lost himself in contemplating the face that Emma had loved. He would have liked to have been this man. Finally he broke in on what Rudolphe was saying and said, "I don't blame you, no, I don't blame you now. It is the fault of fatality!"

That afternoon, little Berthe went to the garden to fetch her father for dinner. His head was thrown back against the wall, his eyes closed, his mouth open, and in his hand was a long tress of black hair. He was dead.

When everything was sold, twelve francs, seventy-five centimes remained. These were used to pay for Mademoiselle Bovary's trip to her grandmother who died the same year; old Rouault was paralysed, and it was an aunt who took charge of her. She is poor and sends her to a cotton factory to earn a living.

Since Bovary's death, three doctors have followed one another at Yonville without any success, so severely did Homais attack them. He has an enormous practice; the authorities treat him with consideration, and public opinion protects him.

He has just received the cross of the Legion of Honour.

THE WAY OF ALL FLESH

By

Samuel Butler

SAMUEL BUTLER (*1835–1902*) was an English author, born in
Langar, Nottinghamshire. His parents tried to raise him for
the ministry but his personal opinions were at variance with
their desires. He emigrated to New Zealand where in five
years he accumulated a competence and indulged in literary
activities. In 1872 he published his *Erewhon* which was a
utopian novel satirizing the Darwinian theories and conventional religion. Butler was a man of great versatility and pursued studies in painting, biology, Shakespearian criticism and
writing. He is probably best known for his posthumous novel
The Way of All Flesh.

THE AUTHOR, when he was a small boy, knew old Mr. Pontifex, a
gentleman of nearly eighty, who was a carpenter by trade, and
who was a rather talented amateur painter and musician. The old
man had married in the year 1750 and had had a son about fifteen
years later. The son, George Pontifex, was a bright child, obstinate
and sturdy by nature, who gave every promise of a successful
career. His mother's sister, who lived in London, took the boy to
her home and her husband put him into business. He made a very
rapid progress and at twenty-five was taken into partnership with
his uncle. Two years later he married a lady who brought him a
handsome dowry and who died after the birth of her youngest
child, Alethea, in 1805. George Pontifex did not marry again.

In the early years of the nineteenth century, old Mr. Pontifex
was visited regularly at Paleham by his five little grandchildren and
their two nurses. In 1811, Mrs. Pontifex died and, in accordance
with an old custom, a penny loaf was sent to everyone in the
neighborhood. The author, a boy living at the rectory with his
father received one also and, in common with all the other chil-

dren of the neighborhood, became solicitous about the health of all
the old people in the vicinity for, should they die, the treat would
probably be repeated. One year later Old Pontifex himself died but
his son did not believe in the custom of penny loaves.

The manner in which George Pontifex raised his children was
a very strict one. He would repeatedly tell them that he would see
them through school but that they should not get a penny from
him after that. They must try to emulate him by making their own
ways in the world without the help of another. He convinced his
younger son, Theobald, to try to get a fellowship at Cambridge
and then to prepare for the clergy. Theobald, who could not compete in business with his elder brother, John, accepted his father's
decision as something that might give him some independence and
free him from parental tyranny. When it came to his ordination,
however, Theobald became frightened and wrote his father that
he had decided against entering the clergy. His answer was a brief
note threatening to cut him off without a penny if he changed
his mind at this late stage. Theobald was ordained.

The reverend Mr. Allaby, rector of Crampsford, had little money
and many unmarried daughters, five in fact. A friend managed to
get Theobald to go to Crampsford as aid to Mr. Allaby, but really
as a victim for the wiles of one of the unmarried daughters. Theobald came to dinner and was treated very cordially; when he departed, however, a storm rocked the Allaby household. All of the
daughters could not be attentive to him. The young man would
merely become confused. Their father settled the problem. Let
them play cards for Theobald. They did and Christina, a girl of
twenty-seven—four years older than Theobald—won him. The
others thereupon promised that, when the young man came to the
house, they would not be in evidence.

The inexperienced victim of this plot was easy to snare, although
a little push, as it were, from Mr. Allaby was necessary before
he actually summoned up enough courage to propose marriage.
There was little enough romance in Theobald's nature, though he
pretended, even to himself, that he was an impassioned lover.
Christina, on the other hand, was all sentiment and, when Theobald accidentally left his sermon case behind one Sunday, she
slept all night with it in her bosom.

The engagement to a penniless girl on the part of his son gave
George Pontifex an opportunity for the sarcasm and threats which
he so enjoyed and, as a consequence, Theobald postponed the
marriage. He did not break the engagement, however, and when,
in three or four years his father became accustomed to the idea,
the wedding took place. After the ceremony Theobald got sick
with fright and actually quarreled with his wife as to who should
order dinner that night. As Theobald was a little more stubborn,
he had his way and, as a result of winning the initial argument, he
established himself as complete master of his home. Obsessed with
a sense of his own importance, Theobald, who had been so timid
a rebel against his father's tyranny became, in his turn, a household dictator.

Battersby-on-the-Hill was the name of the village of which
Theobald became rector; and a pleasant little place of four or
five hundred inhabitants it was. It was here about five years
later that a son was born to Christina, to the great joy of her husband and of old Mr. Pontifex, who acted as though this were the
first time that Theobald had done anything of which he might
be proud. There was quite a celebration, which even the author
attended, for it gave him an opportunity to see Alethea, Theobald's sister, again, and he had always been in love with her. The
author was godfather to little Ernest Pontifex, for so they named
the child, and from that time took quite an interest in his god-
child.

A little later George Pontifex died leaving less than was expected to young Ernest, but still leaving something. His epitaph,
which some suspected as being not entirely free from guile, read
thus:

He Now Lies Awaiting A Joyful Resurrection
At The Last Day.
What Manner of Man He Was
That Day Will Discover.

The birth of Ernest was but the first of a series; another boy,
named Joseph, and a girl, Charlotte, were born in succession, and
Theobald became aware of the fact that children were a nuisance.
Christina was certainly fond of Ernest, though Theobald never

was, but he received just as regular and just as severe whippings at her hands as he did at the hands of his father. When the author, whose name by the way is Edward Overton, visited the Pontifexes, he found that the children were white and puny, aching for love and understanding, and finding only the firmness of jailers who are sure they have their charges' interests at heart.

When Ernest was old enough to go to school he was enrolled at Roughborough under the famous Dr. Skinner, a man of prodigious learning and little wisdom, whose ferocious temper made him feared by every boy in the school. When Ernest had been a year and a half at Roughborough—he was now almost fourteen—he was in disgrace with all the masters because he always wanted a little more freedom than was allowed him. At this time his aunt, Alethea Pontifex, decided to move near the school so that she might perhaps be of some aid to her nephew and might, in some small way, be able to overcome the influence of Theobald and Christina in the formation of his character.

The youngster won her affection at once by displaying a good knowledge and vast love of music, despite the fact that he had to hide both from his masters, who thought such things reprehensible. Games did not interest Ernest very much, but then he was not very strong. Alethea conceived the idea of having him build an organ, under her supervision, an organ which he could play as much as he liked. In this manner his love of music and desire to play an instrument would lead him to take the exercise he needed so badly.

For about a year and a half things went well; then Alethea suffered a severe attack of typhoid fever. The will she insisted on making was a strange one. She left a goodly sum of money to Ernest, to be given him when he was twenty-eight. Overton was to be executor and was not to let Ernest know that any money was ever to come to him. In this way, Alethea argued, Ernest would make his mistakes with the money his grandfather had left him and then, when he had learned some wisdom, he would come into enough to keep him for the rest of his days. The will was drawn up and shortly thereafter Alethea died.

The Pontifexes had a housemaid by the name of Ellen, a remarkably pretty girl, of whom Ernest was fond in a boyish way.

One morning it was discovered that the girl, who was no more than nineteen, was pregnant. With no foundation for their suspicions certainly, Christina and Theobald none the less fastened on Ernest as the culprit. Ellen was immediately sent away in disgrace. The cook told Ernest the story shortly after the carriage had taken Ellen away; and told him also that Ellen had no money. Taking a shortcut, Ernest ran after the coach and caught it by the time he was out of breath. He said goodbye to the girl, pressing into her hands the little money in his pockets, his knife, and his watch. In tears, Ellen told him that she would never forget him and that some day she would try to repay him for his kindness.

To explain the absence of his watch, Ernest had to say that he had lost it, but when his father discovered it in a pawnshop in a neighboring village and obtained a description of the girl who had left it there, he was more firmly convinced than ever that his son had behaved shamefully in his own home. On learning that John, the coachman, had witnessed Ernest's parting with his watch, Theobald dismissed him at once. John, noticing Ernest's pale and frightened face, told Theobald that he did not mind being discharged but added that, if he learned that Ernest had been treated harshly, he would return and give Theobald a beating that he would not soon forget.

On graduation from Roughborough, Ernest went to Cambridge where his father desired that he follow in his footsteps by becoming ordained. At first Ernest, like Theobald before him, was so frightened that he tried to resist; later he almost became converted to a fanatic cult within the church and was full of schemes for the redemption of mankind.

Shortly after Ernest had been ordained to a curacy in one of the central parts of London, he met a colleague, Pryer, one of a High Church group, who believed in such things as the celibacy of the clergy. Pryer was a strong and unscrupulous personality and Ernest soon fell under his influence. Together they planned to start a College of Spiritual Pathology, which would of necessity be dependent on Ernest's money. Pryer, to make the money grow properly, invested in the stock market, where he seemed to invariably lose, until eventually he absconded with whatever of the money he still had.

In the boarding house in which Ernest resided were two hand-some young women, Miss Snow and Miss Maitland. Miss Snow was a lady of none too rigid virtue but Ernest, with no experience of the sex, could not realize that. Discovering that her rooms were visited by a young man named Towneley, whom he had much admired at Cambridge, he was upset. Suddenly realizing that he was not interested in the young woman to teach her something of religion but for a very different reason, he decided that, since Towneley was with Miss Snow, he could go to visit Miss Mait-land. The latter was an entirely different type of girl and Ernest made it so plain what he wanted that she called the police. Towneley and Overton did their best for him but it was of no avail. Ernest was sentenced to prison for six months.

It was at this time that Ernest broke with his parents, realizing that they were responsible for all his troubles. He refused to ever see them again, though, when he knew death was near his mother, years later, he went to visit her.

On leaving prison Ernest decided, his former career as a clergy-man being over, that he wanted to go into business. At this time he became very friendly with Overton, who was tempted to let him have the money that Alethea had left him at once, but who did not want to spoil the experiment. He helped Ernest set up in business, therefore, and anxiously awaited the results of the new enterprise.

One night Ernest recognized in a passing lady of the streets none other than Ellen, the housemaid to whom he had given his watch. They renewed their acquaintance and Ernest took her home to live with him until they could marry. They worked very hard at the business and had a truly remarkable financial success. In addition Ernest was reasonably happy with Ellen, whom he soon married.

Ernest's success and happiness did not, unfortunately, last very long. Ellen had strange fits of depression and seemed unable to account for a goodly portion of the money which the store had taken in. After a while Ernest discovered what was really at the root of the trouble. Ellen had been a very heavy drinker before she had come to live with him. She had tried very hard to over-come the habit and had said nothing to him about it, but it had become too much for her. Ernest would not subscribe to Overton's advice to divorce Ellen and was made more miserable daily. The business was rapidly being ruined, for Ellen spent all the money on liquor and, worst of all, she was constantly getting into trouble.

One day, as he was walking near the park, Ernest was delighted to see his father's former coachman, John, who greeted him warmly. When John started to talk about himself Ernest was startled, for John told him that he might very well have been the father of Ellen's child and that, when Theobald Pontifex discharged him, he had married Ellen. Ernest's happiness at learning that he was not, and never had been, married was unbounded. Ellen was quite content to leave him and, indeed, shortly after "married" once more and went to live in America, where Ernest sent an allowance regularly. Their children remained in London with Ernest.

Thoroughly aware of the mistakes his parents had made in raising their children, Ernest insisted on sending his away to live in the country with a worthy couple, so they might be well cared-for and still be independent. The income on the money Alethea had left, which now became his, was ample to cover all expenses for the children and to keep Ernest living very well. His studies at last bore fruit and he became an author, though with little concern for what any one thought of his work. He would never have anything to do with reviewers, saying: "What can it matter to me whether people read my books or not? It may matter to them—but I have too much money to want more, and if the books have any stuff in them it will work by-and-by. I do not know nor greatly care whether they are good or not. What opinion can any sane man form about his own work? Some people must write stupid books just as there must be junior ops and third class poll men. Why should I complain of being among the mediocrities? If a man is not absolutely below mediocrity let him be thankful—besides, the books will have to stand by themselves some day, so the sooner they begin the better."

ANNA KARENINA

By

Leo Tolstoy

COUNT LYOV NIKOLAIEVITCH TOLSTOY (*1828–1910*) was a Russian poet, novelist and social reformer. He joined the army as a staff officer in the Crimean war and was at the storming of Sebastopol. Retiring from the army he spent a short time in the most brilliant literary and social circles of St. Petersburg. He married in 1862 and settled on his estates devoting himself to the advancement of the peasantry. Tolstoy's desire was to divest himself of his property. His wife refused to see the family reduced to hardship so he deeded his estates to his family and worked on the land as a peasant and lived as a guest in his wife's house. In the Fall of 1910 he left home as a wanderer and died of exposure. He wrote almost constantly during his life-time and as his years advanced his works became more melancholy. His great volume *Anna Karenina* was produced in the years 1875 to 1878.

ANNA KARENINA, a beautiful and charming young society matron, hurriedly left her husband, her little son and her household in Petersburg, one winter, in order to go to Moscow to act as mediator in the family crisis which was taking place in the home of her beloved brother, Prince Stepan Arkadyevitch Oblonsky, or Stiva, as he was called in the fashionable world. Stiva's wife, Dolly, had discovered that he had been carrying on an intrigue with the French governess of the children and she had announced to her husband that she could not go on living in the same house with him.

While on the train from Petersburg to Moscow, Anna made the acquaintance of the old Countess Vronsky whose son, Count Vronsky, was a suitor of Stiva's sister-in-law, the lovely eighteen-year-old débutante Princess Kitty Shtcherbatsky. The crotchety old countess quite lost her heart to Anna during the journey and when Vronsky met his mother at the railway station Anna was extravagantly introduced to him with many enthusiastic compliments. Vronsky, on his part, was favorably impressed by this energetic, charming woman who pressed his hand in greeting with such frank warmth and who carried her slightly full figure with such admirable lightness and grace. To make the meeting more memorable, it happened that a drunken guard was killed by a train while they were still in the depot. The fact that Vronsky inconspicuously left two hundred roubles for the widow of the man served to accentuate the impression that his distinguished and handsome person had already left with Anna.

Meanwhile, Kitty had received her first proposal from the simple, idealistic country squire and old friend of Stiva, Levin, who had seen Kitty grow up from childhood into a gay and lovely young woman, one of the belles of Moscow. For no tangible reason, since Vronsky had never made a proposal of marriage, and although she was indeed fond of Levin, Kitty had refused him in the hope that Vronsky would propose at the coming charity ball at which the most brilliant society in Moscow would be represented.

Anna played her role well and soon the troubled waters of the Oblonsky ménage were again flowing smoothly; Dolly and Stiva were reconciled and the latter was as genuinely penitent as his somewhat shallow emotional nature permitted him to be for his little extra-marital escapade. Soon the eve of the ball rolled around, and Anna nodded with approval at Kitty's costume when the young girl entered the already crowded ballroom with her mother. Kitty's hopes leapt high that night for she felt this to be the proper occasion on which Vronsky's intentions might become explicit. But Anna was particularly fascinating that night in her simple black dress, fascinating were her round arms with their bracelets, fascinating was her firm neck with its thread of pearls, fascinating the light, graceful movements of her little feet and hands, fascinating was that lovely face in its eagerness, but there was something terrible and cruel in her fascination. Or so at least it seemed to Kitty. She saw that dancing the mazurka Vronsky and Anna felt themselves alone in the crowded room and the submissive look on Vronsky's face, hitherto always so firm and independent, confirmed her in her feeling that she had been a fool to refuse a man who was most attractive to her for one who was so faithless and irresolute. As for Anna, she decided then and there, either through fear or unconscious coquetry, that she would leave Moscow the following day for home.

Returning home to her husband, Alexey Alexandrovitch, Anna resumed the routine duties of managing a large and fashionable household. She managed to forget the slight feeling of shameful excitement which her more or less casual contacts with Count Vronsky had caused and made a genuine attempt to immerse herself in the wifely duties Alexey expected from her, comforting herself with the thought that Alexey was, in spite of his rather unattractive exterior, a good man, truthful, good-hearted and distinguished in his official responsibilities.

Vronsky, however, with no familial responsibilities to tie him down, could not dismiss the mingled feelings and intense admiration and desire which Anna had aroused in him and in order to have freer access to Anna's society, he decided to take up his old diggings in Petersburg and to pay a few visits to old friends so that he might quickly begin to frequent the circles in which Madame Karenina moved. When Anna began to meet Vronsky at various fashionable events, she was at first sincerely displeased with him for daring to pursue her; or at least believed herself so.

Meanwhile, news came from Moscow of Kitty Shtcherbatsky's serious illness which Anna instinctively and rightly attributed to Vronsky's defection. One night Anna deliberately visited the Princess Betsy as she was aware that Vronsky was expected there and she generously and seriously urged that he return to Moscow and Kitty. This was the first time Anna had openly intimated that she was aware of the reason for his presence in Petersburg and emboldened by the love which he read in her eyes Vronsky declared his love in impassioned terms in spite of the fact that Alexey Alexandrovitch arrived at the reception at this moment, and in spite of the fact that the mutual interest of himself and Anna in one another was becoming increasingly evident to the scandal-mongers of this exclusive set. As for Alexey, he was engrossed in a profound discussion of the most recent theological controversies and noticed nothing out of the way in his wife's animated tête-à-tête with Vronsky. But he was too much the man of the world not to notice that to the rest of the company it appeared indecorous.

Alexey decided that it was his duty to warn Anna to behave more circumspectly although he did not feel for a moment that there was any reality to the matter, apart from social demands that appearances always be above questioning. However, when he broached the subject to her, he met with a barrier of amused perplexity on Anna's part and so, although nothing special happened, a new life began for the Kareninas. Their inner relations were completely changed. Alexey, a man of great power in the political world, felt himself completely helpless against the blow which he felt was lifted over him.

And he had not long to wait; for shortly thereafter Vronsky became Anna's lover. But Anna's sense of shame and guilt at their spiritual nakedness crushed all the brief joy out of her and in its turn infected Vronsky. But this passed too, and although all Vronsky's inner life was absorbed in his passion, his external life unalterably followed along the accustomed lines of his social and regimental ties and interests. The regiment was fond of Vronsky and respected him too. They were proud that this man of immense wealth, with brilliant education and abilities, had disregarded the path open to him for every kind of success and distinction and instead devoted himself to the interests of his regiment and his comrades. It need not be said that Vronsky did not speak of his love to any of his comrades, nor did he betray his secret even in the wildest drinking bouts. In spite of that, his love was known to all the town. The majority of the men envied him for just what was the most irksome factor in his love—the exalted position of Karenina. As for the women, who envied Anna and had wearied of hearing her called "virtuous", they were only waiting for a decisive turn in public opinion to fall upon her with all the weight of their scorn.

Their opportunity came sooner than had been looked for. Beside the service and society, Vronsky had another great interest —horses. On the day of the great races at Krasnoe Selo, attended by the most brilliant court and diplomatic society, Vronsky was thrown from his horse and Anna who was in the audience with Karenina, for form's sake, behaved in a manner which was beyond decorum. Karenina, who had been abroad and who now occupied the town house while Anna stayed in the country villa, was furious at this breach of the external proprieties; for it had come to that between them. But, when returning from the races Anna had informed him of her relations with Vronsky and had burst into tears, Alexey for all the fury aroused in him against her, was aware at the same time of that emotional disturbance always produced in him by tears. He felt almost physical pity for her. He subsequently thought the matter over from all possible angles—a duel, divorce, and decided they were out of the question for one reason or another. He concluded that in accordance with the principles of his religion he would devote his energies to his wife's reformation and salvation, although, no doubt, she could never regain his esteem.

As for Anna, she was alternately happy and remorseful that she had thus clarified her position. But visions of shameful ostracism began to haunt her and after making various abortive attempts at a solution, she decided she would first have to reach some understanding with Vronsky. As for Vronsky, his present relation to Anna and her husband was to his mind clear and simple. It was precisely defined in the code of principles by which he was guided. She was an honorable woman who had bestowed her love upon him, and he loved her, and therefore she was in his eyes a woman who had a right to the same, or even more, respect than a lawful wife. But when Anna informed him that she was with child he was caught unawares, and had begged her to leave her husband. But on second thought, he felt that it would be better to avoid such a move. Anna, torn by the condition on which Alexey would give her her freedom, that of leaving him the little boy, decided she would go back to Petersburg to Karenina's establishment and perform, once again, the purely nominal duties of a wife. Long as she was willing not to make her association with Vronsky too apparent to the world at large, Karenina offered, in his turn, all the privileges of a faithful wife without the necessity of fulfilling her duties.

Things went on in this manner for some time, until, one evening shortly before her approaching confinement, Anna summoned Vronsky to her home. As luck would have it, the husband and the lover met on the former's door-step. This outward breach of decorum sent Karenina into a cold rage and he took steps at once toward securing a divorce, regardless of the scandal it was certain to cause. In the meanwhile, however, official duties called him to Moscow and here Prince Oblonsky and his family pleaded with him not to go through with the divorce action. The Princess Kitty had effected a real reconciliation and love-match with the old, rejected suitor, Levin, and all was happiness were it not for this shadow on their beloved Anna. Suddenly a telegram came for Karenina from Anna saying she was dying and imploring him to return. And truly, Anna was near death. The confinement had been successful but the mother was on her death-bed. Alexey granted Anna the forgiveness she begged, not only forgave her but pitied her for her sufferings and remorse. He forgave Vronsky and felt sorry for him too, especially after he heard reports of Vronsky's attempted suicide.

Miraculously, however, Anna got well and once the softening effect of the near approach of death had worn off, Alexey noticed that Anna was afraid of him, ill at ease and could not look him straight in the face. But the rupture could not be healed and Anna conceived a great spiritual and physical loathing for this man who had been so generous and Christian in his behavior. Through the good offices of her brother, Stiva, it was arranged with Karenina that he would grant a divorce and take the charge of adultery upon himself since this was the only basis upon which the Russian Orthodox Church would grant one. But within a month even this last generous gesture was denied Alexey Alexandrovitch and he was left alone with his son in his house at Petersburg, while Anna and Vronsky had gone abroad together, not having obtained a divorce, but having absolutely declined all idea of one.

Anna, in that first period of her emancipation and rapid return to health, felt herself unpardonably happy. The thought of her husband's unhappiness did not poison her happiness. Separation from the son she loved—even that did not cause her anguish in these early days. The baby girl, Vronsky's child, had so won Anna's heart, since she was all that was left her, that Anna thought rarely of her son. Vronsky, meanwhile, in spite of the complete realization of everything he had so long desired was not perfectly happy. Deprived of any real social life due to the irregularity of their position, Vronsky fell back upon an early interest, painting, to satisfy his hunger for achievement of one kind or another. It helped him to fancy himself an enlightened amateur and patron of the arts, who had renounced the world, his connections, and his ambition for the sake of the woman he loved. But almost as suddenly as it had reasserted itself, his interest in painting died away, for Vronsky was too much the man of taste not to finally become aware of how second-rate his aptitude in this direction was. They resolved to return to Russia, to the country.

Back in Petersburg, everyone but Alexey Alexandrovitch perceived that his career had come to a full stop, was over. Although he still filled a position of consequence, nothing was expected from him and from this time on he began to occupy himself with various projects and outlines for judicial reform. But he had one faithful disciple in the person of the religious, elderly and highly unattractive Countess Lidia Ivanovna who, from the day of Anna's departure, hoped to take her place in Karenina's affections. It was she who told Karenina's son that his mother was dead. But the child refused to believe it.

One of Anna's objects in returning to Russia had been to see her son. As soon as she arrived in Petersburg she sent a friendly plea to be allowed to see her son, but influenced by the Countess Lidia, Karenina refused. Anna was wounded to the quick but decided to see the boy anyway. She visited her husband's house and found the child happy and full of memories of her. She was even more upset by this visit than she had predicted and shortly afterward, having been brutally humiliated in her attempt to face out her position in society, she and Vronsky departed for the country.

Levin's country place was not far from Vronsky's estate and Dolly who was visiting Kitty in order to be with her during her confinement decided it was her duty to visit her husband's sister. Both Levin and Kitty disliked the idea of her having anything to do with Vronsky, but Dolly felt she had to indicate to Anna that her affection for her had not changed in spite of her position. Dolly came home completely reconciled to the situation, and even to Vronsky, although she could not understand Anna's refusal to get a divorce which Vronsky so urgently wished so that his child might bear his own name.

But even the country began to pall on them and the growing fear that she might lose Vronsky's love decided Anna to secure a divorce so that she could marry him and in this way tie him to her. When Stiva reached Petersburg as emissary, once again, for Anna to her husband, he heard on all sides how Karenina's affairs were dominated by a clairvoyant, Landau, whom the Countess Lidia had taken up. The matter was left for Landau to settle in a trance and the result was an unconditional refusal from Karenina to grant Anna a divorce. Anna and Vronsky were living in Moscow awaiting a decision and day by day the situation between them became more strained mostly due to Anna's unnatural suspicions and jealousy which, in their turn, produced a real coldness and irritation in Vronsky.

One day after a quarrel, Vronsky left for a visit to his mother who had as a guest a young girl, the daughter of the Princess Sirokin. Anna's by now unsettled mind immediately attributed the visit to the presence of the girl. After much internal anguish, she sent a note to Vronsky asking him when he would be back. She decided subsequently, however, to follow him to his mother's. When she alighted from the train a careless note from Vronsky stating he would be home at ten was handed to her by the porter who also informed her that the coach of the Vronskys was waiting outside for the Princess Sirokin and her daughter. Anna was furious at the fancied "affair."

And all at once she thought of the man crushed by the train the day she first met Vronsky. With a rapid, light step she went to the rails and threw herself under the approaching train. At the same instant she was terror-stricken at what she was doing. She tried to get up, to drop backwards; but something huge and merciless struck her on the head. All that had been in darkness, flickered, began to grow dim, and was quenched forever.

FATHERS AND SONS

By

Ivan Turgenev

IVAN SERGYEVICH TURGENEV (*1818–1883*) was a Russian nov
elist. When he was 22 he assumed a government post but soon
retired to write. His liberalism and letters presently led him
to a short imprisonment. Upon his release he belabored the
mental and moral bankruptcy of the upper classes which he
held was a result of idleness ensuing from overworking the
serfs. *Fathers and Sons* probably marks the apex of his critical
period and in this work the term "nihilist" was first used. The
animosity of his critics finally turned the melancholy of his
earlier works into pessimism.

NIKOLAI PETROVITCH KIRSANOV, a landed proprietor in Russia, was
happy, in the spring of 1859, to greet his son, Arkady, who had just
graduated from college and was returning home, bringing for the
vacation his friend, Bazarov, a medical student, of whom he thought
highly. Nikolai lived quietly, a widower, happy in the companionship of his brother, Pavel, a retired army officer.

When they arrived at the house they were greeted by Pavel, exquisite, delicately-featured, handsomely erect. His reaction to
Bazarov was that the young man was an unkempt creature, while
Bazarov's reaction to him was that he was a museum piece. The
servants were happy to greet their young master but one young
woman, Fenitchka, did not come forward to greet them, remaining in a small back room in which a child slept peacefully.

The next morning Arkady asked about Fenitchka, who still remained in her room. In confusion his father told him that he was
living with Fenitchka and that they had a baby son. The young
man, realizing that Fenitchka was ashamed to meet him, went to
her room to greet her and kissed his little step-brother. When

Pavel joined them, he asked about Bazarov and was told that he
was a nihilist. In astonishment he asked the meaning of nihilism
and was told that it derived from the Latin word "nihil" which
means nothing. A nihilist was one who accepted nothing or, perhaps more accurately, one "who regards everything from the
critical point of view . . . who does not bow down before any
authority, who does not take any principle on faith, whatever
reverence that principle may be enshrined in." Bazarov comes
along with a sack of frogs which he plans to use for experiment.

"So he's going to cut them up," observed Pavel Petrovitch. "He
has no faith in principles, but he has faith in frogs."

When Bazarov sat down with them Pavel interrogated him
concerning his nihilism but was met with indifference, though he
did evoke one statement of Bazarov's belief: "A good chemist is
twenty times as useful as any poet."

Arkady chided Bazarov in private about the manner in which he
treated his uncle. He told him the story of Pavel's life, which re-
volved around an unhappy love affair. The story made little impression on Bazarov, who said that as a physiologist he knew what
aesthetic nonsense such talk about love really was. What can enig-
matical glances mean to a man who has studied the anatomy of the
eye?

Nikolai, a somewhat romantic and impractical soul, very fond
of German poetry, did not manage his little farm over-well, as
Bazarov was quick to notice and to tell Arkady. Though Arkady
was not pleased at the attitude toward his uncle of the young man
whom he regarded as his master, he was glad that Bazarov obviously liked his father and approved of the affair with Fenitchka.
However, on one occasion Arkady was hurt. Bazarov was amazed
to hear the sweet strains of Schubert's "Expectation" on a violoncello and inquired the name of the player. When Arkady told him
it was his father, Bazarov burst into roars of laughter at the
thought that a man of forty-four, who was the head of a family,
should still play on the violoncello.

Pavel's antipathy to Bazarov flared up, especially when Nikolai
told him that he had overheard Bazarov telling Arkady that his
father's day was over. Arkady, prompted by Bazarov, had even
taken away his father's copy of Pushkin and given him a scientific

German text to read. Things came to a stage where Pavel argued with Bazarov, attempting to defend an aristocratic liberalism. Bazarov retorted that those were mere romantic phrases, meaning nothing. In the course of the discussion the meaning of nihilism became somewhat clarified. What was necessary was to clear the intellectual atmosphere of all the rubbish in it which kept men from breathing properly. Nihilism was a purely destructive force, for the time was not yet come for construction nor, indeed, had Bazarov given it any thought.

Since the time was drawing near when Bazarov must return to his own home, the young men decided that for a few days, pleasure, they would go to the nearby town of X—, where Nikolai Petrovitch knew some of the important officials. Once there, on their way to visit the governor of the province, they encountered by chance another disciple of Bazarov's, one Sitnikov, who told them that while they are in town they must meet a very remarkable woman, Evdoksya Kukshin, known to her friends as Kukshina.

Off they went to Kukshina's, to discover a fairly young and very dishevelled young woman of the most "emancipated" type. She chattered of great names and of the latest articles but Bazarov said little except to ask if there were any beautiful women in town. There was a Madame Odintsov, a charming widow, but not fully "emancipated." After several quarts of champagne the atmosphere became oppressive and the three men departed.

At a ball a few nights later Arkady made the acquaintance of the charming Anna Sergyevna Odintsov, and talked to her so much of his friend that she invited them both to call. This they did promptly and Arkady was surprised to note that Bazarov, contrary to his habit, was talking a great deal and obviously trying to interest the lady. When she invited them to visit her nearby at her country home, they accepted promptly. As they left Madame Odintsov, Arkady asked his friend what he thought of their hostess, and was answered in a typical Bazarovian manner: "What a magnificent body. Shouldn't I like to see it on the dissecting-table."

Three days later the friends traveled to Anna Odintsov's country home, where she, her aunt, Princess H—, and her eighteen-year-old sister, Katya, constituted the entire household except, of course, for the servants. They were received very well, and were introduced to the family as well as to Porfiry Platonitch, an elderly neighbor, who often drops in to play cards, of which he is inordinately fond. Arkady soon discovered that Anna spent most of her time with Bazarov and, although he enjoyed being with Katya, he could not help feeling a trifle jealous.

Bazarov found himself in a strange state. He loved feminine beauty but regarded love in the abstract as sheer lunacy. He had always said that if a woman took a man's fancy, he should try to win her; but, if she proved difficult, forget about her and try someone else. Now, however, he discovered that directly he thought of Anna Odintsov, his blood was on fire. And he could not keep her out of his thoughts. He expressed himself constantly to the effect that these were physiological matters and that one woman was as desirable as another, provided she be as handsome. None the less he found himself thinking of kissing Anna, and Anna alone. One day he could stand it no longer and said abruptly that it was time for him to go home.

That night and the next morning Anna talked to Bazarov, telling him that she was unhappy, that if he went away she would miss him terribly, and that she wanted him to change his mind and to stay. She was normally a creature of regular habits, calm and rather silent; in short, not unlike Bazarov. But now there was something she wanted terribly and she was not sure what it was. Bazarov was encouraged and suddenly rushed at her with an animal-like passion. Believing the things he did, he could behave in no other manner, for he could not act in the tenderer manner of a lover. His violent manner frightened Anna so much that she flung him away and looked as though she were about to scream.

The next day Bazarov departed for his home and Arkady insisted on going at the same time, although he was more than a little loath to leave Katya. When they reached Bazarov's home, his father and mother were overwhelmed with joy and love. Bazarov treated them as calmly as he treated every one else, commenting to Arkady that his father was queer enough in many ways but harmless and sometimes fairly pleasant. The old parents absolutely idolized him and when Arkady talked to Bazarov's father in the enthusiastic manner in which he discoursed of his friend at any opportunity, the old man almost cried for joy.

When Arkady talked to Bazarov in this new environment, he learned a great many things that aided him to understand his friend better than he had before. Bazarov felt very insignificant insofar as he was a man and shared the abilities and fate of man in general. But he was extraordinarily conceited and thought very well of himself as an individual in comparison with others. "When I meet a man who can hold his own beside me," he said, "then I'll change my opinion of myself."

Arkady wanted to leave for his home and Bazarov decided to go with him. His poor parents were quite crushed by seeing their son for only three days after an absence of three years; nevertheless they tried not to show how much he had hurt them. On the way they stopped at Anna Odintsov's home and were greeted coolly, though Anna apologized by saying that she was not well and hoped that they would return soon. When they reached Nikolai Petrovitch's home, however, they were greeted with great joy, even by the usually imperturbable Pavel.

They had not been at Arkady's home long before that young man felt an irresistible desire to return to the Odintsovs. Saying good-bye hurriedly to his family and to Bazarov, on the pretext of studying the Sunday schools in the neighboring villages, he took a box of letters that had been written to his mother by Madame Odintsov's mother, and hastened to his goal. On his arrival he was greeted warmly by Anna and by the shy Katya.

Bazarov, left behind, pursued his scientific studies with vigor, talking little to any one, except to Fenitchka, with whom he became friendly. Once, while they were talking, he leaned forward to smell a rose which was close to her face. Turning his head slightly he kissed her vigorously on her parted lips. She pushed him away feebly and at that moment Pavel Petrovitch made his appearance.

Two hours later Pavel presented himself at Bazarov's door and said that he wanted his opinion on a matter that had been engaging his attention. What did Bazarov think of the institution of the duel? Bazarov answered that theoretically he thought it absurd but that practically he would not endure an insult and would fight if necessary. In that event, Pavel said, let them decide on the conditions for he was determined that they should fight.

The next morning they repaired to a nearby wood with Pavel's pistols. At the first exchange of shots Pavel missed but Bazarov, without taking aim, hit his opponent in the thigh. He quickly bound the wound, Pavel's honor was satisfied and they agreed to tell Nikolai that they had quarreled about politics. When they returned to the house Pavel, realizing that his brother had not married Fenitchka for fear it might offend him, and learning the truth of the incident with Bazarov from the girl herself, asked Nikolai to marry his mistress. Nikolai, who had long wanted just that, was overjoyed. Pavel, thinking of his own ruined life, was happy for his brother. Closing his eyes to fall asleep, he peacefully came to the end of his life, for indeed there was no more life for him to lead, nothing he was interested in, nothing to do, though in body he still lived.

Bazarov came to the Odintsov residence and told Arkady of the duel, assuring him that his uncle was not seriously injured. He learned that Arkady and Katya were in love and desired to marry. Then he told Arkady that he had no more interest in him and was sure that Arkady secretly felt the same way. Saying good-bye to Anna, he returned to his own home.

Always desirous of helping the peasants, Bazarov treated one old man who had typhus, from whom he contracted the disease. When she learned that he was dying, Anna Odintsov hurried to his side, bringing with her a German doctor. But it was too late to do anything for Bazarov. Before he died, he told Anna what he had never dared tell her before, or even admit to himself, that he loved her. He had not kissed her before and he asked her to kiss him now. She kissed him gently on the forehead, knowing that it would be the only time.

Two old people visit a little graveyard and stand speechless looking down at one grave in which all their hopes, all their aspirations lie buried. And then they move off slowly, supporting each other, for they are very feeble.

THE SCARLET LETTER

By

Nathaniel Hawthorne

NATHANIEL HAWTHORNE (*1804–1864*) was one of the earliest American novelists. He was born at Salem, Mass. He graduated from Bowdoin College in the class of 1825 with the poet Long-fellow. He wrote stories and verses for about 12 years after his graduation. Some of his short fiction gained such favorable notice from London that in 1837 a group of them to which he gave the name *Twice-Told Tales* was issued in one volume. He joined the semi-socialistic community at Brook Farm near Boston in 1841. Before he found the experiment unsatisfactory he wrote a series of stories for children from New England history. In 1850 he completed *The Scarlet Letter* which at once gained great renown and is claimed as the best of his works. Later he wrote *The House of the Seven Gables* and *The Wonder Book*. He was made consul at Liverpool by President Pierce. After four years he retired to Rome to write. In 1860 he returned to America and died while staying with his friend, ex-President Pierce. He was buried at Concord, near the graves of Emerson and Thoreau.

A THRONG OF BEARDED MEN, in sad-colored garments and gray steeple-crowned hats, intermixed with women, some wearing hoods, and others bare-headed, was assembled in front of a wooden edifice, the door of which was heavily timbered with oak and studded with iron spikes. But on one side of the portal, and rooted almost at the threshold, was a wild rose-bush, covered, in this month of June, with its delicate gems which might be imagined to offer their fragrance and fragile beauty to the prisoner as he went in, and to the condemned criminal as he came forth to his doom, in token that the deep heart of Nature could pity and be kind to him.

All eyes on this particular summer morning not less than two centuries ago were intently fastened on the iron-clamped oaken door. Suddenly it was flung open from within by the town-beadle, a grim and grisly presence, with a sword by his side and his staff of office in his left hand. He laid his right upon the shoulder of a young woman, whom he thus drew forward, until on the threshold of the door she repelled him by an action marked with natural dignity and force of character and stepped into the open air as if by her own free will. She bore in her arms a baby of some three months old, who winked and turned aside its little face from the too vivid light of day; because its existence, heretofore, had brought it acquaintance only with the gray twilight of a dungeon or other darksome apartment of the prison.

When the young mother stood fully revealed before the crowd, she clasped the infant closely to her bosom; not so much by an impulse of motherly affection, as that she might conceal a token fastened to her dress. There on the breast of her gown, in fine red cloth, surrounded with an elaborate embroidery of gold thread, appeared the letter A.

"She hath good skill at her needle, that's certain," remarked one of the women spectators, "but did ever a woman, before this brazen hussy, contrive such a way of showing it? It is but to laugh in the faces of our godly magistrates and make a pride out of what they, worthy gentlemen, meant for a punishment."

Some thought it should have been branded upon her forehead or that she should have had the death sentence passed upon her. With a haughty demeanor, she followed the beadle to the scaffold in the market place where she was to stand until an hour past noon. On the balcony of the meeting-house just above her head, the governor, several counsellors, a judge, a general and the ministers of the church sat or stood looking down upon her. Apparently she failed to see them for her mind wandered to other scenes—to the native village in Old England, to her father's bold brow, reverent white beard and old-fashioned Elizabethan ruff, to her mother's anxious face, but especially to the countenance of her husband, a man well-stricken in years, a pale, thin, scholar-like visage, with eyes dim and bleared from poring over ponderous books. The figure was slightly deformed with the left shoulder a trifle higher than the other.

Suddenly, accompanied by an Indian, that figure appeared on the outskirts of the crowd and a keen, penetrative look was fixed upon her. When she appeared to recognize him he slowly and calmly raised his finger, made a gesture with it in the air and laid it on his lips. He asked a townsman who she was and learned that she was the wife of a learned Englishman who resided in Amsterdam and two years before had sent her here while he remained behind to look after some necessary affairs but was never heard of again. The woman had refused to name the father of her child and so must stand in the pillory for three hours and wear the scarlet letter for the balance of her life.

Just then John Wilson, the eldest clergyman of Boston and a great scholar, addressed her. Since his own efforts had been futile, he was turning her over to her young pastor, the Reverend Mr. Dimmesdale.

This worthy bent his head in silent prayer and then came forward.

"Hester Prynne," he said leaning over the balcony, "I charge thee to speak out the name of thy fellow-sinner and fellow-sufferer. Be not silent from any mistaken pity and tenderness for him; for, believe me, Hester, tho he were to step down from high place to join thee there, it were better for him to do so than to hide a guilty heart thru life."

Hester shook her head.

The Reverend Mr. Wilson reminded her that the young minister spoke wisely and demanded that she speak out that name.

"Never!" she replied, looking not at him, but into the deep and troubled eyes of the younger clergyman. "Would that I might endure his agony as well as mine! My child must seek a heavenly Father; she shall never know an earthly one."

"Wondrous strength and generosity of a woman's heart!" he murmured. "She will not speak."

For the better part of an hour then the elder minister preached a sermon on the evils of sin. When it was over, she was led back to the prison, so exhausted and nervously excited that the prison attendants were unable to cope with her and sent for a physician. Roger Chillingworth, the old man she had seen on the outskirts of the crowd, was ushered into her presence. First, assuring her that he meant no harm, he quieted the child with a draught of medicine and then turned his attention to her. He had never been a fit husband for her, he said, should never have married her but he nevertheless intended to seek the father of her child since she would not divulge the secret, but she, too, was not to reveal that the old doctor was her husband.

Upon her release from prison shortly thereafter, Hester took up her abode in a small, thatched cottage on the outskirts of the town. There she supported herself by her needle. She made the gorgeously embroidered gloves that officials wore at public ceremonies, deep ruffs, baby linen, scarfs for military men, shrouds, coarse garments for the poor. She was patient—a martyr, indeed—but she forebore to pray for enemies, lest, in spite of her forgiving aspirations, the words of the blessing should stubbornly twist themselves into a curse. Clergymen used her as an object lesson; children cried after her in the streets; strangers stared at her badge of shame.

Her sole comfort was her beautiful baby. Pearl, she had named her, for she had purchased her with all she had. She dressed her in the finest of materials and thus arrayed she accompanied her mother everywhere holding a forefinger with her whole grasp, and tripping along at the rate of three or four footsteps to one of Hester's. She never mingled with other children for instinctively she felt their scorn, but the spell of life went forth from her ever-creative spirit, and communicated itself to a thousand objects, as a torch that kindles a flame wherever it may be applied. The pine trees, to her, were the Puritan elders, the ugliest weeds, their children. She played with a visionary throng but always she created enemies, never a friend. Early she had noticed the scarlet letter and often amused herself by throwing flowers at it. To the neighboring townspeople she was a demon offspring, to her mother, an enigma, an odd mixture of pain and joy.

At length the good people of the town decided that her child was not receiving the proper upbringing and should therefore be given into the charge of some more fit person to be reared. To secure the governor's help in preventing this, one morning she and Pearl set out for the Bellingham mansion. The child looked like a jet of flame garbed as she was in a crimson velvet tunic of a peculiar cut, abundantly embroidered with fantasies and flourishes of gold thread. She was the scarlet letter endowed with life!

When they reached the governor's mansion, they were informed that he was busy so they awaited him at the garden entrance where presently he appeared in company with three worthy gentlemen— the Reverend Mr. Wilson, whose beard was white as a snowdrift, the Reverend Arthur Dimmesdale and old Roger Chillingworth who for two or three years past had been settled in the town. He was a physician of some note and had become the friend as well as the medical adviser of the young minister whose health was suffering from overwork in the performance of his pastoral duties.

Soon they found themselves close to the little scarlet image.

"Prithee, young one," said the old man, "who art thou, and what has ailed thy mother to bedizen thee in this strange fashion? Art thou a Christian child or one of those naughty elves or fairies whom we thought to have left behind us in merry old England?"

"I am mother's child," answered the scarlet vision, "and my name is Pearl."

"Ruby, rather, or Red Rose, judging from thy hue!" responded the old minister attempting vainly to pat her cheek.

Just then Hester appeared and the governor told her of their decision to deprive her of Pearl. To her pleadings that she was well able to instruct her in the teachings of the church, he begged the old preacher examine the child in the catechism.

"Canst thou tell me, my child, who made thee?" he asked.

All this Pearl knew for Hester Prynne, herself the daughter of a pious home, had carefully instructed her in the New England Primer as well as the first column of the Westminster Catechisms, but the child was perverse this day and answered that she was not made at all, but had been plucked by her mother off the bush of wild roses that grew by the prison-door. The proximity of the governor's red rose, together with the recollection of the prison rose-bush which she had passed in coming hither no doubt was responsible for the answer.

Here was convincing proof that the magistrates were right. Old Roger Chillingworth, with a smile on his face, whispered something in the young clergyman's ear. Hester, looking at them, was startled to see what a change had come over the old man's features—how much uglier they were, how his figure seemed to have grown more misshapen. She caught hold of Pearl and drew her forcibly into her arms, confronting the old Puritan magistrate with almost a fierce expression.

"God gave me the child!" she cried. "Pearl keeps me here in life, punishes me too. See ye not, she is the scarlet letter, only capable of being loved, and so endowed with a million-fold of the power of retribution for my sin? Ye shall not take her! I will die first!"

Here by a sudden impulse she turned to the young clergyman. "Speak thou for me!" she cried. "Thou wast my pastor, and knowest me better than these men can. I will not lose the child! Look thou to it!"

Thus appealed to, the young man came forward, pale and holding his hand over his heart. He looked careworn and emaciated. He pleaded that the child was meant for a blessing—the one blessing of her life, to preserve her from the sin into which she might otherwise have fallen.

"You speak, my friend, with a strange earnestness," said old Roger Chillingworth, smiling at him.

The worthy gentlemen agreed that he was right. Hester should keep her child. Pearl stole softly towards the young minister then and taking his hand in both her·own laid her cheek against it. The minister looked round, laid his hand on the child's head, hesitated an instant, and then kissed her brow.

"A strange child!" remarked old Chillingworth. "It is easy to see the mother's part in her. Would it be beyond a philosopher's research to analyze that child's nature, and from its make and mold, to give a shrewd guess at the father?"

For some time, this husband of Hester's had been living under the same roof with the young minister, ostensibly to look after his health. The man's condition interested him for he seemed to be suffering from an illness of the soul that was affecting his body. In vain he tried to persuade the minister to reveal his secret, but he replied that he would disclose it only to God.

One day coming upon Reverend Mr. Dimmesdale asleep in his chair, Chillingworth laid his hand upon his bosom and thrust aside the vestment that had always hidden it from the professional eye. A look of wonder, joy and horror appeared in his face. He was filled with ecstasy but what distinguished the physician's ecstasy from Satan's was the trait of wonder in it!

Chillingworth now that he knew the minister's secret could play upon him as he chose. The victim was forever on the rack; it needed only to know the spring that controlled the engine: and the physician knew it well. Dimmesdale was conscious of some evil influence watching over him, but could never gain a knowledge of its actual nature. He hated the old man, but took himself to task for it and continued on terms of friendship with him.

In his sacred office the young minister had achieved a brilliant popularity overshadowing those more learned because his own burden gave him sympathies so intimate with the sinful brotherhood of mankind; so that his heart vibrated in unison with theirs, and received their pain into itself and sent its own throb of pain through a thousand other hearts, in quakes of sad, persuasive eloquence. People thought him a miracle of holiness. The very ground on which he trod was sanctified.

He was tortured by this public veneration and often vowed to tell them the truth, but the words he spoke were always vague. And yet, by the constitution of his nature, he loved the truth, and loathed the lie, as few men ever did; therefore, above all things else, he loathed his miserable self. In private he reverted to old outworn modes of penance. He scourged himself in his secret closet and laughed bitterly the while, fasted rigorously until his knees trembled beneath him, kept long night vigils in utter darkness. His brain, then, often reeled so that he saw visions, visions through which glided Hester Prynne, leading along little Pearl in her scarlet garb, and pointing her forefinger, first at the scarlet letter on her bosom, and then at the clergyman's own breast.

One night a new thought struck him. He dressed in his ministerial robes and strode forth to the scaffold in the market-place where Hester had suffered seven years before. The town lay asleep. Bodily pain over his heart caused him to shriek aloud, and, fearing discovery, he covered his face with his hands. At length he grew calm and noticed a glimmering light in the distance coming steadily nearer. It was the Reverend Mr. Wilson coming from the death chamber of Governor Winthrop, but he passed onward without noticing the crouching form. Frightened and fearing that morning would find him there half-frozen, he burst into laughter, a laughter that was echoed by a child's voice. Hester Prynne and Pearl approached.

He invited them to join him there. They mounted the steps and he took the child's hand. He felt stronger then. Would he stand thus with them at noon-day on the morrow, she asked, but he said not then but on the great Judgment day. Again the child laughed. Suddenly a meteoric disturbance illuminated the scene. In the sky the minister discerned a scarlet letter but Pearl's gaze was fixed on more tangible things. She pointed her finger toward old Roger Chillingworth who stood at no great distance from the scaffold looking malevolently at them.

"Who is that man, Hester?" the minister gasped, overcome with terror. "I shiver at him! Dost thou know him?"

Hester remembered her oath and was silent. The physician drew near and reminding him that this was not a fit preparation for the morrow's work led him home.

Next day, however, he preached an eloquent sermon, but as he came down the pulpit steps, the gray-bearded sexton met him, holding up a black glove, which the minister recognized as his own. It had been found on the scaffold. Moreover a great meteoric "A" had appeared in the night sky which the people said meant angel, for worthy Governor Winthrop had just died.

Hester, returning home, remembered him as he had once been, saw the present weakness and decided to help him. He was surely on the verge of lunacy. In the years she had matured and thought so deeply that she felt herself a match for Chillingworth.

One afternoon walking with Pearl in a retired part of the peninsula she beheld the old physician with a basket on one arm and a staff in the other hand, stooping along the ground in quest of medicinal roots and herbs. Bidding Pearl go play with shells and seaweed at the water's edge, she accosted him. She noticed he had an eager, searching, almost fierce, yet carefully guarded look which he tried to mask with a smile.

"Hast thou not tortured him enough?" she asked. "Has he not paid thee all?"

"No, no! He has but increased the debt. See what I have become and who made me so?" he answered.

Hester blamed herself. He should have avenged himself upon her, but the scarlet letter had done that, he reminded her. She must tell him the old man's identity for "There is no good for him, no good for me, no good for thee, no good for little Pearl. There is no path to guide us out of this dismal maze."

Chillingworth pitied her for the good that was wasted in her nature, but he could not pardon. However she might go her way and deal as she chose with her former lover. He waved his hand, then, and betook himself again to his employment of gathering herbs.

Hester marvelled how she had ever married him. In so doing he had committed a fouler offence than any which had since been done him, for he had persuaded her that she would be happy at his side.

A few days later she learned that Mr. Dimmesdale had gone to visit Eliot among his Indian converts and would probably return the next day. With Pearl for a companion she went into the forest and rested on a luxuriant heap of moss a little off the beaten path. A brook babbled near by. Soon the minister appeared coming along the path and she bade the child go play but to stay near the brook. There was a listlessness in his gait, as if he saw no reason for taking a step farther, nor had any desire to do so but would have been glad, could he be glad of anything, to fling himself down at the root of the nearest tree and lie there passive, for evermore. He still kept his hand over his heart. Hester called him and he put forth his hand, chill as death, and touched hers.

She led him to the heap of moss where she had been sitting and after speaking of ordinary occurrences he said, "Hester, hast thou found peace?"

She smiled drearily looking down upon her bosom but answered, "Hast thou?"

Then he told her of his despair, the hypocrisy of his life. She reminded him of the good he was doing among the people but he was unconvinced.

"Had I one friend—or were it my worst enemy!—to whom, when sickened with the praises of all other men, I could daily betake myself, and be known as the vilest of all sinners, methinks my soul might keep itself alive thereby."

The friend he had in her. The enemy she told him dwelt under his own roof. It was Roger Chillingworth, her husband.

He buried his face in his hands and upbraided her for keeping the secret from him for so long, but she clasped him to her bosom and at length he became quiet. They sat down side by side on the mossy trunk of a fallen tree and planned their future. He could not go on in the life he was in, neither had he the courage to seek a new environment alone.

"Thou shalt not go alone!" she answered in a deep whisper, for she, having lived so long apart from society, was not trammelled by its laws.

Joy filled her heart. She threw the scarlet letter into the nearby bushes, let her rich dark hair fall over her shoulders; a radiant and tender smile beamed out of her eyes. Love, whether newly born or aroused from a death-like slumber, must always create a sunshine, filling the heart so full of radiance, that it overflows upon the outward world. She called Pearl to her for she must know her father, but the child felt estranged because this new person had entered the picture. Not until her mother had confined her hair beneath the cap and restored the scarlet letter to her bosom did she rush to her side.

"Now thou art my mother indeed! And I am thy little Pearl!" she exclaimed kissing her brow, both cheeks and the scarlet letter, too.

Her father kissed her brow but she washed her forehead in the brook and then stood apart silently watching until the minister took his leave.

Three days hence, a Spanish vessel then lying in the harbor was to depart for Bristol. They would embark on that. The arrangements suited Dimmesdale perfectly, for he would be able to preach his Election Sermon and could leave feeling that he had honorably discharged his duties.

Due to the excitement he walked home rapidly. His attitude toward life had changed. He wanted to shake hands with a drunken seaman, to snub a devoted virgin. He took refuge in his study and set to work upon the sermon, a new draught, for the one already begun no longer satisfied him. To Chillingworth's request that he take drugs he replied that the sight of Eliot and the free forest air had completely restored him. He ate a hearty supper and spent the night on the sermon. When morning came, there he was, with the pen still between his fingers and a vast, immeasurable tract of written space behind him.

The morning of the great day arrived. Hester Prynne and little Pearl stood among the throng of craftsmen, Indians, visitors from other towns, beside the scaffold in the crowded market-place. It was a New England holiday. Wrestling matches were held, a friendly bout at quarter-staff, on the platform of the pillory there was an exhibition with broadsword and buckler. Among those interested were the crew from the Spanish vessel, rough-looking desperadoes, with sun-blackened faces, and an immensity of beard. They smoked tobacco and frequently quaffed from their pocket-flasks. Soon their captain appeared in close conversation with old Roger Chillingworth who smiled at Hester, a smile that conveyed secret and fearful meaning.

The noise of the drum and clarion announced the arrival of the procession. The sun shimmered on the weapons and armor of the military men; Bellingham and his associates were models of ponderous sobriety; but Hester's eyes were fixed on Arthur Dimmesdale who seemed imbued with a new spirit as he moved proudly past. Mistress Hibbens in gaudy dress remarked upon the transformation.

"Couldst thou surely tell," she questioned, "whether he was the same man that encountered thee on the forest-path?"

Hester evaded the question. The procession entered the meeting house whose doors were left open that the crowd in the square might hear the sermon. Pearl, playing about the market-place, attracted the attention of the shipmaster who took the gold chain from his hat and presented it to her, requesting at the same time that she tell her mother that the old doctor was to join their party. Curious people, sailors included, crowded near Hester to stare at the letter as did some of the town's own inhabitants to whom the sight was no novelty.

At the same moment the admirable preacher was looking down from the sacred pulpit upon an audience whose utmost spirits had yielded to his control.

Finally the services were over and babbling with applauses of the minister, the audience emerged from the meeting house. The subject had been the relation between the Deity and the communities of mankind, with a special reference to the New England which they were here planting in the wilderness. He had foretold a high and glorious destiny for the newly gathered people of the Lord. Apparently he felt he was about to die; he had reached the height of his power. Exhausted by his efforts, he staggered along but paused opposite the scaffold when he saw Hester and little Pearl. Turning toward them he stretched forth his arms.

"Hester," he said, "come hither! Come, my little Pearl!"

The child flew to him and clasped her arms about his knees. Hester slowly drew near, but paused before she reached him. Old Chillingworth sprang from the crowd and caught the minister by the arm.

"Ha, tempter! Methinks thou art too late!" he said. "Thy power is not what it was! With God's help, I shall escape thee!"

He again extended his hand to the woman of the scarlet letter. "Come, Hester, come!" he cried, with a piercing earnestness. "Support me up yonder scaffold!"

The amazed crowd beheld the minister, leaning on Hester's shoulder, and supported by her arm around him, approach the scaffold, and ascend the steps, while still the little hand of the sin-born child was clasped in his. Chillingworth followed. Then the Reverend Mr. Dimmesdale turned to the dignified and venerable rulers; to the holy ministers, to the people.

"People of New England!" he cried, "ye that have loved me!—ye that have deemed me holy!—behold me here, the one sinner of the world! At last! I stand upon the spot where, seven years since, I should have stood, here, with this woman, whose arm sustains me at this dreadful moment. Lo, the scarlet letter which Hester wears! Ye have all shuddered at it! But there stood one in the midst of you, at whose brand of sin and infamy ye have not shuddered!"

Fighting back the bodily weakness, he stepped passionately forward a pace before the woman and the child. With a convulsive motion, he tore away the ministerial band from before his breast. It was revealed! Then, down he sank upon the scaffold! Hester partly raised him, and supported his head against her bosom. Old Roger Chillingworth knelt down beside him, with a blank, dull countenance, out of which the life seemed to have departed.

"Thou hast escaped me!" he repeated more than once.

"May God forgive thee!" said the minister. "Thou, too, hast deeply sinned!" He withdrew his dying eyes from the old man, and fixed them on the woman and child.

"My little Pearl," he said feebly and smiling gently, "wilt thou kiss me now?"

Pearl kissed his lips, and as her tears fell upon her father's cheek, they were the pledge that she would grow up amid human joy and sorrow, nor forever do battle with the world, but be a woman in it.

Nothing was more remarkable than the change which took place, almost immediately after Mr. Dimmesdale's death in the appearance and demeanour of Roger Chillingworth. All his strength and energy—all his vital and intellectual force—seemed to desert him at once so that he positively withered up, shrivelled away, and almost vanished from mortal sight, like an uprooted weed that lies wilting in the sun. It is a curious subject of observation and inquiry, whether hatred and love be not the same thing at bottom. Each, in its utmost development, supposes a high degree of intimacy and heart-knowledge; each renders one individual dependent for the food of his affections and spiritual life upon another; each leaves the passionate lover, or the no less passionate hater, forlorn and desolate by the withdrawal of his subject.

Within a year, he died and by the terms of his will, of which Governor Bellingham and the Reverend Mr. Wilson were the executors, he bequeathed a very considerable amount of property, both here and in England to little Pearl. Mother and daughter then left for Europe where the latter blossomed into womanhood and married well. Then Hester returned to her old home. Letters came with armorial seals upon them. In the cottage there were articles of comfort and luxury such as Hester never cared to use and only wealth could have purchased. A new life had dawned for Hester. People brought all their sorrows and perplexities to her, and besought her counsel, as one who had herself gone through a mighty trouble. Women especially sought her help. She comforted and counselled them, as best she might, and assured them, too, of her firm belief that, at some brighter period, when the world should have grown ripe for it, in Heaven's own time, a new truth would be revealed, in order to establish the whole relation between man and woman on a surer ground of mutual happiness.

When after many years she died, she was buried near an old and sunken grave, yet with a space between, as if the dust of the two sleepers had no right to mingle. One tombstone served for both. It was a simple slab of slate with an engraved escutcheon that bore a device, a herald's wording of which might serve for a motto and brief description of our now concluded legend: so sombre is it, and relieved only by one ever-glowing point of light gloomier than the shadow—

"On a Field Sable the Letter A Gules."

PRIDE AND PREJUDICE

By

Jane Austen

JANE AUSTEN (*1775–1817*) was an English novelist who wrote mainly about domestic life. She was educated at home by her father, a village rector. Her first four novels, including *Pride and Prejudice,* which was written before she was 22 years old, were published anonymously. *Northanger Abbey* and *Persuasion* were published in 1818 posthumously. It was not until after her death that her authorship and all of the six books were made public.

"MY DEAR MR. BENNET," said his lady to him one day, "have you heard that Netherfield Park is let at last?"

Mr. Bennet replied that he had not.

Indeed it had been let to Mr. Bingley, a young bachelor and therefore of great interest to Mrs. Bennet whose business in life was to get her five daughters married. She therefore saw to it that Mr. Bennet made an early visit to Netherfield, before Sir William and Lady Lucus called, for they also had marriageable daughters.

At a ball given in town, Mr. Bingley proved himself very eligible for he was good-looking and gentlemanlike with a pleasant countenance and easy, unaffected manners. His friend, Mr. Darcy, soon drew everyone's attention for his fine, tall person and handsome features, but it was soon discovered he was proud and disagreeable. He particularly antagonized Elizabeth Bennet, next to oldest of the girls, for she overheard a conversation in which he refused to dance with her, calling her merely tolerable in appearance. Mrs. Bennet was pleased to note that Mr. Bingley obviously favored Jane, her oldest daughter, above all other girls present, and was already anticipating their marriage. The Bingley sisters thought that the oldest Miss Bennet was very sweet but Elizabeth detected a certain superciliousness in their manner. It was generally agreed that Mr. Darcy was unbearable.

At a party given later at the Lucus', Mr. Darcy found himself admiring Elizabeth, but she rebuffed any attempts at conversation or dancing on his part. Her resistance did not injure her with the gentleman. Jane received an invitation to visit Netherfield. While she was there she contracted a cold and Miss Bingley insisted that she stay, for Longbourn, Jane's home, was five miles away, and the weather would not permit the journey. Mrs. Bennet, after learning that her daughter was not seriously ill, was rather pleased, for the more Jane saw of the Bingleys, the better for her plans. Elizabeth, worried about her sister, insisted on going to see her. Her appearance on arriving at Netherfield, in consequence of her long walk through the mud, did little to put her in the good graces of the Bingley sisters, nor did the attention which Mr. Darcy paid her, for it was obvious that Miss Caroline Bingley was seeking his favor.

When the girls arrived home a few days later, they were informed that Mr. Collins, a cousin, to whom their father's estate was entailed because of a lack of male heirs, was coming for a visit. Mr. Collins, a pastor, had decided to be noble and marry one of the Bennet girls to ease his conscience about his inheritance. Although he found Jane most attractive, he very soon switched to Elizabeth, when it was suggested to him by Mrs. Bennet that the eldest was likely to be very soon engaged. His decision was very annoying to the young lady who thought her cousin stuffy. Mr. Collins brought news of his patroness, Lady Catherine de Bourgh, whom he greatly admired. She was a cousin of Mr. Darcy's.

On a walk to Meryton, Mr. Collins was unable to hold Lydia's and Kitty Bennet's attention for they were occupied with admiring the officers. One in particular, far handsomer than all the rest, was the object of their chatter. This was Mr. Wickham. As the group was talking together, Mr. Bingley and Mr. Darcy passed. Only Elizabeth caught the look which passed between Mr. Darcy and Mr. Wickham but she soon related their consternation to the other Bennets and the mystery of the glance was a topic of conversation for some time. They soon learned from Mr. Wickham, however, for he became a frequent visitor at Longbourn, attracted by Elizabeth, that he had been deprived of a valuable living by Mr. Darcy, that his intended profession had been the Church, and that the living which he had lost was the very one which Mr. Collins now held. Elizabeth's dislike for Mr. Darcy increased on hearing this, but Jane could not believe him so contemptible.

Mr. Collins soon made his declaration in form. Elizabeth, much surprised, refused as delicately as she could. Mrs. Bennet was much taken back at her daughter's refusal and called out, "Oh, Mr. Bennet, you are wanted immediately; we are all in an uproar. You must come and make Lizzy marry Mr. Collins, for she vows she will not have him; and if you do not make haste he will change his mind and not have her."

Mr. Bennet was unperturbed, however, and secretly pleased. Although his pride was hurt Mr. Collins suffered in no other way for his regard for Elizabeth had been purely imaginary.

One day a letter was delivered to Jane. It was from Miss Bingley and stated that they were all leaving for London, not to return that winter. Jane, who had been seeing Charles Bingley regularly, had heard nothing of it from him. It also expressed Miss Bingley's hopes of having Miss Darcy, who was living in London, as a sister. Jane was depressed, but Elizabeth assured her sister that Mr. Bingley would return, and that Miss Bingley was not such a simpleton as to doubt his affection for Jane. Jane's spirits rose at her sister's encouragement.

As soon as Charlotte Lucus heard of Elizabeth's refusal of Mr. Collins' addresses, she was bound to engage them towards herself and so well succeeded that in three days she announced herself engaged to him. Mrs. Bennet was overpowered and many months passed before she could forgive Charlotte.

Quite a while passed before Jane had any further tidings of Mr. Bingley. A letter finally arrived from his sister which was chiefly occupied with praise of Miss Darcy and the progress of Miss Darcy's romance with Mr. Bingley. Jane after a few days, when she could talk about it, said to Elizabeth of Mr. Bingley, "He may live in my memory as the most amiable man of my acquaintance, but that is all. I have nothing either to hope or fear, and nothing to reproach him with. I have this comfort immediately, that it has not been more than an error of fancy on my side, and that it has done no harm to anyone but myself."

Elizabeth was not so complacent but for Jane's sake agreed not to mention him again.

Mr. Bennet said to Elizabeth on the subject, "Your sister is crossed in love, I find. I congratulate her. Next to being married, a girl likes to be crossed in love a little now and then. It is something to think of and gives her a sort of distinction among her companions. When is your turn to come? You will hardly be long outdone by Jane. Now is your turn. Here are officers enough at Meryton to disappoint all the young ladies in the country. Let Wickham be your man. He is a pleasant fellow and would jilt you creditable."

Mr. Wickham was frequently at Longbourn and now openly declared his claims against Mr. Darcy, so that no gentleman was hated so much by Hertfordshire people. Only Jane Bennet supposed any extenuating circumstances and pleaded allowances.

Mrs. Bennet's brother and his wife, Mr. and Mrs. Gardiner, arrived for Christmas. Mrs. Gardiner, after hearing Jane's story, offered to take her back to London with them for a change of scenery. Jane was pleased and hoped that she might see Miss Bingley some morning when Charles was likely to be out. Before she left, Mrs. Gardiner warned Elizabeth against Mr. Wickham whom she had heard people talk of disapprovingly several years before. Elizabeth only promised not to do anything too hastily.

As soon as the Gardiners and Jane left for London, the marriage of Charlotte and Mr. Collins took place to engage the Bennets' attention. Charlotte extracted a promise from Elizabeth to visit her at Kent, her new home.

In a letter from Jane, Elizabeth's fears were realized. She knew that nothing but chance could make Charles Bingley aware of Jane's presence in London, for Charlotte Bingley had been very cool and returned Jane's visit formally and only after a rude delay. In a second letter Jane felt sure that by this time Mr. Bingley must know that she was there and convinced Elizabeth of the fact so that she lost all regard for the gentleman and hoped he would soon marry Miss Darcy.

In writing to her aunt, Elizabeth was forced to admit that Mr. Wickham had turned his attentions elsewhere and that Miss King, the possessor of a small fortune, was now apparently the recipient of his affections. Because time was dragging at Longbourn, she decided to accompany Sir William and his daughter, Maria, to Kent to see Charlotte. At Kent, Elizabeth found Lady Catherine very condescending and her daughter Anne, unattractive. Sir William stayed only a week, long enough to see that Charlotte was comfortably settled. A few weeks later, Elizabeth learned that Mr. Darcy was expected at Rosings, his aunt, Lady Catherine's estate. Colonel Fitzwilliam, another nephew, came with him. They soon called at the Parsonage. Colonel Fitzwilliam was very attractive and seemed pleased with Elizabeth. Mr. Darcy's interest in her was again apparent. She was always rather curt and once brought him to account for his past uncongenial behavior about which he said, "I certainly have not the talent which some people possess of conversing easily with those I have never seen before. I cannot catch their tone of conversation or appear interested in their concerns as I often see done."

In spite of this explanation and Mr. Darcy's later behavior which was nothing but commendable, Elizabeth was no more favorably inclined towards him than before. Charlotte was thinking of a match between Colonel Fitzwilliam and Elizabeth.

One day while talking to Elizabeth, Colonel Fitzwilliam let it drop that Mr. Darcy congratulated himself on having lately saved a friend from the inconveniences of a most imprudent marriage. He claimed very strong objections to the lady. Elizabeth knew he must have meant her sister and was so upset that she shut herself in her room and the next day declined from going with her cousins to Rosings. While she was brooding over the matter, the door bell rang. Much to her surprise, it was Mr. Darcy.

After a hesitation he began, "In vain have I struggled. It will not do. My feelings will not be repressed. You must allow me to tell you how ardently I admire and love you."

Elizabeth's astonishment was beyond expression. Mr. Darcy continued, mentioning their different circumstances but still begging her hand. Elizabeth's refusal was cold and disdainful arousing Mr. Darcy's anger.

She accused him of breaking her sister's and Mr. Bingley's happiness and of unjust and disgraceful treatment of Mr. Wickham and ended by saying, "You could not have made me the offer of your hand in any possible way that would have tempted me to accept it." Mr. Darcy left hurriedly.

The next day a letter from Mr. Darcy, answered all Elizabeth's charges against him. It said that Mr. Darcy had affected a separation between Jane and Mr. Bingley, but only after he had closely observed Jane's behavior and convinced himself that she had no more than ordinary regard for his friend. He had convinced Mr. Bingley of the fact. As regarded Elizabeth's more serious accusation, the letter explained Mr. Wickham's relations with Mr. Darcy's family to the complete discredit of the former. Mr. Wickham had given up the living of which he accused Mr. Darcy of depriving him, for three thousand pounds. After squandering that, he inveigled himself into the affections of Miss Darcy, then fifteen, and obtained her promise to elope with him, all merely to obtain her fortune. Mr. Darcy had arrived on the scene just in time to prevent the deception. The letter further stated that Mr. Darcy was sorry if he had caused Miss Bennet any pain and called on Colonel Fitzwilliam to testify to his veracity.

Elizabeth read the letter with varying emotions. After a long meditative walk through the park she was forced to admit the justice of everything he had said. She remembered a comment of Charlotte's on her sister's temperament to justify his first claim, and also with a blush of shame her family's actions on occasions. She returned to the Parsonage resolved to repress such reflections as must make her unfit for conversation and tried to look cheerful as usual.

After six weeks, Elizabeth and Maria returned to Longbourn, stopping at London to pick up Jane. Elizabeth told Jane of Mr. Darcy's proposal and all the contents of his letter which regarded Mr. Wickham. Jane was distressed at the latter for she could not believe so much wickedness existed in the whole world.

Mr. Wickham was again a frequent visitor at the house for the Kings had gotten their daughter away from his influence. When he and the other officers left for Brighton, their post, Lydia Bennet also went there on the invitation from friends, Colonel and Mrs. Forester. Mr. and Mrs. Gardiner came again to Longbourn, but this time just to get Elizabeth whom they were taking with them on a northern trip. One of the show spots they were to visit was the estate of Pemberly.

Elizabeth, when she and the party arrived at Pemberly, was much chagrined to learn that Mr. Darcy was the owner. She heard him praised highly by the housekeeper and that he was acclaimed everywhere. As she turned around from a picture of the late Mr. Darcy, she was much embarrassed to encounter his son. Mr. Darcy was very cordial to her and to Mr. and Mrs. Gardiner and was surprised to find them related to Elizabeth. Elizabeth, on the other hand, was proud that here were some relations about whom she need not blush. Elizabeth met Miss Darcy, and found her shy rather than proud as was her reputation. The Gardiners were surprised at Mr. Darcy's courtesy and his acquaintance with their niece but said nothing.

Mr. Bingley soon appeared on the scene and Elizabeth was kept quite busy trying to find something in the attitude of either Mr. Bingley or Miss Darcy to justify the contention of Caroline Bingley and was happy that she could see nothing to uphold it. It became obvious to the Gardiners that Mr. Darcy was in love with Elizabeth but they refrained from questioning Elizabeth.

Letters from Jane gave quite a shock to the party for they announced that Lydia had gone away with Mr. Wickham and that it was generally believed that they were not married. Mr. Darcy when he heard the news, blamed himself, for not having revealed Wickham's character thereby preventing any further nonsense from him. The party left immediately for home. Elizabeth thought that now with this new disgrace in the family Mr. Darcy would certainly be through with her.

Mr. Bennet and Mr. Gardiner went to London to look for the couple as that was the most likely place for people who wanted to hide. The father soon returned disheartened. After a few days news came from Mr. Gardiner saying that Mr. Wickham and Lydia were in London and unmarried, a situation soon to be remedied under certain conditions. Lydia was to receive her share of the five thousand pounds secured among the girls and one hundred pounds per annum. A second letter from Mr. Gardiner revealed that Mr. Wickham had been taken out of the militia and put in the regular army and given a northern post.

PRIDE AND PREJUDICE

After the wedding in London, Lydia came home for a while with Wickham. She was the same light-hearted, gay creature as before. During her chatter, she let it drop that Mr. Darcy had been at the wedding and Elizabeth immediately wrote to Mrs. Gardiner for further particulars. She learned that Mr. Darcy had paid all of Wickham's debts and purchased his commission in the army. Mrs. Gardiner suggested that his affection for Elizabeth might have been the cause and ended by asking that no one know of his action, except perhaps Jane.

Soon after Lydia and Mr. Wickham left, Mr. Bingley and Mr. Darcy arrived at Netherfield and soon called at Longbourn. Mrs. Bennet was barely civil to Mr. Darcy, a fact which hurt Elizabeth because of her secret knowledge. After several visits, Jane happily announced her engagement to Mr. Bingley. The whole family was very happy and Mrs. Bennet triumphant.

Jane said to Elizabeth, "I am certainly the most fortunate creature that ever existed. Oh! Lizzy, why am I thus singled from my family and blessed above them all? If I could but see you as happy! If there were such another man for you!"

A few days later Lady Catherine visited Longbourn and in a private conversation with Elizabeth tried to extract a promise from her not to marry Mr. Darcy, for she had heard rumors to that effect. Elizabeth, who was not to be cowed, sent an extremely angry lady away. The discomposure of spirits into which this extraordinary visit threw Elizabeth could not be easily overcome. Mr. Darcy had only been civil in his recent behavior. A letter from Mr. Collins revealed that the lady had also expressed her views to him on the subject. It also made Elizabeth the object of many gibes, particularly from her father who could not conceive of such a possibility as marriage between Elizabeth and Mr. Darcy.

On a walk with Mr. Darcy, Elizabeth took the occasion to thank him for his kindness to her sister. He assured Elizabeth that it was done only for her. The young lady was too much embarrassed at this to say a word. Mr. Darcy then asked her if her feelings toward him had changed since last April, saying that his affections and wishes were the same. Elizabeth immediately, if not fluently, gave him to understand that her sentiments had undergone so material a change since the period to which he alluded,

[99]

as to make her receive with gratitude and pleasure his present assurances.

That night Elizabeth opened her heart to Jane. Jane was absolutely incredulous when she heard the news and said, "You are joking, Lizzy. This cannot be! Engaged to Mr. Darcy! No, no, you shall not deceive me. I know it to be impossible."

However, after Elizabeth convinced her sister that she really loved Mr. Darcy, Jane was very happy, for as she said, "You will be as happy as myself."

The next morning Mr. Darcy arrived with Mr. Bingley, much to Mrs. Bennet's disgust, for to her he was still a disagreeable man. He went immediately to Mr. Bennet for his consent which he quickly received. Elizabeth was called in for an interview with her father, however, and he tried to dissuade her from marrying this man whom Mr. Bennet was convinced she hated. With difficulty, Mr. Bennet was assured of her regard.

Now Elizabeth feared her mother's reaction to the news. When she heard it, Mrs. Bennet sat quite still and was unable to utter a syllable. When she really comprehended what she had heard, she was delighted and went into rhapsodies over the wealth which would come into the family as a result of Elizabeth's and Jane's marriages. With this behavior in private, Elizabeth feared what it might be in front of the gentleman in question, but fortunately Mrs. Bennet stood in such awe of her intended son-in-law that she ventured not to speak to him, unless it was in her power to offer him any attention, to mark her deference for his opinion.

Happy for all her maternal feeling was the day on which Mrs. Bennet got rid of her two most deserving daughters. Mr. Bennet missed his second daughter exceedingly. Elizabeth and Darcy resided at Pemberly, as did Georgiana Darcy with whom Elizabeth got on admirably. Mr. Bingley bought an estate near Pemberly so that the sisters were within thirty miles of each other, a happy circumstance for both.

With the Gardiners, the Darcys were always on the most intimate terms. Darcy as well as Elizabeth really loved them; and they were both ever sensible of the warmest gratitude toward the persons who, by bringing her into Derbyshire, had been the means of uniting them.

ADAM BEDE

By

George Eliot

GEORGE ELIOT (*1819–1880*) was the pseudonym of the English
novelist, Mary Ann Evans. She used her early life as material
for *The Mill on the Floss.* When she was 21 her father moved
to Coventry where she met George Bray who persuaded her
to translate Strauss's *Life of Christ* which changed her evan-
gelical views of religion. She became a magazine editor and
friend of the literary lights of the day. She formed a union
in 1854 with George Henry Lewes, an editor, which both regarded as matrimony but which was not legalized because
Lewes could not divorce his wife. Under his encouragement
she began her great career as a novelist which was arrested by
the crushing blow of his death in 1878. Two years later she
married John Cross, a long time friend of the Leweses, but
she died the same year.

ON THE EVENING of the eighteenth of June, in the year of our Lord,
1799, there was an unusual appearance of excitement in the village of Hayslope, and through the whole length of the little
street, from the Donnithorne Arms to the churchyard gate, the inhabitants had evidently been drawn out of their houses by something more than the pleasure of lounging in the evening sunshine.

Mr. Casson, the innkeeper, had been revolving the problem in
his mind as to how to reconcile his dignity with the satisfaction of
his curiosity by walking towards the Green, when his thoughts
were diverted by the approach of a horseman pulling up at the
door of Donnithorne Arms.

"Why, what's up in your pretty village, landlord?" said the
traveller getting down. "There seems to be quite a stir."

"It's a Methodist preaching, sir; it's been given out as a young woman's a-going to preach on the Green," answered Mr. Casson.

"Well, I wish I had time to wait and see her, but I must get on. I've been out of my way for the last twenty minutes to have a look at Squire Donnithorne's place in the valley. It's a pretty spot, and one meets some fine strapping fellows about, too. I met one, just before I came up the hill—a carpenter, a tall broad-shouldered fellow with black hair and eyes, marching along like a soldier."

"Ay, sir, that's Adam Bede, that is, I'll be bound. Thias Bede's son. He's an uncommon clever stiddy fellow, an' wonderful strong. But he's a little lifted up and peppery-like."

"Well, good evening to you, landlord; I must get on."

"Your servant, sir; good evening."

Dinah Morris was the preacher woman's name. She was possessed of one of those faces that make one think of white flowers with light touches of colour on their pure petals. The eyes had no peculiar beauty, beyond that of expression; they looked so simple, so candid, so gravely loving, that no accusing scowl, no light sneer, could help melting away before their glance. She spoke simply, with the quiet depth of conviction that seemed in itself an evidence of the truth of her message.

In less than an hour from that time Seth Bede, Adam's brother, was walking by Dinah's side along a hedge-row path towards her home. Seth was but three and twenty, and had only just learned what it is to love—to love with that adoration that a young man gives to a woman whom he feels to be greater and better than himself. And that night, as Seth and Dinah were walking home, Seth gathered courage to press his suit. Dinah answered that although if there were any one man whom she might consider as more than a Christian brother, it was Seth, she couldn't think of marrying, as she had been called upon by God to minister to others, not to have joys and sorrows of her own.

The next day Captain Donnithorne and Mr. Irwine appeared at Hall Farm where lived Dinah's aunt, Mrs. Poyser, and Mr. Poyser. Mr. Irwine was the parson, and Captain Donnithorne the son of Squire Donnithorne. Mr. Irwine was come to see Dinah, of whose preaching he had heard. And Captain Donnithorne, although he mentioned being interested in trading horses with Mr. Poyser, was chiefly concerned with securing the promise of a few dances with Hetty Sorel, Mr. Poyser's niece, at a dance to be held in the near future.

Hetty was in the dairy. She blushed a deep rose-colour when Captain Donnithorne entered and spoke to her; but it was not all a distressed blush, for it was enwreathed with smiles and dimples, and with sparkles from under long curled dark eyelashes; and while her aunt was discoursing to him about the troubles the dairy gave, Hetty tossed and patted her pound of butter with quite a self-possessed, coquettish air.

"I hope you will be ready for a great holiday on the thirtieth of July, Mrs. Poyser," said Captain Donnithorne, when he had sufficiently admired the dairy. "And will you promise me your hand for two dances, Miss Hetty?"

Hetty dropped the prettiest little curtsy as she said, "Yes, thank you, sir."

Mrs. Poyser had in mind that Hetty should one day marry Adam. But Hetty had never given Adam any steady encouragement. Hetty had now become aware that Mr. Arthur Donnithorne would take a great deal of trouble for the chance of seeing her; that he was constantly finding reasons for calling at Hall Farm, and always would contrive to say something for the sake of making her speak to him and look at him. Adam had in mind, at the same time, a strong desire to make Hetty his wife. He had loved her dearly for some time, but he had too cool a head not to estimate to the full the obstacles to be overcome. To be sure, if she loved him very much, she would be content to wait for him: but *did* she love him? His hopes had never risen so high that he had dared ask her. In the meantime, Dinah had gone home to Snowfield. And thus matters were standing when the holiday on the thirtieth of July arrived.

At the dance, Adam's eyes followed Hetty eagerly in spite of himself, and took in deeper draughts of love. He thought she behaved so prettily, so quietly; she smiled less than usual; there was almost a sweet sadness about her. "God Bless her!" he said inwardly; "I'd make her life a happy 'un, if a strong arm to work for her, and a heart to love her could do it." At last the time came for his dance with her. As he was standing with her, waiting for the music to begin, Hetty's string of beads was broken. The locket leaped out of her frock, and Hetty helpless, the next moment saw beads and locket lying on the floor. "My locket, my locket!", she said, in a loud frightened whisper to Adam; "never mind the beads."

It had fallen on the raised wooden dais where the band sat; and as Adam picked it up, he saw the glass with dark and light locks of hair under it. He turned it over on his hand, and saw the enamelled gold back.

"It isn't hurt," he said, as he held it toward Hetty. Soon the dance music started. But the pleasure of the dance with Hetty was gone; a puzzled alarm had taken possession of him. Had Hetty a lover he didn't know of? The dance ended, and Hetty was claimed by another youth. Adam was determined to stay no longer; no one wanted him or would notice if he slipped away. As soon as he got out of doors, he began to walk at his habitual rapid pace, busy with the painful thought that the memory of this day, so full of promise, was poisoned forever.

Suddenly he stopped, startled by a flash of reviving hope. Perhaps Hetty had had as much as a guinea in her Christmas boxes, and there was no knowing but she might have been childish enough to spend it in that way. The little ring of dark hair he felt sure was her own, and the light hair might well be a bit of her father's or mother's who had died when she was but a child. And so Adam went to bed comforted, having woven himself an ingenious web of probabilities—the surest screen a wise man can place between himself and the truth.

It was beyond the middle of August—nearly three weeks after the holiday, that Adam was walking through the beech grove. He strode along the winding path, delighting in the fine trees about him. But for the rest of his life he remembered the moment when he rounded a bend in the path and his eyes fell on two figures about twenty yards before him. The two figures were standing opposite each other, with clasped hands; and while they were bending to kiss, Gyp, Adam's dog, caught sight of them, and gave a sharp bark. They separated with a start—one hurried through the gate out of the grove, and the other turned around and walked slowly toward Adam. Arthur Donnithorne, it was, who came up, offered some remark about the beeches, and would have passed on but for Adam's saying, "Stop a bit, sir," in a hard, peremptory voice. "I've got a word to say to you."

Arthur paused in surprise. "What do you mean, Adam?" he said. "I mean, sir," answered Adam, "I mean that you don't deceive me. This is not the first time you've met Hetty Sorel in these woods, and this is not the only time you've kissed her."

When Arthur could not prove that his intentions were honorable, he angered Adam so that the latter insisted upon fighting. Adam was much the stronger and the blow soon came that felled Arthur. Afterwards, when Arthur had regained consciousness, both were sufficiently calm to discuss matters more calmly and in a saner light. The result of the affair was that Arthur wrote a letter to Hetty taking blame upon himself for behaving as he had no right to do to a young woman not his equal.

Hetty was stricken with grief when she read that fateful letter. The shattering of all her little dream-world, the crushing blow on her new-born passion, afflicted her pleasure-craving nature with an overpowering pain that annihilated all impulse to resistance, and suspended her anger. And the constant hinting and insinuations of her uncle and aunt finally wore her down until she cared not what she did, so that it made some change in her life. Why should she not marry Adam Bede? Her uncle and aunt obviously wished it so, and she felt confident that he would still want to marry her.

The weeks went by, and at last Adam felt the love in his heart so strongly that he spoke out. "I could afford to be married now, Hetty—and I could make a wife comfortable; but I shall never want to be married if you won't have me." It was then November and the marriage was set for Easter.

It was a busy time for Adam—the time between the beginning of November and the beginning of March, and he could see little of Hetty, except on Sundays. Hetty's mind was oppressed during these days; she knew not where to turn from a swift-advancing shame inside her; understanding no more of this life of ours than a foolish lost lamb wandering farther and farther in the nightfall on the lonely heath; yet tasting the bitterest of life's bitterness. Whenever the thought of writing to Arthur had occurred to her, she had rejected it; he could do nothing for her that would shelter her from discovery and scorn among the relatives and neighbors who made all her world. She had had a letter from Dinah lately, full of kind words about her approaching marriage; and when Hetty had read the letter aloud to her uncle, he had said, "What do you think, my wench, o'going to see her as soon as you can be spared, and persuading her to come back wi' you?" Hetty had not liked the thought of going to Snowfield where Dinah lived, so she only said, "It's so far off, uncle." But now she thought this proposed visit would serve as a pretext for going away. She would tell her aunt that she should like to go to Snowfield for a while, and then, when she got on the road, she would ask for the coach that would take her to Windsor. Arthur was at Windsor, and she would go to him.

A long, lonely journey, with sadness in the heart; away from the familiar to the strange; that is a hard and dreary thing even to the rich, the strong, and instructed; a hard thing, even when we are called by duty, not urged by dread. Hetty had a hard time of it. She found she had not enough money to take her to Windsor by coach, and was forced to walk a good part of the way. When she finally arrived, she was footsore, tired, hungry, and weak. She stopped at an inn in Windsor to inquire the way. The kindly wife of the proprietor saw her poor condition and insisted on feeding her. When Hetty was done, the landlady remarked, "You're not very fit for travelling," glancing while she spoke at Hetty's ringless hand. "Have you come far?"

"Yes," said Hetty, roused by this question to exert more self-command. "But I'm better now. Could you tell me which way to this place?" Here Hetty took from her pocket a bit of paper; it was the end of Arthur's letter on which he had written his address.

The landlord came in then. He took the paper and said, "There's no one there now. It's shut up—been shut up this fortnight. Who was it you were looking for? Perhaps I can let you know where to find him."

"It's Captain Donnithorne," said Hetty tremulously. "Captain Donnithorne? Stop a bit," said the landlord slowly. "He was the one in the Loamshire Militia, which is a fine sight o' miles away from here. It's gone to Ireland—been gone this fortnight."

"Look there! She's fainting," said the landlady, hastening to support Hetty. They carried her upstairs and put her to bed.

The next morning, Hetty woke up early and thought about what she ought to do. In looking through her things, she came across the letter she had gotten from Dinah, and she remembered how kind Dinah had been to her when she was staying with the Poysers. The impulse to go and see Dinah came to Hetty, and after considering every angle of this proposition, she decided to do so. So she got up and dressed herself and went downstairs. The good landlady was amazed when she saw Hetty come down soon after herself, neatly dressed and looking resolutely self-possessed. She told the landlady that she was much better and had better be going. About eleven o'clock, after breakfast and many well-wishes of the good landlord and his wife, Hetty set out on the long and weary road to Snowfield.

But fortune was against her, and the mounting tide of fate caught up with her on the journey. Her baby was born, and in a fit of dread and panic, she killed the little thing. Soon afterward she was arrested for the murder of her child. At the trial, the jury found her guilty and sentenced her to be hung by the neck till she be dead.

As soon as Dinah Morris heard of Hetty's sad condition, she hurried as fast as possible to be near her and comfort her in her last few hours. She rode with the condemned girl in the cart on the way to the gallows, and in a low voice, as the cart went slowly along through the midst of the gazing crowd, she poured forth her soul with the wrestling intensity of a last pleading, for the trembling creature that clung to her and clutched her as the only visible sign of love and pity. But just as the cart stopped at the fatal spot, a sudden shout of excitement rose at the sight of a horseman cleaving the crowd at full gallop. The rider is Arthur Donnithorne, returned from Ireland at the news of Hetty's plight, and he is carrying in his hand a hard won release from death.

One autumnal afternoon in the year 1801—more than eighteen months after the trial and Hetty's rescue from death, Adam Bede came to Hall Farm to ask Dinah to come and comfort his mother, who was suffering from some minor illness. He had come to know Dinah well in those eighteen months. She had been a great help to his mother, and he had grown to love her. And when he learned that afternoon that Dinah was going back to Snowfield again, the realization of all that Dinah had come to mean to him suddenly struck him. And Dinah had something of the same feeling in her heart towards Adam. Thus it was not long after that the time came when Dinah said to Adam, "Adam, it is the divine will. My soul is so knit to yours that it is but a divided life I live without you. And this moment, now you are with me, and I feel that our hearts are filled with the same love, I have a fulness of strength to bear and do our heavenly Father's Will, that I had lost before."

Adam looked into her sincere eyes and said, "Then we'll never part any more, Dinah, till death parts us."

And they kissed each other with a deep joy.

Seth was quite willing and happy that the two should be married, for now, in truth, he would indeed be a Christian brother to Dinah, by marriage as well as by feeling.

In a little more than a month after the meeting on the hill when Dinah and Adam pledged themselves to each other, they were married on a rimy morning in departing November.

What greater thing is there for two human souls, than to feel that they are joined for life—to strengthen each other in all labour, to rest on each other in all sorrow, to minister to each other in all pain, to be one with each other in silent unspeakable memories at the moment of the last parting?

JEAN VALJEAN

(From *Les Miserables*)

By

Victor Hugo

VICTOR-MARIE HUGO (*1802–1885*) was a French poet, novelist and dramatist. At the age of 14 he produced a tragedy. At 20 he published his first work. At 21 he produced another play followed by about one each year. In 1831 he published *Notre-Dame de Paris,* a historical romance, and also a sheaf of lyric and contemplative verse in which is included some of his best poetry. His next twelve years were occupied largely by politics, oratory and journalism. He was a Royalist and worshiped Napoleon. When he was 50 he commenced writing again and when he was 60 he published *Les Miserables.* In Paris during 1870 Hugo distinguished himself by summoning the Germans to withdraw from France and proclaim the German Republic. Hugo's plays were all magnificently written although the situations and personages are somewhat remote from general experience. His complete works in 47 volumes appeared before his death.

THE DEATH-AGONY of the barricade was approaching. The attack was a hurricane. The narrow street was filled with a column of infantry of the line and National Guards. They came inexorably for the barricade. The impact was that of a steel ram against a mud wall.

But the wall held.

The barricade was like a mane of fire. For a moment it was overflowed by assailants; but it shook off the soldiers as the lion does the dogs, and it was covered with besiegers only as the cliff is with foam, to reappear, a moment later, steep, black, and formidable.

The column fell back helplessly, and remained massed in the street, subject to the most terrible slaughter. The insurgents shot down the soldiers at musket-point. The bravery of both sides was almost barbaric, and suffused with an heroic ferocity.

When the wave of the first attack had subsided the leader of the insurgents, Enjolras, stood exposed on his battlement, listening intently. He was followed an instant later by Marius Pontmercy, his lieutenant. Enjolras thought he distinguished the peculiar sound that is made when canisters of grape are removed from the caisson.

"Heads down, keep close to the wall!" he cried.

Before his order was executed a fearful charge of grape-shot poured into the barricade through the opening of the redoubt. It ricocheted upon the wall, killing two men and wounding three.

The utmost confusion reigned in the barricade. They could not hold out long against grape.

The voice of Enjolras rose in ringing command:

"Plug the opening with a mattress!"

"We have none," said Combeferre, "the wounded are on them."

At that moment a man, who throughout the fighting had remained seated on a block in a corner of the barricade, rose and approached Enjolras. It was Jean Valjean.

"Can you lend me a double-barrelled carbine?" he asked.

Enjolras, who had just reloaded his, handed it to him.

Jean Valjean turned and faced a house of six stories standing a little outside the barricade. From the window in the garret hung a mattress, suspended from two ropes almost invisible at that distance. They stood against the sky like hairs.

He raised the rifle, and in the same motion fired. One of the two ropes of the mattress was cut. He fired the second barrel, and the mattress fell into the street.

The barricaded applauded.

All cried:

"There is a mattress."

"Yes," said Combeferre, "but who will go after it?"

Jean Valjean went through the opening, and entered the street. A fusillade of musket balls whistled by him, but heedless of them he walked to the mattress, placed it on his back, and returned to the barricade. He thrust the mattress into the opening.

This done, they waited the charge of grape.

The cannon vomited its package of shot with a roar. But there was no ricochet. The mattress blanketed the shot. The barricade was preserved—for a time.

Enjolras turned to Marius:

"Who is that man?"

"I know him," said Marius. "He is M. Fauchelevent." Then Marius turned away, for the vision of Cosette, the daughter of M. Fauchelevent, floated before his eyes.

It would be too much to say that this action of Jean Valjean saved the barricade and its defenders. Their fate was only postponed, for the cartridges of the besieged were becoming exhausted. Enjolras, knowing this, began to place his men at the barricade in such a way that every shot would tell. When this was done only one thing remained—to make a proper disposition of his prisoner.

He entered a doorway that stood in the shadow of the barricade, and walked to the center of the room where, on a large table, lay the bound figure of police inspector Javert.

"I haven't forgotten you," said Enjolras.

"Nor have I you," said Javert, coolly.

Enjolras drew his pistol, and cocked it. A hand was laid on his arm. It was Jean Valjean.

"Do you think that I deserve a reward?"

"Certainly."

"Well, I ask one."

"What?"

"To blow out that man's brains myself."

Javert raised his head, turned to Valjean, and said:

"Very appropriate."

"Take the spy," said Enjolras.

Almost at the same moment a wild burst of firing had begun. The infantry, exasperated at the stubbornness of the insurgents, was attacking savagely.

When Jean Valjean was alone with Javert he cut the ropes that bound the prisoner, then, with pistol in hand, motioned him to the door. Of all the insurgents Marius alone saw them pass, victim and executioner. Hardened as he was by the blood and suffering of the last few days he could not help shuddering at the grim procession.

Jean Valjean led his captive into a little side-street about fifty yards from the barricade. Except for the subdued clamor of the fighting the street was silent. And well it should have been for its only occupants were the corpses of the insurgent dead.

Jean Valjean fixed upon Javert a look which had no need of words to say:

"Javert, it is I."

Javert answered:

"Take your revenge."

Jean Valjean drew his knife, and swung Javert around so that his unprotected back was toward him.

"That suits you better, Valjean."

Valjean stooped, and cut the cords that bound his prisoner's wrists.

"You are free," he said.

Javert was not easily astonished, yet he could not escape an emotion. He stood aghast.

Jean Valjean continued:

"I don't expect to leave this place alive. Still, if by chance I should, you will find me in the Rue de l'Homme Armé, Number Seven, under the name of Fauchelevent."

Javert restored the military stiffness of his shoulders, and walked off in the direction of the markets. After a few steps he halted, turned around, and cried to Jean Valjean:

"You annoy me, kill me rather."

"Go away," said Valjean.

Javert receded slowly, and when he had gone Jean Valjean fired the pistol in the air.

The barricade was in its death-agony. All but a handful of its defenders lay in puddles of blood. Marius, still fighting, was so hacked with wounds, particularly about the head, that his countenance was lost in blood. Enjolras, by a miracle, was untouched. The others were bleeding from innumerable wounds, and as Valjean turned the corner of the side-street three more were shot down. They fought breast to breast, foot to foot, hand to hand, with pistols, with sabers, and even with fists. They were one against sixty, but they fought like a brigade.

A final assault was now begun, and where all the others had

failed this assault succeeded. A bristle of bayonets appeared at the top of the escarpment, and the few insurgents who were defending the center fell away before the fury of the attack. Marius fell with a ball through his shoulder, and as he passed into unconsciousness he felt the shock of a vigorous hand seizing him. Mingling with his last thought that he was taken prisoner, and would be shot, was the memory of Cosette.

Marius was in fact a prisoner—the prisoner of Jean Valjean. The whirlwind of the attack at that instant was concentrated so fiercely upon Enjolras and the few who were left alive that nobody saw Jean Valjean cross the unpaved field of the barricade and make for the side-street which he had left only a moment ago. But the path which Javert had taken was now cut off. The escarpment over which Javert had climbed at the end of the street was now ringed with bayonets. There was to be no escape for the insurgents now that their defense had crumbled.

In desperation Valjean's eyes roved over the façade of the house before him, but its solid exterior was impenetrable. He turned his gaze to the ground with the violence of a last extremity. Beneath his persistent look he perceived a few steps from him, half hidden in a jumble of paving stones, an iron grating, flat and level with the ground. He sprang forward, seized the corner of the grating, and pulled it toward him. It was but the work of a moment to place Marius on his back, to insert himself into the opening, to replace the grating over his head, and to descend with Marius into the subterranean gloom of the sewer. Overhead, like a faint murmur, he could hear the fearful tumult of the barricade.

How long he struggled in the slimy grip of the sewer he could not have told. In the sewers of Paris there is no passage of time—only an enveloping blackness. Holding Marius on his shoulder with one hand Jean Valjean felt his way with the other. He walked in an enigma. In that colossal madrepore Jean Valjean had to invent his route. Each step might be his last.

Valjean had been walking for hours with the dead weight of Marius across his shoulders. Behind him was half of Paris, before him was—the fontis. He knew of it only when the pavement gave way to slime. He hesitated. To retrace his steps was impossible. But the farther he advanced the deeper he sank. The mud rose to his knees, then to his waist. He held Marius above his head. The mire was dense enough for one man's weight, but Valjean thrust the thought from his mind. He sank still deeper. Death was close, but even closer was the thought of Cosette. He made a desperate effort. His foot struck the ascending pavement. They were saved.

This terrible effort exhausted him, and he lay prone in the mire with Marius' head resting on his chest. Later he raised his eyes, and perceived in the distance a faint light. It was the outlet. With renewed strength he swung Marius to his shoulders, and hastened toward the gleam of light.

Jean Valjean reached the outlet, and there he stopped. It was indeed an outlet, but it did not let him out. It was closed by a heavy iron grating, which to all appearances had not been opened for years. Beyond the grating Valjean could see a narrow strip of beach. He laid Marius on the floor of the outlet, and then, walking to the grating, he clenched the iron bars in his fists. They were immovable. He shook them frenziedly; the bars showered him with rust. He applied all his strength to a single bar in an effort to wrench it from its socket, and use it as a lever to pry the grating from its frame; the bar was invincible. They were trapped.

Jean Valjean dropped upon the pavement more prostrate than sitting, beside the yet motionless Marius, and his head sank between his knees. No exit. This was the last drop of anguish.

Of whom did he think in this overwhelming dejection? Of himself, of Marius? No! He thought of Cosette.

In the midst of this annihilation a voice spoke low into his ear:

"Go halves."

A man stood before him. He was barefoot, and held his shoes in his hand. Thus he had reached Valjean without being heard.

"Go halves," the man repeated.

"What do you mean?"

"You have killed the man. I have the key."

The man took him for an assassin. He pointed to Marius.

"Give me half of what you found in his pockets, and I will open the door for you."

Valjean did not answer.

[114]

"Come on. How much did you find in his pockets?"

Without another word the stranger dropped to one knee, and began to fumble through Marius' coat. Valjean did not interfere with him. In the semi-darkness of the outlet he searched the pockets of the coat. At the same time his right hand, unseen by Jean Valjean, tore a strip from Marius' scarf, thinking perhaps to identify the assassinated man, and through him his assassin. His search, however, revealed only thirty francs. And forgetting his offer to "go halves" he took the whole. Then he took the key from under his blouse.

He slipped the key into the lock, and the bolt slid quietly. It was plain that the lock and the grating had been oiled with care. He half opened the door, and motioned to Valjean, who was placing Marius on his shoulders. In a moment they were outside, and the grating closed noiselessly behind them.

They were free. Blessed night with its mantle of darkness was descending on the river. It was the undecided and exquisite hour which says neither yes nor no. Jean Valjean was overcome with the ecstasy of liberation. Then, hastily, as his sense of duty returned, he scooped some water from the river, and bathed the face of the motionless man. A sigh escaped his bloodless lips.

Valjean had turned to the river again when he was overcome with a feeling of uneasiness.

He turned around, and before him stood an apparition with folded arms.

It was Javert. It was he who had driven the mysterious stranger into the outlet which he was now guarding with the tenacity of a bulldog. It was evident to Valjean why the stranger had been so willing to open the grating for a mere thirty francs. Knowing that Javert was on guard he had hoped that by delivering an assassin into his hands to clear the field for his own escape.

"Inspector Javert," said Valjean, "I did not give you my address at the barricade with the intention of escaping you. I am your prisoner. Take me. Only grant me one thing. Help me to carry this man home. Then dispose of me as you wish."

Javert seemed not to hear. He was in a kind of savage reverie.

"The man is wounded," continued Valjean, "and if he is to live he must be taken home immediately." Again the thought of Cosette entered his mind. "He lives with his grandfather in the Marais, Rue des Filles du Calvaire."

Javert was like a black statue, immobile.

"It will take only a few moments," said Valjean. "Look! There is a fiacre on the embankment. Grant me this one favor, Javert."

The graven image became liquid. Javert motioned toward the embankment. Marius was saved.

In less than a half hour the fiacre drove up to the door of M. Gillenormand. In less than a minute after the porter had answered the bell Marius was placed in his own bed.

They re-entered the fiacre, and the driver mounted upon his box.

"Inspector Javert," said Jean Valjean, "grant me one thing more."

"What?" asked Javert roughly.

"Let me go home a moment. Then you shall do with me what you will."

For a few seconds Javert remained silent. Then he lowered the window in front.

"Driver," said he, "Rue de l'Homme Armé, Number Seven."

Jean Valjean wished nothing more than to tell Cosette that Marius was safe.

The fiacre entered the street, and came to a stop before Number Seven. They got out. Javert paid the driver and dismissed him. Jean Valjean thought this strange in view of the fact that he would be gone for only a few moments.

Javert turned to him.

"Very well," he said, "go up. I will wait here for you."

Jean Valjean was nonplussed at Javert's mysterious behavior. Still, he had promised to give himself up, and there was no reason why Javert should have followed him.

He entered the house and began to climb the stairs. On the first landing he paused. The window on the landing was open and had a view upon the street. Mechanically, Jean Valjean gazed through the window. It was a short street, and the lamp lighted it from one end to the other. Jean Valjean was bewildered with amazement; there was nobody there.

Javert was gone.

Inspector of Police Javert had plunged into the deserted streets.

Unconsciously his feet took him toward the Seine. One thing had astonished him, that Jean Valjean had spared him, and one thing had petrified him, that he, Javert, had spared Jean Valjean.

The thought that he, Javert, owed his life to a malefactor, that he had not only acknowledged the debt, but had paid it by giving Valjean his freedom, overcame him. He had betrayed society in order to appease his conscience. He had taken it upon himself to release a convict. A single resource remained—to return immediately, and place Jean Valjean under arrest.

But he could not.

He thought himself base. He was a horror to himself. His ideal was not to be humane, not to be sublime; it was to be irreproachable. And now he had failed.

He reached the Seine, and leaned with both elbows on the parapet. For some moments he remained motionless, his attention fixed on the turgid waters of the river.

To have the unknown over his head, he was not accustomed to that.

There was a dull splash, and the form with its secret slid into the depths.

We leave the dead—for a time—and return to the living. The convalescence of that young republican, Marius, was never in doubt. Within a few days he passed from the red and purple dreams of delirium into the intelligible world around him. Of those dreadful days at the barricade he had only the vaguest recollection, of the blood and suffering he could recall only the shock of the ball crashing into his shoulder.

But throughout his delirium there had been one vision that had never left him—the vision of Cosette.

During the early stages of his illness a dignified and white-haired gentleman had been calling every day, and inquiring after his health. It was M. Fauchelevent. As Marius gained in strength M. Fauchelevent was accompanied on these morning calls by that lovely and adorable young lady, Cosette.

Cosette, on seeing Marius for the first time in weeks, was enraptured. Her first impulse was to throw herself into her loved one's arms, but she was ashamed to show her love before Marius' family. Behind her walked the dignified M. Fauchelevent, neatly dressed in a new black suit. Who could have recognized him as the bloodied corpse-bearer who had left his burden at the door of that house only a short time ago? Under his arm he carried a package, the shape of an octave volume.

Marius' grandfather, old Gillenormand, stood beaming. Then he cleared his throat a few times, and began:

"Monsieur Fauchelevent, I have the honor of asking you, for my grandson, the hand of Mademoiselle."

Monsieur Fauchelevent bowed. The lovers threw their arms around each other, oblivious to the two old men.

When this pleasant little outburst subsided M. Fauchelevent turned to the old grandfather.

"Before we go into the details of the wedding," he said, "I wish to say that Mademoiselle Fauchelevent brings to this union the sum of six hundred thousand francs."

The old grandfather gasped.

M. Fauchelevent opened his package; it was a bundle of bank-notes.

As for Marius and Cosette, they were gazing into each other's eyes.

Throughout the happy courtship, and after the marriage, a struggle was being waged. M. Fauchelevent, or as we know him, Jean Valjean, was in the grip of conscience. Jacob wrestled with the angel but one night. Alas! how many times Jean Valjean clenched in the darkness with his conscience, and wrestled desperately with it. Was it his right to introduce himself as a member of Marius' family? Should he place upon the peaceful andirons of the Gillenormand parlor his feet which dragged after them the infamous shadow of the law?

A few weeks after the marriage Jean Valjean called at the house of Gillenormand. Marius received him warmly in his study, and reproached him for the infrequency of his visits.

"How glad I am to see you, father," he said. "We have missed you."

Valjean mumbled that he had been away on a journey.

It was early morning, and Cosette had not yet risen. Valjean was relieved for what he had to say was intended for the ears of Marius alone.

"Cosette loves you so much," said Marius. "You must not forget that your home is here. We will have no more of the Rue de l'Homme Armé, or you will have a bone to pick with Cosette."

Jean Valjean was mute. The struggle within him was reaching its climax. For a moment he said nothing, then he gazed fully into the eyes of the young man.

"Monsieur," he said, "I have one thing to tell you. I am an old convict."

Marius stood aghast.

"What—what does this mean?"

"It means that I have been in the galleys."

Marius caught a glimpse into the future of a hideous destiny for himself.

"My name is not Fauchelevent, it is Jean Valjean. I am nothing to Cosette."

Marius was petrified.

"Cosette is innocent of all this," said Valjean, "she knows nothing of what I have told you, and she must never know. Promise me that you will never tell her."

Marius aroused himself from an abyss of thought.

"Be calm," he said, "I will keep your secret for myself alone."

"And as for me," said Valjean, "I shall efface myself. I shall never again embarrass the house of Gillenormand with my presence. For Cosette's sake you may tell her that I have left on a journey. It will break her heart when I do not return, but it will be best."

When the old man had left Marius sank into a gloomy reverie. It was during this fit of brooding that there flashed before his mind's eye a specter.

The specter was Javert. All the bloody incidents of the barricade flashed through his mind with startling clarity. That which in retrospect had been a wild confusion was now sharply etched in his brain. Those indistinct scenes were clear again, and he almost cried aloud in horror at the memory of the victim and his executioner, of Javert being dragged away from the barricade by Jean Valjean. He heard again that frightful pistol shot. It was plain that Jean Valjean had gone to the barricade to avenge himself. He had probably learned through some underworld channel that Javert was a prisoner there.

Of the mental tortures that Marius underwent Cosette had no inkling. Marius was always the doting husband and lover. That she was innocent of any knowledge of Valjean's past he had not the slightest doubt. Her simple devotion exalted him, and to some extent dispelled the miasma of uncertainty that clouded his mind. But now another matter had come to plague him—the marriage portion of six hundred thousand francs. The origin of that huge sum vexed him. A convict could not have come by it honestly. What deviltry had been its source? His bitterness toward Valjean grew at the thought of the man's wickedness. It had not been enough to dishonor the name of Gillenormand by representing himself as an honest citizen, but to add to this Valjean had further clouded the marriage with what was undoubtedly evil booty.

His suspicions of the dubious origin of the money were confirmed when one day an old clerk of the banking house of Lafitte, which managed Marius' accounts, recounted a scandal of many years ago that had rocked the business world of Paris. Marius dared not ask too many questions, but this unsolicited information, a little hazy here and there, seemed conclusive enough. Marius now felt that he had a solemn duty to perform—the restitution of the six hundred thousand francs.

What had been a warm liking for M. Fauchelevent gave way to an almost savage hatred for Jean Valjean.

And of Jean Valjean? A tree deprived of light must wither away.

One day, not long after the confession, there came to the house of Gillenormand a visitor the like of which Marius had never seen before. He was dressed like a seedy statesman, with his hair smoothed over his brows after the manner of an English coachman. Marius received him in his study, and after much bowing and scraping he cleared his throat and began:

"Monsieur, I have a secret to sell you."

"A secret?"

"Yes."

"Well, what is it?"

"Monsieur, you have in your house a robber and an assassin."

Marius shuddered.

"This man has glided into your confidence under a false name."

"Well?"

"His name is Jean Valjean, known to you as M. Fauchelevent."

"I know it."

"He is an old convict."

"I know it."

These laconic answers nettled the visitor.

"I know what you have come to tell me," said Marius, "that Jean Valjean is a robber because he robbed M. Madeleine, a rich manufacturer, and an assassin because he killed the police officer Javert."

A superior smile began to play over the visitor's lips.

"You are mistaken, Monsieur," he said. The smile of triumph was quite evident.

It was Marius' turn to be upset.

"Do you deny the facts?" he asked.

"Javert committed suicide," said the visitor quietly. "Here is the proof."

He drew from his pocket two yellow and faded newspapers, both tightly folded. He placed one on the table next to him, and the other he began to spread out. It was the *Moniteur,* and it carried the full story of Javert's suicide. Before destroying himself, according to the account, Javert had written his last report to the prefect. The report said that having been taken prisoner in the barricade of the Rue de la Chauverie his doom was sealed until an insurgent, to whom had been committed the task of killing him, had released him. Javert told of Valjean's subterfuge, how he had fired his pistol in the air instead of blowing out his brains.

The authenticity of the article could not be doubted for it was an official communication from the prefecture of police to the *Moniteur.*

Marius could not restrain a cry of joy.

In the second newspaper, the *Drapeau Blanc,* Jean Valjean was himself identified as M. Madeleine, the rich manufacturer. The story of Jean Valjean's regeneration, his rise from the galleys to the position of a wealthy manufacturer, was recounted in simple terms. This account was an utter repudiation of the garbled story Marius had heard from the old clerk at Lafitte's. The *Drapeau Blanc* called Jean Valjean the savior of a depressed region.

In the eyes of Marius the shadowy figure of Jean Valjean had become grand.

"Nevertheless, Monsieur," the visitor said, interrupting Marius' thoughts, "Jean Valjean is a robber and an assassin."

He raised his hand as though to sweep away Marius' objection.

"Monsieur," he said, "I was a witness to the incident I shall describe. On the sixth of June, just passed, in one of the outlets of the Paris Sewer I saw Jean Valjean with the body of one of his victims. The body was that of a young man, completely disfigured with blood. This convict is as you know a man of terrible strength, and when he insisted that I open the grating of the sewer I had to comply with his wishes, but not before I obtained a piece of evidence. When Valjean's back was turned I tore a strip of cloth from this young man's scarf. No doubt Valjean threw the assassinated man into the river."

The visitor drew from his pocket a strip of ragged cloth, discolored with dark stains.

Marius had risen, pale, hardly breathing, his eyes fixed upon the fragment. Without a word he moved toward a closet, his gaze never leaving the scrap in his visitor's hand. Reaching into the closet he fumbled for a moment, and then drew forth a long stained cloth. Walking toward the extortionist he snatched the fragment from his hand, and fitted it to the gap in the scarf. The edges fitted perfectly.

A volcano of emotion erupted within him.

"That young man was myself, and there is the scarf," cried Marius.

The visitor was petrified.

Quivering with rage, Marius pointed his finger at the trembling man.

"You are a wretch, a liar, a slanderer. You wanted to destroy Jean Valjean, and you have only succeeded in glorifying him."

Marius was aflame.

"Get out of my sight," he shouted, "go before I kill you."

.   .   .

We said that a tree deprived of light must wither away. Jean Valjean was that tree; Cosette was his light. When Marius called on the old man he was in his last hour. Cosette, on seeing his tragic and wasted face, uttered a piercing cry.

Clasped in Cosette's arms, Jean Valjean exclaimed:

"Forgive me, Cosette, forgive me."

He turned to Marius.

"Forgive me, Marius," he said.

The sorrow that was swelling in Marius' heart burst forth. He fell upon his knees before the broken man, and wept bitterly.

"You ask my forgiveness. I owe you my life—I, who was the pitiless judge. Forgive me, Jean Valjean, forgive me," he cried.

Gently the hand of Jean Valjean came to rest on the young man's bowed head.

CARMEN

By

Prosper Mérimée

PROSPER MÉRIMÉE (*1803–1870*) was a French novelist, archaeologist, essayist, and in all these capacities one of the greatest
masters of French style during the nineteenth century. He
was born in Paris, and his father was a painter of repute.
Mérimée had English blood on his mother's side. His sympathies were against democracy and his cynicism and irre-
ligious prejudices made legitimism distasteful to him. He was
a friend of Napoleon III. Although he was a person of warmth
he had the reputation of being a cold-hearted cynic. He was
kind to his friends and had a scorpion-like scorn for foes. His
literary work has a Renaissance character. He had an admirable style, sound scholarship, and a strong intellectual grasp of
whatever he handled.

A YOUNG FRENCHMAN, happening to voyage in the region of An-
dalusia, in Spain, decides to investigate the locale, and discover
for himself whether the battles of Caesar had been ascribed to
the proper terrain or not. Motivated by this abstract archeological
interest, he hires a guide and several horses, better to explore the
countryside. His original purpose is quite driven out of his mind,
however, by a series of unusual events. It all begins by a strange
encounter in a deserted woodland patch, near a stream. There our
author spies a ferocious-looking Spaniard, unkempt and haggard,
sitting with an old blunderbuss across his knees. To all appearances, this is a typical highway thief, or even murderer. Fascinated somewhat by the promise of adventure, and literally unable to withdraw, our author strikes up a conversation with the
man.

First, he asks the stranger if he cares to smoke. The reply is

"Yes." Some excellent cigars are forthwith produced. Then he offers him food, and the man eats ravenously—like a man who has been starving for several days. When the repast is over, the sullen look of the reserved and forbidding guest begins to thaw a bit, and a friendly and lively conversation gets under way. The man, it appears, is a Basque; he does not know the immediate country-side very well. When he hears, however, that his host is on the verge of setting out for an inn nearby, he offers to come along. It is such a bad inn, he explains, yet it is the only available one. Still, he knows the old woman who keeps it, and perhaps his presence will be some protection. At least he can help his host of the afternoon, to secure better food than if he arrived at the inn totally unknown and unaccompanied.

Meanwhile, our author's guide motions excitedly to him; and it is not difficult to guess his meaning. He has placed this Basque as a robber or a "dangerous character" of some sort; he would like his master to be rid of him; and he cannot understand why they must journey to the inn together. In truth, our young French writer has become interested in the Basque; although he knows that in all likelihood he is a bandit, he also knows that no pro-vincial Spaniard who has eaten your food, smoked your cigars, and spent an afternoon in your company talking, and singing native songs, will ever harm you, or let harm befall you if he can help it. Accordingly, he ignores the worried glances and fur-tive signalings of his guide, and the three set out for the inn.

A more broken-down, filthy, uncomfortable place could not be imagined! Yet the Basque adventurer manages to procure them a seasonable meal. Impromptu beds are assigned them, on the floor; and the Basque asks his new friend permission to choose one close to him. The guide, still restless, leaves for the stable, pre-sumably to look to the welfare of the horses. But he is immedi-ately followed by the careful Basque, who apparently does not trust the guide to be by himself. He returns soon, however, and falls into a deep sleep. Then our author, who has been unable to sleep in such hot and close quarters, tiptoes out to sit on a bench before the inn. A moment later, the guide comes out of the stable, leading his horse. But he has been careful to muffle the horse's hooves with rough cloth. Challenging him to stop, our author demands to know where the guide is going. He is told that the mysterious Basque has been recognized as the notorious Don José; that he is wanted for murder, and a reward of two hundred ducats is on his head. Despite every attempt of his master's to keep him there, the guide rides off to "inform on" the sleeping bandit. Our author, with a few misgivings of guilt, cannot refrain from waking the bandit, warning him to take off at once to the mountains, and even supplying him with more cigars before his departure. Don José is deeply grateful, and the chance friendship of these two men, struck up in the afternoon, is cemented more closely.

The author continues his journeys—his friend of yesterday having left a pleasing sense of adventure and excitement with him. One day he chances to be passing through the quaint old town of Cordova. He is leaning on the quai, overlooking the sea, smoking and thinking when a beautiful gipsy girl, dressed casually but dashingly in a short skirt, a loose blouse, and a bright shawl drawn invitingly over one shoulder, the other exposed, stops a short distance from him to watch the bathing women. Noticing that the smoke of his cigar is drifting her way, he asks if it is bothering her. She replies that on the contrary, she likes the smell of a good cigar, and sometimes smokes a bit of tobacco herself. They continue to talk, and the gipsy girl, whose name is Carmen (or Carmencita) confesses that she is adept at telling fortunes, and even at practicing certain kinds of witchcraft. Our author, who has always been intrigued by the mysterious arts, cannot resist the temptation to have this alluring and exciting woman tell him what the future has in store for him. So they set out for Carmen's abode, for the crowded streets of Cordova are not suitable for an occupation of this sort.

An old gipsy woman of unsavory appearance lets them into an uninviting house, where Carmen has her rooms. They settle themselves, and our author is fascinated to see Carmen chant her "magic" phrases, mix her potions, and dance her mad gipsy dance to the accompaniment of castanets. She is just about to begin telling his fortune, when a man bursts angrily into the room. He advances furiously on our author, is about to seize him, when their eyes meet, and they perceive that they know each other. Indeed, it

·is none other than the bandit Don José, whom our author had been pleased to befriend a few weeks ago. A heated conversation ensues between Carmen and Don José, in the course of which she makes the gesture of hand across the throat—indicating that she wants the man to be killed. Our author suspects it is he that is being so disposed of, and forever after he feels little sympathy for Carmen, and women of her kind. But Don José doesn't comply with Carmen's wishes; instead, he walks Carmen's bewildered victim half-way back to town, and then, abruptly, leaves. Our author is glad to be free of distasteful complications, and makes plans to voyage on at once, to some other, perhaps friendlier, towns. Before leaving, however, he discovers that his elegant watch, which Carmen had greatly admired, is missing: nor is it difficult to imagine the manner of its disappearance!

It is many months later, after a long tour of the provinces of Spain, that our author, returning, is forced to pass through the township of Cordova, again. On his arrival, he chances to meet an old monk who had heard about the disappearance of his watch, and who hastens to inform him that the watch was returned the following day, by a man who is now in a prison nearby. Further questions reveal to our author, that the prisoner is Don José, and that he voluntarily gave himself up to the police after having committed a murder. Our author determines to visit him; and there, seated in the jail, is Don José: calm, but bathed in gloom and melancholy. Refusing all aid, he confides to the author the story of his life.

.   .   .

As a proud and fierce young Basque, he leaves his mountain home after a fight, in which he was the victor. He falls in with some dragoons and enlists with the cavalry. He soon distinguishes himself, and becomes a corporal. He is instructed that he is in line for becoming a sergeant; but, unfortunately, just at that time he is stationed at the Seville Tobacco Factory. Here he sees for the first time that dark and exciting gipsy beauty, Carmen, of whom we have already heard. He is still a loyal and simple youth, and the memory of innocent Basque girls is recent in his mind. He tries to ignore Carmen; but she hates indifference, and so she seizes every opportunity to taunt and mock him.

One day the porter from the cigar factory rushes out, shouting for the officers; a fight has broken out inside, and a woman is badly wounded. Our hero is forced to go in only to find that the injured woman has been gashed in the forehead by the vicious Carmen. He places her under arrest, and soon sets out with two young privates, to escort Carmen to the jail. They must cross some mountain roads to reach it. As they walk along, Carmen pleads with him to release her; he explains he cannot do it. Then she proceeds to ask him if he is a Basque, and when he replies affirmatively, she breaks into the Basque dialect. Now the Basque dialect is very beautiful to the ears of natives, and our young hero, knowing in his heart that Carmen is more probably gipsy than Basque, is yet willing to swallow her lies for the sake of hearing and talking that language which is so dear to him. Finally, by appealing to his Basque courage and pride, Carmen is able to convince him to enact a little comedy for her aid. She turns around and pushes him; he falls; Carmen takes madly to her heels. The lumbering young privates take after her, but she is too fleet for them, and far outstrips them. The three army men then return to town, minus the prisoner. Suspicion falls upon the young corporal for his share in the affair, and he is imprisoned, and loses his rank.

This is the first step of his undoing; but it is also the first step of his association with Carmen. While he is in prison, she sends him some tokens: a file, to aid his escape, and money to purchase civilian clothes, once he has effected it. He chooses to serve his time more honorably, however. But when he is released, Carmen gets in touch with him. He is now a private in the army, and he feels his humiliation very keenly. But by this time he has fallen madly in love with the bewitching, irresponsible creature who has caused him so much trouble. Carmen, in turn, finds him courageous and pleasing, and is perfectly willing to let him become one of her men. She favors him with occasional affection and attention; but this only inflames his love the more, while it arouses a burning jealousy of the other men who play a part in her life. One day, when Carmen is to meet him in a little out-of-the-way gipsy cafe and to take him home with her, she comes upon the scene with someone else—an officer in the army. The young

Basque lover, infuriated, insults his superior officer, and they come to blows. The officer unsheathes his sword, wounds the Basque on the forehead, but in a minute is killed by the quicker blade of his adversary. Carmen speaks a few hurried words to the old gipsy woman who owns the place; and then orders the young Basque to run off with her.

Carmen takes care of him, and when he recovers she outlines for him a career of plotting, thieving, smuggling, and trickery, a career which is a passion only with the gipsies, and which only they have developed to a fine art. He cannot return to the army, however, nor stay in any region where he might be known. And so he must comply; and the desperado Don José is the character that is born out of this good Basque youth, fallen upon evil circumstance. So the years pass. Carmen is always the genius of the little band of thieves that work together. But every once in a while she engages in a kind of "gipsy business" that remains maddening and revolting to Don José. She captivates some rich merchant, or officer, or foreign traveller, lives with him, steals his money and rings, and then notifies her band of a specific time when she and her paramour are to pass on a deserted road. The group of bandits then descend upon them, overpower the man, steal his belongings, and depart with the triumphant Carmen.

Don José pleads with her and threatens her; but she refuses to promise to give up this way of "earning" money. It is only the command of a husband that is law for the gipsy woman, Carmen tells him. But Carmen is already married; and her husband is expected to join the band now. He has just been released after many years in prison; and he is the ugliest, meanest-looking gipsy Don José has ever seen. When Don José becomes aware that Carmen hates her husband and would be gladly rid of him, he fights a duel of knives with him, and kills him. Then Don José makes Carmen his wife, and forbids her to have anything to do with other men. For a few years they manage to live on their smuggling and thieving. But Carmen grows restless, and takes a fancy to a young bull-fighter. Don José warns her, and pleads with her to give up this life, and come with him to some new country where they can begin to live honestly, renouncing all the crime and vice which has been their practice for years. Carmen refuses.

Shortly after, in another city, Don José finds out that Carmen has been flirting with the bull-fighter again. This time he is beside himself with rage. After the bullfight, he meets Carmen and threatens to kill her unless she promises to be faithful to him, and come away with him to lead a new life. Carmen, realizing fully that her life is in danger, says that she has always known it would be her lot to be killed by the man she had once favored more than any other, and then married. She makes no attempt to resist. Scornfully, she throws aside the ring which Don José had given her. Tested beyond endurance, he leaps upon her and chokes her to death. He then buries her in the forest, visits a priest and pays him to say mass for somebody now dead. When mass is over, Don José, defeated and alone, turns toward the city. When he arrives, he makes straightway for the police. There he confesses that he has just murdered Carmen, and is put in jail to await execution.

And this is the tale that the unfortunate prisoner told to our author. Our author could not refrain from thinking that in the evil fate which awaited Don José some of the characteristic gipsy resignation to suffering would be displayed. Unable to offer any material aid, he promises Don José to take a golden medal and chain to Don José's old mother, telling her that her son is dead "but not how he died."

ICELAND FISHERMEN

By

Pierre Loti

Louis Marie Julien Viaud (*1850–1923*) was a French novelist, born at Rochefort, who assumed the pen-name of Pierre Loti. He joined the marine service when he was 17 and continued in it for thirty-one years until he resigned. He traveled extensively while he was in his naval office. He became widely known to his contemporaries for his impressionistic writings in exotic settings. The settings included Turkey, Senegal, Tahiti, Brittany, Algeria, Japan and the Basque country.

THERE THEY WERE, five huge, square-built seamen, drinking away together in the dismal cabin of the *Marie* which reeked of fish-pickle and bilge-water. They had been drinking wine and cider in their pannikins, and the sheer enjoyment of life lit up their frank, honest faces. Now, they lingered at the table chatting, in Breton tongue, on women and marriage, subjects which they treated humorously without being indecent. In the midst of all this merry-making sat Sylvestre Moan, a lad of only seventeen yet already a man for height and strength. A fine curly black beard covered his cheeks, his eyes were childlike, bluish-gray in hue, and sweet and tender in expression. His usually serene brow was faintly lined with worry. What is keeping Yann? he asked himself. Is he lashed to his work on deck?

As if in answer to this unspoken question the captain drew himself to his feet, and raised the scuttle with his head.

"Yann!" he shouted, "Yann! Look alive, matey!"

The only answer was a rough growl, to be followed in a few moments by the sound of a man in clogs coming down the wooden steps.

He entered bent in two like a big bear, for he was a giant. In fact, he was so huge in all his proportions, though he was as straight as a poplar in less confined quarters, that he seemed a trifle grotesque. The muscles of his shoulders stood out like great globes. His large brown eyes were mobile, with a grand, wild expression.

Sylvestre threw his arms around Yann, and drew him toward him tenderly, after the fashion of children. Except for his old grandmother there was none other so dear to Sylvestre. He was betrothed to Yann's sister, and he treated him as an elder brother. And Yann allowed himself to be pulled about like a young lion, answering by a kind smile that showed his white teeth.

After they were seated the important topic of marriage was revived.

"You ought to be ashamed, Yann," said the master, "a hulking chap like you, twenty-seven years old, and not yet spliced. What must the lasses think of you when they see you roll by?"

Yann's retort was a contemptuous one. It was not for nothing that he had spent the required five years in the government naval service. There he had learned not only to speak good French but also to hold skeptical opinions of the sentimental feelings of his mates. With love he was not concerned, and to the men in the cabin he rattled off his latest love adventure in Nantes. He told the story with coarse words and oratorical flourishes which seemed out of place among the simple men of the crew, with the grand solemnity of the ocean around them.

Sylvestre, who had been brought up in respect for holy things, was greatly pained. He expected to marry Yann's sister soon, but never yet had answered any girl's love advances. He could not understand Yann's strange behaviour when the sacred subject of marriage was mentioned. It was his secret hope that Yann would undergo a change of mind before he, Sylvestre, left Breton shores for his long period of naval service. But Yann was obdurate, and would have nothing to do with the lovely maidens of Paimpol, or, for that matter, with all the maidens in Brittany.

Early that morning when they were on deck with their hand-lines baited for the cod that swam the cold green seas of Iceland Sylvestre thought of Gaud, his cousin, the daughter of M. Mêvel.

Gaud was adorably young, very fair, with great gray eyes between almost black lashes. A deep dimple under her lower lip foiled it up delightfully. From time to time when she was absorbed by a particular idea, she would bite this lower lip with her white teeth, making the blood run in tiny red veins under the delicate skin. In her supple form there was no little pride which she inherited from the bold Icelandic sailors, her ancestors.

Sylvestre recalled the first time that Gaud and Yann had met. It was at the "Pardon des Islandais," the fête-day of Our Lady of Bonne-Nouvelle, the patroness of fishermen. It was a day of great rejoicing, and the streets of Paimpol were filled to overflowing. There were throngs of sailors and happy girls, and side by side with them were the sweethearts of dead sailors quitting the chapel of the dead in their long mourning shawls and their smooth tiny coifs.

Sylvestre and Gaud had but a confused impression of this seething activity. As her glance played over the roving crowds she was struck by a group of young Icelanders who were crowded around the singers of "complaintes." One among the Icelanders was a giant with shoulders almost preposterously broad. She said to herself, perhaps with a touch of mockery, "There is one who is tall, to say the least. What an incumbrance he'll be to the woman he marries, a husband of that size!"

Yann turned around as if he had heard her, nodded his great head to Sylvestre, and stared at Gaud as if to say, "Who is this girl who wears the coife of Paimpol, who is so elegant, and whom I have never seen before?"

Quickly he bent his eyes to the ground, and then turned again to the singers. The fine profile, the grand half savage look, the brown, almost tawny pupils moving rapidly on the bluish opal of his eyes, impressed her and made her timid. Sylvestre made a move to fetch Yann, and lead him to Gaud, but he was already moving off with his friends.

Every detail of this meeting Sylvestre recalled vividly. He turned to Yann who was hauling in the cod from the steel-gray waters, and suddenly and very seriously said: "You really ought to marry, Yann."

"Me! Yes, some day I'll marry." He smiled. "But I'll have none

[133]

of the lassies at home. No. I'll wed the sea, and I'll invite you all to my wedding."

It was not until some time after the *Marie* had put in at Paimpol that Yann and Gaud met again. It was at a wedding feast. At the appointed time all were assembled except Yann. Time passed and yet he did not come. It was then Gaud discovered that it was for Yann alone she had donned her best dress.

At last he arrived, in his best clothes also. He excused his lateness, saying that an unexpected shoal of fish had been reported from England as heading for a point a little off Aurigny. Along with the *Marie* the other boats had set sail, and Yann was hard put to find a substitute for his place aboard the *Marie*. It was this that had made him late, and in order not to miss the wedding he had abandoned his share in the profits of the catch.

Later, while he was dancing with Gaud, he roughly said to her: "You are the only person in Paimpol, indeed in the world, for whom I would have missed such a windfall. Truly, for nobody else would I have missed my fishing, Mademoiselle Gaud."

"Thank you, Monsieur Yann," she said, "I, too, would rather be with you than with anybody else."

Each time he spoke to her he looked deep into her eyes, as though to divine the opinion hidden there. And she smiled as she gazed at him full in the face; answering seldom, but listening with her whole soul, more and more astonished, and more and more drawn toward him. His earnest voice, short and blunt to others, was soft and tender as he spoke to her.

When the dawn came they took leave of each other like betrothed ones who are sure to meet the following day.

But that night had long since passed, and many others, and Yann had never returned. What change had come over him? Meeting him by chance he seemed to avoid her, turning away his look as though he had been done some injury.

Except for these chance meetings Gaud did not see Yann again until the day poor Sylvestre left for his period of naval service. Yann, who had also come to bid good-bye to Sylvestre, feigned to look aside when Gaud saw him. They accompanied Sylvestre to the train, he blubbering a little, and his grandmother silently weeping. When the train had left the station for Brest Gaud turned around, but Yann was gone. Her anger began to rise at his disappearance. To think that she, as lovely a lass as any in Britanny, should be treated in this manner by a common sailor. And with her mounting indignation a plan began to evolve in her mind.

Her father had formerly had mutual interests with Yann's father, and owed him a hundred francs for the sale of a boat. It was a complicated business, or so the two men thought, and the transaction had been attended with a certain amount of friendly bickering. At any rate, a hundred francs remained to be paid. At least, this was the contention of M. Mêvel. But like all Bretons Yann's father was stubborn. The hundred francs, he maintained, was not enough to close the deal, it was but an installment. He would not accept payment until M. Mêvel agreed to this. It seemed as though the matter would never be settled until one day, a few months after Sylvestre's departure from Paimpol, Gaud approached her father, and said to him:

"You ought to let me take the money to him, father. Old Gaos may be in good humor, and I shall be pleased to see Marie Gaos. Besides he may listen more readily to me."

Need one be told the thought uppermost in Gaud's mind?

M. Mêvel gave his permission, and she started out. Her path took her along narrow roads dotted here and there with Calvaires, ghastly highway ornaments of Our Saviour on His cross, to which Bretons are given. The ground was undulating and rocky, and from all the heights the open sea could be seen. No more trees now, nothing but the shorn heaths with their green reeds, and here and there consecrated crosses rose, their outstretched arms outlined against the sky. At one of these crossways, guarded by a colossal image of Christ, she hesitated between two roads running among thorny slopes.

A child passing by came to her rescue: "Good-day, Mademoiselle Gaud!"

It was one of the Gaos children, one of Yann's wee sisters. Gaud kissed her and asked if her parents were home.

"Father and mother are, yes. But brother Yann," said the little one, without intent, of course, "has gone to Loguivy; but I don't think he'll be gone very long."

What could Yann be doing at Loguivy? Courting the girls, perhaps.

As night drew near they came to the home of the Gaos family, which was built against a high cliff. A dozen granite steps led up to it. Trembling a little at the thought that Yann might have returned, Gaud crossed the small garden where chrysanthemums and veronicas grew.

Indoors she explained that she had come to bring the money for the boat, and they very politely asked her to sit down to await the father's return. But her eyes were already searching for Yann. They were very friendly, chatting and laughing with her. She had not been seated very long when a heavy footstep on the stairs made her tremble. It was old father Gaos returning from fishing. After he had saluted her Gaud mentioned the object of her visit. The old man, in a friendly way, refused to accept the hundred francs as a final payment; he would speak to M. Mével again about the matter. Gaud smiled to herself.

They made excuses for Yann's absence, telling her that he had gone to Loguivy to buy nets. Perhaps the father had guessed with the shrewdness of an old salt that there was more to Gaud's visit than the mere payment of a hundred francs, and also that Yann was not as indifferent to this lovely girl as he pretended to be.

Gaud dreamily lengthened out her call, although conscious that it was too long already, and feeling a tug at her heart that she would not see Yann after all. But night was falling and the work had been folded up. The little ones on the benches drew closer to one another, saddened by the gray dismal gloaming, and eyed Gaud hard, seeming to say:

"Why doesn't she go now?"

Suddenly the blood rushed to her face at the idea of having remained so late. She got up, and took her leave. The old man accompanied her. As they walked along together the impulse to unburden herself became strong, but the words were stifled in her throat. At the cross of Plouëzoc'h she bade him good-bye for the lights of Paimpol were already in view.

One day in June, shortly after Gaud's visit to Yann's family, old Granny Moan was summoned to the naval registry office with a peremptoriness that is characteristic of the government. Of course, it concerned her grandson, Sylvestre, but that did not frighten her in the least. All those who draw their living from the sea are used to the Naval Registry, which is like an impersonal guardian of the lives of seafarers. Perhaps Sylvestre had distinguished himself, thought Granny Moan.

She put on her best dress and a clean white cap, and started for Paimpol. The old grandmother trotted along swiftly. The desolate countryside was beaming with life. The rocky crevices of the low hills were brimming with flowering shrubs. But Granny Moan saw none of this, for in her mind anxiety had begun to grow. Nearing Paimpol she became more and more uneasy, and improved her speed until her old legs began to creak. She did not hesitate before the registry office, but marched directly in.

The commissioner was not in just then, and an ugly little creature sat at his desk. When she gave her name he rose with a look of importance, and reached for a set of impressive looking documents. He spread them out before her, and old Granny Moan suddenly began to tremble. In her blurred mind there appeared the memory of twenty years ago when in the same way she had been told of the death of her son, Pierre. The commissioner had behaved in the very same way then.

Now he was reading mechanically: "Moan, Jean-Marie-Sylvestre, registered at Paimpol, folio 213, number 2091, died on board the *Bien Hoa,* on the 14th of——"

The old lady gasped in bewilderment: "Wh—What?"

"Discharged—dead," he answered, in the detached manner of an official.

The old lady was so dazed that the clerk repeated himself in Breton.

"Marw éo," he said, "marw éo."

In an aged and pitifully tremulous voice she repeated the words after him. She wept not, nor did she lament, for in her long lifetime her well of grief had been too often sounded.

"Marw éo! Marw éo!"

The words tumbled from her quivering lips in a kind of echolalia.

"Marw éo! Marw éo!" and nothing more.

Thus did Gaud find her in her cottage that evening; her hair dishevelled, her arms hanging down, and her head resting against the stone wall, with a falling jaw grinning, and whimpering plaintively like a child. How she managed to drag her old body home she could not have told.

"My grandson is dead," she wailed. The old woman threw the papers into Gaud's lap.

Hastily scanning them Gaud saw that the news was true, and fell on her knees to pray. On the hearth the cricket that brings joy was chirping his shrill music. The dusk entered through the narrow window into the dwelling of the Moans, who had all been devoured by the sea, and whose family was now extinguished.

At last Gaud said: "I'll come to you, Granny, to live with you. I'll bring my bed, and I'll take care of you, and nurse you—you shan't be alone."

She wept for her little friend Sylvestre, but in her sorrow she was led involuntarily to think of another—he who had gone back to the deep sea fishery.

The sad weeks followed, one on another, until the biting winds began to sweep down from the north. The two women seldom left the little house. Old Granny Moan was becoming difficult to tend —her poor mind was going. There were days when she stumbled around the cabin with an expression in her eyes that was terrifying in its lifelessness. On those days she could remember nothing of her grandson.

"Sylvestre? Sylvestre?" she would repeat dazedly, "Oh, my dear, I've had so many of them, when I was young, boys and girls together, that now I can't remember their names."

Winter came on, and the great sea sighed around them, filling the vacant night with its profound voice. The two women, one old and lifeless, the other adorably young, huddled close to the smouldering fire on the hearth. Through the dusty corridors of the old woman's mind floated vague memories of the past, a past that swarmed with the faces of the long dead. And for Gaud, too, there were faces, one of which seemed never to fade. She had but to see it in her mind's eye for the old ache to rise anew.

That season the fleet had been late in returning to Paimpol. The Iceland storms had been so severe that many of the ships had run before them into whatever harbors they could find. But now, one by one, they were rounding the point, and slipping into the harbor of Paimpol. The *Marie* was among the last to return, and hardly had she been made snug at the dock when the crew, Yann among them, swarmed over the sides and into the arms of their joyous families. The wharf fairly simmered with so much happiness. There were loving arms for everyone. Yann, who was usually the gravest and most impassive of men, was inarticulate with joy. Terrible indeed must have been that winter on the Iceland seas.

Slowly the crowd dispersed, and Yann set off with his father, trailed by his little brothers and sisters. They had not gone very far when the old man turned to Yann with eyes that were deeply sad. The story poured from his lips—Sylvestre's death in the Orient, the old grandmother's heartrending grief, and, last, Gaud's loving kindness and noble sacrifice. Yann listened benumbed, his head bowed in grief. They walked together in silence for a time, and then Yann turned to his father.

"I must see Granny Moan," he said, abruptly, and without another word he took the road that led to the old woman's cottage.

He was humble for the first time in his life as he crossed over the threshold. Touching his hat to the two women his eyes fell upon Sylvestre's portrait in its small black frame. For what seemed an interminable time to the two women Yann gazed at the face of Sylvestre. His eyes were no longer proud and flashing, but full of suffering.

Gaud stood with her hands resting on the table. She watched Yann silently inspect the poverty of the cottage. The old grandmother appeared not to notice him. Yann and Gaud stood facing each other in silence. Indeed, no words could have expressed the emotions in their hearts. They gazed at each other more and more searchingly, as if in solemn expectation of some wonderful, exquisite event, which was too long in coming.

"Gaud," he said, in a low grave voice, "if you're still of a mind now——"

If she were still of a mind! What was he asking of her? Had she heard aright? She felt almost crushed under the immensity of the event.

"We could make a splice of it—a marriage, right off, Gaud, if you are of a mind?"

[139]

It was not surprise but ecstasy that prevented Gaud from answering; no words at all came to her relief.

"Well, Gaud, why don't you answer?" said Granny Moan, who had risen and come toward them. "Don't you see, it rather surprises her, Monsieur Yann."

She turned to Gaud, and said petulantly: "Why don't ye kiss each other, my children? Lor', but they're dumb! Dear me, what strange grandchildren I have here. Pluck up, Gaud! Say something to him. In my time lovers kissed when they plighted their troth."

Yann raised his hat, as if suddenly seized with a hitherto unfelt reverence, before bending down to kiss Gaud. It seemed to him that this was the first kiss worthy of the name he had ever given in his life.

She kissed him also, pressing her fresh lips, unused to refinements of caresses, with her whole heart, to his sea-bronzed cheek.

Among the stones the cricket sang of happiness, being right for this time.

In the ten days that remained before Yann was put to sea again they lived a lifetime of happiness. From the moment of the wedding in Ploubazlanec church Gaud's joy knew no bounds. In spite of the storm all Ploubazlanec had turned out to look at them. Nearly all Yann's mates, the Icelanders of Paimpol, were there, and they cheered the bride and groom all the way to Yann's home where the wedding feast was to be held.

The house was a scene of merry confusion and disorder, with all the friends and kinsmen of the young couple gathered there. Boiled and roasted meats were served with poultry. There were different kinds of fish, omelets and pancakes. Despite the wind which was raging outside the laughter and jollity of the guests pervaded the house. The happiest of all were Yann and Gaud, who, when they were not thinking of each other, were overcome at the knowledge that only a few days of married life remained before Yann must put to sea. Gaud was appalled at the imminence of this separation, and at the thought that all their plans of life together, of peaceful joy and settling down, must be put off until Yann's return.

Yann, in his loving way, did all he could to comfort her. Once, when the shrieking wind made itself heard even above the noise of the celebration he hugged Gaud close, and jokingly said: "The sea is wrathy and jealous, because I'd promised I'd be wedded to her."

That blissful week soon came to an end. On the day of the sailing Yann and Gaud set out, arm in arm, like sweethearts, for Paimpol. On the way they murmured a thousand tender things to each other. The day was one of universal serenity. The air had a delicious balmy scent, as of spring itself. All this made the pain of parting sweeter and longer drawn out.

Yann was to sail on the *Leopoldine,* the *Marie* having been taken out of service by her owners. The wharf was crowded with people. The departures for Iceland had begun the day before, and with each tide there was a fresh fleet off. On this particular morning the *Leopoldine* was to start with about fifteen other vessels, and the wives and mothers of the sailors were all present at the getting under sail. At the very last minute Yann caught up his wife in his arms. Without saying a word they were enfolded in a long and silent embrace.

He embarked; the gray sails were unfurled, and spread out to the light wind that rose from the west. Even as she watched the *Leopoldine* faded out of vision.

It can be told in few words. The long summer faded into autumn, and when the first cold winds began to blow the Iceland fleet returned to Paimpol one by one. All through the country joy returned with them. The *Leopoldine* was among the belated, but there were yet another ten expected. In another week all would return. Gaud waited in happy anticipation for Yann, keeping their home bright and tidy for his return.

Three more ships appeared, then another five, until there were only two lacking, the *Marie-Jeanne* and the *Leopoldine*.

"Surely," said Yann's father, "the *Leopoldine* won't be long now. When one of them begins to start home the others can't hold back long in any peace."

But the days succeeded one another without result. Gaud assured herself that this delay was but natural; was it not the same every year? At night, however, a nervous shiver of anguish would run through her whole frame.

One day at the end of September a group of anxious women

[141]

had rapidly formed on the wharf. Gaud, pale and trembling, was there, and with her Yann's father.

"I'm almost sure," he said, "I'm almost sure it's them. A red sail and topsail that clews up—it's very like them anyhow."

He squinted seaward for a moment, and then his eyes fell. It was the *Marie-Jeanne,* the last but one of the Iceland fleet.

Every day, like a poor crazed woman, Gaud dressed in her brightest lest she be taken for the widow of a shipwrecked sailor, feeling exasperated when others looked furtively and compassionately at her. She would turn her head so that she would not meet those glances that froze her very blood.

September had passed. The sorrowing wife took scarcely any nourishment. She remained at home, crouching with her hands between her knees, with her head thrown back, and resting against the wall behind. She was half crazed with grief. At times a hoarse animal-like cry rose from her throat, and was repeated in spasms, while her head beat backward against the granite wall.

Alas! where was the *Leopoldine* now? Where could she be? Out afar, on the slate-gray seas of Iceland, forsaken, crushed, and lost.

All ended by a never fading vision appearing to her—an empty sea-tossed wreck, slowly and gently rocked by the vast sea; almost with soft mockery, in the midst of the silent calm of deadened waters.

EUGÉNIE GRANDET

By

Honoré de Balzac

HONORÉ DE BALZAC (*1799–1850*) was a French novelist who studied law and was admitted to the bar but never practised as he devoted his life to literature, struggling with poverty for years. From his twenty-sixth to his thirtieth year he engaged in business as a publisher and printer. Unsuccessful, he retired to the country where he gathered material for his first successful novel *Les Chouans*. His mature life was involved in a series of love affairs the last one ending in his marriage to Evelina, a Polish-Russian countess shortly before his death. Balzac wrote about 100 novels and tales besides a number of unsuccessful plays. His books are noted for their vigor and power and exuberance of life. Among his many works are *Le Curé de Tours, Modeste Mignon* and *Les parents pauvres*.

IN CERTAIN FRENCH PROVINCIAL TOWNS there are dwellings which inspire us with a melancholy similar to the sadness evoked by dark cloisters, mournful waste lands, or dismal ruins. In just such a house in Saumur dwelt M. Grandet, a wealthy cooper, who, in 1789, had married the daughter of a prosperous lumber merchant. Known as an ardent Republican, he had considerable influence both politically and commercially. Of their marriage a daughter Eugénie was born and, during the ensuing years, Grandet's fortune increased rapidly. In addition to his cooperage business he augmented his revenue by real estate transactions and by speculating in the wine-crops of the vicinity. Only two persons in Saumur had even a remote idea of the extent of the cooper's fortune: M. Cruchot, the notary, entrusted with Grandet's usurious money-lending activities, and M. des Grassins, a wealthy banker, with whom he had secret financial dealings in the accomplishment of which

Grandet possessed the characteristics of the tiger and the boa constrictor. He would crouch, lie in wait, and pounce upon his prey; then he would open the throat of his money bag, swallow a mass of gold and silver coins, lie down calmly and, like a serpent, coldly and methodically digest the food. His neighbors experienced toward him a feeling of admiration mingled with respect and terror, for few were those among them who had not felt the scratches of his sharp claws.

He never bought food, for his farmers supplied all the necessities of his table in part payment of their rent. His sole expenses were clothes for the family, payment for chairs in church for his wife and daughter, candles for the house, the meager wages of Nanon, the devoted servant, and household repairs. He never went anywhere because he did not want to invite people to his home; the Cruchot and des Grassins families were his only guests. The nephew of M. Cruchot, a man of thirty-three years and judge of the higher court of Saumur, was a possible suitor for the hand of Eugénie. He had a rival in des Grassins, ten years younger than he, whose mother was doing all in her power to advance her son's interests.

The tall and gaunt servant Nanon was the only human creature capable of accepting the despotism of such a master. She served the household for thirty-five years, assuming all the heavy tasks, and toiling from early morning until late at night.

Mme. Grandet was a thin, awkward woman, yellow of complexion, one of those women who seem born to be tyrannized. Her husband never gave her more than six francs at a time for her expenses. Rarely leaving the house, she wore very few new clothes. She never asked for anything for herself.

One evening, when the des Grassins and the Cruchots were playing lotto in Grandet's sitting-room on the occasion of Eugénie's birthday, an unexpected visitor arrived. It was Charles Grandet, the handsome young son of M. Grandet's brother, who had come from Paris by stage-coach. Splendidly dressed, he had brought with him two trunks filled with clothes of the latest Parisian fashion.

The newcomer produced a profound impression upon Eugénie. Convinced that she alone was capable of understanding the ideas and tastes of her cousin, she immediately prevailed upon Nanon to have his bed warmed and to start a fire in his fireplace. Feeling that the odor of tallow candles would be offensive to the Parisian bred dandy, she sent Nanon out to purchase wax candles and also some sugar for his drinking water. She had to provide the money from her own pocket, for Grandet kept the key to the cupboard and daily rationed out the household supplies.

During the course of these preparations Grandet was studiously perusing a letter from his brother which Charles had delivered to him. One can readily understand what must have been his feelings as he read:

"When this letter reaches your hands I shall no longer be living: in my present position I do not feel able to bear the shame of bankruptcy. It is my misfortune to have liabilities of four million francs and assets of only one-quarter of that sum. My creditors have failed in their payments to me and my wine business has been ruined by the abundance and the quality of your crops. I ask you now to be Charles' father. Be a good father to him. Do not wean him too suddenly from the leisurely life which he has led, for it would kill him. After a short while he will perhaps feel able to go to the Indies and start a career for himself. Farewell, my brother. God bless you for accepting, as I am sure you will, this guardianship. There will always be a voice praying for you in the world where we all must go some day and where I already am.

VICTOR GRANDET."

Without showing the slightest trace of emotion, Grandet calmly folded the letter in its original creases, put it into his pocket, and went to find Charles.

"Well, my nephew," he said, "if you are tired, Nanon will conduct you to your room. It is not very elaborate, for we are poor vintners and haven't a cent. The taxes eat up all our profits. To-morrow, if you wish to look around town a bit, you are free to do so. You will excuse me for not accompanying you, for I have my work to do. If any neighbors tell you that I am rich, don't believe them. I let them talk, for it does no harm; in reality I am very poor and have to work hard."

As Charles ascended the worm-eaten staircase and entered his desolate room, he wondered why his father had ever sent him to so unattractive a place.

.   .   .

Into the pure and monotonous life of young girls there comes a moment when the sun casts its rays upon their souls. Love had come into Eugénie's heart. Rising early the next morning she found new charms in the ordinary objects surrounding her. A thousand confused thoughts arose within her. Although she took special pains with her dress she reflected: "I am not beautiful enough for him; he will pay no attention to me." She went down to the kitchen and tried to prevail upon Nanon to bake a cake but Nanon objected because of the extra amount of flour and butter. Just at that moment they heard Grandet descending the stairs.

"There is your father," remarked Nanon; "ask him for the necessary provisions." But Eugénie ran out into the garden. For the first time in her life she was afraid of her father.

When Grandet reached the kitchen, Nanon asked him for the extra butter and flour. Upon his grumbling refusal Nanon pointed out to him that she would need eight pieces of sugar on account of the arrival of Charles. Again Grandet refused, stating that he would do without the two lumps that he habitually took in his coffee. Nanon abandoned the sugar question in order to obtain the cake, and Grandet finally unlocked the cupboard and doled out a portion of butter and flour.

Shortly after Grandet had departed to visit one of his estates, Charles blithely came down to breakfast, remarking that, since he was not particularly hungry, a trifle, such as a chicken or a partridge would be quite sufficient. However, when he sat down to his meal, the sight of the tastefully prepared boiled eggs and coffee soon made him forget his partridge. Before he had finished, a knock was heard; Grandet had returned.

To Charles's astonishment, Eugénie whisked away the saucer of sugar, leaving a few pieces on the table; Nanon removed the eggs; but Grandet had already sized up the situation. "Well, my nephew," he remarked, "it seems that these women are pillaging the whole town of Saumur for your benefit. When you have finished we shall go into the garden. I have some things to tell you that are not exactly sugary."

Several moments later, in the garden, Grandet handed to Charles a newspaper containing the news of Victor Grandet's bankruptcy and suicide. Charles burst into tears and Grandet left him to his misery.

In the women, however, Charles found sincere sympathizers. They did everything in their power to soften the terrible blow that had fallen upon the young man. They would gladly have worn mourning, but Grandet refused on account of the expense, explaining that mourning is in one's heart, not in one's clothes.

Grandet immediately consulted the lawyer Cruchot to see what could be done to save the Grandet name from the impending dishonor that might be caused by his brother's bankruptcy. With these facts at hand, Grandet prevailed upon the banker des Grassins to go to Paris, consult the creditors, and endeavor to have them sign over their claims to Grandet himself, who would later undertake to make a settlement out of court.

.   .   .

One day when Grandet had gone to Angers and Eugénie went to speak to Charles, she found the door of his room ajar. As she entered she saw Charles asleep in his chair next to the writing table upon which were several letters, one of which was open and unfinished. Unable to restrain her curiosity upon noticing that it began "My dear Annette", Eugénie began to read the letter. It acknowledged his love for Annette, marriage with whom was now impossible inasmuch as he was penniless and must go to the Indies. Filled with compassion, Eugénie went to fetch a purse filled with gold pieces which her father had been giving to her over a long period of time. Awakening Charles, she confessed having read the letter and offered him her savings to make a start in life. After a slight hesitation Charles accepted. In return he entrusted to Eugénie that which he treasured most—a gold box containing the portraits of his father and mother, in pearl-studded frames.

During the ensuing days, Eugénie's affection for Charles developed into a lasting love, and Charles declared his love to her. They met frequently in the garden, under a beautiful walnut tree, Mme. Grandet and Nanon aiding them in concealing their love from Grandet who surely would have disapproved. Finally the day for

Charles's departure arrived, after which Eugénie spent many lonely hours made bearable only by her faith in his love and her confidence that he would return to her as soon as he had made a name for himself.

.   .   .

Des Grassins had little difficulty in coming to an agreement with Victor Grandet's creditors. The latter had consulted the Bank of France and discovered that both des Grassins and Grandet of Saumur were men of wealth. They were convinced that eventually Grandet would repay them in full. After nine months, each creditor received forty-seven percent of the amount due him, the money being derived from the sale of the property left by Victor Grandet. Then Grandet assumed a waiting policy over a period of three years, attempting to tire out the creditors. Finally he announced to them that his nephew Charles, having made a fortune in the Indies, expected to return and pay them in full. Grandet himself, therefore, could not pay off these debts without consulting Charles.

.   .   .

Snow and ice held the town of Saumur in its grip on New Year's Day in 1820. For some time Eugénie and Mme. Grandet had been fearing the arrival of this day, for it would be the occasion of the annual gift of a gold piece from Grandet, and he would certainly ask to see Eugénie's collection of coins. And now the dreaded moment had arrived. In vain did Eugénie seek pretexts to avoid revealing her secret; Grandet insisted upon seeing the gold, and she finally was compelled to admit that it was no longer in her possession. But try as he might, Grandet could not oblige her to tell what she had done with her money; and finally, in a fit of rage, he locked her in her room and submitted her to a diet of bread and water.

Grandet's inflexibility so preyed upon the mind of Mme. Grandet that she became seriously ill. Day by day her condition grew worse. In the meantime Eugénie was permitted to leave her room only to go to church. The neighbors began to speculate upon the curious state of affairs in the Grandet household. When the secret finally leaked out, the entire community censured Grandet for his inhuman conduct. Finally Cruchot determined to have a word with him. He began by approaching the subject from the standpoint of common decency and humanity, but this made little impression upon Grandet. But when Cruchot pointed out that if Mme. Grandet died, Eugénie would receive all her money, Grandet, thoroughly frightened, decided to make peace with his daughter.

Returning home, he went up to his wife's bedroom and the sight that greeted his eyes amazed him. Eugénie had brought to her mother the box that Charles had left in her care, and the mother and daughter were examining the portraits. Grandet pounced upon the box like a tiger leaping upon a sleeping child. "Gold," he cried, "it is made of gold! It must weigh two pounds! Ah! Charles gave you that in exchange for your gold pieces. Why didn't you tell me? You have made a good business deal, my daughter." Grandet drew a knife from his pocket and attempted to pry the gold from the cover of the box. Pleading with him in vain, Eugénie seized a knife from the table and threatened to commit suicide if Grandet continued desecrating the box entrusted to her care. In the meanwhile Mme. Grandet had fainted and it became imperative to summon a doctor.

Mme. Grandet, in spite of the tender care of her daughter, rapidly grew worse and it was not long before death put an end to her physical suffering and to her mental anguish over the future of Eugénie who would no longer have her mother to protect her from her father's despotism. However, immediately after his wife's decease, Grandet's attitude toward Eugénie underwent a complete change: he actually trembled before his daughter. Neighbors attributed this alteration to his very advanced age, but the reason for his conduct soon became apparent. He explained to Eugénie that if she signed a document renouncing her mother's heritage Grandet would avoid the payment of heavy government taxes. Eugénie gave her immediate consent, thereby putting herself financially under the complete control of her father.

After this transaction, five years passed without any event to break the monotonous existence of Eugénie and her father. Eugénie's profound melancholy became quite apparent. Her only friends were the Cruchot family who had taught her to play whist and came in frequently for an evening game. Toward the end of the year 1827, Grandet was stricken with a paralysis which made rapid strides. During her father's infirmity, Eugénie's patience and devotion were sublime. His money was even more than ever a constant obsession and his dying words to his daughter were: "Take care of my fortune, for you will have to render me an accounting of it in the next world."

. . .

Eugénie was now alone in the world except for the devoted Nanon. After her father's death, she learned through Cruchot that she possessed a total fortune of seventeen million francs. One of her first acts was to bestow upon Nanon an annuity of 1200 francs, which made the servant a desirable match. She soon became the wife of Antoine Cornoiller, and the latter was entrusted with the supervision of Eugénie's landed property.

Eugénie had lived without ever having enjoyed any of the real pleasures of life. She had enjoyed a few days of happiness with Charles, but he had departed, leaving a world between them. For seven years her love for Charles had dominated her; and yet she had received not a single letter from him in all this time.

During this interval, Charles had been making a fortune in the Indies. Eugénie's money had given him a start. Then, engaging in the negro slave trade, he had amassed a capital of 1,900,000 francs when he finally returned to Bordeaux in 1827. On board the homeward bound vessel he had met a courtier of Charles X, M. d'Aubrion, whose extravagant wife had plunged the nobleman into debt, and who was anxious to marry off her ugly daughter Mathilde to any husband who would accept her without a dowry.

Thus, a real opportunity seemed to present itself to Charles. Believing that Grandet had settled his father's affairs, he was anxious to be received in Parisian society. He accompanied the d'Aubrion family to Paris and proposed to Mathilde. Des Grassins, hearing of Charles's return, immediately went to consult him about his father's affairs, warning him that a bankruptcy might be declared unless these debts were settled. "Monsieur," said Charles, "in a few days I shall be the Count d'Aubrion. My father's affairs are not mine. Furthermore, when a man has 100,000 francs a year income, his father is never declared a bankrupt."

In the month of August, Eugénie received a letter from Charles in which he explained to her that their mutual declaration of love had been a childhood silliness, that a man's duty was to marry for position, and that love in marriage was an illusion. He enclosed a money order for the sum which she had loaned him, together with the accumulated interest.

What a terrible and complete disaster! "My mother was right," sobbed Eugénie; "our destiny is to suffer and die." Determined to enter a convent, she talked the matter over with her confessor, but he indicated to her that it was rather her duty to society to marry, so that she might have someone to help her protect her fortune and continue to interest herself, as she had done for a long time, in the poor of Saumur.

Just at that moment Mme. des Grassins arrived to tell Eugénie that she had received word from her husband that Charles had been back from the Indies for a full month. Eugénie's contempt for the actions of Charles was now complete. Upon the occasion of the next visit of the magistrate Cruchot de Bonfons she said to him:

"I know full well that you are attracted to me for my money alone. If you will swear to leave me free during my entire life and demand of me none of the rights that my marriage should give you over me, my hand is yours. The only feeling that I can offer my husband is that of friendship. You will possess my hand and my fortune, but nothing more. And you must perform one service for me. I shall give you 1,500,000 francs. You shall leave immediately for Paris, go to M. des Grassins, get the names of all my uncle's creditors and pay what is due them, capital and interest at five percent."

The magistrate agreed.

"When you have received receipts for these payments," continued Eugénie, "you will take them together with this letter to Charles Grandet."

When the magistrate had left, Eugénie fell into an armchair and burst into tears. The magistrate accomplished all that Eugénie had asked, including the delivery of the following letter:

"My Dear Cousin:
"M. Cruchot de Bonfons has been good enough to deliver to you the receipts for the money owed by my uncle. A bankruptcy has

been rumored. It occurred to me that the son of a bankrupt might not be able to marry Mlle. d'Aubrion. Be happy according to the social conventions to which you are sacrificing our love. To make your happiness complete, all I can offer you is the honor of your father. Farewell. You will always have a faithful friend in your cousin,

"Eugénie."

"Well," said the magistrate, "it seems that there will be a double wedding, for I am marrying Eugénie."

"Congratulations," answered Charles, "she is a fine girl." Then, a suspicion entering his mind, "Is she rich?"

"Well," replied the magistrate, "four days ago she was worth nineteen millions, but today she has only seventeen."

When Charles had recovered from his astonishment, he stammered: "Well then, I hope that we may be able to advance each other's interests."

Three days later, the magistrate published the banns of his marriage to Eugénie. Six months later he became counsellor of the royal court of Angers. He hoped that before long he might rise step by step until he obtained a seat in the House of Peers in Paris. But these ambitious ideas never materialized; he died a week after being elected deputy from Saumur.

Thus Eugénie was a widow at an early age. Her face was pale, reposed, calm. Her voice was gentle. In spite of her vast fortune, she lived as simply as she had before her father's death. Her charitable work among the poor became her entire interest. Such is the history of this woman who, in the midst of the world was not of this world. Born to be a wife and mother, she was left without a husband, children, or family.

WUTHERING HEIGHTS

By

Emily Brontë

EMILY BRONTË (*1818–1848*), the English novelist, was a sister of the talented Charlotte Brontë. Patrick Brontë, a clergyman of the Church of England, was the father of six unusual children. In 1846 a volume of verse appeared called *Poems,* by Currer, Ellis, and Acton Bell, the pseudonyms Charlotte and Emily and Anne used. Emily had contributed twenty-one of the poems that were published and it was later agreed that in this volume Emily revealed a true poetic genius. Her *Wuthering Heights* won great acclaim. She died when she was quite young. Within eight months Branwell, the brother, Emily, and then Anne passed away.

1801. I have just returned from a visit to Mr. Heathcliff, to whom I introduced myself—Mr. Lockwood, his new tenant at Thrushcross Grange. Heathcliff is strangely reserved; he seemed reluctant to admit me to Wuthering Heights. A gypsy-dark man, he is as inhospitable as his crew of furious dogs, but I shall call on him again. There are few people to talk to in this lonely moorland country.

A few days later. Yesterday I arrived at Wuthering Heights just as the snow began to drive thickly. Joseph, the vinegar-faced man-servant, would not let me in, but a young man of rough appearance yet free bearing appeared from the yard and admitted me. In the apartment to which I was led sat a beautiful young woman; most unnaturally, in her lovely eyes was an expression of mingled scorn and desperation. These people were even more silent than Heathcliff. When the master of the house came in, I learned that the girl was the wife of Heathcliff's dead son, and that the young man was Hareton Earnshaw. Never have I seen an odder, gruffer household, or one where hate seemed to exist more strongly.

I was obliged to spend the night at the house because of the fury of the storm. On the windowsill of the unused room where I slept were scratched names—Catherine Earnshaw, Catherine Heathcliff, Catherine Linton. The books in the room had belonged to Catherine, and one had a sort of diary, dated a quarter of a century back, written on the blank pages. I had fallen asleep over the diary when I heard a scratching at the pane. A ghostly voice sobbed, "Let me in—let me in!" "Who are you?" I asked. "Catherine Linton," it replied; "I'm coming home; I'd lost my way on the moor! It is twenty years!" I yelled in fright, and Mr. Heathcliff came running. He sent me out of the room, but before I descended to the kitchen I heard him cry out in anguish, "Cathy, do come, at last!"

When I finally arrived home, I was exhausted by the long walk through the snow and the strange events of the night. I was glad to sit and rest before the fire, listening to what my housekeeper, Nellie Dean, told me about the family at Wuthering Heights.

MRS. DEAN'S STORY

When I was young I used often to be at Wuthering Heights; I helped about the place, and played with Hindley Earnshaw (the father of Hareton, whom you saw) and Cathy. One night their father, Mr. Earnshaw, returned from a trip to Liverpool with a strange dark gypsy of a child whom he had found starving in the city. The child, who was given the name Heathcliff, early bred bad feelings in the house. Cathy, who was six, about his age, took to him, but the older Hindley tormented the child until his father turned against Hindley. Heathcliff was oddly silent and sullen, and seemed to pay heed neither to the kindness of his benefactor nor the insults of his oppressor.

In the course of time Mr. Earnshaw failed and died, and when Hindley, who had been sent to the university, came home for the funeral he brought a wife with him. The wife took a great dislike to Heathcliff, and the boy was banished to the servants, and his lessons with the curate stopped. But Cathy taught him what she learned, and the two children were happy as long as they could be together, particularly when running about the moors. One night they were near Thrushcross Grange, and decided to peek through the windows to see how the children there spent their time. As they ran away, Cathy was caught by the bull-dog and her foot injured. When the Lintons found out who she was, they petted her and made her stay, but Heathcliff, who cursed at them, they sent home. Mr. Linton scolded Hindley for the way the children were being brought up, and Mrs. Hindley began to pet and flatter Cathy, and take her pretty clothes. When Cathy returned from the Lintons' five weeks after her injury, she was very much tamed, and hurt Heathcliff's feelings by laughing at his dirtiness. Heathcliff hated the Lintons, who had made such a change in Cathy, and they disliked him for his wildness.

The next summer a child was born to Hindley and his wife. The child, Hareton, lived, but its mother died of a consumption that had long been coming upon her. His wife's death changed Hindley. He did not weep, but cursed and defied God and man. All the servants but Joseph and me left, so bad were the master's ways and companions. He treated Heathcliff diabolically, and the boy took a savage delight in provoking the master to degrade himself. The only caller we had was Edgar Linton. Cathy had kept up her acquaintance with the Lintons; she showed her best side to them, so they all were fond of her. Indeed, at fifteen she was the queen of the country-side—headstrong, haughty creature that she was. But her prettiness was such it was no wonder Edgar loved her. He proposed to her, and she accepted him.

Yet after she did, Cathy was unhappy. Something in her soul and heart told her she should not marry him—and she told me that if Heathcliff had not been brought so low, she would not have thought of it, for Heathcliff was more herself than she was. As she told me this, Heathcliff was listening, though we had not known he was in the room, and when he heard her say it would degrade her to marry him, he left the room, never hearing her say how necessary he was to her. He did not come home that night, nor the next, and Cathy took a fever mourning for him. She became more spoiled than ever during her convalescence. Heathcliff did not return. About three years after this time, Catherine married Edgar Linton. I went to live with her. I wanted to stay and care for five-year-old Hareton, but Hindley ordered me out of the house, saying he wanted no more women there.

Things went on well for a while at Thrushcross Grange. Catherine behaved fairly well, and Edgar and his sister Isabella catered to her every whim. About half a year after her marriage, as I walked in the garden one evening, I met Heathcliff. He insisted on seeing Cathy, though I begged him to go away. When he entered the family living-room, we were all amazed to see how he had changed. He was tall and well-formed; his face was intelligent, bearing no marks of his former degradation; his manner was dignified, though stern. Cathy was half-mad with joy to see him. He told her he had intended to come back just to see her and pay back his old score against Hindley, but that she had changed his mind. He was going to stay at Wuthering Heights, that he might see her often.

Linton was disturbed by Heathcliff's return, but soon it was not for Cathy's sake, but because Isabella fell in love with him. Cathy tried to tell her sister-in-law that Heathcliff was a fiend, but the infatuated girl would not believe her. Then Cathy mischievously told Heathcliff that Isabella was in love with him. The tormented girl fled, but Heathcliff mused upon the fact that she was Edgar's heir. A few days later I saw him kiss Isabella, and when Catherine scolded him, he told her that she herself had treated him infernally, and that he would be revenged upon Linton. Linton, hearing their quarrel, drove Heathcliff from the house. Catherine flew into such a frenzy of temper that she was almost out of her mind. For three days she locked her door against us all, and when she opened it, she was strangely wasted, and told me that she was dying. She certainly seemed to be, for her mind wandered queerly. To cap our troubles, I discovered that Heathcliff had run off with Isabella. Edgar refused to send anyone to bring her back, since she had left of her own accord, but from that day on he disowned her.

They were absent for two months, and during all that time Catherine was ill with brain fever. Her husband nursed her tenderly, and finally she grew better. About that time I received a note from Isabella. She had just arrived at Wuthering Heights. Already she loathed the place as she loathed Heathcliff. Heathcliff treated her shockingly, and the house was horrible and uncivilized, as were all the people in it. She begged me to visit her. I found her wan and unkempt, and tormented by her husband. Heathcliff, berating her and Linton, was anxious to hear about Catherine. He made me promise to arrange a meeting with her. He would not believe me when I told him that it might unseat her tottering reason, but swore he would force his way into her room if I would not admit him quietly. The following Sunday, when the family was absent at church, Heathcliff walked into Catherine's room. He clasped her in his arms, and as he gazed upon her he groaned, for he too saw that she had not long to live. Wildly she blamed him for causing her death; wildly he raved of his love for her. She pleaded with him never to leave her, and as he held her fast in his arms, the master's footsteps were heard without, and she fainted. As Linton rushed to aid her, I pushed Heathcliff into the garden. There I found him soon after sunrise the next morning, and had to tell him that a puny seven-months' child had been born at midnight, and that Catherine had died two hours later. I was appalled at the passion into which he burst. He beat his head against a tree-trunk. He groaned to think that she lay in peace. "Haunt me!" he cried to her. "May you not rest as long as I am living! Be with me in any form, but do not leave me alone in this abyss!" Four days later, she was buried, not in the Linton tomb, but in a grassy corner of the church-yard where the heath creeps in from the moor.

The next day, as I nursed the moaning doll of a baby, little Catherine, Isabella suddenly appeared before me. She was wet with the storm without; her face was white, and under one ear was a deep cut. She made me order a carriage for her, and tell a maid to pack her clothes. She had fled from Heathcliff and Wuthering Heights. The night before had been particularly dismal at the house; Hindley had sat silent for hours, brooding upon his sister's death. For once he was not drunk, as he desired to go to her funeral. As they heard Heathcliff's step without, Hindley had turned to Isabella and asked her to aid him to revenge himself on Heathcliff. He was desperate, for his enemy had encouraged him to drink and gamble, and had won well-nigh all his possessions from him. Heathcliff knocked at the door as Hindley stood behind it with knife and pistol. Isabella called out to warn him, as she could not help Hindley murder him. Heathcliff burst his way in, seizing Hindley's pistol and forcing the knife back into its owner's wrist. In rage, he kicked and trampled the unconscious man until he had lost his own breath. The next morning, Hindley was very ill, but became furiously angry when Isabella told him how he had been treated while he was unconscious. She then taunted Heathcliff, who was sitting weeping in the chimney-corner, with the fact that he had tormented the brother of the girl he was mourning. "But if you had married her you would have treated her as you have her brother," Isabella cried. Heathcliff snatched a knife from the table and hurled it at her, striking her beneath the ear. As she ran from the house, she saw him and Hindley engaged in mortal combat.

After telling me her story, Isabella departed, never to revisit this neighborhood. She and my master later corresponded. A son was born to her a few months later, and christened Linton; from the first, he was an ailing, peevish creature. Heathcliff asked me where she lived, but I refused to tell him, and he answered that all he wanted was never to see her again.

Only six months after Catherine died, Hindley died in his drink. He was only twenty-seven, my own age. Hareton was left little more than a beggar, for Hindley died in debt to Heathcliff, and the whole property had been mortgaged to him to supply cash for Hindley's gambling. When I told Heathcliff that Mr. Linton wished to bring up Hareton, he threatened to take Isabella's child from her if Mr. Linton persisted in his desire. This was enough to tie Mr. Linton's hands, and the child remained to be brought up by Heathcliff.

The next twelve years were the happiest of my life. Little Cathy became the center of everything for us. She was a real beauty, a winning little thing, with high spirits, but softer than her mother. Till she was thirteen, she had never been beyond the park, though she had long desired to go on the moors. At last, her father was called away to his sister's death-bed, and Cathy took advantage of his absence to steal out of the park. I knew she had particularly wanted to visit the Crags, some distance beyond Wuthering Heights, and sought for her in that direction. To my surprise, I found her in the kitchen of Heathcliff's place, talking to Hareton, a great, strong lad of eighteen. I tried to make her leave, but she did not want to go, for she enjoyed talking to Hareton. But when the housekeeper told her that Hareton was her cousin, she burst into tears at the idea that such an ignorant brute (for the boy could not read or write, having been brought up without any schooling) was related to her. It was easy now to persuade her to leave, and when I told her that her father objected to the whole household at the Heights, she promised not to tell that she had been there.

Soon came news that Isabella was dead, and that Mr. Linton was returning with his nephew. He proved to be a pale, delicate boy, very like my master in looks. No sooner had they arrived, than Heathcliff sent Joseph to claim his son. Mr. Linton could do nothing but let the boy go, though he feared what Heathcliff would do to the ailing, fretful child. I was obliged to take him to the Heights, early the next morning, lest Cathy know when her new plaything was taken away from her. Heathcliff laughingly promised to be good to the boy, since he was the prospective owner of Thrushcross Grange, and he wanted to see his descendants lord of the Linton estates. I left little Linton with some foreboding, and returned to console Cathy as best I might.

Time wore on, and Cathy was sixteen. One day we went walking on the moor, and found ourselves far from home before we knew it. We met Heathcliff and Hareton. Heathcliff insisted that Cathy go see Linton, and she had curiosity enough to desire to do so. He told me quite frankly that he wanted to see the two cousins fall in love and be married. We found Linton a pretty boy yet, but languid and over-fond of himself. Cathy could not understand why Heathcliff, if he was her uncle, never visited the Grange, and when she was told her father and he had quarreled, resolved to be friends with Linton anyway. I could see that Heathcliff scorned his son, but was secretly very fond of Hareton, though he rejoiced to see him a brute, to have brought the boy's first-rate qualities low. He enjoyed seeing the boy wince when Cathy laughed at his ignorance.

When Mr. Linton found where Cathy had been, he told her enough of the old story to show her Mr. Heathcliff's character. I thought her very deeply impressed, but that night found her weeping because Linton expected her the next day and she could not return to him. Though forbidden, she found a means to send him books and notes, and one day I found out that they had been writing love-letters to each other. This was put a stop to, and for a while no missives passed between the Heights and the Grange.

When fall came, Mr. Linton was taken ill. Life was very sad at the Grange, and Cathy moped dismally around the place. One day, when we were walking near the road, Heathcliff rode by. He told Cathy that Linton was dying for love of her. He begged her to go see the boy. Her heart was divided between her father and Linton, and the next day I had to ride with her to Wuthering Heights. We found Linton more fretful than ever, and quite ill and feverish. The servants neglected him as much as possible, and he was miserable. The two children quarreled a bit, but soon were happy together, as Cathy petted the boy and told him stories. I forbade her to visit the Heights again, but I was taken ill, and unable to watch her for a while. Apparently she divided her time between her father and me, but I later found out that she visited Linton every day after tea.

She and Linton quarreled often, for the boy was irritable, but they always made up. Once she heard Heathcliff scolding the boy for quarreling, and then she told her uncle not to interfere, and was surprised when he laughed. Altogether, their friendship had grown amazingly. But when I learned of it, and told her father, the visits were forbidden. Edgar wished the boy to visit the Grange, but he was not strong enough to do so. It was the next summer before Edgar yielded to Catherine's entreaties, and she was allowed to visit her cousin. She was not supposed to go to the Heights, but to meet him on the moor. We found him feeble and frailer than ever. He did his best to appear strong and well, but the hollows around his eyes showed how ill he was. His peevishness had changed to apathy. He seemed to feel it a punishment to endure our company, but when Cathy proposed our going, he glanced fearfully toward the Heights, and prayed her to stay longer.

A week passed, during which Mr. Linton grew more and more feeble. The day came when Cathy had promised to return to see Linton, but she did not feel like leaving her father. Since she needed exercise, I forced her out of the house and on to the moors. Linton was waiting for us, as before, but seemed no more anxious to see us. When his father came along suddenly, he grovelled with fear at his feet. The boy seemed so ill that Heathcliff persuaded us to go with him to the Heights. When we arrived, Heathcliff locked the door on us, and said that we could not go until Cathy married Linton. Five nights and four days I was locked up before I was allowed to return to my master, and Cathy would not have escaped then, though she was married to Linton, had not he finally given in to her tears and unlocked her door. She was with her father when he died.

After the funeral, Heathcliff arrived and took her back to Wuthering Heights. A few days later Linton died. Heathcliff had forced his son to will all his possessions and his wife's to him.

MR. LOCKWOOD RESUMES HIS STORY

Yesterday I went to the Heights, to tell my landlord I was going to London for six months. I took Miss Catherine a note from Mrs. Dean, and talked with her and Hareton. I saw that Hareton was trying to be friends with her, and that he was trying to learn to read to gain her approval, but that she still delighted to scorn him.

1802. By chance I returned to the Grange this autumn. Going over to the Heights, to see Mrs. Dean, who had moved there, I found that all was changed. As I looked in the window, I saw Hareton, handsome, respectably dressed, being given a reading lesson by Catherine, and rewarded with kisses when he had finished his task. I hurriedly sought Mrs. Dean, who told me that Heathcliff was dead. About a week after I had left the Grange, Heathcliff had summoned her to live at the Heights, and bade her keep Catherine out of his sight. It now pleased Catherine to make friends with Hareton. She told him she was glad she was his cousin. Little by little she wooed him, taught him, grew to love him as he loved her. His brightening mind brightened his features until he looked like an entirely different individual. Heathcliff, a very preoccupied man those days, became more and more apathetic. "It is a poor conclusion, is it not?" he said on seeing the growing friendship of Hareton and Catherine. Suddenly one day a glad look displaced his usual gloom; for three days he did not eat, and on the fourth he lay dead. He was buried, as he had asked, on one side of the first Catherine, while her husband lay on the other. Tales were told that his ghost and that of a woman had been seen walking on the moors. And now Cathy and Hareton were to be married, and the old unhappiness was done.

JANE EYRE

By

Charlotte Brontë

CHARLOTTE BRONTË (*1816–1855*) was an English novelist whose
life almost to its close was one of sorrow and struggle. Her
mother died early and her father's meager means as a clergyman forced the Brontë sisters to seek livelihoods as governesses.
The three girls published a book of verse which was little
noticed, and then they turned to prose. Charlotte's first novel
The Professor was rejected by the publishers but her second
book *Jane Eyre* gained a great success. She married her father's
curate at the age of 38 and her brief year of married life was a
happy one although her husband had no sympathy with her
literary endeavors. Her life and writings are very closely connected, as she herself is the heroine of *Jane Eyre*. *Shirley* was
intended to be a portrait of her sister Emily.

IT WAS A BLEAK, cold day. My aunt, Mrs. Reed, had gathered her
little darlings, Eliza, John, and Georgiana, about her by the fireside, but had sent me away, saying I was an unsociable child. I
was sitting happily in another room, reading, when the children
broke in upon me. I was afraid of John; he was fourteen and I
was only ten, and he bullied me. Now he struck me, telling me
that since I was a dependent I had no business to read his mother's
books. Lifting the book I had been reading, he hurled it at me
and hit me so that I fell and struck my head against the door. As
he hit me again I turned upon him, but in a moment his shouts
brought the servants, and I was carried away and locked in the
red room. It was a lonely room, the room in which my uncle had
died nine years before, and I screamed in terror. But my aunt
would not allow me to be released, and I fell unconscious.

When I awoke, it was to see the kind face of Mr. Lloyd, the

apothecary, bending over me. He was very kind to me; I told him of my unhappiness at Gateshead. I was the daughter of a poor clergyman whom my mother had married against her family's wishes. Her brother, my uncle Reed, had taken me to his heart when my parents died, soon after my birth, and on his own death-bed, very little later, had told my aunt to bring me up as one of her own children. But this she had not done, and my life was very miserable. Mr. Lloyd suggested to my aunt that she send me away to school, and she, only too glad to be rid of me, fell in with the plan. It was not until several months later that I was sent for by my aunt and presented to the principal of the school which I was to attend. He was a tall, black pillar of a man with a grim face and a sanctimonious manner. My aunt told him that I had a tendency to deceit, and asked him to see that the teachers kept a strict eye on me. I left Gateshead feeling that I owed my aunt nothing.

It took all of a long day to travel the fifty miles to Lowood school, and I was exhausted when I arrived. A tall, dark lady with a grave face, Miss Temple, the head of the school, greeted me in a kindly way; she sent me with one of the teachers, Miss Miller, into a dim study room; after a supper of oat-cake and water, and after prayers, the girls filed off to bed, I so tired that I slept without dreaming until dawn. The next day my real life at Lowood began. We arose before dawn, dressed in the bitter cold, and had prayers and an hour of classes before breakfast. The food was of the plainest, and so was the dress of the students. All the eighty girls of the school were dressed alike in plain brown dresses; not a curl was allowed to disturb the drabness of their appearance. I found that life at school was marked by a Spartan simplicity, for since it was partly a charity school, the head felt that the girls should not enjoy even the simplest comforts.

I soon made a friend, Helen Burns, a pale girl with a cough, somewhat older than I was. She was a good, patient girl, and never complained, even when she was scolded unjustly by one of the teachers who was particularly cruel to her. She helped me to endure that winter at Lowood, for the cold and the poor food made life physically miserable. About a month after I came to the school, Mr. Brocklehurst, the principal, visited us. He took a pious joy in reproving what he thought were any signs of vanity—naturally curly hair in one girl, and plaited hair in the older girls. His hatred of vanity did not extend to his own family, however, for his wife and daughters were decked out in curls, silks, and furs. I was so unfortunate as to attract Mr. Brocklehurst's attention. He remembered what my aunt had said to him, and in front of the school branded me as a liar, made me sit on a high stool, and commanded that no one speak to me for the rest of the day. Helen Burns, however, smiled at me, and at tea-time tried to comfort me. As we were talking together, Miss Temple came into the room and led us to her own apartment. She listened to my story, and promised to verify it. If she could do so, she said that she would clear me before the whole school. After giving us tea, and inquiring about Helen's cough and the pain in her chest, Miss Temple dismissed us. I long remembered that pleasant evening, and how Helen and Miss Temple had talked so eloquently of books and things entirely unknown to me. A week later, Miss Temple heard from Mr. Lloyd, the apothecary, and I was cleared of the charge of perjury before the whole school. Now I did well with my lessons; spring came on, and I was happy.

But suddenly an infection struck the school; semi-starvation and neglected colds had weakened most of the girls, and forty-five out of eighty were ill at one time. Helen, too, was ill, and lying in Miss Temple's room. I knew that she was going to die, and one night I crept upstairs to say goodbye to her. I got into bed with her, and we talked together. She spoke of God, and how glad she was to go to Him. I fell asleep with my arms around her neck. When I awoke, I was being carried back to the dormitory, for Helen had died in her sleep.

Things at the school were better after that. The virulence of the fever had drawn attention to the school; Mr. Brocklehurst was replaced as head, and conditions were greatly improved. I remained there for eight more years, six as pupil and two as teacher. At the end of that time, I became restless; I wondered if there were not something for me in the real world, if I must spend all my days in those narrow walls. I determined to advertise for a position as governess, and did so. When I received an answer from a place called Thornfield, stating that a governess was needed for a little girl under ten, I decided to apply for the position. I was able to send references from the trustees at Lowood, and was accepted.

I arrived at Thornfield to be received by an elderly woman, Mrs. Fairfax, who proved to be the housekeeper. She told me that little Adela Varens, the ward of Mr. Rochester, was my pupil. Adela was a pretty little thing, but her mother had been a French actress, and the child had many little artificialities which she had learned from her mother. We got on very well together. I could learn little about my employer; he visited Thornfield but rarely, as he travelled a great deal. Life went on very pleasantly for me, with only one slight disturbance. One day, as I was in an upper hall, I heard a very loud and strange laugh. Mrs. Fairfax said it was that of Grace Poole, one of the servants, so I thought no more about it.

One cold January afternoon, I went for a walk. As I went along, a horseman passed me. Suddenly the horse slipped and fell, the rider with him. I ran to help the man, who had sprained his ankle. I aided him to get on his horse again, and he rode off, after inquiring where I lived and thanking me. When I went home, I found out that this man was no other than the master of the house, Mr. Rochester, who had strangely failed to introduce himself to me. The next day Adela and I were invited to take tea with him. He was a dark, rather grim-faced man; I should have been afraid of him, as I was very shy, had he not been rather brusk and rude. He asked me a great many questions about myself and seemed interested in my answers; at nine o'clock he abruptly dismissed us. I saw little of him for some time after that. Then one afternoon he told me Adela's story. Her mother, the French actress, had once been Mr. Rochester's mistress. He had left her when he discovered that she had another lover at the same time. The actress claimed that Adela was Rochester's child, though he had never felt that she was, because she was so unlike him, and when the mother abandoned the child, he adopted it.

I had grown to like Mr. Rochester very much. Though he was very proud and harsh to inferiority of every description, he always was very cordial to me, and made me feel that I was able to amuse him. I ceased to pine for the kindred I had never had, and became very happy with this new interest in life. One night I again heard the demoniac laugh. Going to my door, I saw a cloud of smoke rushing from Mr. Rochester's door. When I rushed into his room, I saw that his bed curtains were afire, and that he lay stupefied, surrounded by flames. I drenched him and the bed with water from his ewer, and of course awakened him. He would not allow me to call any of the servants, but took a candle and went out of the room. After a long while he came back, and told me that it was Grace Poole who had caused the damage. He thanked me in such a warm manner for saving his life that I went back to bed and stayed happily awake until morning. I was surprised to find the next day that Grace Poole had not been dismissed, and that it was said the fire had been caused by Mr. Rochester's upsetting his candle.

Mr. Rochester went off to spend a week or so with fashionable society at the Leas, and I was very lonely, particularly when I heard that one of the party was to be the Honorable Blanche Ingram, a beautiful woman to whom Mr. Rochester was reported to be attentive. When I heard this, I knew that I was a fool, little plain thing that I was, to feel that I was a favorite of Mr. Rochester. Particularly did I feel insignificant when my employer returned, bringing a gay party, of whom the Honorable Blanche was one, with him. I saw little of the guests; only in the evening were Adela and I called to sit in the living room with them, where I felt very out of place. I did not like Miss Ingram; she was handsome, but very proud and satirical. Yet I felt sure that Mr. Rochester was going to marry her, for he paid much attention to her. One night, a stranger, handsome though rather repellent, appeared in the drawing room to wait for Mr. Rochester, who was not at home. A servant brought word that a gypsy-woman, an odd old hag, desired to tell the fortunes of the guests. I had my fortune told also, and was surprised when the gypsy told me much that was true: that I was cold and alone, longing for love, and that I would not beckon it to approach. Suddenly the gypsy revealed herself to be Mr. Rochester, and I wondered if I had given too much of myself away.

That night, I again heard a cry, and the noise of a struggle. The guests rushed out into the hall, but Mr. Rochester told them that a servant had had a nightmare, and sent them off to bed. After stillness had returned to the house, Mr. Rochester came to my room. He took me to a chamber in which lay a stranger, Mr. Mason. His arm and shoulder were bandaged, but blood trickled from a wound and his face was white. Mr. Rochester left me to take care of the man while he went for a doctor. When the doctor had cared for the wound, my master smuggled Mr. Mason down the back stairs and away from the house. As he went away, Mr. Mason cried, "Let her be taken care of; let her be treated tenderly——" Mr. Rochester thanked me for the help I had given him, and told me that Grace Poole had again caused trouble; to the guests, he said that Mr. Mason had gone away early.

Very soon after this, I had a message from Mrs. Reed's maid Bessie. Her husband brought news that John Reed, my old tormentor, had ruined and then shot himself. His mother was very ill, and calling out for me. Mr. Rochester gave me leave to go to her. I found her daughters quite unconcerned about their mother's illness. Georgiana was fussing about the parties she was missing, and Eliza was concerned with her crucifix and the altar-cloth she was embroidering. Mrs. Reed had something she wanted to tell me before she died. It was days before she was able to talk to me, and then she told me of a great harm she had done me. Some time before she had received a letter from an uncle of mine on my mother's side; he was living in Madeira, where he had made a small fortune, and he wanted me to go to him there. Because Mrs. Reed disliked me so, she had been unwilling to think of my enjoying prosperity, and had written to him that I had died in the typhus epidemic at Lowood. I told her that I would forgive her, and she died soon afterwards. No one wept her.

Several weeks later, when her affairs were arranged, I returned to Thornfield. Mr. Rochester seemed glad to see me, and I told him that I was glad to return, that where he was was my only home. He was kinder than ever to me, and one day, to my overwhelming surprise, he asked me to marry him. When I replied that I would, his exultation was great, but I could not imagine why he murmured, "It will atone, it will atone." The wedding was set for a month from that time, and I went about buying some simple clothes for my trousseau. I wrote to my uncle in Madeira and told him I was going to marry Mr. Rochester. A few nights before the wedding, I had a bad dream. I dreamed that in the night a strange woman, tall and dark, came into my room and looked at the new clothes hanging in my wardrobe. Then she took my wedding-veil from its place and threw it over her head. Her savage, discolored face was ghastly as she removed the veil from her head, rent it in two parts, and trampled on them. She glared at me—I fainted—and awoke from the dream with daylight. But when I arose, I saw that it could not have been a dream, for the veil lay in two pieces on the floor! When I told Mr. Rochester, he said that the woman must have been Grace Poole, and that when we had been married a year and a day he would tell me why he kept her in the house.

We started for church early the next morning. As we took our place at the altar-rail, the clergyman read, as is the custom, the charge that any who knew of any impediment should step forward. Not once in a hundred years does anyone answer that charge, but this morning a voice cried out, "I declare the existence of an impediment. Mr. Rochester has a wife now living!" Mr. Mason, Mr. Rochester's former guest, stepped forward. He said that Mr. Rochester had fifteen years ago married his sister, who was now a lunatic, and confined at Thornfield Hall. Then Mr. Rochester confessed all. He *had* married Bertha Mason, who had gone completely mad after the marriage, having inherited insanity. For long years he had been tied to her. Feeling cheated of life, he had decided to marry me, when he had fallen in love with me. He took us all to see his wife, who was in Grace Poole's care. I need scarcely mention that the wife was responsible for all the things which we had attributed to Mrs. Poole. When we saw the struggling, bloated maniac, there was no one who did not feel the tragedy of Mr. Rochester's position.

I learned that Mr. Mason had been in Madeira, that he knew my uncle there, and that when he heard from my uncle of my approaching marriage he had hastened to England to stop it. My hope was blighted now, my confidence in Mr. Rochester dead. Still more was I cut to the heart when he proposed to me that I live with him as his mistress, since I could not be his wife. Though I loved him more than life, I could not comply with his request, and early the next morning I stole away from Thornfield Hall.

I had little money in my purse, but I rode by coach as far as my thirty shillings would take me. When the coachman set me down, I wandered for several days and nights, absolutely destitute. I was unable to find work; I was too proud to beg. Finally, weary beyond death and almost starved, I knocked at the door of a little cottage. The servant was unwilling to admit me, but just as I was turning away, the master of the house came in the gate. He was a clergyman, and at once led me into the house, where he and his sisters cared for me. Mr. St. John Rivers, Diana and Mary nursed me for many days before my health returned. I would not tell them my real name, but said I was Jane Elliott. I told them much of my story, but the name of the place from which I had just come and the name of the people with whom I had been living I would not reveal.

The inmates of Moor House were very kind to me, and the more I knew them the better I liked them, for we had many similar tastes. Mr. Rivers I knew less well than his sisters, for he was seldom at home, as his work took him abroad in the parish. He was a very zealous Christian, and, I learned later, determined to be a missionary. This saddened his sisters somewhat, for they hated to have their family circle broken. After I grew strong, I asked Mr. Rivers if he knew of any occupation by which I could earn my livelihood. In his parish, he told me, there was need of a schoolmistress for a school of poor children. The salary would be thirty pounds a year, and a little furnished cottage would be provided. Mr. Rivers was pleased when I said I would accept the position, for he had told me that the work would be hard, and that I would have no use for my accomplishments. One day Mr. Rivers came home with the news that their Uncle John had died. This uncle had quarreled with their father, and had left them in his will only ten guineas apiece, all the rest of his fortune going to another relative.

The next day I went to my own cottage. Work in the school was hard, but I was sure that I had done right in refusing to live in luxury as Mr. Rochester's mistress. Mr. Rivers came to call on me my first evening there. As we talked, a lovely young girl approached us. Mr. Rivers introduced me to Miss Oliver, the heiress, who was much interested in the school. I saw Mr. Rivers' eye glow as he looked upon her, but he curbed his emotion. I saw that he loved her, and that he felt he must sacrifice his love to his mission. I continued my labors in the school. I grew very friendly with Rosamond Oliver, and saw that she loved Mr. Rivers, but he remained firm in his determination.

One day Mr. Rivers brought me the news that he had discovered I was Jane Eyre. On my easel he had found a paper on which I had written my name. His name was St. John Eyre Rivers, we were kinsmen, and from the uncle who had just died I had inherited twenty thousand pounds. I hastened to divide the money among the four of us, since I felt that Mr. Rivers and his sisters deserved it just as much as I did.

At holiday time I was happy with my new relations, happy until Mr. Rivers asked me to marry him. He had desired me to learn Hindostanee some time before, and I had enjoyed lessons with him. Now I learned that he felt that I could help him in his work, and that he wanted me to marry him and go to India as his fellow-laborer. I could not accept his offer, for I still loved Mr. Rochester. When he urged upon me the glory of self-sacrifice, I told him that I would go with him as his helper, but that I could not marry him. He would not accept me upon such terms, and grew very cold toward me. He made me feel what punishment a good yet stern man can inflict on one who has offended him. Finally I weakened, and told him that if I felt it were God's will, I would marry him. As I waited for the divine voice, I suddenly heard another voice somewhere crying "Jane! Jane!" It was the voice of Rochester, and it spoke in pain, urgently.

The next day I set out for Thornfield. After a journey of thirty-six hours, I approached the house. To my horror I saw a blackened ruin! From the landlord of the nearby inn I learned that the lunatic had set the fire; Mr. Rochester had saved the servants and tried to save his wife, but she had jumped off the battlements and killed herself. Mr. Rochester had been blinded by the fire, and had had one hand so badly crushed that it had been amputated. He was now living at Ferndean, a manor belonging to him.

You can imagine how I hastened to Mr. Rochester, how gently I introduced myself, how I assured him that I would never leave him, how he could scarcely believe that I had returned to him. Blind as he was, he was happy, and his face, which had been tormented ever since I had gone, they said, was glad once again. We were married. His eyesight so improved that when his first-born was put into his arms, he could see that the boy had his own eyes.

DAVID COPPERFIELD

By

Charles Dickens

CHARLES DICKENS (*1812–1870*) was an English novelist, the second of eight children and the son of a clerk in the navy office. When he was about 12 years old his mother and father were confined to debtor's prison and Charles did the meanest sort of drudgery, living on wretched fare in an attic. The family fortunes revived and Charles gained an education. At 20 he became a newspaper reporter of Parliament and successfully joined the staffs of several London papers during which time he wrote many of his sketches. With the publication of the *Pickwick Papers* Dickens found himself famous at home and abroad at the age of 25. He then rapidly produced several novels and in 1842 made an extensive trip through the United States where he was heartily welcomed. After his return to London he satirized American faults and stirred up considerable resentment in America. After several editorships he began a weekly periodical which was chiefly to encourage young authors. In 1853, he began to give public readings from his works, originally for charity, but they were so well received that five years later he began the first of his exhaustive reading tours which sapped his strength and hastened his end. His American lecture tour earned him $100,000 in six months. He was buried in Poets' Corner, Westminster Abbey. A few of his many works include *David Copperfield*, his favorite book, *Oliver Twist* and *A Tale of Two Cities*.

I WAS BORN IN BLUNDERSTONE, Suffolk, a posthumous child. On the afternoon of the day on which I was to be born, Miss Betsey Trotwood, my father's aunt, who had been displeased by my father's marriage to a "wax doll" half his age, called upon my mother. Miss Trotwood was quite won over by the soft, frail little thing, so much so that she put cotton in her ears and waited through the long evening while I was coming into the world to welcome what she hoped would be little Betsey Trotwood Copperfield. But when she was told by Mr. Chillip, the doctor, that the baby was a boy, she disappeared, never to return. So I grew up with only my mother, who petted me, and our maid Peggotty, who cared for us both, for company. One evening, a gentleman whom I disliked on sight, escorted my mother home from an evening party—a gentleman whom Peggotty disliked, too, but to whom my mother was grateful for companionship and skilful flattery. After that, the gentleman, Mr. Murdstone, was seen more and more frequently at our house.

One day Peggotty asked me if I should like to go with her to visit her brother in Yarmouth; to my surprise, my mother was quite willing to let me go. Mr. Peggotty, his nephew Ham, his niece Little Em'ly, and his partner's widow, the disconsolate Mrs. Gummidge, lived in a fascinating "ship-looking" thing, a grounded superannuated barge, as trim and nautical a place (though smelling somewhat strongly of fish) as one could wish. I promptly fell in love with the blue-eyed Little Em'ly, and the fortnight at the sea-shore slipped happily away. But dismay fell upon me on our return home when a strange servant opened the door, and when Peggotty told me that my mother had married again, and that the new father was Mr. Murdstone.

Things changed then in the once-peaceful house. Mr. Murdstone insisted that his weak little pliable wife should be "firm," and she dared caress me only secretly. All the household arrangements were taken over by Mr. Murdstone's sister, a grim dark female, as firm as her brother. Between them, the Murdstones disseminated an atmosphere of gloom and fear. They insisted on being present at the lessons my mother gave me, and succeeded in terrifying me into a sullen, dull and dogged state. The only thing that saved me was the store of my father's books which I discovered; *Tom Jones, Don Quixote* and the others kept alive my fancy and my hope. One day when I could not learn my lessons my mother burst into tears, and Mr. Murdstone, with the excuse that I had tormented my mother, beat me unmercifully, redoubling his blows when I bit his hand. For five days he kept me imprisoned on bread and water, brought to me by Miss Murdstone. On the last night,

[173]

faithful Peggotty dared to whisper through the keyhole the news
that I was to be sent to school. In the morning I was seen off with
"firmness" by the Murdstones, with reproaches by my mother,
who had been convinced that I was a hardened rascal, and with
cakes by Peggotty. When the carrier who was taking me to the
London coach tasted the cakes, he told me to send to Peggotty
the message that "Barkis was willin'."

I arrived at the rather shabby Salem House, near Blackheath, to
find that it was vacation time. Mr. Murdstone had been anxious
to get me out of the way. Furthermore, he had sent instructions
that I was to be treated severely; a placard bearing the words:
"Take care of him. He bites" was fastened upon my back. I
dreaded the return of the boys, but fortunately the first to come
back was Tommy Traddles, a jolly sort of fellow, who helped me
through the difficult time. Quite a different sort was J. Steerforth,
one of the oldest boys, who at once offered to take care of my
money, and who spent the entire seven shillings on a moonlight
feast for the boys in his bedroom. I was very proud of the friendship of the handsome, careless Steerforth, and even introduced
him to Ham and Mr. Peggotty, who called on me at school. I
speedily forgot how he caused the dismissal of Mr. Mell, a half-
starved tutor, and thought of him only as something shining and
great. So in a jumble of struggle and strife, of beatings and poor
food, the year passed.

I went home for the holidays to find I had a new baby brother.
For one happy afternoon, while the Murdstones were out calling, my mother, Peggotty, and I talked together as we used to
do, but with the return of the Murdstones, gloom settled upon
me again. After two more months of school, I was called home
again. My frail little mother had died, and with her, my baby
brother. After the funeral Peggotty was dismissed, and the Murdstones were glad to have her take me with her for a while when
she returned to Yarmouth. We were conveyed thither by Mr.
Barkis, who, I found, was still "willin'," for Peggotty later confided in me that she was going to marry the carrier. I found the
barge still a friendly place, with little changed save Little Em'ly,
who was prettier than ever. All of them liked to hear tales of
my idol Steerforth, especially Little Em'ly. Barkis came calling

on Peggotty every evening, and on the last day of my stay at the barge, they were quietly married.

For a while after my return home I was completely neglected; then, school being expensive, I was shipped off to London, at the age of ten, to earn my living in the service of the firm of Murdstone and Grinby. Mr. Murdstone paid for my lodging, clothes and laundry, but my food and pocket money came out of my own small pay of six shillings a week, with the result that I was usually half-starved. I lodged with Mr. Micawber, a cheerful incompetent, continually hunted by his creditors, but always hoping for something to turn up, and Mrs. Micawber, who in spite of all disaster, vowed she would "never desert Micawber." She even, on one occasion, moved into the Debtor's Prison that she might be with him. I slaved on at my work in the cellars of the wine firm, associating unhappily with my common companions, growing more and more shabby, more and more of a drudge. Finally, when Mr. Micawber was released from prison and went with his family to seek employment in Plymouth, I could bear my lonely drudgery no longer. Writing to Peggotty, I obtained from her the address of my aunt Betsey and half a guinea.

My small box of clothes and my half-guinea were stolen from me by a dishonest porter, and it was with only three-halfpence in my pocket that I started for Dover. Selling my clothes as I went along, I plodded weary mile by mile to Dover. Starved, exhausted, my hat crushed, my shoes burst, my whole form powdered with chalk and dust, I staggered at last into my aunt's neat little cottage and burst out crying. Miss Betsey was too dismayed to know what to do, beyond pressing a quantity of bottles of restorative upon me. She sent at once for Mr. Dick, a poor dim-witted gentleman who lived with her. Dim-witted he might be, but he had enough sense to say, when Miss Betsey asked him what to do with me, "I should wash him!" As I relaxed into a warm bath, I heard the cry of "Donkeys!" and saw my aunt and her maid Janet sortie out to their daily warfare with the donkeys and donkey-boys who swarmed over the patch of green in front of the house.

A day or two later I heard the cry again, and saw Miss Murdstone come riding over the grass plot. She and her brother had come to Dover in response to a letter from Miss Betsey, informing them that I was safe with her. Miss Betsey quickly took the measure of the Murdstones, and though she had been undecided about me before, now decided to keep me. So I stayed with my aunt, who became more and more fond of me. I also advanced in friendship with Mr. Dick, who spent every day writing his Memorial, out of which he could not keep the head of Charles I. Finally my aunt arranged to have me sent to school in Canterbury. She took me first to the house of Mr. Wickfield, her lawyer. We were let in by a crop-headed youth without any eye-brows, the "'umble" Uriah Heap, Mr. Wickfield's clerk. Since we were unable to find a suitable boarding-house for me, Mr. Wickfield offered me the hospitality of his own home. There I was happy in the companionship of his daughter Agnes, a placid and sweet little girl, though I was somewhat uncomfortable in the presence of the damp-handed Uriah, who despite the fact that he insisted he was a "'umble" person, spent the evenings diligently studying law.

I was most happy at school. Dr. Strong, the head-master, was a very kind man. He had a beautiful wife, many years younger than he, and was pursued by his wife's poor relations, especially by her mother, who never ceased mentioning how much older the doctor was than his wife. Mrs. Strong's cousin, Jack Maldon, surreptitiously made love to her, upsetting her extremely, particularly when he stole a ribbon from her on his departure to assume the position the doctor had obtained for him. Miss Betsey visited me frequently, and Mr. Dick came every week, once with a strange tale of a man who hovered about Miss Betsey's cottage, and to whom she gave money. One day I kept an old promise to have tea with Uriah Heep and his mother, who succeeded in drawing out of me a large store of information about my affairs and those of my friends. Much to my surprise, I saw passing by my old friend Mr. Micawber, who came in at my cry, and was introduced to the Heeps. He was still "waiting for something to turn up," and the next day was off to London.

The years passed, and I was seventeen, and through with Dr. Strong's school. On my last evening in Canterbury, I went with Mr. Wickfield and Agnes to visit the Strongs. I saw that Mrs. Strong was still bothered about something, that her mother was still constantly talking about her friendship with Jack Maldon, who was coming home from India because of the climate, and that Mr. Wickfield narrowly watched Mrs. Strong, as though something were wrong. Something was wrong with Mr. Wickfield himself. He seemed to drink more and more, and I noticed that when he was at his worst he was sure to be summoned on business by Uriah. But I was to leave these things behind for a while. Aunt Betsey sent me to Yarmouth to spend a while with the Peggottys, a brief vacation before I decided upon my life-work. I went by way of London, and there was overjoyed and amazed to come upon my old idol Steerforth, who took me home with him to Highgate. There I met his doting mother and her companion, Rosa Dartle, a sharp-edged sort of woman.

When I left for Yarmouth, Steerforth went with me. We arrived just in time to be present at the announcement that Ham and Little Em'ly were going to be married. It was a pleasure to see how Steerforth entered into the pleasures of my humble friends, how gay he was with them, and how they all loved and admired him. Steerforth seemed very fond of the sea, and bought a boat, which he had his valet, Littimer, come down from London to put in order. It was in Yarmouth that I met the queer little dwarf, Miss Mowcher, and saw again Martha Endell, once a seamstress, and now a wanderer from the narrow way, to whom Little Em'ly was very kind when every one else turned from her.

After two weeks in Yarmouth I returned to London to meet my aunt, who suggested that I might like to become a proctor, and who took me to the legal firm of Spenlow and Jorkins to apprentice me. On the way there I observed that we were followed by a rough-looking man; when my aunt saw him, she was much upset, but insisted that she must speak to him, and I observed when she rejoined me, that her purse had been lightened of its guineas. We went on our way, and soon I was accepted as a probationer by Mr. Spenlow. My aunt went back to Canterbury after finding some chambers for me in the Adelphi. There I was visited by Steerforth, and there I gave a dinner to him and two of his friends. After having dined too well, we went to the theatre, and there, to my great shame, I met Agnes again. The next day she sent me a note to say that she was staying with a friend of her father's, Mr. Waterbrook. I was invited there to dinner, where to my amazement I met my old friend Traddles, now studying for the bar. Agnes informed me that Uriah Heep, who was also at the dinner, had made himself so useful to her father that he was now her father's partner, and Uriah, soon afterwards, told me that his heart was set on no less a prize than Agnes herself.

My mind was soon taken off my Canterbury friends, however. Mr. Spenlow invited me to spend the week-end at his home, and there I at once fell in love with his pretty little daughter Dora. I was much surprised to find that her companion was none other than my old enemy Miss Murdstone, whom reduced circumstances had forced to accept a position. Soon afterwards I came upon another old friend of mine. When I went to look in upon my friend Traddles, I found that he lived in the same house with Mr. and Mrs. Micawber.

Steerforth, who had been out of town for a while, appeared with the news that he had been in Yarmouth for a week, seeing about his boat. He brought a letter from Peggotty saying that Barkis was dying, and I resolved to go to see her. Steerforth persuaded me to wait a day or two, and to visit him at Highgate in the meantime. There I found that Rosa Dartle was acting more queerly than ever, and seemed to be suspicious of Steerforth. I stayed overnight, and then went down to Yarmouth. I arrived just before Barkis died, and was able to speak to him before he went. Little Em'ly seemed to be terribly overcome by the presence of death; she was quite unlike herself. The day after the funeral, Ham broke the news to me that she had run away with Steerforth. It would be difficult to imagine the shock this was to Little Em'ly's family. Peggotty at once vowed that he would go to seek for her. On his way abroad he went to see Steerforth's family, to find his mother and Miss Dartle wild with torment because he had deserted them; they had no pity for the "common" girl whom he had betrayed.

Meanwhile my affection for Dora was flourishing. I was able to meet her privately at the home of her friend, Miss Mills, and we became engaged. My friend Traddles was also engaged, to a "dear girl" who lived down in Devonshire—one of ten. A shadow fell over me, however, when my Aunt Betsey and Dick came up from Dover with the news that she was ruined. Agnes came to town to see my aunt. She was much relieved when Aunt Betsey told us that her own speculations had been the cause of her ruin, for Agnes had feared that her father, who was drinking more and more and who had come further and further into the power of Uriah Heep, had been at fault. Agnes brought the news that my old head-master, Dr. Strong, had retired and was living in London. He was in need of a secretary, and I at once assumed that position in addition to my other duties. I found Mr. Jack Maldon still in evidence, still slyly pursuing Annie, who kept trying to avoid him, while her husband insisted on throwing them together, feeling that she needed youth near her. At this time, Mr. and Mrs. Micawber, who were constantly in financial straits, went back to Canterbury, where Mr. Micawber had obtained employment from Uriah Heep.

Suddenly, the greatest possible calamity befell me. My secret meetings with Dora and my love letters to her were discovered by Miss Murdstone, who conveyed the news to Mr. Spenlow. He forbade me ever to speak to Dora on the subject again. I was still overwhelmed by the suddenness of this blow when Mr. Spenlow died very suddenly, without leaving a will. It was discovered that he had much less money than had been thought, and that Dora would not be very well off. She went to stay with two maiden aunts, to whom I wrote asking for permission to see her. This had been recommended to me as the best course by Agnes. I had seen her when I had gone to Canterbury on some business for my aunt. The change in the Wickfield household seemed greater than ever. Uriah and his mother now lived in the house, and Mr. Micawber—even he seemed changed, and not so frank as he had been—lived in Uriah's house. It was apparent that Uriah had a singularly strong hold over Mr. Wickfield, but even that did not prevent Mr. Wickfield from denouncing Uriah when he announced that he wished to make Agnes his wife. Uriah was forced to withdraw, but told me the next day that he knew how to wait, and that the fruit would yet fall into his hand.

Unexpectedly, I saw Mr. Peggotty again, one snowy night. We went into an inn to sit down and talk. He was still searching for

Little Em'ly, and had decided to return to the Continent once more to look for her. As we talked, I saw the door pushed open, and the poor face of the lost Martha looked in, and presently was gone again. Sadly, I saw him off on the Dover Road.

Happiness now came to me again, for Dora's aunts allowed me to see her, and consented to our engagement. They had become quite fond of her, and my aunt became fond of her also, though it bothered me a little that they seemed to treat her as if she were a toy. She was so young and had so little sense of responsibility! She did not seem to realize that she was marrying a poor man. Agnes loved her too. Agnes had come to town to visit Mrs. Strong. Uriah followed her, fearing that Mrs. Strong would propose a rival for him. In order to spite Mrs. Strong, he told the Doctor that she and Jack Maldon were in love with one another. The Doctor was inexpressibly grieved, for he believed Uriah, but he did not say a word of the accusation to his wife; he only mourned in silence.

I attained the dignity of twenty-one. I was very busy, for I had learned stenography in order to report Parliamentary debates and earn more money for Dora. I had also taken to authorship, and had some little things accepted and paid for. At last, one glad day, I was married to Dora. Our housekeeping was a strange thing; we knew less about it than two young birds. We had trouble with the servants and trouble with the accounts; the meat was often raw and the dishes smashed by hundreds. But we kissed and made up after our tiny squabbles, and were very happy. Through the kind offices of Mr. Dick, Mrs. Strong and her husband were made happy again and the cloud between them dispersed; she told him that she had always loved him only, in spite of his age, and that she had long ago repulsed her dishonorable cousin. "There can be no disparity in marriage like unsuitability of mind and purpose," I heard her say, and the words rang strangely in my mind.

About a year after my marriage, as I was passing Mrs. Steerforth's house, one day, I was called in by Miss Dartle, who told me with cruel pleasure that Little Em'ly had run away from Steerforth. She had never ceased mourning for her home, and gradually he had tired of her; finally he left her. He had planned to marry her to his servant, Littimer, but when she heard this, she ran away. Mr. Peggotty and I thought that she would be sure to come to London if she returned to England, and that very likely she might try to find Martha, or that Martha might come upon her. Martha promised to look for her, and tell us if she was successful.

Dora became rather ill at this time, and did not seem to improve as quickly as she should have done. My mind was distracted momentarily with anxiety about her when I received a very cryptic letter from Mr. Micawber, stating that he wished to see me, and would meet me in London. Traddles and I met him, and were surprised to hear him burst into a violent denunciation of Heep, whom he characterized as a scoundrel. He made an appointment with Traddles, Mr. Dick, Aunt Betsey and me in Canterbury a week from that time. Before that day came, I received word from Martha that she had found Em'ly. Mr. Peggotty and I went to her, just in time to keep her from crumbling before an attack launched upon her by Rosa Dartle, who had also found out her hiding place, and who was still jealous of her. Mr. Peggotty took Little Em'ly away with him, and began plans to emigrate, since she did not feel she could ever face any of her old friends again. Mrs. Gummidge decided to go with them, but Ham remained in his old home.

The day came when we went to Canterbury. There we had the greatest pleasure in aiding to unmask the villainy of Uriah Heep. Mr. Micawber, though himself in the toils of Heep, had been far too honest to witness Uriah's treatment of Mr. Wickfield. By diligent study, he had discovered how Uriah had tricked that poor man, how he had made him sign papers he didn't wish to sign, how he had made him believe that all his property was lost. My aunt had believed Mr. Wickfield responsible for the loss of her money, and was delighted to find it was Uriah who was responsible. Traddles had aided in discovering the villainy, and now he and Mr. Micawber tried to set all right again. My aunt recovered her money, and Mr. Wickfield's affairs were finally straightened out. He retired from the business he was unable to carry on, and Agnes started a school that she might support him. Uriah and his mother, disgraced, left town.

Now sorrow came upon me, for little Dora, long ailing, faded away. Just before she died, she sent for Agnes that she might give her a message, and it was Agnes who bore me the news that Dora was dead. Fortunately I was unable to feel my grief fully for a time, for we were all very busy getting the Micawbers ready to emigrate. My aunt felt that in a new land they might prosper and she aided them with money in an effort to repay Mr. Micawber for all he had done in righting her affairs. Mr. Micawber was not out of trouble until he finally set sail, for Uriah Heep, who owned several of his notes-of-hand, was continually having the poor man sent off to jail, from whence he was as promptly rescued by Traddles or me. Another sorrow came to me just before the emigrants left. I went down to Yarmouth, to take news of them to Ham. I arrived on the day of a great storm. The tempest rose high that night, and a ship from Spain foundered just off Yarmouth. It was impossible to get a life-boat out to her. Ham, who had been very careless of his life since Little Em'ly had left, offered to take a line out to her. He tried bravely several times, but was at last washed ashore, dead. And soon another body was washed ashore —a curly-headed figure I had seen clinging to the wreck. It proved to be my old friend Steerforth. I can never forget the wildness of Rosa Dartle or the frozen immobility of his mother as they received the news of his death.

At last the travellers left for Australia. The Micawbers and Mr. Peggotty and his family travelled on the same boat. I introduced them to each other, that they might be friends in the new land to which they were going. Mr. Peggotty, always kind, took with him Martha, that she might have a new start in a new country. It was at this time that my aunt told me that another of her troubles was over. The strange man who had so haunted her had been her husband, whom she had loved devotedly for a while, but who had broken her heart. After long years, he had returned and plagued her for money, which she had given him because of her old fondness for him. He was at last dead, and she free from an intolerable strain.

Now at last the full burden of my grief fell upon me, and I left England to try to lose my sorrow in travel. For three years I was away from England. During part of that time I was well enough to write, and with Traddles marketing my work for me, I gradually acquired a sort of fame. Finally I felt that I could go home.

I found Traddles happily married, caring not only for his wife but for her pretty sisters as well. I happened to visit a prison with Traddles, and there we found two old enemies of ours—Uriah Heep, who had been sent up for forgery, and Littimer, who had been sent up for theft. The dwarf, Miss Mowcher, had been instrumental in capturing the latter. She had never forgiven him his share in the destruction of Little Em'ly. Both of them professed to have found salvation, but no one who really knew them could believe this. I then went down to Dover, where Aunt Betsey had returned, and found her and Mr. Dick well and happy. I often rode over to Canterbury to see Agnes. My aunt told me that Agnes had never married because she had an old attachment for someone. I was made very happy when I found that this attachment was for me.

We have been happily married for many years now. All our old friends are prospering, including those far across the ocean. As I close my task, these faces fade away, but one remains before me— that of Agnes.

PIERRE AND JEAN

By

Guy de Maupassant

GUY DE MAUPASSANT (*1850–1893*) was born in Normandy and
became a great friend of Gustave Flaubert. His first volume
of lyrics and also a play were published in 1880. Among his
more famous novels are *Monsieur Parent, Notre Coeur* and
Pierre et Jean which latter was published in 1888. He became
insane in 1892 and died in an asylum.

GÉRÔME ROLAND, a retired Parisian jeweller, established residence in
Le Havre, purchased a boat, and became an amateur boatman and
fisherman. He and his wife had two sons, Pierre and Jean, who
remained in Paris to complete their studies, spending their vaca-
tions in Le Havre and sharing their father's enthusiasm for the
sea. Pierre, five years older than Jean, intelligent and impetuous,
somewhat of a dreamer, became a doctor. Jean, as calm as his
brother was nervous and as good natured as Pierre was spiteful,
had studied law. Both were awaiting an opportunity to set up
practise in Le Havre.

The brothers were fond of each other and yet a vague jealousy
existed between them. Mme Roland had always succeeded in
smoothing out their petty quarrels, but now she began to have
misgivings. The family had become intimate with a certain Mme
Rosémilly, the young widow of a sea captain. She seemed to
prefer Jean, and Mme Roland feared that a rivalry between her
two sons might lead to disastrous consequences.

One day, as they were all returning from a fishing excursion to
which Mme Rosémilly had been invited, Mme Roland asked the
widow to come home with them to dinner and Mme Rosémilly
accepted with pleasure. "Hem," muttered Pierre, "the widow is

'horning in' again." And from that time on he kept referring to her as "the widow."

Arriving home they discovered that the notary, M. Lecanu, had left word that he would call that evening on a matter of importance. After dinner they were still discussing in wonderment what this affair might be when the notary arrived, a messenger of good tidings. An old friend of the family, M. Maréchal, had died in Paris, leaving his entire estate to Jean Roland. In case of Jean's refusal of acceptance, the estate would revert to a foundling institution. Mme Roland was the first to recover from the general astonishment and with tears in her eyes she stammered: "Poor Léon, our poor friend . . . dead!" The doctor murmured: "He was a fine man; he often invited my brother and me to dinner." Jean remarked in a gentle voice: "He seemed very fond of me; he always used to kiss me when I went to see him."

After M. Lecanu's departure, M. Roland related the story of their past connection with M. Maréchal who, years ago, used to spend most of his evenings with the Roland family. He would go and bring Pierre home from school. The day that Jean was born it was M. Maréchal who went for the doctor. No doubt remembering that he had contributed somewhat to the birth of Jean, on his death bed, having no heirs, he had thought of Jean.

M. Roland, continuing his reminiscences, openly displayed his joy at the windfall that had come to Jean; but Mme Roland's face bore an expression of uneasiness for she realized that Pierre would feel hurt because he was not even mentioned in the will.

Mme Roland's premonitions were well founded. Pierre left the house and took a walk along the docks to regain his composure after the visit of M. Lecanu. After considerable wandering he dropped in on his friend the pharmacist and related what had happened. "You know," remarked the pharmacist, "this will make people talk. In such a case one should leave equal shares to two brothers."

The doctor awoke the next morning with the thorough determination to make a fortune by finding a way to capture the wealthy clientèle of Le Havre. The family having an appointment with the notary and Pierre himself feeling that his presence would be quite useless, he strolled about town in search of an apartment in which he might set up practise. Then he dropped in at a café and, failing to find a table companion, invited the serving maid to have a glass of beer with him. What impelled him he did not know, but he had soon related to her the complete circumstances of his brother's inheritance. "Your brother is lucky," she remarked. "It certainly is curious that he bears you so slight a resemblance." It was quite evident to Pierre that this girl believed Jean to be the son of M. Maréchal.

Gradually, but very definitely, a feeling of jealousy toward his brother grew in the heart of Pierre. When Mme Roland announced that she had hired an attractive apartment in which Jean was to start his law practice, Pierre felt a sudden flush of resentment. He took long walks to free his mind of his anger and also of the growing conviction that Jean was the son of M. Maréchal, but his thoughts inevitably reverted to the same subject. He reflected upon the slightest incidents of his childhood, seeking to discover the truth. He remembered that M. Maréchal was blond as was Jean. He also remembered a miniature portrait that formerly stood on the parlor mantel but which had disappeared some time ago. No doubt his mother had put it away. He inquired of her what had become of the portrait and she answered: "Oh! I don't remember; perhaps I put it away somewhere in my desk." The next day, in the presence of his father, Pierre inquired of Mme Roland whether she had found the portrait and she attempted to evade making an answer when M. Roland reminded her that he had seen her take it from her desk several days before. Mme Roland, therefore, had deliberately told a lie; and Pierre was more certain than ever that Jean was an illegitimate child. To make matters worse, Pierre felt that his mother must realize that he was suspicious and a painful uneasiness seized him, for he knew that she must be suffering.

Several weeks later Mme Roland began to have nervous spells. Pierre, in his doctor's capacity, attempted to prescribe for her, but she seemed to resent his attentions. Finally the day came when Jean was to take possession of his new apartment and the family decided to invite Mme Rosémilly to help them celebrate the occasion by a picnic on the seashore, returning to Jean's new home after dinner.

PIERRE AND JEAN

On the excursion Jean and Mme Rosémilly went off by themselves, climbing over the rocks in search of shrimp in the inlets
along the coast. When the couple returned to join the others,
Jean joyfully announced that he had just proposed marriage to
Mme Rosémilly and that she had accepted.

They all returned to Jean's new home and enjoyed a jovial
celebration. M. Roland saw Mme Rosémilly home. Mme Roland
busied herself putting some final touches to the decorations in
the bedroom, leaving the two brothers in the living room. Pierre's
jealousy had reached the breaking point and unable to bear his
resentment any longer he grumbled: "The widow looked worn
out this evening; evidently picnics do not agree with her."

Jean flared up in anger. Silent until this moment, he now poured
forth his pent-up feelings, reprimanding Pierre for his attitude
of jealousy which, Jean declared, had been apparent to everyone
for some time. Pierre, exasperated, retorted that it was Jean who
had dishonored the family by accepting the inheritance. "Everyone
is saying," he told Jean, "that you are the son of M. Maréchal. A self-
respecting man does not accept an inheritance that dishonors his
mother." And with these words he rushed from the house.

Jean realized that their loud argument must have been overheard by his mother. Going into the adjoining room he found her
sobbing on the bed, her face buried in the pillow. It took some
moments for him to calm her and he kept repeating: "Mother
dear, it isn't true; I know it isn't true." But when she finally lifted
her pale face from the pillow she turned to him and said: "Yes,
Jean, my child, it is true." She tried to leave the house, but he
knew that if she ever left he would never see her again. He endeavored to make her remain with him, threatening to join the
army and give up his entire future if she refused. Then Mme
Roland revealed to him the entire story of her relations with
M. Maréchal. He had been the only man she ever loved; the
only happy moments of her life had been with him. She had no
regrets over the past, but the future frightened her, and together
with Jean she tried to find a solution. Finally they decided that
Pierre would take her home and they would try to make arrangements the following day.

On the morrow, in a calmer frame of mind, Jean deliberated at

[187]

length upon the problem. Constant contact with Pierre had become impossible; and certainly Mme Roland could not remain under the same roof with her elder son. Jean asked himself whether a respectable man would keep such an inheritance. For a moment he thought of giving the money to the poor. Then he thought of Mme Rosémilly and remembered that if he gave up the money he would have to renounce his marriage. He could not think of accepting money from M. Roland, either now or after M. Roland's death, for this would be equivalent to robbing Pierre. Finally he decided to accept the inheritance, since he was M. Maréchal's son, and refused to accept anything more from M. Roland. Next he attempted to find a solution to the question of the presence of Pierre in the family circle. Suddenly the whistle of a steamboat in the harbor gave him an idea. He left the house to see if the execution of his plan was possible. Then he went to the home of his mother.

In the presence of the family Jean explained what a wonderful opportunity it would be for Pierre to become a ship's doctor on one of the transatlantic liners that docked at Le Havre. He told them that he had heard that there was a vacancy on the *Lorraine* which was due to make her maiden voyage on the seventh of the following month. M. Roland exclaimed: "Why, I know M. Poulain very well, and he has intimate connections with the steamship company. I'll pay him a visit immediately." They also thought of several friends who would be only too happy to give letters of recommendation.

Pierre had no difficulty in securing the appointment, and the *Lorraine* sailed on the scheduled date. He regretted having revealed to Jean the secret of his brother's birth, for he felt that it was a contemptible action. He felt relieved, however, now that it was over. Once upon the high seas he would no longer have to face his mother and brother. He wondered what they had said to each other that night after he had rushed away from Jean's apartment. Had she denied or had she affirmed the accusation? He would never know. And he also wondered exactly what his brother thought of him. Then he remembered Jean's gentle disposition and how incapable he was of bearing a grudge. Then, too, would not Jean soon forget, for he would be entirely preoccupied with his plans for marrying Mme Rosémilly?

GREEN MANSIONS
A Romance of the Tropical Forest

By

W. H. Hudson

WILLIAM HENRY HUDSON (*1841–1922*) was a British naturalist and author who was born in Argentina of American parents who had settled there. He lived in South America until he was 29 and many of the inspirations for his works were gained on the pampas. Later he moved to England where he occupied his entire time in observations and writing. His best known works include *Green Mansions, The Book of a Naturalist,* and his last volume, *A Hind in Richmond Park.*

MANY YEARS HAVE PASSED since I left Guiana, and with that departure went the sole intimate of Abel Guévez de Argensola, known simply as "Mr. Abel"—a man of the rarest charm, but also of the greatest mystery to everyone (save, as I said, myself). The legends which spring up about any man who is a stranger— Abel was a Venezuelan in our British colony of Georgetown—and to boot, reserved in character, were multiplied intensely by one strange incident. After Abel's death, a darkened room was found containing only an ebony stand on which stood a cinerary urn, ornamented with a floral pattern through which was wound the figure of a serpent, and inscribed with seven short words which no one could understand or interpret. That was all; yet that was enough to arouse the imaginations of the romance-weavers. Since to me alone was the truth known, in its interest, and in friendship and respect for the memory of Abel, I determined to write down his story exactly as he told it to me. Perhaps some of his original gayety and sensitivity, and some of his profound love of nature, indeed, his deep attunement with it, may be felt as his story unfolds; just as it may become evident why, in the closing years of his life, when I had the good fortune to earn him as my friend, his spirit was tinged with melancholy, burdened by his wonderful but ultimately tragic experiences.

An impulsive quarrel, due to Abel's candid charge that a temporary illness of mine was due to indolence and the use of stimulants, drew an excuse that the criticism was tendered in the name of friendship. I turned on him passionately and exclaimed that one condition of friendship was that the partners in it should be known to each other; and while *my* life was an open book to him, *his* was a closed and clasped volume to me. The challenge was given, and within the day, I knew that Abel had accepted it. A note, inviting me to dine, was the first step. And then, after dinner, as we sat smoking and sipping black coffee, Abel began talking, calmly and gently. And this is his story.

·　　　·　　　·

I will begin to explain my life to you from my twenty-third year; for it was then that a great decision was forced upon me. The Venezuelan "republic" was a corrupt, inefficiently run government; so much so, that it was not at all unusual for the young and educated and wealthy men, to plan to overthrow the haphazard government of the moment, replacing it by themselves, the more worthy. Usually these outbreaks failed, and the men were punished, but not regarded as immoral. And so it was that I—a young man of unblemished character, not ambitious of political distinction, wealthy for that country, popular in society, a lover of social pleasures, of books, of nature, allowed myself to be drawn into a conspiracy of this type. Our adventure had an unhappy outcome, because the authorities got wind of the matter, seized some members of our party, and shot them. I happened to be away visiting a friend, a leader in the conspiracy, when we got news of our imminent danger. We had to act quickly. I had always had a longing to visit the vast and almost unexplored territory south of the Orinoco, where primitive and unspoiled peoples lived quite unadulterated by contact with Europeans. I had even gone so far as to master several Indian dialects of the northern states of Venezuela. If I could manage to penetrate to the interior in the western part of Guiana, and go on to the Amazonian territory bordering on Colombia and Brazil, I would be almost certainly safe from arrest. The Guiana authorities concerned themselves little enough about the political upheavals at Caracas. I lost no time in securing myself a passport, which stated my object as a collector of information about the native tribes, the vegetable products of the country, and anything else which would be of interest or advantage to the republic. The complaisant government employee who arranged it for me, added a proviso that the authorities should afford me whatever protection and assistance I might need.

Thus I was introduced to a new life. For the first three months, I wandered about visiting some Christian communities, and then travelled further learning to speak more and more dialects, and stopping at small settlements of native tribes. During this time, my guiding star was hope for literary fame. Each day I recorded my adventures and experiences in a journal, which I guarded jealously as the means to establishing my reputation should I ever return to my native land. My literary plans were interrupted however, when I fell ill with a severe fever, and was rescued from death by the instinctive kindness of some natives. My journal was lost, and I was easily persuaded to forget about the writing of experiences, and to turn instead to the life of action and adventure. So I proceeded further on, until hearing that the natives of the famous Parahuari mountains were always decked in necklaces of pure gold, I became inflamed with the desire to visit that region. Now the hope for gold replaced my earlier hope for fame; and by dint of much effort, cajolery and trading (for I had a small stock of calico and trinkets for this purpose) I managed to find my way to the Parahuari mountains. I should add that although I encountered many dangers, and even narrowly missed death twice or thrice, I was singularly well received by natives of every kind; and here, I think, it was my facility with their native tongue that impressed them, and made them feel that since it would be no easy task to outwit me, they might as well befriend me. But the purpose which had drawn me on—the hope of finding gold—was once again doomed to failure. I searched feverishly every rock and creviss but found no trace of the precious metal. So in utter discouragement, I fled the Parahuari, and made my way to the village which nestled in the midst of a high broken country of forest and savannah and many swift streams, near one of these, called the Curicay. The chief of this tribe was Runi, an old, dignified but taciturn savage. Bleakness and despair had seized hold of my soul; and who knows what my end might have been. But everything was changed by a chance walk, on the evening of the day that I arrived at this village. The exquisite beauty of the mountain tops, bathed in the diffused ruddy light of the setting sun, the blue and ethereal sky, the fresh, caressing winds, and the lyrical chirping of flocks of tropical birds—struck my parched and shattered soul like the fertile drops of rain; and suddenly, a deep calm took possession of me, and my first two quests, for fame and gold, seemed less than worthless. Now only one desire remained; and that was to stay on, in this enchanted country, to make my peace with myself and with nature. But to do this, it was necessary to make friends with Runi and his tribe.

Runi was reserved and stolid, like most Guiana natives. He shared the native admiration for *staying* power, however; so I made a long speech to him, about all the tribes I had visited, naming them, and their chiefs; that everywhere I had been received with great friendliness, and that I had merited it; that I was a friend to the natives, and had their welfare at heart. Then I proceeded to give him my last remaining trinket, a small silver tinderbox. We smoked together, and then Runi called for drink. Casserie, the native drink of low alcohol content, but sweet and insinuating, was brought; and all the members of the tribe drank; only Runi and I, being the principals, had to drink the most. By the time a few hours had passed, we were all affected by the drinks, I even more than the others, being less accustomed to this kind of liquid. But staggering to my feet, I shouted to them that the enemies of Runi and his people must beware of this:—pulling my revolver from my pocket, I sent a bullet through the air. The women screamed, and a thrill of shock and awe went through the assembled tribe. Satisfied that these people feared, and therefore respected me, I barely managed to stumble to my swinging hammock, where I fell into a long sleep.

There followed many peaceful weeks of learning the ways of

these childish yet primitive people. But it was not long before my days became transformed with a new and exhilarating pastime. One day, walking at random in the countryside, I came upon the thickest, greenest, most fertile patch of woodland I had ever seen. Charmed by its profuse herbiage, its myriad birds, its abundant animal life, it suddenly occurred to me that it was strange that my Indian hosts had never come here for hunting, but confined themselves to the far inferior neighboring woods. I therefore made a point of questioning them, only to find the stubborn evasiveness which cloaked every effort to penetrate any of their real "secrets," which were usually superstitions of one sort or another.

I returned to the magic forest frequently, drawn on now by an additional interest. A beautiful and hauntingly human voice, sweet and dulcet in tone, and infinitely varied and flexible in expression and inflection, had presented itself to me. Yet I could nowhere discover its owner. Day after day I would revisit my green mansions, only to hear the exquisite voice, communicating to me every shade of emotion—sometimes warning, sometimes reproach, sometimes sheer lyric song. On one occasion I induced the reluctant young warrior, Kuá-Ko, to accompany me; and this attempt to learn the secrets of the forest from him, resulted in Kuá-Ko's own undignified terror and flight from "the evil spirit." The forest, it seemed, was inhabited by a daughter of the Didi; and thus, it was forbidden to hunt there, on pain of earning the fury and perhaps the evil eye of this feminine enemy spirit. Seeing that I remained incredulous and apparently unfrightened by his story, the craft of young Kuá-Ko became awakened. Patiently, day after day, he tried to teach me how to shoot with the traditional poisoned arrows, which are used for hunting by most Guiana natives. I was a clumsy pupil, but willing—until it dawned upon me why Kuá-Ko had gone to such lengths to appoint himself my teacher. Since I, a white man, and a stranger, had expressed that I was unafraid of any young woman, "evil spirit" or otherwise, perhaps I could be put upon to go into the thick of the forest one day, discover the owner of the now familiar voice, and shoot her with the poisoned arrows. The forest would then be freed of its evil spell, and Runi and his tribe would be free to hunt game and birds there. My horror and disgust at this barbarous plot were almost uncontrollable; but prudence dictated a cautious reply to the effect that white men killed with guns, not arrows; and that they killed only men who were threatening their lives, but never women.

And so I took to daily walks in the wood, in search of the elusive and enchanting voice, which clearly enjoyed its communications to me. Finally I was rewarded; but only again to lose the cherished prize. Far in the interior, in a remote and leafy grotto, I came upon the divinest and most ethereal girlish form one could well imagine. It was reclining gracefully, clad in a short chemise-like filmy garment. A look of surprise crossed the lovely face, when my footsteps betrayed my presence; and then, like a breath of wind, still with face turned toward me, the slight creature faded effortlessly out of sight, leaving only a faintly rustled heap of leaves as testimony of her reality.

I became obsessed with visions and dreams of "the daughter of the Didi," and sought for her patiently in every likely sheltered grove for many days thereafter; but nowhere could I find a trace of the mysterious creature. But accident brought us a new encounter—one that proved to be the most momentous of my life.

I was making my way through the darkening forest (a storm was brewing overhead) when directly before me I saw one of the beautifully colored, but deadly poisonous "coral" snakes. Instinctively, I reached for a rock, threw it, but just missed the snake. Thus angered, it approached me; I bent for another rock, when sharp cries of anger in that unmistakable voice (half human, half bird) assailed my ears. I whirled in its direction, and there stood my wild forest creature, her eyes flaming with wrath. I motioned that I would not hurt the snake, but she pointed at the rock, still grasped firmly in my hand. I cast it aside. Then, to my amazement, I saw the snake approach the girl's bare feet—only to wind itself quietly around her ankle. I realized that this girl was one of the few people who calmed poisonous snakes, as well as any wild creature. So I stood beside her, trying to explain by motions (for she did not seem to understand the Indian tongue) that I was sorry I had angered her. But suddenly notes of agitation, distress, and even warning seemed to seize her speech. Following her gaze, I looked down at the forgotten snake who, irritated by a chance motion of my foot, had raised his head again, and, before I could move or act, darted his poisonous fangs into the fleshy part of my leg. How horrible to be dispatched thus from the beloved presence I had just gained, forced to flee, perhaps mortally wounded. I started to run frantically for the Indian village, just at the moment when a heavy thunderstorm broke loose, and beat upon the ground. I must have lost my way; for I ran into thicker and thicker wood, and finally found myself on the edge of a cliff. If I could jump off it, I remember thinking, I will be nearer home. And then I spied a huge tree which, rooted in the soil below the cliff, yet had its branches on a level with it. It was a mad and desperate chance; and I, maddened enough by fear and exhaustion, to take it. I jumped, and remember only the feeling of rushing through the air; for then I lost consciousness, and seemed to be sinking into a deep sleep.

I awoke to find myself in a strange hut, with a warm fire burning, although the storm was still raging outside. An old man was sitting Indian-fashion, watching me. I spoke to him in the Indian tongue, and he looked up. Smilingly, he said, "Why do you not speak in your native Spanish? I see you are Venezuelan, by birth." Free to speak once again in my native tongue, we conversed rapidly. He told me that he and his grandchild lived alone in this hut, in the very wood I liked to frequent; that the Indians were hateful, anxious to kill them and burn their shelter, but that they were ignorant cowards. "Do you know, they are afraid of my little granddaughter, a child of seventeen summers." So saying, he called her over, calling her by the name of *Rima*. I turned to look at this second person, whose presence I had not noticed, and to my astonishment saw she was the girl of the forest, the creature of the enchanting voice. But how different she appeared, now. In contrast to her luminous outdoor self, she was quiet, tidy, humble in attitude, and quite bereft of the sparkle and delicious animation that I had always associated with her. But it was she who saved me; she, who had run to the hut, after my fall, and brought her grandfather to carry me back to their shelter, and to safety. Miraculously, no bones were broken; and the snake bite, my constitution had successfully warded off.

I stayed on in the hut, at the invitation of Rima and her grandfather. For my part, I was determined to penetrate the mystery of this strange child who was feared by the Indians, and who lived so calmly with this old man. Could he really be her grandfather? She told me that her mother was dead; but that whenever she was out in the forest, she was with her mother, who had become part of the earth. Religion, she apparently confined to her domestic life in the hut—perhaps only to please the old man. But to find out more from Rima was impossible.

In the daytime, when I would go out walking in the forest, she would play her ancient mocking game with me. Calling here, and scolding there, challenging me to follow, then mocking me for my slowness—Rima remained still elusive, still wild and untamed. I decided to use a bit of stratagem with her. I would feign sorrow, and lack of interest. Then her childlike compassion would overcome her, and she would stop her taunting, and her mad racing, and come to sit beside me. She would let me hold her hand in my own; and hers was an altogether human little hand, soft and velvety to the touch. Examined at close range, her hair was of infinitely fine texture, billowing and soft; her skin so lustrous that it seemed transparent, and able to take on different colors, depending on whether the sun shone, or there were shadows. Her eyes which could be burning flames when she was angry, were a soft and deep red, blending wonderfully with her alabaster skin. She was truly a rare and heaven-sent being; and I wondered why God had not made a race of humans to look like this. Perhaps he had, and Rima was one of the last of these favored children of nature.

At last, one day, under a mora tree I asked Rima to call me by my name, Abel; and begged her to look into my eyes. She looked, long and deeply. Instantly I felt certain that there had been some mark of spiritual feeling in her softened eyes. But a moment later she looked troubled, and was eager to cover her agitation with flight. It was a bit later, at the suggestion of an odd phrase or look, that I understood. She yearned to be able to communicate with me in her own thrilling, subtle, but alas for me, inhumanly varied language. Perhaps dimly she sensed that a union, even of love, could never be complete while she must imprison her thoughts and feelings. "You are still you, and I am I" was a phrase I heard repeated, accompanied by a baffled and anxious expression.

Troubled as Rima was, she soon revealed to me a strange plan. With childlike persistence she questioned me about the world; how large it was, what the names of adjoining lands and peoples might be. Naming the adjacent territories in order, I came to that mountain which skirts the border of Guiana, and which is known as the Riolama. At that name Rima uttered a sharp cry, her face quite transfigured with excitement. "That is it," she exclaimed. Then she explained that that was the place where her mother had come from, and that it had been her long cherished hope to revisit the country of her childhood, where she hoped to find other people like herself—people who loved all animals, and ate only vegetation; people who could understand her beautiful and limitless bird-like speech; people who looked as she, and dressed as she—in simple garments, spun through the efforts of myriad willing spiders. When she heard that it was a good twenty days' journey, she remained undismayed. I urged that the journey would be too much for the old man; but Rima, infuriated at his unwillingness to help her in the past, had no compassion for him. She flew off in a rage; and I knew that the religious old man, who looked on Rima as a child of divinity, and as his protector in the heavenly scheme of things, would give way.

In a few days, we set out—not without secret misgivings on my part at the behavior of the Indians when they would discover the wood freed of its human occupants. And indeed, had it not been for a chance encounter on the road with three travellers, they might never have learned of our departure! Still I was not sure that the travellers would pass Runi's settlement, and besides, it was too late to turn back. After twenty days, exhausted and footsore, we arrived at Riolama. The condition I had imposed upon old Nuflo, Rima's grandfather, was that in exchange for accompanying us on so arduous a journey he must tell me the story of Rima's origin. And by the time we arrived I knew that Rima had come on a futile quest. For as Nuflo related the circumstances to me, Rima's mother, beautiful as Rima, and speaking the same language, had been discovered by him one day in these very hills.

Nuflo had thought she was a saint at first, because of her pure beauty and spiritual appearance. But to protect her from his own band of unscrupulous thieves and murderers, he fled with her to the town of Voa, where medical attention as well as the solicitations of the priest could be provided her. Shortly after, the saintly woman gave birth to a girl—whom she named Rima. In the few years that she managed to live, in the hot and moist climate of the town of Voa, she taught her child to speak her language. It was this language which Rima alone could speak, and understand. And from Nuflo's tale I knew that Rima's mother had been separated from her father, and from all his tribe; and that probably none of their kind existed anymore, any place on this earth.

But Rima was restless with our arrival at the mountain, Riolama. She prepared to go in search of her people, further and further, until they were found. I saw that I would have to disillusion her, brutal shock though it might be. And so I told her the probable truth—that she was the last of her people; and that no search for them could possibly end well. The life seemed to flow from her face, and then her body grew limp. Just in time, I caught her in my arms, and carried her back to the cave where Nuflo and I had arranged to sleep. I watched over her all that night, my eyes fastened on her face, waiting for signs of life to return. Unable to control my sorrow and love any longer, I kissed her tenderly on her pale lips, again and again. And then it seemed that a rosier flush came over her face. At last she opened her eyes, and looked at me, serenely, and as if purified. I bent close to her to say that now that she knew of my great love for her, and now that she loved me in return, it was no longer important to lament that nobody could share her language. No closer communication could be desired than that of love; no need could she have to *tell* that which both she and I so deeply felt and understood.

On the morrow, my profound happiness was marred by Rima's intention to depart for our forest alone. Argue and plead as I would, she remained determined to precede slow Nuflo and myself; to reach the forest ahead of time, and there prepare herself for our happy life together. Indeed, she was gone before I could detain her. Two days later, we followed; but inclement weather and bad luck at securing food made our journey last for twenty-six days and nights. Imagine our distress and terror when we reached the forest to find our hut completely demolished, apparently burnt to the ground by the savage Indians.

Frantically, I turned to seek for Rima; but evil forebodings already had me in their grip. I remembered the hatred of the Indians for "the daughter of the Didi." I searched all the familiar places, calling Rima; yet I heard nowhere the sweet, warbling voice for which I longed with all my being. Suddenly I came upon the seated form of an Indian, and then I saw another, and still another. They approached me hostilely. I determined to act the role of friendship and innocence. I dared not ask about Rima yet; but a few days later, back in Runi's long hall, a virtual prisoner, I asked to accompany Kuá-Ko and several others on a hunting expedition. Once alone with the young savage Kuá-Ko, whose hatred of Rima I knew only too well, I asked him how it was that he was no longer afraid to hunt in the "magic" forest. Then from the lips of this coarse and primitive brute poured the story of Rima's capture: how they had surrounded her in the forest, and she had climbed to the top of a high tree; how they had placed dry bushes high all around the tree, and set fire to them; and how, when the flames reached the top, the girl was heard to cry out "Abel, Abel," and, with that, fall, like a large white bird, to her flaming death.

Misery such as mortals rarely suffer, pounded my heart, body and head. I willed for life to leave me while at the same time ravaged with the consuming desire to choke the savage beast beside me. I hardly know how I suffered through the night; and in the morning, I knew myself to be half mad. Somehow I must destroy Kuá-Ko and all the members of Runi's tribe who had plunged Rima to her burning death.

In this period of anguish and mental frenzy, I cursed the author of my being. But truly, at that time, I was a man mortally sick in mind. Suffice it to say that through stratagem, I worked upon Managa, Runi's ancient enemy, to such an extent that he and his tribe made a surprise attack upon their enemy and annihilated them completely. I returned to the forest which Rima had made so blessed for me, and day after day, week after week, slipped by in brooding and sorrow. Finally, I grew to hate the solitude and the fiendish memory of my onetime happiness. My last labor there was to search for Rima's burial heap. There I gathered up the delicate bones that remained, and placed them in a large and ancient jug which had belonged to Nuflo. Alas, poor Nuflo, deserted by me had met his fate at the hands of the Indians too. This jug I stained with the berries which Rima had been wont to eat, and I inscribed the few short words which pledged my undying love. And then I turned my face in the direction of Venezuela, and pushed on firmly and steadily—anxious to leave behind me forever the sight of native peoples, and their villages. Back in Venezuela, with the precious funeral urn, I regained the clear vision that once had been mine. I knew then that the beautiful creature who had made me so ecstatically happy, was like the rarest of flowers—of which there can be only one, at any one time. But she, like they, are eternally beautiful in the minds of men who have been fortunate enough to look upon them. And to this very day, in the midst of friends and wealth, the one tragedy of my life is still *the* profound sorrow; and it is this winning of the self through the deepest suffering that alone would make me able to meet Rima's eyes, were she ever again to face. Neither she nor I believed in austerities or good works. Nevertheless there is a way, which every soul can find out for itself—even the most darkened with crime and tormented with remorse. In that way I have walked; and self-forgiven and self-absolved, the eternal sorrow in Rima's eyes would not be in them now.

THE ADVENTURES OF TOM SAWYER

By

Mark Twain

SAMUEL LANGHORNE CLEMENS (*1835–1910*), originally known as "Mark Twain", was an American humorist, born at Florida, Mo. After a brief frontier school education he became a printer and then a Mississippi River pilot. From the cant of the river he gained his pseudonym which means "mark two fathoms." Later he tried silver-mining in Nevada, reporting in San Francisco, lecturing there and then in New York. In 1867 he journeyed to Europe where he gathered material for his *Innocents Abroad*. He married an Elmira, New York, girl while he was an editor in the city and later moved to Hartford, Conn. His books were sold by subscription for the most part which yielded him a handsome income. A publishing concern, of which he was a member, failed involving him in a great loss but he left his daughter a fortune of about $500,000. Among his more famous books are *Tom Sawyer, The Prince and the Pauper, The Adventures of Huckleberry Finn* and *Connecticut Yankee at King Arthur's Court*.

"TOM!"

No answer.

"You *Tom!*"

Still no answer.

Aunt Polly pulled her spectacles down and looked over them about the room; then she put them up and looked under them, scanning every nook and corner. She reached under the bed with the broom, and resurrected nothing but the cat. She gazed out into the garden and then raised her voice again, this time for distance.

But Tom was discovered in the small closet behind her, and there was evidence that he had been making free with the jam pot. He escaped the threatened switching by diverting his aunt's attention, and that afternoon he played hookey, arriving home barely in time to help Jim, the small colored boy, saw and split the wood for the morrow. At least, he sat and told of his adventures while Jim did three-quarters of the work, at the same time that his younger half-brother, Sid, who had no adventuresome and troublesome ways, quietly performed his task of picking up the chips.

Aunt Polly, with whom Tom lived, his dead mother's sister, never had the heart to punish him properly, though she certainly had enough provocation. But this time she had steeled herself to turn his Saturday holiday into captivity, for work was the thing he most hated in all the world. Tom was commanded to whitewash the fence, and as he began the hated task a great, magnificent inspiration dawned upon him. He set to work in earnest, stepping back every few minutes to admire his handiwork, and one by one the neighborhood boys, passing by, paused to watch. They came to jeer but remained to whitewash, for as Tom seemed to take pride in his work and remarked "Aunt Polly's awful particular about this fence" he soon had the boys pleading "Say, Tom, let *me* whitewash a little." Tom demurred, but finally let Ben Rogers have a share in the noble work in return for his apple. After that it was easy to trade off chances on the whitewashing for various small possessions the boys had that he coveted.

By the middle of the afternoon Tom was literally rolling in wealth, he had had a nice, idle time, and the fence had received three coats of whitewash. Aunt Polly, summoned to inspect the work, would not believe that it had been completed, and great was her astonishment as she admitted, "Well! you *can* work when you've a mind to." The rest of the afternoon was free for play, and Tom engaged in sham military maneuvers with the boys, his company being victorious. Homeward-bound, the fresh-crowned hero fell captive, without a shot being fired, to love, and a certain Amy Lawrence, whom he had thought he had adored to distraction, vanished out of his heart and left not a trace of herself behind. The lovely little blue-eyed creature with yellow hair in pigtails, wearing a white summer frock and embroidered pantalettes, whom he espied in the garden, was Becky Thatcher. Tom worshipped with furtive eyes, and then began to "show-off" in all sorts of absurd boyish ways, and as she disappeared into the house she tossed a pansy over the fence, which he cherished tenderly and returned to supper in such high spirits that his aunt wondered what had got into him.

Next day at Sunday-School, miracle of miracles, Tom was presented with a Bible, coveted prize given the scholar who could produce ten yellow tickets, signifying that he had memorized two thousand Bible verses. Through an intricate system of blue, red, and yellow tickets, these precious slips might be accumulated over a period of months or even years. But as it was impossible to believe that *this* boy had achieved this remarkable feat, the presentation of the prize lacked something of the gusto appropriate to the occasion, especially so as Tom had replied miserably "David and Goliath" when questioned as to the identy of the first two disciples. On the superintendent, Mr. Walters, had slowly dawned the suspicion that these tickets had not been come by in the approved manner. He had expected no application for the Bible prize for ten years at least; this had been the most stunning surprise of the decade, but also a mystery that could not well bear the light.

And indeed Tom had obtained the tickets by waylaying boys as they came in to the Sunday-School, and trading tickets of various colors for odds and ends of trifles he had on hand. Too late the boys saw that they had been duped, but by that time Tom had his Bible. As the company passed into the church on this Sabbath morning, Tom amused himself with the antics of a pinch-bug beetle which he had in a percussion-cap box in his pocket. Others of the congregation, becoming weary of the long sermon, took pleasure in watching the insect, and a vagrant poodle-dog who happened in played with the pinch-bug as it lay on its back in the aisle and then gave a yelp of agony as the creature bit it sharply and dashed down the aisle and right in front of the altar. It was a relief to everyone when the benediction was pronounced and the long service was over.

Monday morning at school, Tom's excuse in regard to his lateness "I stopped to talk with Huckleberry Finn" drew upon him a terrible flogging in which the schoolmaster's arm performed until it was tired. But the punishment was worth it, for afterwards Tom was sent to sit with the girls, which meant in this case next to Becky Thatcher. This was bliss for Tom, but for a long time Becky would not notice him. Finally she deigned to look at the pictures he drew for her, and when he wrote the words "I love you" on his slate he pretended not to want her to see, but gradually withdrew the hand that was hiding them. The master, now noticing what was going on, descended on Tom and fastening a close grip on his ear bore him across the room to his own seat. That noon, however, the two children remained in the deserted schoolroom and Tom drew more pictures for Becky. The sweet tale "I love you" was whispered softly each to the other, and they became "engaged." But alas, before the hour was out they had quarreled and Tom left the school in anger, leaving them both miserable. Steeped in melancholy, Tom wandered disconsolately through the woods, and then came the happy thought to be a pirate. "Tom Sawyer the Pirate—the Black Avenger of the Spanish Main!"

The adventure that night in the graveyard with Huckleberry Finn proved to be of tragic import and rather more than the boys had bargained for. Huck Finn was the son of the town drunkard, the juvenile pariah of the village. His society was forbidden to all the "nice" boys of St. Petersburg, and all the mothers hated and dreaded him because he was such a glamorous figure to their sons on account of the freedom of his life. He was accountable to no one, fished and swam when he pleased, slept on doorsteps in fine weather and in empty hogsheads in wet, wore queer discarded clothing, and smoked a pipe. Huck had this time acquired a dead cat, and the two boys had arranged to go to the graveyard at midnight to the grave of a person recently buried and wait for the spirits to take away the body. They would then throw the dead cat after the body, and this, accompanied by the proper incantation, meant, Huck said, a sure cure for warts.

They met as scheduled, and while they were rather fearfully waiting for the spirits of the dead to appear, three figures were seen in the distance who turned out to be not the three devils they expected but three humans they knew well. Young Doctor Robinson, who had arranged with the other two, Injun Joe and Muff Potter, that they should open the grave and get the body in it for him, was killed during a quarrel with his two helpers over their pay. And the doctor's murderer was Injun Joe, who had done the awful deed with Muff's knife, and because Muff had been knocked out while the murder took place and had been drinking heavily it was easy for the half-breed to fasten the crime on Potter.

Huck and Tom, horror-stricken at what they had witnessed, ran from the grave. Through fear of Injun Joe they made a compact to tell nothing of what they knew as to the correct identity of the murderer. During the weeks to come they visited Muff Potter in jail and brought him small comforts. Tom's conscience began to trouble him more and more, and finally the night before the trial, it harassed him so that it drove him to the judge's with the story of what he knew. When the truth came out next day, Injun Joe, fleet of foot, escaped from the court-room and was not caught.

Tom now was a glittering hero by day, but to him the night became a season of horror. Injun Joe infested all his dreams and he hardly dared set foot out-of-doors after twilight. Huck Finn was in the same state of wretchedness and terror, though his part in the dread night's proceedings had not come out. And also Huck had lost his confidence in human beings since Tom, who had sworn with the most dismal and formidable of oaths, had nonetheless revealed the secret they had agreed to keep to themselves.

Both Huck and Tom had their attention diverted from the grewsome business by a new adventure, as Tom, to whom life had again become a gloomy affair, mostly because he had been slighted by Becky, felt that this was a good chance to become the pirate he dreamed of. He discovered that Joe Harper was of the same mind, having been unjustly punished at home. These two hunted up Huck Finn, and the three resolved to meet on the river at midnight. They were going to capture a small raft and provision it with what they could steal at home, and set sail.

At midnight, the Black Avenger of the Spanish Main (known up to this time as Tom Sawyer) arrived with a boiled ham, and a few trifles, the Terror of the Seas (Joe Harper) contributed a side of bacon, while Huck the Red Handed, provided a skillet, and a quantity of leaf tobacco and corncobs for pipes. No one smoked but himself, but when the long evenings of their self-imposed exile began to drag, he lost no time in teaching this art to his companions, with sad results at first.

It was fun the first night—they had arrived at their retreat about two o'clock in the morning,—as they built a great fire and ate their bacon and corn pone. They had a good sleep, a swim the next morning before their breakfast of the fish that they caught and bacon and more pone. Exploration of the island followed, revealing nothing extraordinary. But as time went on, the novelty of the adventure wore off, and little by little the boys became homesick, though they would not have admitted this for worlds. During that afternoon they heard a peculiar sound in the distance, which seemed to be the ferryboat's whistle and which was often repeated. It slowly dawned on the boys that this was the signal heard "last summer when Bill Turner got drownded." They parted the bushes and could see the ferryboat with crowds of people aboard, and knew that the river was being searched. "Boys, I know who's drownded—it's us!" exclaimed Tom, and they all felt like heroes. It was good to be missed.

That night Tom swam and waded to the nearby Missouri shore and crawled into the skiff of the ferryboat that was about to depart. Making his way home after he had crossed the river, he hid and overheard Mrs. Harper and Aunt Polly and the rest saying with many tears that the boys had been given up for dead, since the raft had been found wedged against the bank. If the bodies were not found by Saturday—it was now Wednesday—funeral services for the three would be held Sunday morning at church time. Tom had gone home with the good intention of leaving for his aunt a message "We ain't dead—we're only off being pirates," but now a brilliant idea came to him, and he did not leave the message after all. The boys would stay on the island till Saturday, make their way home and hide in the church for their own funerals, revealing themselves when the time seemed ripe.

This plan was carried out. After a final adventure of a terrific thunder-storm on their last night, when the thunder and lightning crashed and cracked around them, and their makeshift tent of an old sail was destroyed and they were soaked to their skins, the boys dried themselves out as best they could, and departed for home. They hid in the church gallery and listened to the eulogies of themselves and the sobs of the mourners, and at the proper moment marched down the aisle in a very fine climax. As their families threw themselves upon them in a frenzy of emotion, in which Huck was included too at Tom's insistence, the minister in a flash of inspiration gave the signal for "Praise God from Whom All Blessings Flow," and Old Hundred swelled up with a triumphant burst and shook the rafters. Thus was ended an extraordinary funeral service, and Tom knew this to be the proudest moment of his life.

At this point Tom resolved that he could be independent of Becky Thatcher; he would now live for glory. Probably she would be wanting to "make up" now that he was a hero, but he would show her that he could be indifferent. He pretended not to notice Becky and did not even plead for an invitation to her picnic. Each of them took up a "flirtation" with another to get even, but this seemed curiously unsatisfying to both of them.

There came a day in school when Tom received two whippings, one for the inky page in his speller which had been thus smeared by his hated rival for Becky's favor, Alfred Temple, "that St. Louis smarty!" And the second when in an impulse of chivalry he took the blame for the torn page in the schoolmaster's book that Becky had mutilated. The gratitude and adoration which shone out of Becky's eyes were pay for a hundred floggings, and though he had to stay two hours after school as added punishment, he was happy, for he knew that she would wait all that weary time for him. As he fell asleep that night, her last words lingered sweetly in his ears "Oh Tom, how *could* you be so noble!"

The long summer vacation was marked by a rainy and disappointing Fourth of July, a few days of the circus, some parties, a revival in the town, and then an attack of the measles for Tom. After long, weary days he recovered from the latter, and then one afternoon he was suddenly smitten with the raging desire to go somewhere and dig for buried treasure. "Where'll we go dig?" inquired Huck sensibly when approached on the subject, and Tom answered "Oh, most anywhere." But, on further consideration, he admitted that the treasure would probably be buried under a ha'nted house or on an island or "under a dead tree that's got one limb sticking out." The boys had already tried Jackson's Island when they were off playing pirates. Long and wearisome experiments were made with the other two types of hunting for buried treasure. "Do they always bury it as deep as this?" inquired Huck as they toiled away with their shovels. "Not generally. I guess we haven't got the right place," his companion replied.

After more back-breaking work, Tom remembered that they should find out where the shadow of the dead limb fell at midnight and dig there. This project did not work out either, however, and the next day as they returned for their tools they approached the ha'nted house, and then remembered that as it was a Friday they must not dig for buried treasure that day. They fell to playing Robin Hood.

But the day following they came back to the haunted house and ventured inside. As they examined the place with interest and familiarity modified their fears, they finally dared to go upstairs, and thereby met with a frightening adventure. For who should enter the house presently but two figures, one of whom they both identified (by his voice) as Injun Joe, in the disguise of a deaf-and-dumb Spaniard that had lately appeared about town. The two boys overhead quaked with fear, but they listened with all their ears and watched through a knot-hole, as the two unkempt men talked a long while, had a lunch, and a sleep. Tom wanted to escape while they slept, but the floor creaked so menacingly at his first step that he gave up the idea. So Huck and Tom waited in agony until the men awoke.

In digging in the fireplace preparatory to burying the money-bag they had with them containing six hundred dollars, the men came upon another treasure trove of thousands, left by some former gang. They would have left both stores buried in the fireplace, had it not been for the pick and shovel with fresh earth on them that they had discovered in the house. "Who could have brought these tools here? Do you reckon they can be upstairs?" queried Injun Joe, and the boys' hearts stood still. The half-breed turned toward the stairway and was creaking up when suddenly there was a crash of rotten timbers and he fell to the ground amid the ruins of the collapsed staircase. This mishap of Injun Joe saved the boys, for he gave up any further attempt to see if the house were occupied, and shortly the two companions departed toward the river with their precious box.

Bitter, bitter luck that the tools had ever been brought to the house, thought the boys as they proceeded soberly homewards. The men had spoken of some revengeful job Injun Joe was anxious to get finished. Tom had an awful thought. "Revenge? What if he means *us?*" Tom's dreams were mightily tormented that night.

In figuring out what hiding place for the money the men had meant by Number Two, Huck and Tom came upon some promising clues, and Huck agreed to keep watch every night on the room in the tavern which seemed to be the place and wait until Injun Joe departed from it. It was on the night of the day that Tom went to Becky Thatcher's picnic that Huck's chance came, but let us take up Tom's story first.

The chief event of the long-delayed picnic that had been promised Becky Thatcher was exploring McDougal's Cave, a fascinating cavern of stalactites and glittering crystals. Its vast labyrinth of crooked ways, leading ever farther down into the earth, was a fascination to the children, as they explored the passages, holding their candles aloft.

But to Becky and Tom who wandered far away from the main body of picnickers it became a place of torment. At last they realised that they were lost, their last bit of candle flickered into nothingness, and they were tired and hungry. Tom had a cake in his pocket, but this did. not help for long. Fortunately they had water to drink, for owing to Tom's good sense they had stopped by a spring when the candle went out. Becky forlornly cried herself to sleep in Tom's arms, and when she waked she groaned, "Oh, how *could* I sleep! I wish I never, never had waked!" Tom tried to comfort her, but he was badly scared himself when he realized that Becky's mother had expected her to spend the night at the home of a friend near the ferry-landing, and thus would not miss her for a long time. And indeed it was not until Sunday afternoon that searching-parties were sent out for it was after church that Mrs. Thatcher and Aunt Polly perceived that Becky and Tom had not returned from the picnic with the rest.

Wild was the excitement in St. Petersburg, and it was not long before two hundred men were off to explore parts of the cave that had never been visited before. To Becky and Tom the three days and nights dragged interminably, once they heard faint sounds as of rescuers but could not reach them. At last as Tom decided to explore some of the side passages near them, he came to a "jumping-off" place, and as he leaned down to gaze as far around the corner as he could, he saw unmistakably the form of Injun Joe! Tom was momentarily paralyzed, but the half-breed made off as fast as he could, and Tom said nothing to Becky of the encounter. He resolved to stay close to the spring after this, but after another night of wretchedness and an awaking to raging hunger, he decided to try once more, and moved off in another direction, with the aid of the kite-line. Becky was very weak, and said she was willing to wait and die where she was.

The long vigil of the children was now almost over, for after exploring three corridors in vain Tom spied a faint speck of daylight at the end of a fourth, hastened to it joyfully, and beheld the broad Mississippi rolling by! Becky refused to believe the good news, but with Tom was overjoyed when they finally pushed their way out into daylight again, and waited for a skiff to take them home. The point where they had emerged was five miles down the river below the valley the cave was in!

The searching-party in the cave was tracked by the twine clues they had left behind them, and told the good news. Tom and Becky were weak and bedridden for days. But as soon as Tom was able he was off to see Huck Finn, who had been delirious with fever and was still ill at the home of the Welshman half-way up Cardiff Hill. The Widow Douglas, whose life he had saved on that Saturday night when Tom and Becky got lost in the cave, was caring for him. Tom was not allowed to talk with Huck of exciting things, but he learned at home of most of the happenings of that eventful week-end, and gradually he pieced the story together.

Huck had seen Injun Joe and his ragged, unkempt companion come out of the door-way he had been watching so long, bearing the heavy box of money with them, and had tracked them up Cardiff Hill. He there learned of the plot to rob the Widow

Douglas and torture her. It was because her husband, the justice of the peace, had had him horsewhipped, "horsewhipped in front of the jail, like a nigger," that Injun Joe demanded his revenge by leaving her to bleed to death after he had "slit her nostrils and notched her ears." His companion had objected to this part of the program, but was persuaded, and as they were waiting for the lights to be turned off at the house, Huck had time to run down the hill and tell his incredible tale to the Welshman. He with his two sons hurried up the hill, fired on the two plotters and frightened them off.

Next morning Huck described the two men to the tavern-keeper, though insisting that no one must know that he was the one who tracked them. He let out the fact which he tried at first to conceal, through fear, that the "deaf-and-dumb" Spaniard was really Injun Joe. And of this outlaw's miserable end the people learned when a party went to the ill-fated cave and discovered him dead at the entrance. Judge Thatcher had had the door of the cave sealed up and triple-locked, so no one else could get lost in it, and Tom had not learned of this till two weeks after his own rescue.

So the half-breed was dead, and a sense of relief and security swept through the community. But the treasure had not been found, and there remained one more adventure for the boys. The heavy treasure-box, whose contents they placed in small bags they could carry, Tom and Huck discovered right underneath the point in the cave where Tom had seen Injun Joe make a mark with candle smoke on that awful day of his captivity in the cave. On this trip of discovery Tom and Huck had used the entrance from which he and Becky had emerged, and this was now to be the headquarters of "Tom Sawyer's Gang" (the decision had been made to be robbers instead of pirates, and Huck approved. "Why, it's real bully, Tom. I b'lieve it's better'n to be a pirate." "Yes, it's better in some ways, because it's close to home and circuses and all that," agreed Tom.

As Huck and Tom lugged home the discovered treasure in a small wagon, intending to hide it in the loft of the widow's woodshed, they were overtaken by the Welshman, made to dress up, and hauled into a party that the Widow Douglas was giving in gratitude for having been saved from a terrible fate. To Huck, whose share in the affair had leaked out, being set up as a target for everybody's gaze and laudations was only more uncomfortable than the nearly intolerable discomfort of his new clothes. He was promised a home and education by the grateful widow and a start in business when the time came, but Tom broke in, "Huck don't need it. Huck's rich."

At the incredulous smiles of the company, who thought he must be crazy, Tom merely ran out-of-doors and brought in the sacks of money. It was counted, and the sum amounted to a little over twelve thousand dollars. It was more than any one present had ever seen at one time before. So vast a sum seemed incredible, everybody took to ransacking haunted houses, without success. The village paper published biographical sketches of the boys.

Judge Thatcher invested Tom's share of the money at Aunt Polly's request. The judge had conceived a great opinion of Tom. No ordinary boy could have gotten his daughter out of the cave, he was sure, and Becky had told him of Tom's nobility in taking her whipping at school, and pleaded grace for the lie he told in so doing until the judge, visibly moved, declared it a generous, magnanimous lie, worthy to rank with George Washington's truth about the hatchet. Judge Thatcher hoped for the career of either a soldier or a lawyer for Tom, and he promised to help him achieve the one he should choose.

Huck, being under the Widow Douglas' protection, was perforce dragged into society, and made miserable by new clothes, clean beds, meals at regular times, and going to church. After three weeks, Tom discovered him asleep in his accustomed haunt in an empty hogshead behind the abandoned slaughter-house, clad in his old rags, and happy with his pipe. To Tom's pleas to return, Huck protested, "No, Tom, I won't be rich, and I won't live in them cussed, smothery houses. I like the woods, and the river, and hogsheads, and I'll stick to 'em, too." Huck was won over though when Tom assured him that their turning rich was not going to prevent them from being robbers, and Tom promised to intercede with the widow that she "let up" on Huck a little. When Tom declared, "Huck, we can't let you into the gang, you know, if you ain't respectable," and assured him that "a robber is more high-toned than what a pirate is—as a general thing. In most countries they're awful high up in the nobility—dukes and such," Huck saw that he must endure civilization and its drawbacks for the sake of belonging to the gang, and he declared with finality "I'll stick to the widder till I rot, Tom; and if I get to be a reg'lar ripper of a robber, and everybody talking 'bout it, I reckon she'll be proud she snaked me in out of the wet."

TREASURE ISLAND

By

Robert Louis Stevenson

ROBERT LOUIS BALFOUR STEVENSON (*1850–1894*), a Scottish novelist and essayist, intended to become an engineer because his father and grandfather were lighthouse engineers but he changed to law and was admitted to the bar. But the impulse to write gained ascendancy and he indulged in long leisurely trips to gather material. These journeys ended in his final residence in Samoa in 1889. He died after a long battle with tuberculosis and was buried on a mountain top in the South Seas. Before his end he was probably the most conspicuous personality in English letters and had the affection of all classes of readers. Among his most famous works are *Treasure Island, The Strange Case of Dr. Jekyll and Mr. Hyde* and his *New Arabian Nights.*

I, JIM HAWKINS, have been asked to write down all the particulars about Treasure Island, omitting only the bearings of the island, because there is treasure there not yet lifted. I begin to write in the year 17—, and go back to the days when my father kept the "Admiral Benbow" inn, and the old seaman first took up his lodging with us. I remember him as he came up to the door with his sea-chest carried behind him—a heavy, brown man with scarred hands and a sabre-cut across one cheek, breaking out into that old sea-song I was to hear so often:

> *"Fifteen men on the dead man's chest—*
> *Yo-ho-ho, and a bottle of rum!"*

The inn pleased him, for it had very little company, and nearby there was a cliff from which he could scan the sea for ships. He spent a great deal of time on the cliffs. I noticed that he never went into the main room of the inn until he had examined the company there. He was anxious about something, and I was presently made the sharer in his alarms, for he promised me a silver four-penny a month if I would keep a weather-eye open for a seafaring man with one leg. This man haunted my dreams. When the captain got drunk, he would sing wild sea-songs, and tell dreadful stories of hanging and walking the plank, and wild deeds on the Spanish Main. Once he became so violent that Dr. Livesey, who had come to see my sick father, threatened him with the law.

Early one morning, a pale tallowy man wanting two fingers of his left hand came to the house looking for the captain, whom he called "Bill." The captain was frightened to see him. I heard the sound of quarreling, the clash of steel, and saw the man whom the captain had called Black Dog running from the house, the captain pursuing him. The man escaped, and the captain, over-wrought by the excitement, was seized with a stroke. When he had partially recovered, he told me that if anything happened to him, I was to take care of his sea-chest, which was what his enemies were after.

My father died. The day after his funeral, a blind old seaman came tapping at the door. He demanded to be taken to the captain, and so strong was his grip on my arm that I was forced to obey him. He dropped something into the captain's hand and skipped out the door. "Ten o'clock!" cried the captain, reeled, and fell to the floor dead. Fearing the return of Black Dog and his friends, my mother and I hastened to the neighboring hamlet for aid. The people there were so terrified that they would not help us, except to send a messenger to Dr. Livesey. But my mother determined we must go back alone to get the money that was due us. As we searched the captain's body to find the key to the chest, we noted a little black round of paper on the floor, the black spot, and on the other side the words: "You have till ten to-night." It was then only six, but as we counted out the money due my mother from the captain's chest, I heard the tapping of the blind man's stick upon the road. Seizing what money we had counted and an oilskin packet we had found in the chest, we fled from the house. As we hid under the low arch of a bridge we heard the men battering their way into the house. When they found us and part of the contents of the chest gone, they were wild with anger and began to search for us. We would have been lost, had not the revenue officers, who had been met by the boy sent for Dr. Livesey, come galloping up. The men fled, but the horses ran down the blind man and killed him.

One of the officers took me to find the doctor, who was at the home of the squire. After the officer had left, the doctor opened the oilskin packet. The packet contained a sealed paper, a map of an island, with its location carefully marked, and in red ink the notation: "Bulk of treasure here." This paper must have been the precious thing which the pirate Flint had given the captain, who had been his first mate (as he had told me), when he lay dying, and this must be his treasure. The squire, in great excitement, offered to outfit a ship to search for the treasure. I was to be cabin-boy. The doctor agreed enthusiastically, but warned the squire, who was a talkative man, to hold his tongue.

I remained at the squire's house while the squire went to Bristol to fit out a ship. After a short visit with my mother I joined the squire and the doctor in the sea-port. There we found that the squire had been talking rather too much about the treasure. He had en-gaged a one-legged man, Long John Silver, as ship's cook, and Silver had helped him find a crew. For a moment, when I heard of Silver's one leg, I remembered the fear of the captain who had stayed at our inn, but when I saw the man, and observed how smil-ing and cheerful he was, I was sure he had not been the cause of the captain's terror. Once, when I was visiting Silver's little tavern, I saw Black Dog, but he hurried away, annoying Silver very much because he had not paid his bill, and because, being a stranger, he probably would not return to do it.

We were finally ready to sail on the *Hispaniola*. Her captain, Smollett, was worried about the trip. He found that the crew knew what he had not known, that they were going for buried treasure, and where the treasure was; and he was disturbed because he had not chosen his own crew. The captain feared a mutiny, and al-though the others laughed at him, they allowed him to make a gar-rison of the stern of the ship. The voyage proved fairly prosperous. The men were cheerful, and Silver took great pains to make and keep them so. In spite of his one leg, Silver was one of the most active men on board, and certainly he seemed one of the most trustworthy.

It was only by chance that I learned otherwise. An apple barrel stood on deck that we might help ourselves whenever we wished. One night, when I went for an apple, I found the barrel so nearly empty that I had to climb into it. As I sat there, I heard voices outside, one of which I recognized as Silver's. To my horror, I learned that he had been Flint's quartermaster, and that he was now trying to make one of the men join him and the old pirates he had brought on board as crew. Hands, one of the men, was all for taking the ship over at once, but Silver had enough sense to know they were not able to set her course. His plan was to let Smollett sail the ship for them, let the squire and the doctor find the treasure, finish with them on the island, and make his way home with his rascals and the treasure. I was almost discovered when one of the men started to get himself an apple, but they all went off for rum instead. Just then I heard the cry "Land ho!" We had come to Treasure Island.

In the confusion I was able to whisper to the doctor that I had terrible news for him. He, the squire and the captain went to the cabin, and shortly thereafter sent for me. They were thunderstruck by my news. We were able to count three men who would be loyal to us, making seven against nineteen.

It took us a long time to get the ship into its anchorage between the big island and little Skeleton Island, and the men were very sullen before we got through, in contrast to their cheerfulness on the voyage. Only Silver retained his good humor; one would never have known he was a traitor. The captain allowed the men to go ashore, thinking to quiet them, and I sneaked into one of their boats. I gave them the slip as soon as I landed, and ran off to explore the island. Hiding behind some low trees, I saw Silver talking to one of the seamen trying to make him join the mutineers. As they talked, a cry rang out far off, a death yell. The man walked away from Silver, shaking his head, and suddenly I saw Silver knock him down with his crutch, and then knife him. I fled.

As I ran I saw a dark, shaggy figure leaping ahead of me. When he stopped I walked up to him, and to my surprise he flung himself on his knees before me. He told me that he was Ben Gunn, and that he hadn't spoken to anyone for three years. Gunn had been in Flint's ship when he had buried the treasure and the six men who had hidden it. Afterward, sailing on another ship, he had passed the island, and persuaded his shipmates to hunt for the treasure with him. When they had been unable to find it, having no chart, the sailors had marooned him. While we were talking, we heard the sound of gunfire. Running toward the noise, I saw the Union Jack fluttering above a wood.

THE STORY IS CONTINUED BY THE DOCTOR

After most of our piratical crew had gone ashore, I decided to explore with one of the loyal men. Not very far from the shore, we came on a stockade enclosing a stout log-house. Inside the house was a spring. I at once determined that this was the safest place for us. Hurrying back to the ship, I gathered together those of us who were loyal, and we quickly stored a boat with provisions. One of the mutineers who had been left on board looked as if he could be persuaded to join us. We were able to add him to our band, and shoved off with a second boat-load of provisions. But the pirates had their guns ready now, and shot at us. Our boat sank under us a few feet from shore, and we had to flee to our stockade. We were pursued, and just as we came to the stockade Tom Redruth, the squire's old steward, was shot down. He died soon after we gained safety. We raised the Union Jack over our fort, and it was this which Jim saw as he came toward the sound of shots.

JIM HAWKINS RESUMES THE NARRATIVE

When Ben Gunn saw the flag he stopped. He told me that he would not go into the fort with me, but that I would know where to find him when I wished. A white thing in the hand and the words "Ben Gunn has reasons of his own" would be the signals he would recognize. He told me where he had a little boat hidden, and then he ran away. The next morning Silver came with a flag of truce and tried to get the chart with a promise of our safety, but he went away unsuccessful. Later in the day the pirates attacked the stockade. Captain Smollett was wounded and two of our men were killed, but when the battle was over there were only nine of the mutineers left.

Later in the day, the doctor went off to see Ben Gunn. I envied him his walk through the cool woods, and slipped out after him, though I knew I should not go. I wanted to find where Ben Gunn's boat was hidden. When I came to it I saw it was only a coracle made of goat-skin. Under cover of darkness, I manoeuvered her out to the *Hispaniola*. Only two men had been left on board her. Peering into the cabin window, I saw them with their hands on each other's throats. They were too drunk to know that I had cut the anchor-rope, and it was not until the ship began to move with the tide that they knew something was wrong, but they could do nothing. I lay down in my coracle and went to sleep, so tired was I, in spite of the danger I was in. When I awoke in the morning I was half a mile from the ship, which was moving drunkenly, as if no one was steering her. Suddenly a wind came up, and she skimmed before it. Down she bore on the coracle, and before I could think, my little craft had been run down, and I was clinging to the *Hispaniola's* boom.

Then I saw the two watchmen: one stretched out as stiff as a hand-spike; Israel Hands propped against the bulwarks, his face white as a candle. The deck was spattered with blood. To my astonishment, Hands was still alive. When I gave him brandy, he revived still further. We struck a bargain to beach the ship on North Inlet, on the opposite side of the island from the stockade. I did not entirely trust Hands, which was just as well, for when he did not know I was looking I saw him secrete a dirk. While I was busy guiding the ship into the inlet, he started toward me with the dirk, and I turned just in time to save myself. I clambered up the mast and seated myself on the cross-trees, but he climbed after me. I felt a blow, and I was pinned by the shoulder to the mast. In my surprise, the pistols with which I had been holding him at bay went off, and he plunged into the water. The *Hispaniola* ground into the sand. The schooner was free from buccaneers and ready for our own men to board. I made my way ashore and finally reached the block-house. Stumbling in the dark, I found myself in the midst of my enemies.

Silver told me that he had given my friends safe passage from the stockade in return for our provisions. He tried to make me join his party, but I refused, telling him that I had been the cause of all

the disasters which had befallen him. His crew wanted to kill me
at this, but he restrained them. They wanted to kill Silver too,
but by showing them the chart of the treasure, which Dr. Livesey
had given him, he regained his old power over them. I awakened in
the morning to find that Dr. Livesey had come to tend the
wounded men. Having a chance to talk with him privately, I told
him about the stranded ship. He was grateful to Silver for protecting me, and offered to help him if he could.

After breakfast we started to look for the treasure. We made
our way to Spyglass Hill and were ascending the slope when we
came upon a terrible sight—a human skeleton with only a few
shreds of clothing upon it. It lay in a most unnatural position, very
straight, its hands pointing over its head. We discovered that this
was one of the pointers from which we were to take compass
bearings. This grisly joke of Captain Flint did not cheer the men,
nor were they happy when they heard a thin, trembling voice
among the trees strike up:

> *"Fifteen men on a dead man's chest—*
> *Yo-ho-ho, and a bottle of rum!"*

I knew this was Ben Gunn, but the men thought it was a ghost,
and were dreadfully affected. Finally they were able to go on. At
last we came to a great excavation and found—that the treasure
had been lifted! In an instant the men had turned against Silver.
He and I faced them from one side of the pit. Just as they started
toward us, three musket-shots rang out of the thickets. Two men
fell dead, and the other three fled. The doctor, Gray, and Ben
Gunn joined us. It was they who had saved us.

The treasure was safe in Ben Gunn's cave, where he had taken
it, long before. The next morning we transported it to the *Hispaniola,* which we brought around to an anchorage near the cave.
Leaving the mutineers behind, we set sail for the nearest port in
South America. There Silver skipped ashore with a sack of guineas,
and we were glad to be well rid of him. We made a good cruise
home, and in due time reached Bristol. All of us had an ample
share of the treasure, and used it wisely or foolishly, according
to our natures.

THE RED LILY

By

Anatole France

ANATOLE FRANCE (*1844–1924*) the French critic and novelist
was born in Paris. His real name was Jacques Anatole
Thibaut. His father was a bookseller and the future author
acquired much reading from the wide range of books at his
disposal. But it was not until he was thirty-seven years old
that his first novel, *The Crime of Sylvester Bonnard,* was published. The book won immediate success, and Madame
Armand de Caillavet, a woman of wealth and intellectual
brilliance, now used her influence to induce him to work.
Novels, criticism, history, satire, and personal reminiscences
began to flow from his pen. Always an anti-clerical, France
later became a socialist, and gave his support to various
radical and progressive movements. He was a prominent de-
fender of Dreyfus. Anatole France is supreme as a literary
artist. His writing equals that of Voltaire, Rousseau, and
Renan. He was learned, witty, tolerant, skeptical, and possessed to the full the secret of charm. While he liked to
amuse with mischievous phrases, he never forgot that sorrow,
injustice, and uncertainties beset human life. In 1921 France
was awarded the Nobel Prize for Literature. He died at
Tours.

THERESE MARTIN-BELIÈME, beautiful, young, talented, married to a
distinguished French aristocrat with whom she has little more to
do than if he were a casual companion, is very popular in Parisian
society at the end of the nineteenth century. She attends all important social functions and the most important men and women
in France are regular guests at her home. One evening at her home,
Paul Vence, a distinguished young author, tells her that he has
been asking her for a long time to meet a friend of his, Dechartre,
a sculptor, and wants to set a definite time. Casually she says that

she is quite willing to meet the young man some time. Many of the wits and scholars of the day drop in to visit her and she forgets all about Dechartre. Before going to bed that night she sits before the fire thinking of her life. For two years she had been the mistress of Robert Le Menil. "I gave myself to him because he loved me," she muses. And that was the reason. She had found in him the sincerity for which she had always sought, but it was not sufficient. Life had very little meaning or purpose for her. "Ah," she says, "What I want is to be in love."

The next day she meets Robert and insists that he take her to a poor section of the city. She tells him of her friend, the poet, Choulette, who discovered a poor street-walker named Maria and since then has never left her. If Paul Vence is to be believed, Choulette has even gone so far as to try to resurrect an ancient Franciscan order which would revolve about Maria.

Vence at last brings Dechartre to Therese's home and she is rather pleased with his intelligence and sensitiveness. But she forgets about him and the company when some one casually remarks that Robert Le Menil is going away for a while to join some friends fox-hunting. For Robert had said nothing to her about it.

When she next visits Robert at the apartment he maintains for their meetings, she is petulant. He says that he meant to tell her but that he has not seen her since accepting the invitation. She pretends to accept his excuses but still feels a little offended. After leaving him she walks alone past Notre Dame and realizes that she is not really angry with Robert about the incident. It is just somehow as if he has not enough to offer her and it is time that their affair came to a close.

Suddenly she hears a familiar voice. It is Dechartre. They walk together for a while chatting casually and she notices that he seems very pleased to see her. She, too, is glad they met. He is a charming young man, she reflects. But she must return home. Abruptly she leaves him.

That evening she is dining alone with her husband. She tells him that her friend, the famous English poet, Miss Vivian Bell, has invited her to spend a month at Fiesole. The invitation was never received, though of course she knows that Miss Bell would be pleased to have her. She even says that Madame Marmet, a charming old lady who is a friend of hers, is going to accompany her. Madame Marmet was a very respectable companion and she knew that her husband could have no cause for complaint. She wonders why she felt moved to say these things but decides that she probably felt a need for change. Vence comes to see her and tells her that Choulette is going to Italy also and that the two ladies might enjoy traveling with him.

Everything is arranged quickly. Madame Marmet, Therese, and Choulette travel to Italy and, when they reach Fiesole, they are met by Vivian Bell, who is overjoyed at seeing her old friend once more. The ladies go to stay with Miss Bell and are presented to her admirer, Prince Albertinelli, an Italian Adonis made human by a straight black beard. Therese is a little startled to learn that Dechartre is in Fiesole, having followed her, and that he will call very soon.

When Dechartre arrives Therese is delighted with him. They visit churches and museums together and take occasional walks in the garden. She discovers in him an imagination richly endowed, a brilliant mind, and a charm that becomes increasingly difficult to resist. She thinks unhappily of Robert, knowing that her affair with him is terminated, but fearful lest she hurt him. He had written her, asking why she went away without a word to him, afraid that in some way he had offended her. She writes an evasive answer.

Finally what she has been expecting momentarily happens. Dechartre tells her that he loves her, that he cannot live without her, that he must have her. She does not want anything more than a friendship at the time, although she realizes that she cares more for him than she has ever cared for any one. He says that, if he does not have her, he cannot tell what will happen to him. Therese knows that she is only happy in his presence and that if anything happened to him she could never forgive herself. So she yields to him and writes Robert a letter in which she is still evasive and vague but in which she says sufficient for him to guess what has happened, certainly sufficient for him to know that anything that had existed between Therese and himself is over for ever.

Florence is gay at holiday time and the red lily, which is Florence's emblem, seems to Therese to be the emblem of her feeling for Dechartre. Before she can fully taste her new-found happiness she is startled by a letter from Robert. He is at a hotel in the city and wants her to come there immediately. When she arrives he reproaches her with having left him in Paris and asks her what has happened that has made her treat him in such a manner. From her words he guesses that she has a new lover and strikes her. He is so unhappy at losing her that, had he a pistol, he would certainly have shot her. She wants him to be friendly to her but that seems impossible. At last she leaves him, the memory of his bitter words ringing in her ears. Quickly she goes to Dechartre's apartment and flings herself in his arms. Now she knows that she is fully in love and, for the first time, is madly happy with him.

The next day she receives a note from Robert to the effect that he is leaving for Paris and would like to see her at the station. When she meets him at the station he is still bitter and, as he turns away from her angrily, Vivian Bell and Albertinelli, who are driving past, see her and stop so they can take her home for dinner. Choulette and Dechartre are dining with them that evening and to Therese's chagrin, Vivian innocently comments that she had recognized Robert Le Menil as the young man at the station to whom Therese was talking. Dechartre obviously begins to sulk and, in saying good-night, does not even press Therese's hand.

When Therese goes to see Dechartre the next day she finds him upset. He asks her about the man at the station and she says that it was a meeting of no consequence. Then she speaks with perfect frankness: she has not asked him about his past, why should he worry about hers? If he is afraid that she does not love him, he is wrong. More than that, she has never loved before. To dispel his anguish she gives herself to him as she has never given herself to any one before. Yet she sees that he is still unhappy. Suddenly her eyes fill with tears. He comments on it and she says: "Forgive me, dear. It is the first time I have loved and been really loved. I am afraid."

She had to return to Paris. Her husband, Count Martin, was clamoring for her return in each letter. Besides it was becoming dangerous to meet Dechartre anywhere but in a very large city; it was too easy to be recognized here. As soon as she reached Paris she wrote her lover long letters. She knew more fully now what he meant to her. She lived only for him. He must return to the city at once. The day of his return she spent a few brief moments alone with him. When she left him, she said: "Jacques, my beloved, we are too happy; we are stealing life."

For over six weeks Therese was ecstatically happy. Jacques Dechartre was all that she had ever wanted of life. But then something happened which upset her. She received a letter from Jacques telling her that he had heard her name coupled with that of Robert Le Menil. Since then he has not known a moment's peace. He thinks that perhaps when she is not with him she is in the arms of this other man. Therese is obsessed with only one thought. She must not lose Dechartre. She writes him at once, saying that she has not even seen Le Menil since that evening at the station in Florence. She loves him and him alone. Having written the letter Therese knows there is more that she must do. She must see him at once.

When she reaches Dechartre's home she finds him at work, pale and unhappy. She reassures him again and at last the pain leaves his face and he permits himself to be soothed. He even comes to visit her and plays billiards with Count Martin, who becomes rather friendly.

One afternoon as she is going to see Jacques, Therese meets Robert, looking haggard and nervous. He says he must talk to her so she walks with him while he tells her that he had never known how much she meant to him. Now he understands that he does not want to live if he cannot have her. If she will take him back he will never mention what has happened and will do everything he can to make her happy. She replies that it is impossible for her to go back to him no matter what happens. He says that he had expected that answer but that he will not accept it yet. He wants her to think about his proposal for a while before she gives a final answer.

Miss Bell comes to Paris, bringing with her the news that she is soon to marry Prince Albertinelli. With Count Martin, Therese and Vivian attend the opera to hear "Faust." A new ministry is in the process of formation and all Parisian society is agog with speculation as to the possible members of the new cabinet. News comes to their box. Count Martin has been appointed Minister of Finance.

He excuses himself and goes to talk with a colleague. Dechartre comes and sits in the box with the two ladies. Their talk is interrupted by the entrance of Le Menil, who keeps talking to Therese. Dechartre becomes pale and leaves the box. As Robert holds her cloak for her, she sees Jacques watching her with sad, reproachful eyes, for he hears Robert murmur: "Every day, after three o'clock I shall be in our flat, Rue Spontini."

All night Therese suffers, thinking of the agony that must be in Dechartre's heart. With the early morning she hurries to his house but he is not at home. He did not return all night, the servant tells her. She waits, knowing that he must have been wandering through the lonely streets of Paris, tormented by what he thought her faithlessness. When he arrives she tries to explain what had happened. She tells him the truth: that she had been Robert's mistress; that her life had been empty; that since she had met Dechartre her life had become meaningful; that she had been and always would be thoroughly faithful to him, Jacques.

He remains inflexible; nothing can make him happy again; he does not believe her. She asks whether he would believe her if she killed herself. He says that he would not. Even if what she says were true, the thought that she had ever been to another what she was to him would prove unbearable. But she never has, she answers, she has never been to any man what she was to him. She flings herself into his arms and for a moment peace comes into his face. He embraces her wildly, then suddenly tears himself away.

"I no longer see you alone," he says. "The other is always with you."

"Silent, indignant, despairing, she looked at him. She rose, arranged her dress and her hair, with a feeling of shame that was new to her. Then, realizing that the end had come, she looked around her in astonishment, with eyes that saw nothing, and went out slowly."

THE RETURN OF THE NATIVE

By

Thomas Hardy

THOMAS HARDY (*1840–1928*) was an English poet and novelist. His early education was received at local schools which he supplemented by reading and studying at night while working as an architect. When he was 27 he forsook his profession for literature. His first accredited success was *Under the Greenwood Tree* which appeared when he was 32. *The Return of the Native,* considered by most critics as his masterpiece, appeared when he was 38. *Tess of the D'Urbervilles,* one of his best known works, provoked considerable criticism upon its publication. Hardy wrote many poems dealing with the World War and two volumes of these appeared subsequent to the war. He died at his birthplace after many years of prolific writing.

A SATURDAY AFTERNOON in November was approaching the time of twilight, and the vast tract of unenclosed wild known as Egdon Heath embrowned itself moment by moment. Only the white surface of the old Roman road remained clear, and along it, beside his wagon van, travelled a strange figure. He was young, and would have been good-looking, had not his face, his hands, and his clothes been dyed a peculiar red. Diggory Venn was by trade a reddleman, purveying to the farmers of the region the red ocher used for marking their sheep at fair time.

From time to time he looked into his van through a small window. Once a cry came from within, a cry from some one uneasy in the sleep of exhaustion. It was a young woman, whom he was bringing from a near-by town to her home on the heath. That morning she had gone away to be married. Now she was returning —unmarried.

It was chance that made the reddleman the one to help her home. But he himself had loved her and proposed to her two years before. She had refused, and later been courted and won by the local inn-keeper, Damon Wildeve, though not without interference. The girl's aunt and guardian, a wise woman and good to her niece, had a few months before forbidden the banns, believing the young man unworthy. Later, seeing the girl's heart was set, she gave way, but would not attend the wedding, to be held in another town. But alas, through pure accident, there was an error in the license, and the minister would not perform the ceremony. The embarrassed girl—Thomasin Yeobright was her name—hastened in modesty away from her lover and came home in the way we have described.

On the heath Diggory Venn discovered from a neighbor that the aunt had gone that evening to Wildeve's Inn, to welcome the supposedly married couple. There he took Thomasin, and there, unaware of the truth, came a gay party of friendly neighbors to wish the landlord happiness and be treated to a good round of mead. Wildeve preferred not to break the news, and it was not till the morrow that the facts were known, and many more things rumored.

While the mead was going round, the company gossipped of this and that, and especially of the bonfires kindled that evening on every hillock in England in memory—they thought—of Gunpowder Plot. Of a truth, the custom was pagan and went back into the dark of history.

One fire, they could see through the windows, was burning still, clear and steady. What they did not notice was Wildeve's excited interest in it. Nor did anyone know that, when all had gone, Wildeve crossed Egdon Heath to that place, and found there another girl waiting for him. None knew, that is, save a little lad whom she had hired to mind the fire, and who, hidden in the night, listened to their talk and learned they had been lovers before Tamsie had come into Wildeve's life. Tonight Eustacia Vye had heard, for word will travel, that Wildeve had not married Tamsie after all, and sure that it was because he really wanted his old love, had signalled to him as she had the year before on the same day, with a bright steady fire.

Half unwillingly, Wildeve had come. The truth was, he did not know which woman he wanted. Not a strong character, yet not definitely weak, he was sentimental to the extreme in preferring that which was denied him to that which was at hand.

Eustacia, he thought, had been easy. She had given herself to him; she had loved him; yet she had been difficult, too, turning away from him at unexpected times. Tamsie was pretty and good and innocent. She had to be won, and married, to be had. But she did not possess the fire and power that the dark beautiful Eustacia owned in abundance.

This particular meeting came to no definite conclusion, except an agreement to meet again on Rainbarrow, a near-by tumulus remaining from olden times, and where they had often been before. It was this, and that they had loved before, which the small boy reported to Diggory Venn the reddleman, whom he chanced to meet on his way.

Now Diggory, loving Thomasin so much he was willing to help her marry another if that would make her happy, managed to be on Rainbarrow when next the lovers met. Convinced of the truth through their conversation, he went to Eustacia the following morning to try to persuade her to give up Tamsie's betrothed. She replied haughtily that she would not, and at that moment she desired Wildeve with all her heart.

Yet she was fully aware that she enjoyed Wildeve as her lover only because she was bored with an empty life—she had come to the heath from the town, on the death of her parents, to live with her grandfather. She hated the heath, nay, though she walked it day or night in practical respects unafraid, she actually feared it as something utterly depressing and ugly, something that was ruining her life. She wanted love, a splendid romantic love, and she knew Wildeve satisfied her only because there was no greater man to be had.

Also, being an epicurean, she had no desire for that which was undesired of others. And so a few days later, when Wildeve announced to her that Thomasin had another suitor, whom Mrs. Yeobright might prefer to him, he immediately lost color in Eustacia's eyes and she told him he would have to wait before she could make up her mind about a new proposal he was making—that they two should go to America.

The other suitor was Diggory Venn, the reddleman, whom Mrs.

Yeobright actually felt to be beneath her Tamsie, though she liked him, and was using only as a bait to tempt Wildeve, whom she did not like, to a speedy marriage.

Going home that night, Eustacia felt that peculiar misery which attends the dawnings of reason in the latter days of an ill-judged, transient love; entering the door, she was greeted by her grandfather. "You have heard the Egdon news, Eustacia? Clym Yeobright is coming home for Christmas."

"Where has he been living all these years?"

"In that rookery of pomp and vanity, Paris."

Yes, Clym had lived in Paris. But he did not love it. He was a serious young man, and though his business was the unphilosophical one of a diamond merchant, he found time to read the sociological ethics of his day, the mid-nineteenth century. And what with the half-consciously imparted solid sense of values received from his mother (Thomasin's aunt) he found himself unhappy in a business that symbolized the cheapest and vainest of all human interests. He wanted to be a teacher—to found a school for the farm boys of his neighborhood and to hold night classes in his home for their elders.

So he had come home bringing all his books and eventually announcing to his startled mother what he planned. Annoyed at first with his "coming down in the world," Mrs. Yeobright soon realized he was choosing the better part, and was happy.

But not for long. It was inevitable that Eustacia Vye, who was not socially acquainted with the Yeobrights, should contrive to meet Clym, and inevitable that he should love her.

For was she not beautiful and cultivated, and rarely charming? She was of the stuff from which Greek goddesses, but not model women, are made. Had it been possible for the earth and mankind to be entirely in her grasp for awhile, few in the world would have noticed the change in government. There would have been the same inequality of lot, the same heaping up of favors here, of contumely there, the same generosity before justice, the same perpetual dilemmas, the same captious alternation of caresses and blows that we endure now.

Hitherto, this celestial imperiousness, love, wrath and fervor had found no scope in Egdon, and this limitation had biased her development. She was idle, unhappy, unreconciled, and at nineteen ready for any way out that might come. Still, she had too much dignity to be cheap and Wildeve had been her only lover.

But now—Clym Yeobright, and over his shoulder as it were, the lights of Paris! She loved him to distraction, for himself and for the future she thought was rising. Oh yes, he had told her of his plans, and she had told him she did not sympathize. Yet, she had added tenderly, marriage to him would be a gain to her whether they stayed or went. If she were only his wife, she secretly thought, she could bend his mind at length, and find herself deliciously happy in Paris.

Wildeve she had gladly sent to Thomasin upon Clym's arrival and those two were now married.

The only obstacle to Clym's marriage was the attitude of his mother. She did not know Eustacia personally, but she knew enough about her, and felt from the depths of her soul that this union could bring only sorrow. She pled and argued, and urged, to no avail. Greatly though Clym loved and admired his mother, he was utterly fascinated for the first time in his life by a beautiful woman, and maternal insight meant nothing to him.

Was not Eustacia sweet? And being sweet, would she not be his mate in every hoped-for way?

So they were married. Mrs. Yeobright did not attend the wedding, and the young couple and she did not visit each other thereafter. Yes—once the mother came, on an errand which only widened the rift. Through an error made by an unreliable county messenger, Thomasin had come into possession of money sent by Mrs. Yeobright to Clym. Mrs. Yeobright was told, mistakenly, that Tamsie's husband Wildeve had the money, and that he would probably give it to Eustacia. Knowing that Clym did *not* have it, the mother went to her daughter-in-law and without explanation of the tangle, asked her whether Wildeve had given her some money. The question meant one thing to the elder woman, quite another to the younger.

In violent rage, Eustacia voiced her resentment of the insult. Bitterly Mrs. Yeobright responded, and they parted in unforgiving hate. Ironically, it so happened that Eustacia had planned that very morning to pay her mother-in-law a friendly visit.

Clym, coming later to hear of it, was saddened and worried, but felt this one evil in his life would somehow in time be got rid of. Cheerfully he bestirred himself to get on with his proposed new work, and took to his books.

For Eustacia this meant added unhappiness and dejection. Cut off from friendly association with Clym's family, who were almost her only social equals in Egdon, and certain now that he would not go to Paris, she saw only a black world, lightened, to be sure, with Clym's love for her and hers for him.

Daily Clym read and studied, hour after hour, and into the small hours of the night, and as fate would have it, developed an eye-strain, which the surgeon pronounced sufficiently serious to require months of remaining in a darkened room. Eustacia stood by loyally enough, comforting him and reading to him, but her mind was darkly mournful with the thought that he might go blind and thus keep her in the status of a constant sacrifice to his needs, with no tiniest prospect left of escaping this lonely bleak heath for Paris.

Her next immediate hurt came from an unexpected direction. Clym, able now to go abroad in twilight, but not to read, came upon a neighbor cutting turf. "If," said Humphrey in sympathy, "yours was low-class work like mine, your condition would not interfere with it."

That put an idea into Clym's head. He was too good a philosopher to despise any kind of work, low or high, and being weary of doing nothing, physically strong and having no particular wealth either, he decided to become for the time being a turf-cutter. To Eustacia, the idea was a positive horror, and the more so because her husband was so unreasonably cheerful about what to her cried aloud as social failure.

Unmoved by her protests, he got him the necessary tools and went to work.

A few days later, Eustacia said to him, "You can sing at your turf-cutting, for me there is nothing but depression. I will lighten my gloom this afternoon by going to dance at the village picnic." Clym grew painfully jealous. Yet he let her go, and would not come himself.

When she arrived at the dancing green, there appeared some

promise of delight or satisfaction in her adventure, for she knew no one there. Resignedly she stood on the outskirts, watching others dance. It was the cool of the evening, and would soon be dark.

Suddenly she heard her name whispered by a voice over her shoulder, and she flushed to her temples. For it was Wildeve. He murmured, "Do you like dancing as much as ever? Then dance with me."

It was dark, and she wore a veil; there were many strange couples there, and no one would make invidious inquiries. Without pleasure, but welcoming the change, she accepted his offer. Fairly launched, however, into the ceaseless glides and whirls of the dance, her feelings began to change, a new vitality entered her form. Moonlight and motion became an intoxicant. And Wildeve? Signing the marriage register with Thomasin and hearing of Eustacia's marriage had had, for a man of his nature, the single effect of making a return to his first and lost love compulsory. And now she was in his arms.

Yet Wildeve was a gentleman. The dance over, he made no moves toward greater intimacy. He inquired after her husband and tenderly commiserated with her over her misfortunes, then accompanied her on her way. They parted when they heard others approaching. But Venn the reddleman had seen them. Later, he learned from Thomasin that Wildeve was frequently away of evenings, and made it his business to keep an eye on him, and if possible make him remain at home with Thomasin. Watching Wildeve, he discovered that while there was no real intrigue between him and Eustacia, there was the romantic ideal of an intrigue in the man's mind, for he had taken to climbing to her cottage, leaning over the gate, and going away sighing.

With this Venn interfered in a thoroughly practical manner by planning annoyances for Wildeve—tying a cord across his path and causing him to fall, frightening him with buck shot, and rapping loudly on one of the doors when Wildeve at last went so far as to make Eustacia aware of his presence. The enemy knew who was hounding him and was angrily thinking of taking measures. In the meantime Venn went to Mrs. Yeobright, who respected his good sense, and told her the whole story. She had not known of Clym's illness. How slowly news travelled before the era of the machine! Venn begged her to help both Clym and Thomasin by visiting at their respective homes, in spite of her hurt feelings. Her friendly and dignified presence would surely avert too obviously impending tragedies.

At length, she assented, and on the morrow actually set forth toward Clym's cottage. She was glad to go. Foolish son and alien woman though she thought them, the marriage was unalterable, and a reconciliation would in a measure lighten her unhappiness.

It was a cruelly hot day. Tender plants wilted in the morning, snug houses were unbearable prisons. Yet at eleven o'clock Mrs. Yeobright believed she could make her journey before the heat was really high. She realized her error when half way there, but now to return was as far as to come and she plodded on. Distressingly agitated, weary and unwell, she sat down to rest on a knoll not far from Clym's house. From there she saw her son in his furze-cutter's outfit go home and enter his own door. She could not know that he was planning to go to her house that afternoon! Later another man approached the house, hesitantly as though he had no business there. He finally went in. This turn annoyed her at first, for she had hoped to find her son and his wife alone, but a moment's thought showed her that the presence of a stranger would make matters easier at the start.

She came down the hill and entered the garden.

Within the cottage, could she have seen, Clym lay sound asleep on the hearth-rug. In the adjoining room, Wildeve and Eustacia were talking.

Why had Wildeve come? Just to see Eustacia. He had calculated on meeting her and her husband in an ordinary manner, chatting a little while, and leaving.

Now he was sympathizing with the wife who had said, "My husband reminds me of the Apostle Paul. He is as grand in character. But the worst of it is, though Paul was excellent as a man in the Bible he would hardly have done in real life. . . . And do I desire unreasonably much in wanting what is called life—music, poetry, passion, war?"

There was no flirting between them; Damon, however, made clear that he still loved her. They stood musingly, when a knock

[234]

came to the door. Eustacia went to a window and looked out. Her color changed to red, and from that to extreme paleness. What did this visit mean? Mrs. Yeobright must not see Wildeve.

She motioned him to an adjoining apartment. At first she thought she would not open the door, then the knocking came again more loudly.

She and Wildeve heard Clym moving in the other room, and he uttered the word "Mother." Relieved that he himself would open the door, she guided Wildeve through the rear to a path down the garden. "One word more, Damon," she said. "This is your first visit here; let it be your last. Our being lovers won't do now. Good-bye."

He said he was satisfied, and left her. She walked in the garden for a few minutes, at last gathered courage to go in. To her astonishment, Clym lay as before, and his mother was not there. Eustacia opened the door and looked out. Nobody was to be seen.

Poor Mrs. Yeobright was at that moment following a path hidden from Eustacia by the shoulder of a hill. She was walking rapidly. Her eyes saw two things—Clym's turf hook at the door, and a woman's face at a window. "'Tis too much," she was crying. "Clym—how can he do it! He is at home; and yet he lets her shut the door against me."

If she had not hurried away so hastily—had she knocked once more! But anyone would have said it was fate.

A little boy—the very one who had tended Eustacia's fire and told the reddleman about her and Wildeve on November 5th—joined her on her path and to him she talked as one in a mesmeric sleep. "I have seen something terrible—a woman's face looking at me through a window pane. . . . Shut out! . . . Tell your mother you have seen a broken-hearted woman cast off by her son."

She grew too tired to go on. In a little patch of shepherd's thyme she lay down. The boy, uneasily as though he should not leave her, trotted along home.

In the cottage his mother had left in such anger and sorrow Clym had awakened. To Eustacia, he said, "I dreamed my mother came here. I must go and see her tonight." Worried and miserable, Eustacia begged that he let her go first, on the morrow, and talk with his mother before he saw her. Clym, however, was anxious, and entirely unaware of the day's events, told her he must go that very day.

So it happened that in the dark Clym stumbled upon someone groaning with pain in the path between his new home and his old, and bending discovered his mother ill and dying and even now unable to speak. Making her comfortable, he ran for the neighbors and had the surgeon summoned, but it was too late. She looked at Clym as though she knew him, and passed away. In the very moment that followed, a little boy appeared in the light and cried shrilly to his own mother who stood beside the dead, "That woman asleep there walked along with me today; and she said I was to say that I had seed her, and she was a broken-hearted woman and cast off by her son."

For Clym it was too much. He drew from the words only their obvious meaning that he had deserted his mother for Eustacia, nevertheless remorse took complete possession of him, he grew light-headed of a fever and for a month was confined to his bed. Eustacia nursed and comforted him, conscience-struck, miserable, aware that she must some time tell him the truth that at this stage in his illness would kill him. She was doubly sick in her mind, for fate had twisted events so as to send Wildeve a goodly fortune from a deceased uncle; and he would gladly have shared it with Eustacia.

After nearly two months, Clym was able to go safely about. By chance, he heard from a neighbor that his mother had been seen going toward his house in the morning that thirty-first of August, and from Venn the reddleman he learned of their conversation on the night previous. There was certainly a mystery about it, and frantic to get the truth, though he had no hint of how terrible it would prove to be, he hit on the idea of talking further to the small boy who had accompanied his mother. From the child's lips came the awful words: "She was walking away from your house. She said there was no worse thing to see than a woman's face looking out at you through a window pane. . . . And I seed the woman looking, too. And I seed the other man go in after you went in."

Eustacia, twisting her black hair in front of the mirror, heard her husband come in, and without turning saw his face reflected, and knew that he had been told. He named her murderess, described her as a devil who had held his happiness in the hollow of her hand and dashed it down. He cried for the name of the man who had been with her, and Eustacia, timid on the surface but daring and defiant at heart, refused to answer. Why, she thought, should she defend herself? Yet finally she volunteered this much, that she could clear herself of half by speaking, if he were not too much a mad man to believe her?

She went out of the house at last. Walking unsteadily to her grandfather Vye's and there finding a kind of comfort. She had been gone but a few minutes when a messenger came to Clym, saying that Thomasin had been delivered of a baby, to be named Eustacia Clementine.

"What a mockery!" said Clym. "This unhappy marriage of mine to be perpetuated in that child's name!"

Eustacia, when she lived at home as a maiden had had as a devoted admirer a servant of her grandfather's, a youth, to whom she was a bright and heavenly being. Now that she had come back ill and forlorn, this boy found ways to please her, and she appreciated his tenderness and thanked him. Once he caught her looking too hungrily at her grandfather's pistols, and on the pretext of cleaning them, locked them away. A few days after her return the fifth of November, bon-fire day, came round once more, and Charley, knowing she had in other years delighted in the fires, thought to surprise her with a beautiful pile of the best wood. For half an hour it burned before she saw it, and when she discovered it, she begged him to put it out, relenting, however, when she saw the disappointment in his face, and thinking that if Wildeve had seen it, it was too late now to do anything.

He had seen it, and he came.

She explained, and he believed her, that the signal was not of her doing. Racked with sobs, she told him how her not letting in Clym's mother was the cause of this worst of her troubles, and in sincere sympathy Wildeve offered to do for her anything she was willing to propose. She suggested that he could help her to Budmouth, from whence she could sail alone to France. It was agreed that if she made up her mind, she would signal him at the stroke of eight, and crossing the heath alone, meet him near his Inn at midnight.

Yeobright, in the meantime, had moved to Bloom's-End, his mother's home, and there he spent his time in physical labor that formed a screen between him and despair; and hoped that Eustacia would return to him. On the evening of November 5th he went to see Thomasin and her husband. Finding his cousin alone, he told her (she had heard no word of it) that he and Eustacia were separated, and why. He suppressed all mention of Wildeve's part in it. Thomasin, feeling he had been unduly cruel to Eustacia, urged him to communicate with her, and at last he agreed to take the first step, and returning home, wrote a letter to Eustacia.

In it he begged her to return—he had been too severe—he would listen to whatever she had to say—he himself now was absorbed in nothing but justifying her.

Hoping she would come of her own will, he waited a whole day and sent the letter on the evening of the sixth. It came to her grandfather's hand, who, going with it to Eustacia's room, found it dark and thinking she slept, carried the letter below and placed it on the mantelpiece. She would find it in the morning. At eleven o'clock he went to bed himself. A little later he heard her moving down the hall and disturbed by the sound of weeping, called to her. There was no answer.

Yes, Eustacia was gone into the night, stealing through bitter wind and sudden furious rain across the heath that she feared and hated to Wildeve. She had made up her mind, signalled him and been answered. But now, thinking miserably of all her circumstances, the dreadful realization came to her that she had no money to live in Paris and could ask none of Wildeve without letting him accompany her, and for this she had no will. The last ray of hope went out from her, she felt the wings of her soul finally broken by the cruel obstructiveness of all about her. Slowly she went on.

At this hour Yeobright was sitting wakeful in his house, wishing she would come. He heard light footsteps and a plaintive female voice—surely—it was she! No. In indescribable disappointment he saw it was Thomasin with her baby—Thomasin in despair, telling him she thought her husband was running away from her. A few moments later old Captain Vye appeared, and told his fears. An elopement, or worse. He had found out about the pistols.

Clym left hastily for Wildeve's place, leaving Thomasin behind.

For her, however, suspense was worse than recrossing the heath, which to her since she was a very practical person, had no evil meaning, as it did for Eustacia. Indeed, to-night it held a friend, for as she picked her way she suddenly found herself at the encampment of Diggory Venn, who hurried with her.

With horse and gig, one of its lamps lit to show the location to Eustacia, Wildeve was waiting two or three hundred yards below the Inn. Over the din of the weather rose the greater noise of the roaring of a ten-hatch weir a little beyond where he stood. Would Eustacia come in the storm? "Poor thing! 'tis like her ill-luck," he murmured.

At this moment a footstep approached. "Eustacia?" said Wildeve. But the person came into the light, and he saw it to be Clym. Hidden in the dark, Wildeve hoped his rival, now loitering uncertainly and looking at the gig, would go.

While they both hung thus in hesitation a dull sound became audible above the wind. Its origin was unmistakable—it was the fall of a body into the stream adjoining, apparently at a point near the weir.

Both men understood. They hastened to the weir, with a lamp from the gig for light, and suddenly Wildeve beheld a dark body slowly borne on one of the backward currents of the weirpool. Without showing sufficient presence of mind even to remove his great-coat, he leaped into the boiling hole. Yeobright sprang into a shallower part of the pool and waded toward the deeper portion, where he perceived Wildeve struggling.

It was Venn and Thomasin who discovered them and summoned help. Three unconscious bodies were carried into the Inn, and of these only one ever breathed again. It was Clym. Late that night, he summoned Venn and the lad Charley to look at the dead. So quiet he was, they thought him resigned. But at last, with a wild smile, he spoke, "She is the second woman I have killed this year. I was a great cause of my mother's death; and I am the chief cause of hers . . . I spoke cruel words to her and she left my house."

In vain they reasoned with him. There was only one truth that he could see, and it would have been an easier one to bear, if in the months and years that followed he could have found anyone to agree with him and blame him.

He did sometimes indeed think he had been ill-used by fortune. But that he and his had been sarcastically and pitilessly handled by a wanton universe he could not for long maintain. It is usually so with men. Human beings, in their generous endeavor to construct a hypothesis that shall not degrade a First Cause, have always hesitated to conceive a dominant power of lower moral quality than their own; and, even while they sit down and weep by the waters of Babylon, invent excuses for the oppression which prompts their tears.

For Clym, there was only one thing worth doing now—becoming an itinerant preacher and carrying moral lessons and words of common wisdom to all who would hear him, on hillock or in lecture hall, on heath or in town. Men differed in what they thought of his words. But everywhere he was kindly received, for the story of his life had become generally known.

Thomasin, who was a practical and normal child of nature, was gradually purged of her grief, as time would never purge Clym of his. When Diggory Venn appeared to her after months of absence as white as other men, and with a substantial farm to which to bring a wife, her heart opened to him and she and little Eustacia Clementine found home.

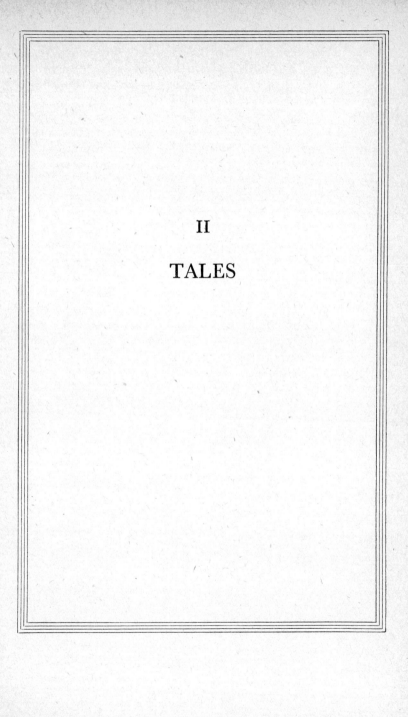

II

TALES

THE ODYSSEY

By

Homer

HOMER is the traditional author of the Greek epic poems, the
Iliad and the *Odyssey*. There is nothing definitely known
about Homer and some scholars even attribute his works as
the output of more than one man. His birthplace is claimed
by a number of cities and the time of his birth has been
ascribed as somewhere between 1100 and 850 B.C. The *Odyssey*
covers 24 books. The exciting and surprising experiences of
Odysseus during his wanderings after the ten years' siege of
Troy, the systematic mythology of the poems, the profusion
of detail, their literary art and poetical diction render the
Odyssey among the world's greatest literature.

AFTER THE CITY OF TROY had fallen to the Greeks and peace had been
established by many deaths, the Greek heroes returned to their
homes. But one, the crafty Odysseus, after many adventures, had
been taken captive by the nymph Calypso, who loved him and refused to let him depart from her island of Ogygia. And Odysseus
yearned for his son, Telemachus, and for his wife, Penelope, who,
unknown to him, was now surrounded by suitors who occupied her
palace and clamored for her hand.

The time ordained by the Gods for Odysseus' departure comes
at last and the Gods meet on Olympus. Poseidon, enemy of
Odysseus, is absent, and Athena, Odysseus' friend, persuades Zeus
to send Hermes, messenger of the Gods, to Calypso to tell her she
must release her captive. Athena, herself, goes to Ithaca to see
Telemachus.

Arriving at the home of Odysseus, Athena enters in the guise of a
man, Mentes, who claims to know the master of the house. She
informs Telemachus that his father is still alive and counsels him

to bid the suitors return to their homes and to urge his mother to return to her father's house. There, if she desires to wed again, let her announce her choice and prepare the marriage feast. Then let Telemachus set sail for the home of one of his father's companions-in-arms, Nestor, or Menelaus, to discover if they can give him news of his father. Having given this advice, Athena returns to her own shape and vanishes.

Telemachus, having recognized the Goddess, is filled with hope and strength. He reproves his mother and summons the suitors to a council of notables of the island to determine whether or not the unwelcome visitors shall return to their homes. At the council Antinous and Eurynomus, two leaders of the suitors, start the attack on Telemachus. Antinous complains that Penelope had asked them to wait for her choice until she completed, on a huge loom she had set up, a winding-sheet for her husband's father, Laertes, against the day of his death. All day she would weave but at night she would undo her work. Now the suitors will be put off no longer. The argument is stilled by an omen of two eagles flying overhead and tearing furiously at each other. A soothsayer interprets this to mean the day of Odysseus' return is near at hand. Telemachus, finding support only in Mentor, his guardian in his father's absence, asks for a ship and crew. He meets with jeers and mockery.

Athena, disguised as Mentor, charters a galley and oarsmen. Telemachus, aided by his old nurse Eurycleia, gets ready the necessary provisions and, with the disguised Goddess beside him, sails from his home.

The voyagers arrive at length at Pylos, home of Nestor, who tells the tragic story of the death of Agamemnon and the horror that befell the house of Atreus. But of Odysseus he knows nothing since he sailed from Troy. Athena takes flight in the form of a sea-eagle and Telemachus travels by chariot to Sparta, the home of Menelaus.

The palace of Menelaus is the scene of a double wedding and Telemachus is entertained lavishly. Helen, over whom the Trojan War was waged, recognizes him, and Menelaus sadly tells him of his father's imprisonment on Ogygia, a tale he had learned from Proteus, an ancient sea-God, who tried to escape him by changing from one terrible form to another. Telemachus says he must return to his ship at Pylos.

When the absence of Telemachus is noticed at Ithaca, Antinous sets forth in a vessel to waylay him at the straits. Penelope weeps for her son but Athena sends her a dream assuring her of his safety.

There is another council of the Gods. Athena complains that Hermes has not yet been sent to Calypso and Zeus sends the messenger at last. Ogygia is wondrously beautiful but Odysseus has no eyes for it. He sits on the sea-beach, dreaming of home. There Calypso, having been given the message of Hermes, comes to give him the news which is all happiness to him and all pain to her.

Odysseus builds himself a ship and, with Calypso's directions, sails in great hope. Poseidon, God of the sea, is still Odysseus' bitter enemy and so the voyage is short-lived. A storm wrecks the bark and Odysseus saves his life by clinging to a spar. A sea-nymph, Ino, takes pity on his plight and gives him a scarf with a charm so potent that so long as he wears it his life is safe. As soon as he is ashore, however, he must cast it into the sea. On the third day after the shipwreck he lands on a strange island and falls asleep, exhausted, on a bed of leaves.

The island on which Odysseus is sleeping is the home of the Phaeacians, a sea-going people, and is named Scheria. The king, Alcinous, has a daughter, Nausicaa, who is troubled by a strange dream about a marriage, in which household stores of good linen are required. In the morning she sets forth with her maidens to the shore, that they may wash the family stock of linens which have been unused for a long time. After washing the linen they eat and play ball. The noise awakens Odysseus who covers himself with an olive bough and comes forth. He seems to Nausicaa the kind of man she wants for a husband and she brings him to the palace of her father.

Alcinous feeds and entertains the stranger and orders games in his honor. After being first coaxed and then abused, Odysseus demonstrates his abilities, putting the company to shame. Then the hero asks a minstrel to sing of the siege of Troy and of the great horse. The minstrel sings of the final stratagem of the Greeks: how they built a vast horse of wood, apparently as an offering to the Gods, then fired their camp and sailed away; how the Trojans dragged the great animal inside the walls; and how a company of Greeks, hidden in the belly of the creature, issued forth at nightfall to open the gates for their returned companions and with them to burn and pillage the proud city. And he sang that Odysseus had conceived the plan and led the closely-hid band. He it was also, who stormed the house of Deiphobus, who had taken Helen to wife after the death of his brother, Paris, and it was he who restored her to Menelaus. Tears are in Odysseus' eyes and Alcinous stops the minstrel. Why is it, he wants to know, that his guest weeps at the tale. And the answer comes: "I am Odysseus."

The whole story of his wanderings pours from Odysseus' lips. He and his companions had landed on the shores of Thrace and had plundered the town of the Ciconians. There they feasted till morning when they were surprised by a large body of the natives, who killed many of them. The remainder returned with their leader to the sea, where they were soon caught in a storm which carried them out of their course for ten days and landed them on the shores of a strange land, that of the Lotus-eaters. Many of Odysseus' company ate of the lotus and as a result were drugged into such forgetfulness and peace that they had to be carried by force to the galleys and there bound securely, for they would not leave.

The next stop was the island of the Cyclops, rude giants having but a single eye and that in the center of their foreheads. Odysseus and his crew set forth adventurously to explore the island, having no presentiment of the doom that awaited them. They found a huge cave with great stores of milk and cream and sat down to await the owner. That owner was a Cyclops named Polyphemus, a son of Poseidon, who, when he returned, imprisoned the adventurers and proceeded to devour them two at each meal. Fortunately, Odysseus had with him a skin of strong wine. This he presented to the giant who drained it and asked the name of the giver. Odysseus answered that he was known as Noman, whereon he received the promise that, since Noman had been so kind, Noman would be eaten last.

Overcome by the drink, Polyphemus slept soundly. Odysseus, meanwhile, hardened a pointed stick of olive-wood by charring it in the fire. Then he and his crew thrust it deep into the single eye of their captor. Blinded and screaming with pain, Polyphemus called for help. The neighboring Cyclops came quickly and asked him who was injuring him. To his answer of "Noman" they exclaimed in disgust and returned to their homes. Polyphemus rolled the huge stone from the door of his cave and permitted his sheep to go out, feeling among them for his captives who, he thought, would try thus to escape. But Odysseus outwitted him by placing the sheep three abreast and tying one of his companions under each middle sheep. Then, clinging to the wool of a huge ram, he made good his own escape. When the Greeks reached the safety of their vessels, Odysseus raised his voice in taunts and mockery of their enemy. Polyphemus hurled a rock which narrowly missed the ship. It was then that Odysseus boastingly told his name. And the blind giant invoked the vengeance of his father, Poseidon, on this Greek who had destroyed his sight forever.

The voyagers went on through seas of which they had never heard and, during their journey, became guests to Aeolus, King of the Winds. When they departed, Aeolus presented Odysseus with an ox-hide bound with a silver cord in which were all the winds, save only Zephyr who would waft them directly home. For nine days and nights they sped toward Ithaca, and during that time Odysseus never once relinquished the helm. At last they saw the rocky shores of their own home and, overcome with exhaustion, Odysseus fell asleep.

The ox-hide bag proved too much for the cupidity of the crew. Surely, they thought, it contained some rare treasure. They undid the silver cord; the winds rushed out and, at terrific speed, they were driven back to Aeolus. Vainly Odysseus pleaded for aid once more. The monarch of the storms said that the curse of the Gods must be on these Greeks and, with harsh words, drove them forth.

The next disaster was at the hands of the giant Laestrygonians, terrifying cannibals, who destroyed all the ships save the one with Odysseus aboard and speared the sailors as they swam for safety. Sailing with his one ship Odysseus reached the island of Aeaea, the home of Circe, daughter of the Sun. Here he sent Eurylochus, his lieutenant, with a portion of the crew, to explore the interior of the island. Deep in the woods was the palace of Circe, a building of marble and silver and gold. Circe herself welcomed them, offering them drugged wine. All but Eurylochus entered and accepted. When they had drunk she struck them with her wands and, though retaining their human senses, they took the form of swine. Eurylochus returned alone and told his leader of the strange happening. Odysseus immediately set forth to rescue his men, meeting, on his way to Circe's palace, the God Hermes, who gave him a wonderful root which had the power to ward off Circe's magic.

When Odysseus entered her home Circe treated him as she had his men but to no avail. Her enchantments were powerless. Thus she recognized him, for his coming had been foretold and, though he could resist her magic, Odysseus could not resist her lips. He sent for the remainder of his crew and dwelt for a year in the halls of Circe, utterly forgetful of Penelope.

Urged by his comrades to remember the shores of Ithaca, Odysseus finally asked Circe to liberate his men and permit them all to depart. With great reluctance she consented, warning him of dangers in his path and telling him that, if he would learn his future, he must seek the Realm of the Dead, and there speak to the shade of Tiresias, the great seer.

So Odysseus traveled on to the land of the Cimmerians who dwell in continual darkness, in a region skirting the realms of Hades. He reached the spot where the rivers Acheron and Cocytus mix at the entrance to Hades. Here he killed a black ram and ewe and spilled their blood into a trench he had dug. Immediately the shadows of the dead rushed forth, lured by the scent of blood. But Odysseus knew that he must not let them slake their thirst with the fresh blood till he evoked the shade of Tiresias. On the arrival of the prophet, Odysseus learned of the future. The flocks of the Sun were pasturing on the coast of Sicily. If he and his companions injured them, he alone would escape and would return home after long suffering. If they did not harm the herds they would soon see Ithaca.

Then the shade of Odysseus' mother, after drinking of the blood, told her son that she had died of grief and that his father, Laertes, was still living in memories and bitterness. The shades of Agamemnon and of Achilles also spoke to their erstwhile companion telling him, one of the faithlessness of Clytaemnestra, and the other of the dark, joyless life of Hades.

The ghosts crowded about Odysseus, thousands on thousands of them, and the hero, for once losing heart, fled to his ship and sailed in haste. With great care he and his men approached the island where the Sirens, twin sisters, lured mariners to their death by the spell of their song. Having been warned by Circe, Odysseus stopped up his crew's ears with wax and had them bind him to the mast, enjoining them not to release him, madly as he might act. As they came within hearing the song made Odysseus strain and tug at his bonds but they held fast.

On they went to the strait that divides Sicily from Italy, where, on one side was the monster, Scylla, and on the other the no less horrible Charybdis. Six of the crew were destroyed but the rest escaped, thanks to the instructions of Circe.

At length the seafarers reached the land where the oxen of the Sun were pastured. Vainly Odysseus urged them to press on; the men were weary and wanted to rest ashore. Eurylochus spurred them to the verge of mutiny and Odysseus reluctantly gave consent, but only after making them swear that none should harm the sacred oxen. They still had sufficient of the corn and wine that Circe had given them and no further food was necessary. But bad weather forbade them putting forth for a month, by which time their store of food was exhausted and they were forced to resort to catching fish and snaring birds. One day, while Odysseus was asleep, Eurylochus persuaded the men to slay some of the oxen and feast on them. The meat groaned aloud while on the spits and the skins crawled after the blasphemers. The Sun, in terrible rage, threatened that unless the sacrilege were avenged, He would never again light the heavens but would retire to Hades.

Zeus undertook the punishment of the mariners. As soon as they put to sea a great storm tossed them about and finally the vessel was shattered by a thunderbolt. Odysseus, in accordance with the prophecy, was the sole survivor. Clinging to the broken mast he barely escaped Charybdis, and after floating for nine days, was cast ashore on Ogygia where Calypso detained him until Athena's intercession won him a pardon from Zeus.

So the tale Odysseus tells is at an end and he begs to be permitted to depart from Ithaca. The Phaeacians load him with gifts and set him aboard a galley which leaves in the evening and arrives in the morning at Ithaca. On reaching their destination the crew carry the sleeping hero ashore and leave him under an olive-tree with his presents heaped beside him. Athena spreads a mist over the island in order that he shall not recognize it and then appears before him in the guise of a shepherd. After listening to his elaborate invention of the manner in which he came to this island, she discloses her identity and tells him of the situation in Ithaca. To keep him from being recognized she touches him with her wand and instantly the majestic Odysseus is an old beggar clad in filthy rags.

Thus disguised he seeks out his swineherd, Eumaeus, himself of noble birth, who acts as a kind of overseer for his absent master. He does not recognize his own prince in the beggar who comes as guest, but he entertains him well, telling him of the plight of Penelope and of the absence of Odysseus. Let not the beggar, like so many others, pretend to bring tidings of his lord merely to earn some reward. The old man tells a fanciful story of his adventures, saying that he knew Odysseus, had even fought by his side. And he will wager that Odysseus will return. Eumaeus is not so hopeful and listens sceptically but he gives his guest warm covering and a place by the fire.

In the meantime Telemachus has been entertained so well by Menelaus and Helen that he has stayed with them a month. Athena comes to him in a dream admonishing him for such delay and telling him that Penelope is being hard pressed, especially by Eurymachus, one of the wealthiest of the suitors. Startled into action, Telemachus and his young friend, Pisistratus, prepare to leave the next day. At their departure an eagle flies overhead with a white goose in her talons. Helen interprets the omen to mean that Odysseus is coming from afar to wreak a terrible vengeance.

The young men embark at Pylos and sail to a sheltered bay whence Telemachus proceeds on foot to the lodge of Eumaeus in order to avoid the ambush which he knows awaits him. The swineherd greets his young lord with great affection and Odysseus with difficulty refrains from discovering himself. Telemachus sends Eumaeus to assure Penelope of his safe return. As soon as father and son are alone Athena appears, unseen of Telemachus, and bids Odysseus make himself known. The rags fall to the ground, royal robes clothe him, and Odysseus is once more his imposing self. For awhile they are overcome by emotion and neither can speak of himself. Then they tell their stories and conspire to discover who, of the entire household, will aid them to slay the suitors, for Odysseus will be content with nothing less.

Telemachus proceeds alone to the palace where the suitors receive him with feigned courtesy. Eumaeus follows with Odysseus, who is once more in the semblance of the aged beggar. Although the disguise hides Odysseus from mortal eyes his old dog, Argus, recognizes him at once, bringing tears to his master's eyes by his fidelity. The last effort to reach his master is too much for him and Argus dies. Entering the hall, Odysseus begs some food from each suitor, none being so hard of heart as to refuse, except Antinous, who hurls a stool at the beggar. This is so gross a violation of Greek hospitality as to draw a rebuke from another of the suitors.

A brawny beggar, Irus, appears and threatens to drive Odysseus from the hall. With one great blow Odysseus breaks his rival's jaw and drags him out into the courtyard. The revellers mockingly present the victor with a prize of mince-meat and blood. One of them, Amphinomus, speaks kindly to him and Odysseus is moved at the fate which lies in store for this gentle young man.

Penelope, descending to the hall, speaks to the beggar, who tells her that her husband is on his way to Ithaca. Grateful for such news she orders the visitor to be taken to the bath and to be treated with great courtesy. He refuses, however, all attendance but that of old Eurycleia. While bathing his feet the aged nurse recognizes her master by an old scar made by a boar's tusk. Odysseus stifles her scream of surprise and swears her to silence.

The next day is a festival of Apollo. In the midst of high revelry the suitors continue to make sport of the supposed beggar. Grim portents of the doom which awaits the revellers are in evidence but pass unheeded save by the seer Theoclymenus. He warns the guests but they jeer at him, saying he is as unwelcome as the beggar. The queen descends, carrying the bow of Odysseus, which he had left behind. Her lord, she says, was wont to drive an arrow through the hollow rings of twelve axe-heads set in a straight line. If any of the suitors can perform the feat, she will choose him for her husband. The rivals try but none can even bend the bow. Then Odysseus, laughed at by the company, picks up the bow and sends a shaft directly to the chosen mark.

The time for vengeance is at hand. The rags fall from him and Odysseus, king of Ithaca, drives an arrow through the neck of Antinous. With Telemachus, Eumaeus, and another retainer, the hero fights his assembled enemies and slays them all. Then he hunts out the mistresses of the suitors among the serving-women and hangs them. Vengeance has been done and Odysseus is satisfied.

Penelope had returned to her chamber but, on being informed of the battle by Eurycleia, she hastens down stairs. Years of waiting and hearing false rumors of her husband have made her sceptical and she is not sure she recognizes Odysseus. So he bathes and, attired in the splendor Athena had put on him at Phaeacia, returns to her presence. He is, in all respects of appearance, just as he was when he left for Troy twenty years before. Now his wife knows his features but fears that this may be some God disguised as Odysseus. She bids the nurse bring her lord his own bed from what was their bridal chamber. But the bed is formed from the stem of an olive-tree, rooted and alive, and hence cannot be moved. Odysseus meets the test easily by answering that no one could move that bed. Penelope, hesitant no longer, takes him in her arms and they retire to their chamber, telling each other of the last twenty years.

In the end Odysseus makes himself known to his father and, quelling a rebellion, resumes his reign over Ithaca, again a peaceful and a happy land.

TROILUS AND CRISEYDE

By

Geoffrey Chaucer

GEOFFREY CHAUCER (*?1340–1400*) who is accredited as the first great English poet was the son of a London vintner. He served his youth in the army and at court. Little is known about him prior to 1367 after which his name occurs frequently in public documents. He rose to the rank of squire in the King's household and was dispatched on several important foreign missions in Europe. He was elected to Parliament in 1382 and held other important government posts until political vicissitudes reduced him. He was buried in that part of Westminster Abbey which afterwards became Poets' Corner. He did not particularly distinguish himself among his contemporaries in prose but he rose far above them in verse and by inventing the seven-line stanza and the heroic couplet later employed by Dryden, Pope and others. Among his more famous works are *Canterbury Tales*, *Troylus and Cryseyde* and the *Assembly of Foules*.

BEFORE I part from you, it is my purpose to tell the double sorrow that befell Troilus, Priam's son. His adventures in love changed from woe to joy and back to grief again for Criseyde forsook him ere she died.

Within the walls of ancient Troy there dwelt an astrologer, Calkas by name, who served the god Apollo. So expert was he in his art that he knew when the city was to be destroyed and what miseries the Greeks would inflict upon the people, but he kept his own counsel. Quietly one night he stole away to their camp where he was well received for they thought that he would advise them of the perils to be dreaded within the city.

At home he left his daughter, Criseyde, blissfully unconscious of her father's treachery. When she learned the truth, she feared for her life, for her fellow-citizens had sworn to burn all the traitor's kinsmen, both skin and bones. She was a widow and in all the city there was none so fair. Indeed so angelic was her natural beauty that she seemed like one immortal. Hector, alone, could stay the people's wrath so clad in brown samite she fell upon her knees before him and with piteous voice weeping bitterly, begged for mercy.

"Let your father answer for his own misdeeds," he said. "You may dwell with us here in Troy as long as you like. Your body shall be saved and men shall treat you with the honor that is your due."

With an humble heart she thanked him and returned home in silence. All respected and loved her.

The war continued, but the Greeks failed to conquer Troy for within the city the sacred Palladium protected them. In April when the fields were green and fragrant with spring flowers, the grateful Trojans held a feast in its honor. To the temple clad in their best array they came, and Criseyde in her black widow's garb was among them. So great was her beauty that she seemed like a bright star, and their hearts rejoiced. Yet she was meek in manner and near the doorway stood alone. There the valiant Troilus found her.

He had always laughed at those who fall under love's sway. He had come with his young knights merely to see the sights and smiled whenever one of them sought some particular lady. His heart was free, but when he beheld Criseyde, he stood speechless. Blessed be love that thus can folks convert! His eyes roamed about the temple, but always they sought her form and rested there as long as the service lasted. Then, amazed at himself, repenting his former scoffing, he left the temple and sought his own palace.

In the mirror of his mind she lived constantly. To be with her became his one desire, to have her before he died. Yet he despaired that this should ever be and in the thick of the fight fought so fiercely that the Greeks dreaded him. He could neither sleep nor eat, but this he pretended was due to an illness, not love, that tortured him. At times, alone, he sang songs in praise of her, then fearing she might never love him, threw himself upon his bed and groaned in pain. Perhaps she had cared too much for someone else. It was thus his friend, Pandarus, found him.

"Alas," he said, "who causes you all this misery? Is some Greek girl to blame or is this remorse of conscience? Have you failed in some devotion?"

In vain he questioned, suggested possible ladies, implored him to disclose his sorrow, but still he lay there like one dead.

"Criseyde is my love!" at length he said.

Pandarus rejoiced for the lady was his niece, gracious, wise and gentle. He would be of service to them both. Troilus in gratitude would have fallen upon his knees, but his friend prevented him and went his way pondering over the matter. Exultant now, the prince mounted his bay steed and rushed into battle where he fought like a lion. Woe to the Greek who met him that day! In his own city so gracious was his manner that all who gazed upon him loved him. He became the friendliest of men, dead were his cruel gibes, gone his lofty manner.

In May, the happy, fertile month when flowers bloom, when every meadow is fragrant and the sun's beams are bright, Pandarus found himself the victim of love's keen arrows. His color changed, he tossed upon his bed. Now, indeed, he was in the mood to plead for Troilus. Early one morning a twittering swallow woke him, and he set forth upon his mission.

He found Criseyde sitting with two friends while a maiden read aloud to them "The Siege of Thebes." Joyously she set a bench for him.

"Is the book of love?" he asked. "Oh, that you might teach me some good!"

"Uncle, your mistress is not here. This romance is of Thebes, and we have heard how King Laius died at the hands of Oedipus, his son."

"Drop the book then. All this I know myself," he said. "Take away your head-dress and let me see your face. Come, let us dance for it is May."

"God forbid! Is that a widow's life? You must be mad. It is more fitting that I should seek a cave and profit by the lives of saints. Dancing is for maidens and young wives."

"I could tell you something that would change your mind," he said.

Her curiosity aroused, she plied him with questions. At last she asked how Hector was.

"Very well, thank God, although he has a little wound in his arm. His brother, Troilus, is well, too. In *him* every virtue lies, all truth and gentleness, wisdom, honor and worthiness."

She was always glad to learn when valor in arms was combined with moral virtue.

Pandarus dwelt upon his friend's bravery. He was the death of the Greeks, shield and life for the Trojans. He loved her, he whispered, and unless she helped him, he would die. In that event her uncle would stab himself. She was merely to be kind to him, not soil her honor in any way. Love for love was reasonable reward.

Criseyde was amazed. It was strange advice for an uncle to give. She didn't want their deaths upon her hands, yet neither would she give herself easily. How had he learned of his friend's plight?

"She who stood in black hath wounded me to my heart's core," Pandarus had heard him cry out in his sleep, had seen him groaning upon his bed.

With this he left. Criseyde sat as still as any stone; she pitied the man. Men began to cry in the street, "See Troilus has put the Greeks to rout! He rides this way to his palace."

She flung the lattice open wide. This Troilus sat on his bay steed, heavily armed except for his head. His wounded horse began to bleed. In twenty places his shield was bruised with swords and maces. There was the mark of many an arrow, too.

The people cried, "Here comes our joy, after his brother, the protector of Troy."

He reddened slightly. His modesty softened Criseyde's heart.

"Who gave me drink?" she said and drew back quickly.

What was best to do? Now her heart was warm, now it was cold. All around the town men loved women, and were they any the worse for it? Quite the contrary. Yet idle tongues would gossip. No doubt he loved her, for she was beautiful, she knew, neither jealous nor shrewish. Even so he might be unfaithful; men were wont to seek new pastures, and where then would be her peace of mind?

At length she rose and went into the garden where her nieces joined her. Arm in arm they strolled along the shaded paths while Antigone, the beautiful, sang a Trojan love song. Its message sank into her heart.

Soon the sun went westward, for his course was run, light faded and the stars appeared. A nightingale, perched on a green cedar bough outside her window, sang clearly in the moonlight. Was his song of love? So lulled, she fell into a deep sleep wherein she dreamed a white eagle set his claws upon her breast and tore her heart out, but in its stead, he placed his own and flew away.

The next day a letter arrived from Troilus beseeching her pity. It was bathed in his tears and delivered by Pandarus who had so instructed him. Daily thereafter similar missives came and according to her answers, her lover was happy or miserable. Day by day his desire increased.

Finally the wary uncle concocted a scheme to bring them together. The false Poliphetes, he pretended, had plotted to bring a law suit against Criseyde. Prominent Trojans, she among them, would meet at the house of Deiphebus, Troilus' favorite brother, to beseech the hero's help for her. He himself was to counterfeit illness when he arrived so that all would be forced to interview him privately in a little room.

It followed as Pandarus had planned. Criseyde, all innocent of his wiles, waited until last to plead her cause.

Then her uncle whispered, "Consider this poor man's plight. Have mercy on him. Why should you fear wagging tongues?"

Did not Troilus hearing them think, "Oh, Lord, right now my destiny approaches! Am I to die or be comforted and yet, what shall I say?"

"Sir, it is Pandarus and I," she said. "Alas, I cannot kneel to do you honor. I have come to thank you for past favors and to beg their continuance."

Troilus, ashamed to answer her, raised himself, and she laid her soft hands upon him. Then he found his tongue. He would be hers until death, would take his own life if it would make her happy; she need only be friendly to him; his whole desire was to serve her.

"Although you are a king's son," she said, "I will not forbear to be angry with you if you do wrong, but while you serve me, I will cherish you as you deserve."

Then she took him in her arms and kissed him. Upon his recovery they would meet at Pandarus' house.

Joy now filled Troilus' heart. All day he fought bravely, but for a part of each night, he thought how he might best serve his lady. They met secretly, but always the fear of prying eyes terminated their visits. Yet he stood so well in his lady's grace that twenty thousand times she thanked God she had met him. To her he was a wall of steel and shield from every displeasure.

One night Pandarus arranged a dinner party at his house. Troilus arrived secretly and concealed himself in a little room where he might watch Criseyde among her friends. When the time to leave arrived, a great storm had arisen, and she was forced to stay the night. The wily uncle induced her to sleep in a little inner room, her women in an outer chamber to be near should she want them.

When all was hushed, Pandarus came to her. "Niece, dear," he whispered, "Troilus has come in all this rain to be with you. He is miserable for a friend has told him that you love one Horaste."

"Horaste, I know him not. Tomorrow I will go and tell him so."

"Tomorrow? He is miserable tonight. Lie still and I will bring him to you."

Troilus, tongue-tied, soon stood beside her. She blushed at his sudden coming, but when he sought to kneel, bade him sit on the side of her bed. Pandarus drew near the fire and pretended to read an old romance.

"It is foolish to let jealousy wreck our happiness," she said. "I love you alone. Criseyde never was untrue to Troilus in thought or deed."

Tears filled her eyes. He cursed himself for coming there, fell upon his knees beside her and swooned. Pandarus, angered by his mouse's heart, tore off his outer clothing and tossed him into bed beside her. Then he upbraided Criseyde. As a woman she should know what to do. Then he left the room.

She noticed her lover's trembling hands, the perspiration on his brow and kissing him tenderly, drew him to her. He stroked her small arms, her back, her sides, her snowy throat, her small, round breasts. A thousand times he kissed her, and she gave herself to him.

"You are my love," he said, "the fairest and the best. How may I ever deserve your thanks, may I never displease you and always I'll be true."

Rings they exchanged and Criseyde pinned upon his shirt a gold and azure brooch in which there was a ruby set like a heart. All too soon day came; the cock crew, the messenger of light. Lest they should be discovered, they parted then, Troilus to seek his own palace, she to await her uncle.

Frequently thereafter, they met thus at Pandarus' house, but the nights were all too short. They called day traitor, envious and worse. So generous and kind did her love make Troilus that his honor spread throughout the world even to the gates of heaven. In battle except for Hector, he was most valorous. The Greeks continued to dread him; this increased boldness came to him from love. In time of truce he hawking went or hunting for wild boar, bear or lions, and often when he returned to town, she greeted him from her window.

But this joy was not destined to last for long, for one day Hector with spear in hand and big bow bent, set out to attack the Greeks. Fiercely they fought, but the Trojans fared the worse. Antenor, Monestes, Santippe, Sarpedon and Polynestor among others were captured. A truce was called to arrange for the exchange of prisoners.

To the Greek council, old Calkas invited himself. For his services to them, he begged that they exchange Antenor for his daughter, Criseyde. It was agreed, and under guard, ambassadors set out for Troy.

Troilus was present at the conference when they arrived, and his heart sank when he heard the strange request, but he made no protest, for he must first consult her.

"Sirs, she is no prisoner," Hector said. "We do not sell women."

Not so thought the other members of the parliament. "Give up Criseyde," they cried, "and deliver Antenor to us."

Thus Hector's objections were overruled. In despair Troilus sought his palace. Like a dead image, pale and wan, he sat down by the side of his bed. Then suddenly he charged about the chamber like a bull beating his breast with clenched fists, dashing his head against the wall. He cursed the day he was born. He would be lost without her.

When Pandarus found him thus, he pitied him and wept in sympathy, but said, "Since you've had your desire, it ought to suffice. The city is full of ladies, fairer than any twelve of her. If she be lost, we shall find another. New love always chases out the old."

"How is it then you suffer from love's pangs yourself if it's so easy to change to another woman?"

"Make her your slave then and keep her here," Pandarus advised.

Troilus would not agree to this, neither could he ask his father for her hand in marriage, for Priam had given his word to exchange her and would not retract it. Neither could he snatch her away from the city without her consent. Perhaps it would be best to consult her.

Meanwhile the news had already reached her ears. A group of friendly women came to visit her. It would be so fine to see her father again, she might even be able to make peace between the two camps. Tears streamed down her cheeks. Her body sat among them, but her thoughts were with Troilus. She wept, she said, because she hated to part from them.

When they had gone, she sought her bed and sobbed bitterly. How was she to live without him! There Pandarus found her.

"Troilus is coming to you tonight," he said. "Women are wiser than men. Perhaps you can think of some way to remedy his misery."

When he came, they clung to each other for a moment speechless. Criseyde begged him to intercede for her and fainted. He kissed her cold mouth, then thinking her dead, unsheathed his sword to slay himself. Just then she awoke. They would spend this last night in each other's arms.

"Within a week or two I'll return to you," she comforted. "I must go since parliament has ordered it, but since it is a time of truce, you'll hear from me every day. My father wants me only because he thinks I am being persecuted here. Peace is near at hand. Any day Helen may be returned and then I'll come back to you. There's another possibility. Men are bought with gold. I'll take all my movable goods to my father and say it is sent from two friends here in the city, and he is to send back for more since the town is to be taken. I, alone, may return for this huge quantity. I'll so enchant him that he'll think his soul's in heaven. His calculating and Apollo's will avail nothing. I'll convince him that the gods speak in ambiguities and for one truth, tell twenty lies."

Hope rose in Troilus' heart, but sank again. Her father was too wise to be swayed thus. Instead he'd try to persuade her to marry some Greek. It would be better to take what wealth they had and go away together. When that was gone, he had friends elsewhere who would help them.

"That would mean only suffering for you," she counselled. "What would they say about you here in Troy where you are needed? If you go now, you will never be able to return when peace is made. They would say you were driven to me by lust, not love, and coward fear. Your honor would be lost forever. And what would they say of me? Trust me, sweetheart. Before ten days are gone, unless death assails me, I'll be with you again. Only be true to me."

Troilus was not convinced, but he kissed her many times, and they lay clasped in each other's arms until day dawned. Then he left the chamber, but he felt as though his soul had been torn from his body.

Truly men never know the grief that women suffer. Her heart was bleeding with sorrow, as led by Diomede, she rode through the city gates. Troilus, too, with many knights accompanied her.

"Why do I suffer? Why do I not rouse myself?" he thought.

It would be simple enough to slay Diomede, to steal her away, but in the ensuing struggle she might be slain. Silently they rode through the valley until at last Antenor appeared. Troilus pretended to be glad to see him, and his heart was light. Upon Criseyde he looked pityingly, drew near to take her hand and she began to weep.

Softly he said, "Keep your spirits up and do not let me die."

Then without speaking to Diomede, he turned back toward the city.

On they rode in silence and the Greek, noticing her beauty as well as her woe decided to make the most of his opportunities. It would not do to speak of love just then, but he assured her that his people would treat her well. He himself would be glad to serve her, she might think of him as a brother. Knights would strive for her hand, but, as his tent was near her father's, she might call upon him at any time.

His words fell on deaf ears. She thought her heart would break, and when her father appeared in the distance, she sank down upon her horse. When they reached the camp, the old man kissed her twenty times. She said she was glad to see him, but could not smile.

Meanwhile Troilus had reached the city where despair seized him again. He knew he would die without Criseyde and sent for Pandarus to arrange his funeral. All but his heart was to be burned, but that should be sent to her in a golden urn.

"It is foolish to mourn thus," his friend admonished. "Other men have suffered; time cures everything. In ten days she'll come again. Let us pass the time at Sarpedon's where there is music, feasts and fair ladies."

He went but amid the crowd, he sought only Criseyde. He wondered how she was faring, re-read her old letters. Within his mind he saw her form, her womanhood and recalled every word and deed that had passed between them.

When the week was over, they bade their host farewell and turned their horses' heads toward home. Troilus sang as they rode toward the palace, but Pandarus' heart sank. He doubted that she'd ever be able to return.

Early the next morning Troilus sought her palace. Perhaps in the interim she had already returned, but every window was barred. Mournfully he re-visited the temple where he'd first seen her, the homes of mutual friends, even the city gate. He would walk upon the walls and gaze toward the Greek camp. The days and nights were longer than they used to be, but at last the tenth day dawned.

On Criseyde's hands, time hung heavily too. It was impossible to get her father's permission to return to Troy. She thought of stealing away at night, but dared not lest she be captured as a spy or worse still, ravished by some man who might see her. Her face became pale; her body thin, all day she looked toward Troy; the nights she spent weeping. She recalled his words to her but dared not show her misery. Why had she not run away with him? The very next night she would go to him, would risk being captured, but two months passed and she did not go.

It was Diomede who changed her mind. With all the tricks that he could muster, he set out to capture her heart. On the tenth day pretending he had business with the old man, he came to Calkas' tent. Criseyde welcomed him, bade him be seated and brought forth wine and spices. Soon they were engaged in conversation. He spoke of the war, asked her opinion of the Greeks, why her father had waited so long to wed her to some worthy man. The city of Troy was doomed, no one would escape alive. To save her from this fate, her father had sent for her. In some Greek she would find a more perfect love than any Trojan could give her. Would she consider him? His voice trembled as he said it, he would come on the morrow to tell her of his grief.

Next day to his pleas she answered, "Oh, Diomede, I love the place where I was born. May God protect it! I loved my husband until his death, but never any other. I know of your worth but do not desire love from anyone, but if I should care for any Greek, it would be you."

Undismayed Diomede continued to press his suit, and at length when she realized there was no chance of seeing Troilus again, she gave him her hand. To him, too, she gave the bay steed upon which she had ridden from Troy, the brooch that had belonged to Troilus and her sleeve for a token. Men say, but not I, that she gave her heart. She was so sorry for what she did that I do not condemn her.

In Troy on that same tenth day with Pandarus for company, Troilus stood upon the walls. Each person in the distance seemed to be she. Perhaps he had miscalculated the time, so for several days thereafter he kept his vigil. Jealousy seized him at last; he neither ate nor drank and forsook the company of friends. One day he dreamed that as he walked through the forest, he saw a boar with great tusks, and clasped in his arms was Criseyde asleep. To Pandarus, the boar was old Calkas; to the wise, Cas-

sandra, Diomede, the descendant of that Meleager who had slain
the great Calydonian monster.

Unconvinced the weary Troilus wrote to her again and again.
Always her answers were the same. She loved him best, he should
always remember that. She would come as soon as possible but
could not say when. In these promises he found further proof of
her infidelity, but he blamed Calkas, not her. He would disguise
himself as a pilgrim and go to her, but discovery would be certain.

His woes increased; Achilles killed the noble Hector. At length
one day he learned the truth. Deiphebus paraded through the
streets a coat that he had captured from Diomede. When Troilus
saw it, his heart went cold, for on the collar was his brooch. She
might have spared him that.

"Who can trust others any more?" he wailed. "Never would I
have believed it of you, Criseyde. I know now that you have cast
me clean out of your mind and yet I cannot for all this world
unlove you a quarter of a day. May God grant that I may meet
this Diomede, and truly I'll make his sides bleed."

Such is the world. In everyone's life there is little heart's ease.
God grant that we may take it as it comes.

Often the two men met, but though they clashed their bloody
swords, stood trial with spears and beat upon each other's helmets,
fortune was determined that neither should fall by the other's
hand. Thousands of Greeks Troilus killed without mercy, and at
last was himself slain by Achilles.

His light spirit floated up to heaven where he beheld the wandering stars and listened to the music of the spheres. Far below
he saw this little spot of earth embraced by the sea. There he
saw the two who wept most for him, but he laughed at their
sorrow for he now despised this wretched world and all its vanity.
Forth at last he went to the place where Mercury told him to
dwell.

THE AENEID

By

Virgil

PUBLIUS VERGILIUS MARO VIRGIL (*70–19* B.C.) was a celebrated
Latin poet who became one of the endowed court-poets
gathered around the prime-minister Maecenas. In 37 B.C. a
collection of ten pastorals entitled *Eclogues* were published
and the prime-minister aided him to achieve affluent circumstances. Virgil lived in a villa at Naples where he worked on
his *Art of Husbandry* which appeared in 30 B.C., and confirmed his position as the foremost poet of his day and age.
The remaining eleven years of his life were devoted to the
composition of his *Aeneid* which is accredited as one of the
classics of all literature.

AENEAS, son of Anchises and the goddess, Venus, was one of the
greatest heroes in the defense of Troy against the Greeks. When
the Greeks departed he rejoiced, happy that the years of strife
were ended. A large wooden horse was left behind and this the
Trojans wanted to take within the walls of their city. Laocoon, a
prophet, warned them against doing this and struck the horse
with his spear. Later two huge serpents came from the sea and
crushed Laocoon and his two sons to death. Interpreting this as a
sign that the horse was sacred, the Trojans took it within the city.

That night a Greek who had been left behind, opened a secret
door in the horse's side and Odysseus and armed followers came
forth. They swung wide the gates and the army of Agamemnon,
which had secretly returned, poured into Troy. Aeneas was asleep
when the shade of dead Hector appeared before him and told
him the city was being sacked. Hector told him to flee with his
family and followers. This he did but in the flight he lost his
wife, Creusa.

The first land they visited was Thrace and Aeneas, mindful of a prophecy that he would found a kingdom in Hyperia, began to lay the foundations of a city. When he learned that Polydorus, a son of Priam, had been killed by treachery in this place he decided, however, to leave a land stained with such a crime. An oracle informed him to seek the land whence his forefathers had come and old Anchises, seeking to remember old legends said he thought the land was Crete. Thither they repaired but pestilence came on them. The tutelary deities of Troy appeared to Aeneas in a dream and told him that Crete was not Hesperia. That ancient land was now called Italy and it was there that he would found a mighty empire. And once more the Trojans set sail.

On their journey the Trojan heroes met Andromache, wife of the slain Hector, who was now wife of one of Hector's brothers, Helenus, who, taken as a slave, had succeeded to the throne when his master died. Helenus predicted long journeys and great trials for his kinsmen, loaded them with presents, and let them depart.

Jupiter, king of the gods, promised his daughter, Venus, that her son, Aeneas would yet found a mighty kingdom and that his son, Ascanius, would lay the foundations of Rome, a city where she would be worshipped as the patron goddess.

Juno persuaded Aeolus, god of the winds to loose a storm upon the Trojans, whom she hated, for the judgment of Paris had gone against her when he pronounced Venus the fairest of the goddesses. Neptune, however, saved the ships and they landed on the shores of Carthage, a new city founded by Dido, who had fled from Tyre, where she had met with treachery. Dido, beautiful as Diana, gave them welcome and told them to rest themselves in Carthage.

Carthage was dedicated to Juno and a city where Juno reigned was cause for anxiety to Venus. She carried off Ascanius and bade her son, Cupid, take his form and, when he was near Dido, infuse his venom in her veins, that she should love Aeneas and thus insure him against any harm. This Cupid did; and Dido was so inflamed for Aeneas that she made him repeat all his adventures and, when all the company had retired, she found she could not sleep. With the first rays of morning the queen summoned to her presence her sister, who was her confidante in all matters, and told her of her affection for Aeneas. She had pledged lifelong devotion to her dead husband but was tempted now to break her vow for the sake of the Trojan hero.

Anna, Dido's sister, was sure that fidelity was no comfort to the dead. Besides Aeneas was a great warrior and could aid to build up a great empire. Dido was happy with this advice which was so like her own real desires. Juno, aware of what Venus had done, proposed to her that they unite Dido and Aeneas. She knew that, if Aeneas left Carthage, he was destined to found a nation that would some day overthrow this city of hers. Venus pretended to acquiesce and it was decided that a hunting-party the next day would be the occasion for the mortals to declare their love.

Scarce had the hunt begun when a storm broke and the hunters sought refuge. Dido and Aeneas, under Juno's guidance, found shelter together in a cave. There, tempted by Dido's beauty, Aeneas uttered words of love to which the ardent maid readily responded. The news of the intended alliance spread quickly and reached the ears of Iarbas, king over the Getulians, who had long been a suitor for Dido's hand. He was a son of Jupiter, to whom he diligently offered worship. Now he prayed to his father to stop the wedding. Jupiter heard and sent Mercury with a message to Aeneas to leave for Italy at once.

As soon as the Trojan chief received the heavenly message his passion for Dido vanished and he was anxious to be on his way. The queen pleaded with him but he was resolute. When his ships had departed, Dido caused a funeral pyre to be prepared and, mounting it, stabbed herself to death with a sword Aeneas had left behind.

Again the ships of the Trojans were halted by a storm and Aeneas decided to stop at King Acestes' land, where his father had died before his countrymen went on to Carthage. Once landed they played many games of skill and strength to break the monotony of their travels. While the games were in progress Juno caused the women of the voyagers to become so dissatisfied with the constant traveling that, in a frenzy, they burned all but four of the ships. The men fell to work to construct others and, nothing daunted, proceeded on their way, leaving some of their companions and most of the women behind them.

The heroes proceeded to the Cumaean Sibyl to inquire of her their fate. She foretold many trials but eventual success. Then Aeneas asked her to instruct him how to enter into Hades that he might hold converse with the shade of his father. The Sibyl accompanied him into the lower regions, warning him first that he would find it difficult to escape. There the hero saw the shade of Dido, who gazed at him with inexorable hatred and would not speak to him. Finally he reached the Elysian fields where he encountered his father's shade. When they had spoken of their love for each other, Anchises showed his son something of what the future was destined to bring about. The land that Aeneas would found was to have a long succession of heroes, the souls of whom Aeneas was permitted to see, even to his great descendant, Julius Caesar, and his, Caesar's, successor, Augustus.

With the aid of the Sibyl, Aeneas made his way out of the lower regions and embarked once more. At last his ships came to Italy and sailed on the river Tiber. The country of Latium at this time was under the rule of King Latinus, whose misfortune it was that the only son who had been born to him had died in the bloom of youth and so his beautiful daughter, Lavinia, was successor to his throne. Lavinia had many suitors, most noted of whom was Turnus, young king of the Rutuli. Turnus was brave and handsome and should, probably, have been already successful in his suit had not there been a number of signs that were interpreted to mean that Lavinia must never marry one of Italian birth. Latinus, seeking to understand the signs, repaired to the tomb of his father that he might ask the shade to prophesy concerning his daughter's future. Faunus, his father, addressed him while he slept under the trees nearby the tomb, telling him not to seek to marry Lavinia to an Italian but to wait till a foreigner came, who was destined to be his son-in-law. From this wedding a long line of mighty monarchs was destined to come, under whose sway would come the furthermost reaches of the world.

Aeneas, feeling now that his travels had come to an end, beached his ships and sent a hundred men as ambassadors to the king of the country to which they were come, to ask him if they could have land, on which they might settle and live in friendship with his people. The ambassadors pleaded thus with Latinus and he, bethinking himself of the oracle, was sure that the leader of these Trojans was the man ordained to marry Lavinia. Therefore he accepted their presents and bade them welcome and sent a magnificent chariot to fetch Aeneas.

Juno, seeing the success of the Trojans, desired to contrive some means of injuring them. She sent a Fury to Amata, wife of Latinus, a woman who had always favored the suit of Turnus for the hand of her daughter. The Fury, Alecto, so enraged Amata that she argued with her husband that the Trojans were pirates. When this failed to move him, she stole Lavinia from the palace and hid her, meantime inciting all the matrons in the town to anger. Alecto then excited Turnus to such an extent that he sent a message to King Latinus to expel the Trojans from the land or else prepare to battle with the Rutuli.

Alecto then prepared some further trouble for the men from Troy. Ascanius was out hunting and she directed his hounds in the path of a tame stag, kept as a pet by the daughter of the keeper of the king's herds. Ascanius wounded the stag who sought refuge in his master's stable. Sylvia, the daughter, seeing him wounded, cried out, and the neighboring rustics came forth with clubs to attack Ascanius. A group of Trojans, seeing the boy's peril, hastened to his side and, experienced warriors that they were, quickly routed the peasants, slaying two of the more important of them. The rustics complained bitterly to their king, as did Turnus, who arrived at the same time, but Latinus held firm to his belief that Aeneas was the man whose coming had been foretold.

Now all Italy was in arms and many chiefs sent men to aid Turnus, who was preparing to attack the Trojan strangers. A message was even sent to the great Greek hero, Diomedes, who had settled in Southern Italy, telling him that the Trojans were attempting to build another Troy in sunny Italy, and that they were preparing for a career of conquest.

In obedience to a dream, Aeneas traveled to a nearby colony of Greeks, who had been hostile to the Latins and asked an alliance with them. King Evander and his son, Pallas, greeted

Aeneas royally and promised him aid. They were not a numerous people, however, and could not be of great service to the Trojans. Nearby, Evander said, a great city of Lydians had been ruled by the tyrant, Mezentius, whom the people drove from the throne. He sought refuge with the Rutulians and the Lydians demanded that he be given up, preparing for war. An oracle had informed them that they would only be successful under a foreign chief and they had asked Evander to command their army. He was too old and would send Aeneas instead, sending with him Pallas and four hundred horsemen.

Aeneas rode forth with the Arcadians, for so these Greeks were called, and on the way Venus appeared, presenting him with armor that had specially been made for him by her husband, Vulcan.

In the meantime Juno informed Turnus that Aeneas and many soldiers were gone from his camp. Turnus immediately attacked the Trojans and lay siege to the camp. Nisus and Euryalus, two brave Trojans, sought to steal through the enemy lines to seek Aeneas, but they were killed, after they had slaughtered many, and their heads put on pikes.

The Trojans, anxious to engage the enemy, opened one of their gates and slaughtered those that came against them until Turnus himself came and drove them back. They closed the gate but Turnus was inside. Then they thought to kill him but, so great was the fury with which he attacked, that he killed many of them and escaped.

Juno and Venus both asked Jupiter for help and he, angry at their bickering, decreed that on that day he would help neither side.

Aeneas, returning with his allies, saw that his camp was besieged and hastened to the battle. When the troops landed Pallas proved himself a great warrior but, before the day was over, was slain by Turnus. Aeneas, great in grief, proved a lion in the fray. Juno, fearful for Turnus, contrived to trick him onto a boat which she then bore away. Aeneas meanwhile wrought havoc, slaying both Mezentius and his son.

On the next day a truce was declared but Turnus returned to his men and argued with Latinus to permit him to renew the

THE AENEID

battle. While he was fortifying the city, somewhat downcast because Diomedes had refused to aid him, he sent Camilla, the warrior queen of the Volscians, to engage the Trojans and their allies. This she did and was slain.

A second truce was made and Turnus proposed that the outcome of the war be decided in single combat between Aeneas and himself. The Trojan hero accepted but as they advanced to combat, the Rutulians broke the peace and the battle started once more. Aeneas, bareheaded, tried to stop his men when he was wounded by an enemy arrow and forced to retire. Turnus, now that Aeneas was no longer in the battle, drove all before him. Venus came down and healed her son, who returned to the fray, rallying his troops. He then decided on a bold stroke and attacked the city itself. Turnus came back swiftly and engaged the Trojan leader in combat.

After a fierce fight Turnus shattered his weapon on the invincible armor that Vulcan had made. Thereupon he fled, as Hector had fled Achilles' wrath, years before. When Aeneas overtook him he was about to spare the life of his enemy when he saw that Turnus wore the gold-studded belt of Pallas, young son of Evander. Then, bethinking himself of his friend, Aeneas raised high his sword and stained it with the life-blood of Turnus.

THE DIVINE COMEDY

By

Dante Alighieri

DANTE ALIGHIERI (*1265–1321*) the Italian poet is considered one of the greatest writers of all time. He was born in Florence of a middle-class family that had been ennobled. He was an observant student and became proficient in languages, theology, painting and music. It is said that the future poet first met his love Beatrice when he was nine years old. When civil war raged in Italy he inclined toward the side that eventually lost and while he was absent on a mission to the Pope his house was burned to the ground and he was banished from Florence. His life then became involved in mystery as he roamed from town to town until 1314 when he went to Ravenna to stay with a friend at whose house he died suddenly of a fever. His *Divina Commedia* is universally esteemed as one of the greatest epics in any language, ancient or modern. He also left a collection of sonnets and short poems, as well as works on lexicography and government.

INFERNO

IN THE MIDDLE of his mortal life, the poet finds himself lost in a dark wood, where he wanders all night until at dawn he reaches the foot of a mountain. This he would fain ascend but his way is blocked by a leopard, a lion and a she-wolf. As he turns back into the wood he meets the dead poet Virgil, who offers to lead him out of the wilderness until a worthier guide in the form of Beatrice appears to lead him higher. Dante doubts his ability to make the journey through the other world but Virgil encourages him and the two, ancient Pagan and modern Christian poets, set forth. When they arrive at the gates of Hell, Dante balks at the inscription over the door—"all hope abandon ye who enter here," but he lets Virgil lead him into a place where cries of lamentation bring tears to Dante's eyes. The cries are from those who are so indifferent to both good and evil that both Heaven and Hell despise them. When they arrive at the first river of Hell, an earthquake rumbles and Dante falls down unconscious.

Upon awakening from his swooning, Dante finds himself on the farther shore of the river, Acheron, on the edge of the great gulf of Hell. Following Virgil, Dante descends into Limbo where he encounters those who are excluded from Paradise solely because they had not been baptized, and must spend eternity in sighing over their fate. Here, also, in a vast expanse of light they meet four poets, Homer and Horace, Ovid and Lucan, who welcome them and reveal to them certain great spirits of antiquity— Electra, Hector and Aeneas; Socrates, Plato and Democritus; Euclid, Seneca, Hippocrates and various others.

From the tranquillity of Limbo, or the first circle, the two poets proceed to the second where they meet the carnal sinners like Paolo and Francesca, the story of whose love makes Dante faint for pity. When the poet comes to his senses he is in the third circle where, lying in mud under a storm of hail, snow and dirty water, are the gluttons. The fourth circle reveals Pluto, ancient god of riches, in whose realm both the avaricious and prodigal are suffering the same punishment, which consists in rolling heavy weights halfway round the circle where, after they have clashed, must be rolled around again to the other side. Now through a gorge where runs a boiling river which stagnates in the marsh, Styx, are found the angry ones; beneath it are the sullen. The shore of the Styx forms the fifth circle where Phlegyas, the ferryman, comes with his boat to convey them across. On their trip they are met by a spirit smeared with mud who seizes their boat but is pushed back into the wallow. Now appears the city of Dis at whose gate a host of fallen angels would let Virgil pass but would prevent the presumptuous Dante from entering.

Dante is perplexed at and alarmed by this but regains his composure after Virgil tells him that he has travelled this way before. Still outside the gate, they are threatened by three hellish furies but a heavenly messenger dispatches them and opens the gate and they are now within the sixth circle. Here are found the heretics who are shut in prison-houses or tombs wrapped in flames. Crossing this circle, they come to the edge of an abyss from which foul vapors rise causing them to retreat and giving Virgil an opportunity to discourse upon the various divisions of Hell and the sins which are punished therein. The seventh Hell, which they now enter, has three belts, the first marked by a river of blood, the second by a lugubrious forest, the third by a desert of scorching sand. After they have crossed the plain of sand, Dante meets certain of his Florentine acquaintances and converses with them about the past. Then they encounter Geryon, symbolic of fraud, as well as those who have practiced this in the form of usury.

The eighth circle is called that of the Evil Pits of which there are ten. The first pit, in which the damned all naked are lashed by horned demons, contains the panders and seducers. In the third, with their heads buried downwards in large holes, are those who practiced simony. The fourth pit contains sorcerers, witches and others who endeavored to pry into the future and who are now doomed to walk backwards with their faces twisted round. In the fifth pit, filled with boiling pitch, are the swindlers and thieves generally for which demons with hooks are on the lookout for such as may raise their heads above the surface of the fiery flood, an operation carried on with so much infernal rivalry that two of the demons fall into the flood.

The two poets barely escape these fiends and make their way into the sixth pit where they find the hypocrites whose punishment it is to keep pacing about in mantles made of lead gilded on the outside. Dante is about to engage in conversation two jolly friars of Bologna when his eyes catch a vision of Caiaphas and Annas who lie naked and crucified across the pathway where they are trodden under foot by all who pass by. It is with much difficulty that Dante makes his exit from this sixth pit, since the rock bridges had been broken down, but Virgil lifts him from rock to rock until he is able to mount the bridge leading to the seventh pit which, ridden with a legion of monstrous serpents, provides punishments for common thieves. Among these Dante meets five of his fellow-citizens from Florence, two of whom have been changed into horrid reptiles. Now ghastly changes take place as another of the five is transformed into a snake, another into a kind of lizard, each exchanging form and substance with the others.

Now on jutting stones as stairs the two poets ascend from this pit of horror to the eighth where they come upon certain Pagan spirits combined and concealed in one flame of fire expiating for their evil counsels to men. In a double flame, containing Diomede and Ulysses, the latter relates in brief the long story of his wanderings. In another flame which now glints forth Dante sees a Ghibelline warrior who is being punished for giving false counsel to the Pope. As this flame floats away Dante and his guide make their way along the cliff to the bridge over the ninth pit in which are plunged souls guilty of sowing discord among mortals, like Mahomet and Bertrand de Born who made Prince Henry of England rebel against his father, King Henry the Second.

Since the allotted time for the journey through Hell is waning, Dante and Virgil clamber up to the tenth bridge spanning the last pit in which as in a vast and vile lazar-house and covered with loathsome scabs are pretenders of various sorts—alchemists and a certain man from Arezzo who pretended that, like Daedalus, he could fly through the air. Here, also, disguised by various diseases like dropsy and scurvy, as well as by amputations, are falsifiers of various sorts. Sinon, the treacherous Greek, and Potiphar's wife are enveloped in a fever that seems as it were a cloud of smoke. Dante and his guide are now out of the eighth circle, Malebolge, with its ten pits and are able to pass on to a deep well, the ninth circle, from which towers seem to rise, but these prove to be giants buried up to their navels in the well. These are Nimrod, who built the tower of Babel; Ephialtes, the Titan who threatened the gods; Briareus, the measureless one; and Antaeus, who lifted the poets and then set them down in the bottom of the well, and they are now in the deepest, darkest circle of Hell.

Here in a hole almost indescribable by mortal tongue, Dante beholds one solid lake of ice wherein traitors are locked fast. To his horror, the poet beholds a single hole in which one of the fiends chews upon the other's scalp where the nape is joined with the brain. Lifting his mouth from such a ghastly meal and wiping it on the other's hair, the vile offender announces himself as Count

Ugolino, his victim as Archbishop Ruggieri. Wholly imprisoned beneath the ice are those who have betrayed their friends, and here are also the souls of living traitors which in the very act of betrayal have descended into this place, leaving the body on earth to the control of a fiend for the rest of the villain's life.

In the last ring of the ninth circle, among the wretched traitors to benefactors, is Satan himself frozen fast up to his waist at the very centre of the universe. The satanic countenance presents three faces in which the six eyes are weeping bitterly while in the three mouths he is champing on the arch-betrayers of history—Judas Iscariot, whose head is inside the maw, his legs dangling outside; Brutus, hanging from the black jowl of the Devil; and Cassius, also. As they depart from the infernal abode, Dante looks back and is thunder-struck to behold Satan with his head downward in the ice, his feet thrust high in the air just as he had fallen headlong from Heaven. Now through a passage hidden from sight but discerned by the sound of a gentle rill descending through it, Dante and his guide regain the world of light where their eyes behold anew the stars.

PURGATORIO

Now issuing from the dead air that had afflicted eyes and heart, Dante with his guide beside him beholds the planet Venus and the four stars of the southern sky which man had not seen since the Fall, when he was banished to a northern clime. Gazing north-ward, the poet beholds Cato with the rays of the four stars, the four moral virtues, adorning his venerable countenance. Cato, learning that Dante is no shade but a living being, consents to help him in his journey through ante-Purgatory, but bids Virgil bathe Dante's face that all the filth of Hell be washed away. Cato then vanished leaving the two poets to the guidance of the rising sun. The Angel of God using his wings as sails for his barque and with over a hundred spirits on board all singing, "when Israel went out of Egypt," comes to welcome the visitors. These shades, amazed at perceiving that Dante is still in the flesh of the first life, crowd about and gaze on him. Among them Dante recognizes a former friend, Casella, a Florentine musician, who at the poet's earnest request sings in tones memorable for their sweetness, "love that in my mind recounts unto me," only to have Cato chide them for the delay and bid them hasten to the cleansing hillside.

As they hasten along Dante can perceive his own shadow thrown by the sun behind them, but not Virgil's and is in fear lest he has lost his guide, who reassures him with the explanation that the sun can cast the shadow of him in only the region where his mortal body was buried. Now at the foot of the mount of Purgatory the two poets are in doubt about their way and decide to inquire of a company of souls coming toward them but with such pace as that they seemed not to advance at all. These wandering souls were such as had died in contumacy against the Holy Church and are now condemned to wander here for a period thirty times as long as that wherein they sinned. After leaving these excommunicated spirits, they attempt the ascent of the mount and as Dante grows weary the two poets pause for rest whereupon Virgil seeks to encourage his disciple by saying that the higher they climb the easier the ascent, although this is disputed by a voice from behind a great rock where loll the Slothful, or those guilty of late repentance. These shades are amazed that Dante can cast a shadow and send two of their company as messengers to find out the cause of this strange thing and learn that it is for the reason that Dante is still in the flesh of the first life.

Since so many of these souls implore Dante to bear to their earthly friends tidings of them and to invoke prayers in their behalf, he asks Virgil who such prayers can alter the decrees of Heaven only to learn that the answer to that question must come from Beatrice. Prominent among the Late Repentant is Sordello who, upon learning that Virgil is from his native town of Mantua, embraces him. This reminds Dante of his Italy against which he inveighs for the dissensions between its cities and families, like the Montagues and Capulets. Virgil now informs Sordello as to who he is and states that like other souls in Limbo he has been condemned for the sin of omission of the three holy virtues. As though in return for this information, Sordello reveals the law of the ascent, which cannot be made after sunset, and leads them to a spot where they can tarry for the night. There they come upon a group of neglectful emperors, Rudolph, Ottocar, Henry of Navarre and others, who for selfish reasons or ambitions neglected their duties. Since they are still outside Purgatory and thus susceptible to temptation, it is necessary for them to be guarded by the angels with the fiery swords lest the serpent from Eden enter this place also. In the sky, as Dante observes, the four stars of the moral virtues are setting while the three stars of the holy virtues are now flaming in the sky, as if to warn men that natural virtue is not sufficient for their salvation.

As the first night in Purgatory begins Dante, whose mortal weariness overcomes him, sinks into deep slumber, and dreams that a golden-plumed eagle swooped down upon him and in its talons carried him up to the fiery sphere. Now, as Virgil informs him, he is indeed in Purgatory, for Lucia had taken him away from Sordello and the other fine forms in the valley and carried him hither. As the poets come to the Gate of Purgatory they are challenged by the Guardian Angel with a naked sword in his hand, and he asks them their mission. Virgil responds saying that a heavenly lady had bade them come whereupon they are welcomed. They mount the three steps to the gate—white marble, perse and porphyry, and Dante humbly begs for admission. The Guardian Angel, having with the point of his sword inscribed seven P's (*peccata,* symbols of the seven deadly sins) on Dante's forehead, drew forth a golden and a silver key and opened the sacred portal warning him that he who looks back must return outside again.

Now after the two poets had managed to make their way through a cleft rock, which moved much as a wave recedes and returns, they attain the first circuit of Purgatory. There they encounter the Proud who are being punished by being bent over, knees to breast, much like corbels which support a ceiling. These sad souls repeat the Lord's Prayer as a petition more for the dead than for themselves. As Dante bends down to listen to their words, he hears them discourse upon the vanity of worldly reputation. At Virgil's bidding Dante now straightens up and moves onward meeting such proud souls as Lucifer, Nimrod, Saul, Rehoboam and others. The Angel of Humility now appears, beauteous, robed in white and with outspread wings, and as they, encouraged by his voice, make the ascent they hear voices chanting, "blessed are the poor in spirit." Since Dante's soul has been purged of pride, the first of the seven P's is removed making the journey upward less toilsome.

When the poets mount to the second circuit they behold pathetic examples of the Envious who, apparently because they found no pleasure in the joys of others, are being punished by having their eyelids stitched together by iron wires. Dante tells one of the group that in time his eyes will be closed, although his sin is more that of pride than of envy, and discourses further with other envious souls as Florentines and Pisans. Now another heavenly messenger invites them to ascend and as they enter on a stairway less steep than the others they hear the chanting of "blessed are the merciful." They are now upon the third circuit, that of the Irate, and as Dante is about to behold them he falls into an ecstatic dream of gentle souls like the Virgin Mary and Saint Stephen, but he is aroused by Virgil, and the two journey on into the evening, then into a smoke dark as night. As they grope their way through this foul and bitter air Dante hears voices chanting "Lamb of God" and learns that they are spirits untying the knot of anger. Now their way is challenged by Marco Lombardo, of whom Dante inquires concerning the cause of vice on earth and learns that the reason is not to be found in the stars but in the free will of man himself. Those in authority have corrupted Church and State and the Church of Rome has been guilty of confounding these two powers in herself.

As they issued forth from the cloud of smoke, Dante hears an angelic voice bidding them ascend and when he was at the first step he hears the chanting of "Blessed are the peacemakers." Now that they are in the Fourth Circuit, Dante would learn what sorts of souls are here being purged of their sins, and learns from Virgil that here are the Hateful. Love is the law of the universe, as is shown by the Creator and all His works, but the Hateful are either lacking in love or they pervert it. Such instinctive love is without praise or blame, but can attain to merit when the mind refuses to accept things which have only the appearance of truth and when the will discards the impulses not in harmony with love toward God. Dante sinks again into slumber and again dreams, this time of the sweet Siren who led Ulysses from his wandering. Finally he is awakened by Virgil, hears an angel saying "Blessed are they that mourn," and finds that he is in the Fifth Circle. Here he comes upon the Avaricious and Prodigal whose souls cleave to the pavement not because their eyes are still fixed on earthly things but because they cannot detach themselves from them. One of these souls, Hugh Capet, finds some solace in citing examples of poverty accompanied by virtue, as with the Virgin Mary, Fabricius and Saint Nicholas, followed by lamentable accounts of various avaricious ones in secular and sacred history. As they are leaving the Avaricious, the mountain shakes because of the attempt of some of the prostrate to rise up.

The two poets are now mounting to the Sixth Circuit; an angel removes another scar of sin from Dante's face and pronounces a blessing upon those who hunger and thirst after righteousness. On this circuit they encounter the Gluttonous and find their way checked by a luring tree from within whose foliage they hear a voice discoursing upon the virtue of temperance as exemplified by certain Roman women, Daniel and John the Baptist. The Gluttonous are being punished by withering away to such a degree that the skin takes its form from the bones. After conversing with an Italian poet of the old school, Dante with Virgil comes to a second tree grafted from the tree of Eve and from its branches hears some one speak of the vice of gluttony. While they are rising to the Seventh Circuit, Dante expresses wonder that mere shadows of men such as they have seen among the Gluttonous can experience the sensation of hunger, finding it difficult to believe that the soul can still retain the experiences of the body.

On the Seventh Circuit they encounter the Lustful and in the instances of the Virgin Mary and Diana observe the contrary examples of chastity. Two companies of the Lustful now sweep by kissing each other in passing, one company shouting "Sodom and Gomorrah;" the other, "Pashiphae enters into the cow that the bull may satisfy her lust," and it is explained to Dante that the first group have sinned against the laws of humanity, the second against the laws of nature. The Angel of God now appears outside the bank of flame chanting, "Blessed are the pure in heart," and warning them that they cannot advance unless they pass through the fire. Dante dreads doing this but after Virgil has assured him that in no other way can he see Beatrice, he with the others makes the fiery passage, being guided by a voice on the farther side singing, "Come, ye blessed of my father."

It is now night and the pilgrims can advance no further, hence the pilgrims fall asleep on the stairs. Dante dreams of a fair woman who, as she gathered flowers, sang, saying she was Leah, intent on action, and that her sister Rachel was satisfied with a life of contemplation. In the morning, Virgil tells Dante that, he having passed through the purgatorial fire is now in possession of a sound will which henceforth must be his guide. As the day dawns, Dante enters the divine forest whose air is perfumed with sweet breezes and made melodious with the songs of birds, and meets Matilda who assures him that she is prepared to answer all his questions concerning this new paradise on earth. On this mount raised upward toward the heavens the winds are caused by the First Mover of Creation, the plants have their roots in the air and the waters issue forth from a celestial fount while mortals live in the fabled golden age. As she ended her discourse, Matilda changed her song into a chant, "Blessed are they whose sins are forgiven."

As Dante and Matilda wend their way along the stream she calls his attention to the sudden brightness filling the forest and he beholds a celestial pageant bearing seven golden candlesticks, which seem as seven trees of gold, and seven pennants looking like the trails of flames in the air. These are borne by a band of beings clad in unspeakable white and are followed by the four and twenty elders of the Old Testament, the four beasts of Ezekiel's prophecy and a chariot drawn by a griffin. When the chariot is opposite Dante a thunder clap is heard and the pageant halts, and now a veritable cloud of flowers are flung by the hands of the angelic host and from within the cloud appears a lady clad under a green mantle with the tints of living flame and over her white veil a crown of olive. In his fear at such a sight, Dante appeals to Virgil but discovers that now he is bereft of his former guide. "Dante!" It is the lady who calls him by name, but even though her veil has dropped he does not recognize her hence she says, "Regard me well, for I am Beatrice, am Beatrice indeed.

How didst thou deign to ascend this mount? Dost thou not know that man is happy here?"

While Dante is weighed down with great shame Beatrice relapses into silence, and as a choir of angels chant "In thee, O Lord, do I put my trust," his frozen heart melts down. Beatrice now turns to the angelic host and explains that while she was on earth she had endeavored to sustain but that he had forsaken her for false images of the Good and had sunk so low that he could be saved only by a vision of the lost hereupon she had provided him with a guide to conduct him through the lower world. Dante confesses his sins attributing them to the loss of her countenance only to be told that he should not have trusted in merely earthly beauty which as his eyes now observe is greatly surpassed by her heavenly appearance. As Dante falls senseless to the ground, Matilda draws him into the river Lethe and as he emerges upon the blessed bank beyond he is met by the handmaidens of Beatrice who is persuaded to unveil her face.

When Dante beholds the glory of the celestial pageant, which has wheeled about and is now returning with the sun, his eyes are blinded. As the procession moves through the earthly paradise lost when Eve ate fruit from the Tree of Knowledge, the poet realizes that the place might yet have been peopled but for schism, heresy and corruption in Church and State. Beatrice now foretells the coming of a political Messiah who will purify both Church and State and reunite them upon a proper basis. Much that she says seems Sphinx-like to the poet but this is because he has been following a false school of thought but now with his brain as wax he is prepared to receive her teachings, and since the waters of Lethe have washed away all former memories he is prepared to receive and retain new impressions. Dante is now born again and with his celestial guide is ready to ascend to the stars.

PARADISO

As the glory of God now glows throughout the universe, the poet calls upon Apollo to aid him in his crowning task of describing Paradise. It is high noon and as Dante beholds Beatrice gazing on the sun whose light is thereby so enhanced that it was as though God had created a second orb to add day unto day, this so exalts the poet that he feels himself one of the gods. Now that they are leaving the earth, Dante is perplexed to understand how in spite of gravitation he can rise, but learns from Beatrice that according to a higher law it is as natural for man to move toward his true place in God as for a flame to rise. They ascend to the First Heaven of the Moon whose substance they enter even as at the Incarnation the Deity entered into man. Dante has yet to learn that what he observes in the moon is not to be explained scientifically by natural causes but by the influence of the Divine Spirit diffused throughout the world. Further, when upon beholding what he takes to be mere images of things, he must learn that such faint outlines are true substances and that all souls are controlled by the will of God and in his will is our peace.

Dante must abandon, also, that Platonic doctrine according to which each soul comes to earth from its star and then returns to it, and realize that all souls have their common dwelling-place in God. In practical matters which concern the human will he must come to appreciate the difference between what we do from natural inclination and that which we feel forced to do to escape peril. Dante is now led to see how the will of man can sacrifice its freedom by making vows for the future, for these can become evil things as they were with Jephtha and Agamemnon who by their vows sacrificed their daughters. As they mount to the Second Heavens of Mercury, a thousand splendors drew toward them, each one saying of Beatrice, "Behold the one who will increase our loves!" Chief among those in this heaven which seems to nestle in the rays of the sun is Justinian symbolic of the Roman ideals of law and peace. After Constantine had changed the seat of empire from Rome to Byzantium and two centuries had lapsed, Justinian made his Code. Having noted this he reviews the history of the Rome with which the quarrels of the Guelfs and Ghibellines contrast so harshly, then with the spirits accompanying him he vanishes away, the company rising like sparks from a fire.

Beatrice now takes up the story of man, his Fall and the Redemption by which he first removed himself from Paradise and in which God by His divine courtesy seeks to reinstate him and render him immortal for, as God originally created human flesh He can accomplish the resurrection of the body. They have now attained the planet Venus from which the ancients took the name to symbolize earthly love although, as Dante learns, it signifies the love divine whereby the planets roll circle within circle. On this fair planet, Dante meets Carlo Martello on whose bright brow once glowed the crown of Danube land. From Martello Dante learns that in this higher realm of the Good there is a place for all with their diversity of gifts and that souls are exalted according to their several capacities rather than according to heredity which plan the world below, especially the city of Florence, might well observe and follow.

The Sun to which Dante and Beatrice have now ascended is symbolic of the self-existent God, source of all intellectual light. Here in this bright court of Heaven are many gems of light whose rays seem songs whose notes are caught from the celestial music. Now a double circle of spirits form round Dante and Beatrice and speaking for his group of celestial neighbors Thomas Aquinas extols the greatness of Dionysius, Boethius, Albert of Cologne, Bede and others. Thomas praises likewise the other order founded by Saint Francis of Assisi, who was wedded to poverty and good works which unfortunately is not the case with his followers. The second circle now encompasses the first one the two creating the impression of parallel rainbows and fusing song with song. As Saint Thomas had exalted the merits of the Franciscana now Bonaventura, a member of that order, extols the virtues of the Dominicans naming also with them Nathan the Prophet, Chrysostom, Anselm and Joachim of Floris. As Dante beholds these spirits in Paradise he wonders how the resurrected bodies can be free from their corporeal limitations but learns that the glorified body has strength sufficient to overcome the former weakness of the flesh, and be adequate unto the desires of the soul, a sentiment to which all the redeemed respond with a chorus of "Amen!"

Now they have ascended to the ruddy planet Mars across whose face a white cross shines. The hymn of victory coming forth from the spirits of this planet is not wholly understood by Dante yet he catches the refrain, "Rise and conquer!" The song is silenced and now like a star darting from its constellation one of the celestial warriors greets Dante announcing that he himself is one of the old Alighieri family, whereupon these two Florentines review the ancient history of that city. Dante inquires concerning his own fate there and learns that while he may be persecuted he will finally triumph over his adversaries. From the fiery Mars Dante and Beatrice ascend to the white and temperate Jupiter where the saints flying like birds trace the letters of the motto, "Love righteousness ye who are judges of the earth," to which is appended the head and neck of an eagle symbolic of justice. The eagle discourses upon the depth and obscurity of God's justice thereby comforting Dante with the thought that many of the heathen may be saved, as in the case of Trajan and Ripheus who are already in Paradise.

As they rise to the planet Saturn, Dante's eyes are fixed on Beatrice who bids him change his gaze to the splendor of the seventh heaven where, as he now observes, a golden ladder ascends far beyond his sight. When Dante inquires why the harmonies of Heaven are silent and endeavors also to penetrate into the mysteries of the Divine Will he is warned not to presume too much, and it is as though the reply to his intrepid queries came at last in the form of thunder which vanquishes him. Here Beatrice assuages his fear and bids him resume his contemplation of the celestial lights. He is further comforted by one of the spirits who assures him of the love of the spirits about him and tells him that his desire to see God with uncovered image can be fulfilled only as he continues in that contemplation which at last will extend beyond all space. Now as he approaches the glory of the final sphere, Dante follows the suggestion of his heavenly guide and looks down upon the spheres through which they have passed and beholds the vile semblance of the earth.

Now as they approach the stars Beatrice calls Dante's attention to the celestial glow saying, "Behold the hosts of Christ's triumph," and he sees thousands of lamps like suns commingled and enkindled, and yet out-shining them all was the living light of Christ. And now his vision thus fortified by such mighty things he is able to endure her smile. He beholds also the garden of Christ flowering in the Virgin rose and the lilies of the Apostles. The Angel Gabriel now descends and crowns the Queen of Heaven

[285]

who then ascends beyond the reach of the spirits which with their celestial flames, soar upward after Her. Now is spread a great table for the supper of the Blessed Lamb of God and at Beatrice's request the saints give the mortal Dante of that which falleth from the table. Saint Peter now appears and as he questions Dante concerning faith the poet defines it as the substance of things hoped for, and declares his faith in God as the unmoved mover of all things, as also as the One in Three. Saint James now joins Saint Peter and questions Dante concerning hope, followed by the dazzling brightness of Saint John whose voice confesses that he can find no place in Paradise until he is risen in the general resurrection.

The brightness of Saint John's soul has deprived Dante of his sight but the Saint, after assuring him that Beatrice will restore his vision, questions him concerning the nature of love and is told that love's primary object is God who is to be loved because he in Himself is good and because he is good to man. Dante is silent, the song of "Holy, Holy, Holy" resounds through Heaven and his sight is restored. With his renewed vision he gazes downward toward the earth then with Beatrice he rises to the realm of the Unmoved Mover, or *Primo Mobile,* whence, as Beatrice explains, time and space have their roots, and in the mind of God are so ordained that great becomes greater and small smaller as though God were both the centre and circumference of all, whereby in the mind of the "I am" all space is a here, all time a now. Yet this all-inclusive Being in His light and love is reflected or broken up into the countless mirrors of angels and yet ever remains one in itself.

Now Dante and Beatrice issue forth from the world of space, ruled by the First Mover into the pure light of Heaven, itself surcharged with goodness and gladness. Here the poet is wrapped in a web of light so brilliant that at first it extinguished his sight but then kindled a new vision whereby he beholds the things of Heaven mirrored in symbolic forms and, then, the splendor of God. Here, rank upon rank, are the spirits of the Church Triumphant all-animated by peace and ardor and rejoicing in the three-fold light of the Deity. With his new vision Dante is able to comprehend the general form of Paradise and now, desiring to see Beatrice as she is, he asks, "where is she?" and then beholds her in the third circle from the highest rank. At the prompting of Saint Bernard he raises his gaze higher until finally he beholds the Virgin Mary among a thousand glowing angels making festival. As the voice of Love sings, *Ave, Maria!* and the whole blessed court responds to the divine canticle, the poet beholds the face which is most like that of Christ and suggested a semblance to God.

For Dante's sake the saint now raises a prayer to Mary and with a smile indicates that he may look on high where, his earthly vision purged, he beholds God as in a dream which memory cannot hold. Yet this vision which was a mere glance, was such as to reveal to him the scattered leaves of the universe bound by love into one volume, although to comprehend it were as futile as the effort of the geometer to measure the circle by its radius. Yet when this circle is as the universe which forever rolls on smoothly we know that it is love which moves the sun and the other stars.

GARGANTUA AND PANTAGRUEL

By

François Rabelais

FRANÇOIS RABELAIS (*1495–1553*) was a French satirist and humorist. His father was a prosperous lawyer and after studying at a Benedictine abbey he continued his studies in 1519 at a Franciscan monastery where he took up medicine. He left for Lyons, a great book center of Europe, to practise medicine but presently published two literary works. His forte of humor and burlesque soon gained ascendancy. His publications in this field gained such popularity that he continued the form. By 1540 he had moved to Paris where he read his first two books to the King who was so pleased with them that he granted a license for the publication of the third. When Francis I died a reaction against liberty of thought set in and Rabelais had to flee. Cardinal de Lorraine soon afterward allowed him to return and gave him "the living of Meudon" where he spent the remainder of his life quietly. Rabelais was not a drunken buffoon nor a profound philosopher as legends have represented him but expressed rather in satire what his contemporaries were thinking and talking about.

To you, illustrious drinkers, and to you, beloved sufferers from the pox, my book is dedicated. Once upon a time Alcibiades compared the prince of philosophers, Socrates, to one of those little boxes called *Silenes* whose exterior was covered with every kind of silly and farcical devise but which were used to guard the most valuable objects. Of just such a nature are many books, like *Gargantua and Pantagruel,* whose frivolous and fanciful external appearance is but a cover for profound truths to be discovered by the reader who will seek diligently within. Did you ever see a dog, the most philosophic of animals, with a marrow-bone? Let the reader imitate him and with the same patience and repeated effort gnaw and suck continuously until he has drawn from our book the substantial essence of its marrow.

GARGANTUA

For the genealogy of our hero, Gargantua, father of noble Pantagruel, I must refer you to a document found in an old bronze box dug up in a field not far from Chinon. Written in verse, much spoiled by insects and rotted by the damp, this piece of parchment outlines the descent of the family from Noah's ark down to Grandgousier, the father of Gargantua.

In his prime Grandgousier was as lively a fellow as one could find, preferring his food salty and his wine straight. He married Gargamelle, daughter of the king of the Butterflies, a handsome girl, whom he proceeded to love so vigorously that she became shortly big with a child. She bore the child eleven months, as has happened in the case of many of the children of Neptune, Jupiter and others. This extended period of pregnancy is necessary for the perfect formation of children destined to do great deeds in the world. The true Pantagruelist may consult Plautus, Hippocrates, and Aristotle on all these points.

The day Gargantua was born, his father, Grandgousier, had invited a number of his friends to help him consume a quantity of highly seasoned sausages and tripe that had begun to spoil. Down by the willow-grove the guests ate and drank, danced and gossiped:

> *"Some more wine, boy!*
> *Pour it in!*
> *A truce to thirst!*
> *Which came first, thirst or drink?*
> *By Saint Quenet let's drink!*
> *Here's to you, Guillot!*
> *By my fig, good wife, I am still dry!"*

While the neighbors were enjoying themselves under the willows, Gargamelle began to feel the pains of child-birth. Despite the warning of her husband, she had eaten several barrels of rich sausage. As a consequence, the sphincter muscle was so constricted that the child could not descend. Whereupon, it escaped from the womb, worked its way up through the diaphragm and issued forth by the left ear. Once born he did not cry: *Mies! mies!* as other children, but shouted, Drink! drink! until quantities of milk were brought. The child was baptized as a good Christian should be. He was named Gargantua from the first words uttered by his father when he saw him.

Gargantua prospered. For the first year he was fed the milk of 17,913 cows in addition to the milk furnished by his mother, Gargamelle, which according to certain doctors, pupils of Duns Scotus, amounted to slightly over 1400 gallons at each feeding. At the time of his birth the odour of the September wine-brewing which he had inhaled developed in him a constant thirst. I have been informed by one of his nurses that whenever he was in a bad humour or started crying the sound of clinking bottles and jingling glasses would immediately pacify him and throw him into a state of ecstatic satisfaction.

From the age of 3 to 5 Gargantua was brought up in the regular discipline applied to other children, that is, he drank, ate and slept; he ate, slept and drank; he slept, drank and ate. In addition he was always dirtying his bed, running his shoes down at the heel, chasing butterflies, gaping at the stars, spitting in his soup, rubbing his stomach, pulling his nose, scratching where it didn't itch, scribbling on paper, jumping from one thing to another, eating the dogs' food, skinning the fox, etc.

Gargantua's first studies were pursued under the direction of an ancient doctor, a Sophist, named Thubal Holophernes who trained him for many years using the scholastic texts of the Middle Ages. The boy made little progress, so his father placed him under the direction of a certain Jobelin Bridé, who pursued the same old fashioned educational methods. Gargantua had been studying for several decades under these two teachers when one day a young man named Eudemon, who had studied only 2 years under a young scholar named Ponocrates was presented to Grandgousier. The father was shocked by the contrast between Eudemon, neat in appearance, active on his feet, confident in manner, glib in speech, and his own son Gargantua, who, when called upon to rise and address the audience, could only fumble and stutter and weep like a calf. As a result of this revelation Gargantua was placed under other preceptors, the principal of whom was Ponocrates, the Humanist, and sent to Paris to complete his education.

The king of Numidia had recently presented to Grandgousier an enormous mare with hoofs divided into toes, hanging ears like those of a goat and a tail as large as the tower of Saint Mars near Chinon. Mounted upon this mare, accompanied by his professors and servants, Gargantua arrived in Paris, first inquiring for the names of the learned men in the city and of the best wines drunk there. The next day he walked through the town, sat down on the towers of Notre Dame, attached the cathedral bells to his mare's neck, and then, in relieving himself drowns 260,418 of the inhabitants, not counting the women and children.

Having established himself in a hotel of the Latin quarter, Gargantua received the ceremonious visit of Doctor Janotus de Bragmardo who has been commissioned by the University to ask for the return of their bells. *"Ehen, hen, hen! Mna dies, Monsieur"*, begins the ambassador. "Give us back our bells, we need them badly. We have already refused to sell them to the people of London in Cahors and of Bordeaux in Brie——. In faith, *Domine,* will you dine with me *in camera,* s'blood! We will make *bomum cherubin! Ego occidi unum porcum, et ego habet bon vino!"*

No sooner had our good professor finished than Ponocrates and Eudemon broke into such gigantic laughter that they thought to burst, like Crassus seeing a jackass eat charcoal, and Philemon, when a donkey pushed in and ate the ripe figs on the dining table before him. Doctor Janotus was dismissed and went away, coughing and spitting his Latin and French, with his bells and enough wool cloth to clothe himself and his family.

Before imposing upon his pupil the strict diet and mental discipline of the Humanist system, Ponocrates allowed Gargantua to continue his former life for a while. He would sleep till about 9.00 in the morning, dawdling in bed for an hour or two before rising. He would then put on a long black robe, belching, sneezing, coughing, and blowing his nose all the time. For breakfast, ham, beef, soup, fried tripe and other meats. After lunch, to church where he sat through 26 or 30 masses, mumbling his prayers without cease. A half-hour of study followed his religious practices, and then would come dinner. A dozen hams and another dozen smoked tongues served as appetizers. As the meal proceeded a man was stationed on each side of the giant to throw in mustard and pour in wine between the great mouthfuls of beef and pork and mutton that he swallowed. When the skin over his stomach began to stretch, Gargantua would stop the meal.

Ponocrates slowly modified this vicious manner of life. First he employed a physician who purged the young giant in "canonical" style. Then, having dismissed all his idle associates he established a daily program that filled every hour with the study of letters and the acquisition of "virtue."

Gargantua was awakened at 4.00 o'clock. While he was being massaged and dressed and during the performance of private functions passages of the Holy Scripture were read and commented on. The toilet completed, the lessons assigned for that day were read during three full hours. A period of relaxation followed devoted to athletic games, which were practiced with moderation and halted as soon as the giant began to sweat. Having been washed and rubbed, dressed in clean clothes, he takes a brief, light meal during which talk runs upon matters studied during the morning lesson. During the moments of digestion musical instruments were played or some game requiring thought would amuse the group. The rest of the afternoon was spent in more violent sports, hunting, swimming, running, practice with arms, horseback riding, etc. After a frugal dinner, always enlivened by discussions of serious subjects, the pupil prays earnestly and goes to bed. When bad weather prevented outdoor play, Gargantua was conducted to the stores, or factories of the city, so as to acquire knowledge of trade and industry.

While Gargantua was thus profiting in mind and body under the guidance of Ponocrates, war broke out in Touraine between peace-loving Grandgousier and a bellicose neighbor, Picrochole. Picrochole's people were famous for their cakes, which they sold in all the nearby markets. One day several loads of these cakes were being taken to Chinon through the land of Grandgousier. Stopping near a field where some of Grandgousier's subjects were working, the Picrocholians stopped to address slighting remarks to the peasants. Insults followed, then blows, with the result that some of Picrochole's subjects were injured and the cakes scattered over the ground. Picrochole was enraged and without waiting to defy Grandgousier in proper form, launched his army upon the latter's country

The attack fell first upon the Abbey of Seuillé. The monks in terror fled to their chapel and began singing litanies *contra hostium insidias* and responses *pro pace*. There was in the monastery a young monk named Friar John des Entommeurs, a bold, handsome, young fellow, full of courage and strength, a fine dispatcher of masses and of food, in a word as true a monk as ever monked it in monkdom. He looked through the window of the abbey and saw the troups of Picrochole ravaging the vineyards; from the chapel he could hear the voices of his brother friars: *"Ini, onim, me, ne, ne, tum, ne, onum, num ini. . . ."* "By God's virtue!" he cried out, "that's well sung, but you had better sing: 'Good-bye, baskets, the wine is made.'" Whereupon, seizing an immense cross made of hard wood, he charged the enemy, who being busy with the grapes were caught unprepared. With monstrous blows he began to dash out their brains, to dislocate their backs, to demolish their skulls, to disrupt their shoulderblades, to disjoint their knees and arms and hips, to crush their noses and knock out their eyeballs. The army of Picrochole fled in disorder.

Grandgousier sought by every pacific means to avoid war. Picrochole, however, was surrounded by ambitious advisers, Duke Garlic and Captains Spitfire and Dunghill who persuaded him that once he has conquered Grandgousier he may easily become ruler of the world. One army would move east, through northern Europe, the other passing by Spain into Northern Africa, would join the first army in the orient and then the east as far as the land of Cathay would be brought under the rule of Picrochole. This enthusiasm encourages prosecution of the war, and several strong-places are seized. Grandgousier after many attempts to placate his irate enemy finds himself forced to summon Gargantua from his studies in Paris.

Gargantua's return from Paris to the Castle of Grandgousier in Touraine entailed only minor and unimportant adventures such as are inevitable on a voyage. The meeting between father and son is marked by dignified expressions of affection and filial reverence. They all sit down to dinner, Grandgousier, Gargantua with his retinue and Friar John and the war and its future prosecution are discussed. Some pilgrims, on their way to seek the protection of various saints famous for their cures of divers diseases are brought in. The two giants protest against the habit of pilgrimages which send men on futile and dangerous wanderings far away from home. Grandgousier concludes: "In the name of God, you poor people go back home. Take care of your families, work, each one of you, at your profession, instruct your children and live according to the precepts of St. Paul. In this way you will have the protection of God and his angels and saints against the pest and all ills."

With the help of his son and his wife and courageous companions, Grandgousier is able to bring his war with Picrochole to a quick end. Just as in his unwillingness to undertake the war, so in his eagerness to make peace, we can see in Grandgousier a peace-loving and benevolent ruler. The terms offered the enemy are not marked by anger nor the desire for revenge or aggrandizement.

It only remains to reward those who have contributed to the victory. As Friar John is foremost among these it is he who receives the principal recompense: an abbey, which will be constructed and organized according to his own specifications. The abbey will be built at Thélème on the banks of the Loire and will be generally modelled upon the Italian style coming into fashion, well aired, dry, with attention to beauty and comfort. Friar John requires that life in the abbey be in every detail opposite to that led in other monasteries. Men and women will live together, and marry when it pleases them. No time-pieces are allowed in the monastery, as the Thelemites are not expected to perform duties at certain stated times but when and how they choose. The common ideal will be one of freedom and culture. Over the main door of the abbey shall be carved the words: "Do as you wish", for it is the belief of Friar John that men who are free, sprung from decent parents and well educated, acquire a natural instinct that urges them on to deeds of virtue and withdraws them from vice.

PARADISE LOST

By

John Milton

JOHN MILTON (*1608–1674*) was one of England's greatest
poets. He was educated at Cambridge, for the church. From
his 24th to 30th years he studied literature on his father's
estate in Buckinghamshire when he wrote *L'Allegro*, among
other works. He was appointed Latin secretary to the Council
of State in 1649 and although he became blind three years
later, he continued in office until the abdication of Cromwell
in 1659. Milton's great epic, *Paradise Lost*, was planned in 1640
when the Long Parliament drew him into political and
church disputes and he pled for civil and religious liberty.
Paradise Lost was not finished until 1665 and it was published two years later in ten books. By 1674 it had been enlarged to twelve books. For *Paradise Lost* Milton received five
pounds as the initial payment and five pounds additional on
the sale of the first three editions. Milton's widow finally
settled all claims on the publication for eight pounds, making
a total of eighteen pounds for nearly a decade of work, producing a classic in English literature.

THE POET calls upon his muse to inspire him in his adventurous
song of man's first disobedience and the fruit of that forbidden
tree whose taste brought woe and death into the world, but
appeals with greater fervor to the Spirit that it may instruct him,
illumine what is dark, raise and support what is low that the
author may assert Eternal Providence and justify the ways of God
to men.

The cause of man's fall is attributed to Satan in the guise of a
serpent who having revolted against the Deity and inspired rebellion among the angels was hurled headlong from the ethereal
sky into the bottomless pit, and all his angels with him. In time

Satan recovers from his confusion worse confounded and resolves on strength as his salvation. To be weak, says he, is to be miserable and the weakness which comes from obedience to the law of God must be so repudiated that evil will be his good and to do evil rather than good shall be the sole task of these bad spirits. The new possessor of the infernal world now rejoices in the freedom of mind which suffers no changes of space or time, for the mind is its own place and in itself can make a Heaven of Hell or a Hell of Heaven.

Satan now confers with his legions about the possibility of setting up a new empire to rival the celestial one concluding that it is better to reign in Hell than to serve in Heaven. Thus inspired the fallen angels rise in a mass as numberless as the cloud of locusts which plagued Egypt in old Pharaoh's day. The principal leaders of the hellish host are named after the idols which appeared later in the land of Canaan—Moloch, Chemos, Baalim, Ashtaroth, Thammuz, Dagon and the like. In addressing his cohorts Satan holds out some hope that they may be able to regain Heaven, but inspires them with the more lively prospect of gaining ascendency over a new world which the Almighty plans to create and to people with a generation of beings equal in the divine favor to the sons of Heaven. On these the infernal host will make war, and at the very word millions of flaming swords flash forth to confirm it. Pandemonium, the high capital of Satan and his peers, far superior to the Tower of Babel, now rises from the deep as one gigantic blast from a vast organ. There the demons sit ready for their great council.

II

High on his gorgeous throne Satan raises the question whether they shall risk a battle for the recovery of Heaven, their just inheritance, and whether they shall proceed by force or guile. Moloch is for open war which will at least disturb Heaven and provide revenge even if victory be lacking. Belial thinks victory over the impregnable towers of Heaven an impossibility and counsels the host to endure in Hell with the hope that the Deity will relent in Heaven and forgive them. Mammon would have the host dismiss the thought of war on the ground that they could find no suitable place in Heaven if they did regain it, nor would they find it agreeable to praise God and accept His decrees. Mammon's advice is that they live to themselves and seek their own good on earth which with its gems and gold and other forms of wealth is capable of a magnificence equal to that of Heaven. By popular vote it is decided that the princes of Hell remain where they are, build up their growing empire and undertake some easier enterprise than that of conquering Heaven. This enterprise shall be that of conquering the seat of that new race called "Man" which according to prophecy the Deity is about to create. The Stygian council agrees with Satan that he himself shall fare forth alone to seek out Man while the other members shall give themselves up to their own affairs at home until Satan returns.

Meanwhile Satan on swift wings moves as it were like a comet through the infernal deep until he comes to the Gates Of Hell. These are guarded by two execrable shapes, one which seemed a woman to her waist but with the remainder of her body a foul and scaly serpent, the other almost a shapeless phantasm yet resembling a goblin. The female shape, claiming to be his daughter and calling the infernal phantasm his father, holds the ponderous key of the gate which God has forbidden her to open. But since Satan is her father she will loose the huge portcullis of the place and let him go forth that he may conquer the new world where she will reign at his right hand. Satan now stands on the brink of Hell and faces a region so vast as to be without the forms of time or space; while he is pondering upon what course to steer he is confronted by Chaos to whom he tells his desired destination promising that old Anarch a recompense if he will guide him to the new world and thus conducted Satan is brought in sight of nature, the new world he is seeking.

III

The scene changes from Hell to Heaven, and the poet who has sung of Chaos and Eternal Night must now attune his lyre to the Celestial City. Thus he calls upon the light divine to shine within his soul that he may see and tell of things invisible to mortal sight. The Almighty Father in the pure empyrean enthroned above the utmost height beholds Satan coasting along the wall of Heaven on his way to the newly created world. To the Son sitting at His right hand, God predicts the success of Satan in corrupting man but justifies Himself on the ground that He has created man a free being and one able to withstand temptation. When the Deity declares His purpose to forgive man for the sin he will commit the Son observes that such grace cannot be extended to man without the satisfaction of divine justice, unless perhaps the Divine Father will abolish all creation and unmake at the outset what was to have been His chief glory. When the Deity asks by what means expiation shall be made and man redeemed, all Heaven is silent save for the Son, who offers Himself as the necessary ransom for mankind. This decision on the part of the Divine Son brings forth from the heavenly choir a sublime and swelling hymn of praise.

At this point, Satan with wearied wings and willing feet, lands upon the outer rim of the new world and begins wandering about in search of man's new habitation. But Paradise, the happy seat of man, is not so easily found hence it becomes necessary for Satan to have a guide thither. Since it will never do for him to appear in his true character as the Fiend, he uses his diabolical power to transform himself into a stripling cherub with flowing locks, smiling countenance and wings of many-colored plumes. Thus garbed, Satan affects an innocent interest in creation and an unspeakable desire to behold its wondrous works especially man, the chief favor and delight of the Creator. In this assumed form and mood Satan presents himself to Uriel, regent of the sun, who points to the spot now known as Paradise.

IV

Now that Satan is in prospect of this paradise, or Garden of Eden, the Hell within him seems to stir and boil so that like a devilish engine recoiling upon itself his thought is distracted with doubt and horror. He fain would flee but which ever way he flies is Hell since he himself is Hell. Finally he summons all his satanic powers, bids farewell to hope, fear and remorse, and exclaiming, "Evil, be thou my good!" he is ready for his infernal work. Pensive and slow, Satan completes his journey to the Garden of Eden, bounds over the high wall and in the form of a cormorant takes his seat at the top of the Tree of Life. The Garden seems indeed an earthly paradise with which, however, nothing on earth can compare. Satan now obtains his first sight of Adam and Eve and is moved to great admiration for their bodily beauty, divine appearance and innocent joyousness in their new paradise. And yet the sight of this blissful pair arouses envy in the heart of him who knows not joy nor love and he renews his resolve to bring about their fall.

From the innocent conversation of the happy pair, Satan gathers the knowledge that Eden is not wholly their own, since of the Tree of Knowledge they are forbidden to taste. He will so excite their minds with the desire to know that they will transgress the commandment given by the envious Deity who fears that their knowledge will make them equal with the gods. While Satan is waiting for night to come, Uriel descends from the sun on a sun-beam and warns Gabriel at the gate of the Garden that an evil spirit in the guise of a good angel had escaped from the depths and after passing on his way by the sun had gained an entrance into Paradise. Gabriel promises Uriel he will find the transgressor before another day has dawned.

Night has come and Adam and Eve begin to think of retiring to their bower for rest according to the divine arrangement whereby God, having separated day from night, had provided periods of labor and repose. Within their bower roofed with laurel and myrtle the innocent pair fall asleep. But now the angels guarding the bower come upon Satan instilling a tempting and delusive dream into the ear of Eve. Satan is apprehended and brought to Gabriel before whom he stands abashed; Gabriel's questions he answers haughtily and in his wrath would resort to resistance but the appearance of an angelic squadron hemming him in with spears causes him to desist and flee carrying with him the shades of night.

v

As the rosy steps of dawn approach in the eastern sky, Eve awakens and relates to Adam her disturbing dream. Adam likewise is troubled by what he calls her uncouth dream, finding it difficult to understand how such a fantasy could have sprung up in a heart as pure as Eve's. Further he comforts her with the

[299]

thought that what in her dream she abhorred to do, she will not in her waking hours. After their morning prayer they return to their amiable duties in the flowery Garden. In order that Adam may realize his responsibilities as a man and be warned against any possible temptation, God sends Raphael to admonish him. From afar Adam discerns the approach of Raphael, calls Eve to come and behold what seems like another morn arising and bids her make ready to receive the heavenly guest. Adam greets Raphael upon his arrival, invites him to his shady bower and entertains him with fruits of Paradise which Eve has gathered. Raphael then delivers his divine message reminding Adam of the mortal state of his infernal adversary. When Adam desires to know his enemy and how he came to be the adversary of God and man, Raphael reviews the story of the revolt in Heaven followed by the fall of Satan and his angels.

VI

Having thus begun to answer Adam's question concerning his possible adversary, Raphael continues with the full story of the warfare between Heaven and Hell and how the angels Michael and Gabriel were dispatched from Heaven to embattle Satan and his infernal angels. Raphael relates further how Satan invented diabolical machines with which for the time he is able to resist Michael and his celestial angels, but how at length by plucking up hills with all their loads of rocks and waters and woods and hurling them at their infernal adversaries they are able to overcome the hosts and machines of Satan. But even such a blast from the celestial forces was insufficient, hence on the third day God sent his Son to achieve victory and glory. The Son of God with His multitudinous legions beside Him, and fierce chariots at His command and ten thousand thunders in His right hand drove like a flood quite through the infernal host and drove them all back into the bottomless pit wherein they fell with an insufferable noise.

VII

Since the angel Raphael has been kind enough to come and warn mankind of its possible loss of Paradise, he may be so gracious as to relate aught about the Creation and how both the heavens and the earth were formed. Raphael then proceeds to the story of Creation which followed the expulsion of bad angels from Heaven, and reviews the several creative acts whereby during six days of work the heavens and the earth were formed and the Sabbath finally ushered in. Men, as Raphael tells the listening Adam, were created in God's own image to dwell on earth where they were to worship their Creator and receive as their reward a regency over all God's works and happiness for themselves and their posterity.

VIII

After giving thanks to the divine historian who had thus allayed his thirst for knowledge, Adam makes particular inquiry concerning the nature of celestial motions in a vast system wherein the earth seems but a grain, an atom in the firmament. Raphael advises Adam that whether it is the earth that moves or the sky, whether the heavenly orbs move in cycles and epicycles or in some other manner is of less import for man than his admiration for the wondrous works of God. Adam then addresses Raphael on the subject of his own existence and, while confessing that it is hard for man to tell how human life began, proceeds to relate what he can recall of his origin, of his talk with God concerning his solitude, of the creation of Eve and his first meeting with her. In concluding his human story, Adam begs leave to inquire whether heavenly spirits love one another and if they do how their love expresses itself, whether by looks alone or by the mixed irradiance and immediate touch. Raphael replies to this poignant question with a smile that glowed with the rosy hue of love and tells Adam it will suffice him to know that the angels are happy with the happiness which cannot come without love. Then they parted, the angel to Heaven, Adam to his bower.

IX

Having thus discoursed upon the venial though innocent conversation between man and his angel guest, the poet now changes to the tragic note in a poem whose theme is no less heroic than that of the anger of Achilles. Not having the desire or skill to indite verses devoted to the battles of armed warriors or tilts of

[301]

knights with steeds caparisoned, he is content to repeat what by
night his muse, celestial patroness, has brought to his ear the inspiration of his unpremeditated verse. If it fails to fit into this late
age and alien clime, the fault shall be his, not hers.

By night had Satan fled, in darkest midnight he returns in meditated fraud and malice, assuming the disguise of a mist as it rises
from the earth. After having considered every possible creature
which might serve his wiles, he decided upon the serpent as the
fittest imp of fraud. What foul descent was this that he who had
contended with the gods must now incarnate himself in such a
creature and mix with bestial slime! Satan finds the serpent sleeping, enters its mouth and endows its brute sense with intelligence.
The morning come, Adam and Eve go forth to their labors and at
the suggestion of Eve agree to divide their work, he to wind the
woodbine round the arbor, she to seek her task among roses and
the myrtle. While Adam believes that a wife is safest at her husband's side, he consents to Eve's plan but warns her against the
danger that may be lurking near. Eve feels that they cannot be
happy if they dwell in constant dread and that Eden is not Eden
if it is so frail as to expose them to harm. Adam still demurs but
Eve persists although she fares forth alone with his permission and
feeling duly warned by him.

The serpent now finding Eve alone gazes upon her with silent
admiration and then resorts to spoken flattery praising her above
all other beings in the Garden. Eve marvels that such a thing as a
serpent should have human speech and human understanding, and
asks him how he obtained them. His reply is that he was wanting
in both speech and reason until he tasted of a certain tree of the
Garden. At Eve's request the serpent guides her to that tree, which
is the Tree of Knowledge. Their journey to the Tree seems fruitless to Eve since, as she informs the serpent, those who dwell in
Paradise are forbidden to taste of its fruits. In an oratorical manner
the serpent expresses great indignation that the Deity should thus
have forbidden human beings to eat of the fruit of this Tree and
denies that, as the Deity has affirmed, death will follow from the
tasting. It is rather life which will follow and, as his own case
shows, the touching and tasting result in no death but only more
and more life. After Eve has well considered what the fruit of the

Tree of Knowledge has done for this lowly creature, she puts forth a rash hand and in an evil hour eats of a fruit which will, as she believes, feed both body and mind.

Eve now bows in reverence before the Tree of Knowledge then turns away from it to rejoin Adam in their bower where he is waiting with a fragrant garland for her hair. On hearing Eve with blithe countenance relate how she had eaten the fatal fruit, Adam drops the wreathed garland and stands speechless. At last his love for Eve being so great, he decides that since she must die as the result of her sin also will eat of the fruit and die with her. Eve now leads Adam to the Tree where with a liberal hand she gives him fruit which he dreads to eat but is so overcome with her female charm that he also partakes of the subtle fruit. The effect is intoxicating and erotic so that in lust they burn. Now, their primal innocence gone, they perceive that they are naked and betake them to the thickest woods where they gather fig-leaves to make garments for themselves. In addition to the sense of shame they begin to experience other emotions like anger, discord and distrust and spend fruitless hours in mutual accusation.

Since nothing can escape the all-seeing eye of God, the sin of mankind in Adam and Eve is now known in Heaven, whereupon the guardian angels abandon Paradise and are held blameless for what happened there, since they had no means of preventing Satan's entrance to the Garden of Eden. God now sent his Son to pass sentence upon the guilty pair and, rising from his radiant seat in Heaven, the Son with timeless speed of the gods descends to earth. He questions Adam and Eve, learns that Adam was tempted by Eve as was Eve by the serpent, punishes them with expulsion from the Garden of Eden but in pity clothes their nakedness as it were with his own righteousness. Now Sin and Death, which had been sitting at the Gates of Hell, decide they will no longer remain in Hell but will follow their sire, Satan, to the earth, or man's abode. In order to make the way from earth to Hell easier for transgressors, they pave the way with a broad highway and bridge over Chaos along the line of Satan's flight.

Satan, his dastardly mission accomplished, now returns to Hell, boasting of his triumph over man, but instead of receiving applause he is greeted with a dismal, universal hiss and realizes that like himself all his infernal angels have been turned into serpents. Now there stood a grove hard by and in it one forbidden tree, akin to that whose sweet fruit had acted as bait for Eve, and there of late it had been planted by the Deity to torment the evil spirits. Thus when in their scalding thirst they sought relief they chewed bitter ashes instead of luscious fruit. Sin and Death now return and resolve upon the ruin of mankind and the destruction of all terrestrial life. But the Deity in his divine abode foretells the victory of His Son over Sin and the renewal of life in all created things.

Adam bewails his fate and the curse which will fall upon his posterity if he give heed to the earlier commandment of God to increase and multiply. Eve endeavors to console him but he responds to her fond overtures of sympathy with a tirade against womankind, wondering why God had not been satisfied with purely masculine spirits, angels and men, rather than creating at last this novelty on earth, this fair defect of nature and finding some other way to generate mankind. Eve admits her frailty and then suggests that to save their progeny from sin and death they refrain from the nuptial embrace and languish away without hope. Or, as she continues, they may make short work of it and seek death by their own hands. Adam, however, reminds her of the promise that her seed would bruise the serpent's head and to seek pardon and peace from the offended Deity. They repair to the place where they were condemned and there falling prostrate yield themselves to tearful penitence and supplication.

THE PILGRIM'S PROGRESS
From This World to That Which is to Come.

By

John Bunyan

JOHN BUNYAN (*1628–1688*) was an English religious reformer. He followed his father's trade of tinker and joined Cromwell's army when he was about seventeen years of age. He married when he was about twenty and by the influence of his wife he joined the Nonconformists. After the death of his wife five years later, Bunyan began his work of preaching. He drew great crowds and was in constant demand throughout all the Midland counties. After the Restoration Bunyan persisted in his irregular preaching in the face of an edict that all divine services should be in accordance with the forms of the estab-lished church. He was confined in Bedford county jail from 1660 to 1672. Here he was allowed a large degree of freedom, supported his family and even married again. He was again imprisoned for six months and in 1675 when he probably finished *The Pilgrim's Progress*. After his liberation his fame as a preacher continued to increase until his death by which time ten editions of *The Pilgrim's Progress* had been sold. He wrote numerous other works including *The Life and Death of Mr. Badman, Grace Abounding* and *The Holy War*.

As I WALKED through the wilderness of this world, I fell to sleep, and as I slept I dreamed a Dream. I looked and behold a man clothed with Rags, a Book in his hand, and a great Burden on his back. He dwelt in the City of Destruction, and being persuaded that the place was about to be destroyed by fire and not able to persuade his wife and children to accompany him, he resolved to leave this world, and immediately met with a man named Evangel-ist, by whom he was counseled to proceed to yon Wicket-gate and receive further instructions.

So I saw in my Dream that this man began to run. Two of his neighbors, Obstinate and Pliable, resolved to fetch him back, but Christian persuaded Pliable to go with him, and on the way discoursed to him of the glories of the far country to which he was bound. Now they drew near to the Slough of Dispond, and began to sink in the mire. Pliable struggled out on the side nearest his own house and so returned to his home, leaving Christian tumbling in the Slough alone. He however having managed to reach the opposite side of the miry pit nearest the Wicket-gate, yet could not rise from it because of his Burden. He was pluckt out by a man named Help, and proceeded on his way, only to encounter Mr. Worldly Wiseman who dwelt in the Town of Carnal Policy. This fellow proposed to him an easier way to be rid of his Burden than the way through the Wicket-gate, and directed him to the village of Morality, to the home of Legality who with his Son Civility could shew him how to be rid of his Burden. Christian was about to turn thither, when he became afraid of the Mount by which he had to go, lest it fall on his head.

At this moment Evangelist appeared unto him, and rebuked him for going astray. Christian began to cry out lamentably and repented that he had followed the counsel of Mr. Worldly Wiseman, and Evangelist, warning him not to turn aside again, bade him God speed on his way. So now I saw that he arrived at the Wicket-gate, and when he knocked Good-will opened to him, and gave to him advice about the straight and narrow way he must follow, and told him furthermore that he must be content to bear his Burden until he came to the place of Deliverance where it would fall off by itself.

Christian girded up his loins and addressed himself again to his Journey, and proceeded until he reached the house of the Interpreter. The Interpreter shewed him many excellent and profitable things, which put him in hope and fear, and then sent him on his way to the Celestial City.

Christian now advanced up a highway which was fenced on either side with the Wall of Salvation, and at the top of this ascent, Christian's Burden fell off at the foot of the Cross, and rolled into the Sepulchre beneath, and he saw it no more. Now behold three Shining Ones met him, and he was given a change of raiment to take the place of his rags, a mark was set in his forehead, and he received a Roll with a Seal on it to give in at the Celestial Gate.

Now I saw that Christian proceeded on his way with joy and singing. The three sleepers whom he discovered on the way, with fetters upon their heels, Simple, Sloth, and Presumption, he sought to warn of their peril, but they would not listen. He attempted to reason with Formalist and Hypocrisy, who came tumbling over the wall, but neither would they listen, for shortly these two friends attempted another short cut. Instead of climbing the Hill Difficulty, the one followed the way of Danger, the other of Destruction, supposing these would lead, as did the main narrow way right up the hill to the destination they were bound for, but they did not, and soon the men who had come not in at the door were seen no more.

About the mid-way to the top of the Hill of Difficulty was a pleasant Arbour made for the refreshment of travellers. Refreshed there by sleep, and unhappily having dropped in that place his Roll though he knew it not, Christian proceeded to the top, and there met with Timorous and Mistrust, who warned him of Lions in the way. Resolving boldly to continue on his path notwithstanding, Christian for the first missed the precious Roll he had lost, which was the assurance of his life and acceptance at the desired Haven. Going back to the pleasant Arbour he found it, and then beheld just by the High-way side the Palace Beautiful.

Making haste to reach it, for it was night, he saw two Lions in the way. The Lions were chained, but he saw not the chains, and fearfully he stopped. But the porter at the lodge, whose name was Watchful, called to him that the beasts were chained and that he should keep in the midst of the Path. The beautiful Damsel, Discretion, was summoned by the porter to speak with the traveller, who desired entertainment for the night in that house built for the relief and security of pilgrims. Discretion summoned Prudence, Piety, and Charity, who discoursed with him till supper-time concerning his travels and why he left home.

Christian rested that night in a bed chamber called Peace, and on the day following he was shown of the Rarities and Records of the place. He stayed yet another night, and on the morn beheld far off to the south the Delectable Mountains in Immanuel's Land.

Before continuing on his journey he was provided with armour from the Palace's Armoury. Then Discretion, Piety, Charity, and Prudence accompanied him to the foot of the Hill, and gave him a loaf of Bread, a bottle of Wine, and a cluster of Raisins when they left him.

Christian proceeded on his way through the Valley of Humiliation, and soon spied a foul Fiend, Apollyon, coming to meet him. And I saw in my Dream that there ensued a terrific combat between these two, which lasted above half a day, even till Christian was almost quite spent and began to despair of life, but in the end Christian gave Apollyon a deadly thrust with his sword, and thereupon the Fiend spread forth his Dragon's wings and sped him away, that Christian for a season saw him no more.

Now Christian gave thanks to the Lord for his deliverance, and there came to him a hand with some of the leaves of the Tree of Life, which healed his wounds immediately. After refreshment, he continued on his way, and came to another Valley, the Valley of the Shadow of Death, a very solitary place. There met him two men who were turning back, and they warned him of the coming dangers. The pathway here was exceeding narrow, and on one side of it was a deep Ditch, and on the other a Quagmire. About the middle of the Valley I perceived the Mouth of Hell, out of which flame and smoke came in abundance. The Sword of Christian availed him not in this predicament, and he had to rely on the weapon All-prayer.

Now Christian heard doleful voices, and rushings to and fro, and perceived a company of Fiends coming to meet him, who however gave back and came no further when he declared I will walk in the strength of the Lord God. The second part of the Valley was even more dangerous than the first, and full of Pitfalls, and at the end of the Valley was the Cave of the Giants Pagan and Pope, which however Christian passed without much danger, though many bodies and bones of former pilgrims lay about.

And I saw that Christian now overtook another pilgrim to the Celestial City, Faithful, who had been his neighbor in the City of Destruction, and of whose passage on before him the porter at the gate of the Palace Beautiful had told him when he left. The two discoursed as they went on together of the adventures that had befallen Faithful thus far on his journey.

Christian and Faithful now discovered a companion walking with them, Talkative, the son of Say-well, who dwelt in Prating Row, a man with a beguiling tongue but who knew good things only to *talk* of them. They were finally rid of him, and as they passed through a Wilderness, Evangelist came up to them, and with praise for their victories urged them not to faint but to press on to obtain the Crown which is incorruptible. He predicted for them tribulations in the Town of Vanity which they were now about to enter, and said that one of them must needs die there.

And I now saw that Christian and Faithful approached the Town of Vanity, having got out of the Wilderness, and entered into the Fair that was held there. Now in this Town of Vanity is kept a great Fair all the year long, where tempting Merchandise is displayed and sold to tempt the pilgrims. The Fair was instituted almost five thousand years agone, and he who would reach the Celestial City must needs pass through the Town. When Christian and Faithful arrived there a great hubbub arose around them, both because of their Raiment and Speech which were diverse from the Raiment and Speech of any of them that traded at the Fair. And also because they would not even look upon the tempting Wares offered to them. When mockingly asked What will ye buy, they replied We buy the Truth.

Finally the Great One of the Fair ordered that they be brought to examination, and they were questioned and then beaten and besmeared with dirt and put into a Cage to be made a spectacle to all the men at the Fair. When some of the spectators ventured to defend them, the two pilgrims were beaten yet again and put in irons and led up and down before the Fair, and then their feet were made fast in the Stocks.

At a convenient time they were brought forth to their Tryal, in order to their condemnation, for the men were secretly resolved that they should die. The Judge was Lord Hate-good, and the Indictment was that they had made Commotions and Diversions in the Town and that they were enemies to and disturbers of their Trade. Three witnesses appeared against them, namely, Envy, Superstition, and Pickthank.

Faithful was called up first, and defended himself right boldly, but he was condemned to death by the Jury, the most cruel death that could be invented. And after his tormentors were through with him, I saw that a Chariot and a couple of Horses took Faithful into the Clouds, with the sound of Trumpet, the nearest way to the Celestial Gate. But Christian was sent back to prison and there remained for a space, later he escaped and went on his way. As a new companion, Hopeful, joined himself onto him. And quickly after they were got out of the Fair, they overtook one that was going before them, whose name was By-ends, from the town of Fair-speech.

Now By-ends and the companions who soon joined him differed from others in Religion in two points, they never strove against Wind and Tide, and they were most jealous when Religion went in Silver Slippers. They had all been School-fellows together, taught by one Mr. Gripe-man, a School-master in Love-gain, a Market-town in the County of Coveting, in the North. After some converse together, these hurried up to Christian and Hopeful, who had proceeded on before, with a deceitful question, but Christian shamed them with his answer, so that they fell behind again.

Christian and Hopeful, having proceeded over the narrow plain Ease with much content, at its further side found a little Hill called Lucre and in that Hill a Silver-Mine, over against which stood Demas, to tempt the Passengers to come and see and dig. These two refused, but when By-ends and his Companions came up they at the first beck went over to Demas, and were never seen again, being either smothered or fallen into the Pit.

The Pilgrims now passed an old Monument, hard by the Highway-side, which was Lot's Wife turned into a Pillar of Salt, placed there as a warning for them, and then they came to a pleasant River, the River of God, or the River of the Water of Life. Their way lay along the Bank, and they walked there with great delight, and refreshed themselves with the water of the River and the fruit of the Trees, and they lay down and slept in a Meadow beyond the River.

And I beheld in my Dream that their way left the River, and the new way being rough to their feet, they wished for a better. Now they espied on the left hand of the road a Meadow, By-path Meadow, and a Stile to go over into it, which Stile they crossed, and followed a Path on the other side of the fence which seemed to lead in their direction, though Hopeful was afraid on't at the very first. And indeed a fellow on ahead of them, Vain-confidence by name, assured them that it led to the Holy City. But the night grew dark, and hearing a moaning on ahead of them they found that Vain-confidence had fallen into a deep Pit.

Rain and thunder and lightning came, and the water rose amain, but Christian struggled back over the path which they had come, and had like to have drowned nine or ten times. Nor could they reach the Stile that night, and fell asleep, and the next morning came Giant Despair, the owner of Doubting Castle, in whose grounds they were, and took them prisoners, and threw them into a nasty and stinking Dungeon.

The wife of Giant Despair was Diffidence, and on her advice the men were soundly beaten the next day without mercy, and the next, angry that they were still alive, the Giant urged them, without avail, to make an end of themselves. Christian had some desire to follow this counsel, as their lot was so miserable, but Hopeful persuaded him that they should not be their own murderers, and the Giant would have made an end to them himself, but he fell into one of his Fits.

Having shewed to them in the Castle-yard the Bones and Skulls of former Pilgrims he had dispatched, and threatened them with like treatment, that night, after much prayer, Christian found in his bosom a Key called Promise which would open any lock in Doubting Castle. So they happily escaped, and came to the King's Highway again, and were out of the Giant's Jurisdiction. And making their way to the Stile, they erected there a Pillar, with a writing to warn those who should come after them of the Giant and his treatment of Pilgrims.

They then went on till they came to the Delectable Mountains, on the tops of which they found Shepherds feeding their flocks, whose names were Knowledge, Experience, Watchful, and Sincere. Having entertained them in their Tents, the Shepherds next day shewed them Mount Error and Mount Caution and a By-way to Hell. Christian and Hopeful proceeded on their way, after having glimpsed the Gates of the Celestial City through the Perspective Glass from the top of the Hill called Clear.

And as they were taking leave of the Shepherds, one of them gave them a *Note of the way.* A second bid them *beware of the Flatterer,* and the third admonished them to *take heed that they sleep not on the Inchanted Ground.* The fourth bid them *Godspeed.*

And I dreamed again, and I saw that, as the same two Pilgrims went on their way toward the Holy City, Ignorance came out of the Country of Conceit to join them, by a little crooked Lane. They pressed on ahead of Ignorance, and having been led astray at a place where two roads met by a man black of flesh but covered with a very light Robe, who was Flatterer, they fell into a Net, and there remembered the advice of the Shepherd to *beware of the Flatterer,* as a Shining One with a Whip of small cord in his hand let them out and led them back to the right way, questioning them as to why they had not read their Note of direction, and chastising them sore before he left them.

Now Christian and Hopeful were met by Atheist, who mocked them, but they passed him and went their way. And behold they approached a certain Country, whose air naturally tended to make one drowsy, and Hopeful began to be very dull and heavy of sleep. But Christian reminded him of the warning of the third Shepherd not to sleep on the Inchanted Ground, and to prevent drowsiness said Christian let us fall into good discourse. So Hopeful related how he had become minded to seek the Holy City, and after their discourse, I saw that Ignorance approached them again, but though they gave him good Counsel he yet could not keep pace with them and fell behind once more.

After more discourse on the nature of true Religion, the Pilgrims were got over the Inchanted Ground, and now I saw in my Dream that they were entering into the Country of Beulah, upon the borders of Heaven. The air was sweet and pleasant, the Vineyards and Gardens had been planned for the solace and refreshment of Pilgrims, and the two tarried and slept.

And then I saw in my Dream that they addressed themselves to go up to the City, and on their way they met two men in Raiment that shone like gold, and were told of two more difficulties to meet with before they reached the City which was pure gold. And behold they came to the River of Death, over which there was no Bridge, and the River was very deep, the which when they had entered Christian had hearty fears that he should die in that River, and Hopeful had much ado to keep his Brother's head above water.

But at length they came up out of the River, and found awaiting them on the far side the two Shining Ones whom they had seen before they started to cross. The two Pilgrims had left their mortal Garments behind them in the River, and with much agility and speed they hastened up the Hill on the top of which the City stood, led by these same Shining Ones, who discoursed to them of the Glories of the heavenly Jerusalem.

As they were drawing towards the Gate, behold a company of the Heavenly Host came out to meet them with several of the King's Trumpeters, who saluted them with melodious noise, so that it seemed as if Heaven itself was come down to meet them. And thus they came up to the Gate. And I saw in my Dream that these two men went in at the Gate, after their Certificates had been taken to the King, and lo! as they entered they were transfigured, and they had Raiment put on them that shone like Gold, and they were given Harps and Crowns.

And Ignorance, being got over the River without half that difficulty that the other two men had met with, for one, Vain-hope, a ferry-man with his Boat helped him cross, ascended the Hill to come to the Gate alone, and no one met him with welcome. Having knocked at the Gate, and being asked for his Certificate he had none, and the King commanded the two Shining Ones to bind Ignorance hand and foot and have him away, and he was put in a door at the side of the Hill. Then I saw that there was a way to Hell even from the Gates of Heaven, as well as from the City of Destruction. So I awoke, and behold it was a Dream.

THE LIFE AND ACHIEVEMENTS OF THE RENOWN'D DON QUIXOTE de la MANCHA

By

Miguel de Cervantes Saavedra

MIGUEL DE CERVANTES SAAVEDRA (*1547–1616*), the Spanish writer, was born of pure Castilian stock. It is believed that he was a student of Hoyos and that he contributed verses on the master's memorial volume. In 1569 he moved to Italy where his life is little known for 10 years until he received wounds at the battle of Lepanto which crippled his left hand for life. Sailing later for Spain he was captured by Algerian pirates and held for ransom for five years. The plays he is supposed to have written in captivity are lost. He published the first part of *Don Quixote* in 1604 and the second part in 1615. Although the book was sensationally successful it brought Cervantes little money reward and he lived wretchedly in squalid quarters until his death.

IN A CERTAIN VILLAGE of La Mancha in Spain there lived at one Time an old-fashioned Gentleman of about fifty Years who spent his Time in reading Books of Knight-Errantry; indeed he had pored over them so long that he had lost the Use of his Reason. Many Arguments he had with the Curate of the Parish and the Barber about Amadis de Gaul, the Knight of the Burning Sword, or the Hero whom he most admired, Rinaldo of Montalvan.

His Understanding now quite gone, and all Interest lost in his Household which consisted of his Housekeeper, his Niece of twenty Years, and a Lad who served him in the Field and at Home, the odd Fancy seized him that he must turn Knight-Errant and roam through the whole World in Search of Adventure. Straightway he prepared himself thus to imitate the Lives of the Heroes in his Romances, and he brought out an old Suit of Armour that had belonged to his Great-Grandfather and had it well scoured. His Horse, a Creature of Skin and Bones, seemed to his disordered Mind a nobler Steed than Bucephalus that carried Alexander the Great to Battle, and he spent four whole Days in thinking up a new Name for the Animal, finally concluding to call him Rozinante signifying that what formerly had been an ordinary Horse was now a very special Steed and worthy of a Knight.

This being done, it took him eight Days to choose a worthy Name for himself. Having finally decided on the Appellation of Don Quixote de la Mancha, thereby honouring his Birthplace, nothing seemed now necessary but that he should find a Lady on whom he might bestow the Empire of his Heart. There was a hale, buxom Country Wench of the next Village, by Name Aldonza Lorenzo, whom our Knight decided to take for his Lady fair, and he gave her the new Name of Dulcinea of Toboso to show that she was a Lady of Quality.

Ready now to set forth, one Morning in the Heat of July, without acquainting any one with his Design, Don Quixote armed himself, mounted Rozinante, and from his own Back-yard rode off into the Fields. Ere long he bethought himself that he had not yet been dubbed Knight and that he ought not aspire to knightly Atchievements until he had had that Honour conferred upon him. Resolving therefore to ask the first Person he met to perform this Ceremony, as he had read in his Romances might properly be done, he travelled all that Day without meeting with any Adventure worth the telling, albeit he thought much on the Wrongs he was to redress and the Dangers he would meet. Toward Evening, both he and his Horse exhausted, he espied an Inn which, in his distorted Imagination he took to be a Castle, and two common Wenches at the Door of it two beautiful Ladies whom he proceeded to address as he thought became a Knight in his Position. The hearty Laughter of the Wenches our Knight resented bitterly, and the Inn-keeper when he appeared would fain have joined them in their Merriment on account of the incongruous Appearance of our Hero, but because of his war-like Look he resolved to answer him civilly and offered him what Accommodation he had for the Night. Don Quixote, taking the Inn-keeper to be the Governor of the Castle, dismounted from his Horse and suffered himself to be led within.

The Wenches, whom he addressed as Ladies fair, assisted him to pull off his Armour, but the Helmet he had ty'd so fast with green Ribbons that 'twas impossible to get it off without cutting them. This Don Quixote would in no wise permit, so he was forced to keep his Helmet on all Night. The Knight addressed the Ladies, for so he still took them to be, with rhetorical Speeches, but to these they could make no Answer, and only asked him if he would eat any thing. "That I will with all my Heart," cry'd Don Quixote, and a short and unsatisfactory supper of some Pieces of Salt-fish and bread mouldy and brown was set before him. With some Help he contrived to eat in spite of the Inconvenience of wearing his Helmet all the Time. This poor Fare seemed nevertheless to him of the Finest, and the only Thing that disturbed his Mind was the Thought that he had not yet been dubbed a Knight.

He resolved to settle this last Matter before he departed on the Morrow, and after Supper therefore, with many fine Words, he demanded of the Inn-keeper that he confer the Honour of Knight-hood upon him. "This Night," said the would-be Knight, "I will watch my Armour in the Chapel of your Castle, and then in the Morning you shall gratify me, that I may be duly qualify'd to seek out Adventures in every Corner of the Universe, to relieve the Distress'd."

The Master of the Inn perceived from his strange Words that his Guest was disordered in his Mind, and decided to humour him in his Desires, telling Don Quixote that he was highly to be commended for his choice of such an Employment, which, he pretended, was the same as the Inn-keeper's own in his Youth. There was no Chapel in the Inn, but the Keeper said that his Guest might lawfully keep the Vigil of his Arms in the Courtyard. Questioning the would-be Knight as to whether he had any Money, Don Quixote reply'd that he had never read in any History of Chivalry that any Knight-Errant ever carry'd Money about him. "You are mistaken," cry'd the Inn-keeper, and assur'd him that though the Histories did not think it necessary to mention Things so evidently necessary as Money and clean Shirts, there was no reason to believe that the Knights went without either. "I must even charge and command you," he said, "as you are shortly to be my Son in Chivalry, never from this Time forward to ride without Money, nor without the other Necessaries" such as a Supply of Lint and Salve to dress his Wounds.

Promising to obey all these Injunctions, without more Ado, our Knight repaired to the Court-yard to watch his Arms throughout the Night. The Inn-keeper acquainted all the other Guests with the Extravagancies of the Stranger, and they took Pleasure in observing him at a Distance as he pass'd his Vigil. One of the Carriers who lodg'd in the Inn went out to water his Mules, and had the ill Luck to be set upon by Don Quixote as he removed from the Trough where our Hero had placed them the Arms and threw them on the Ground. Calling upon the Lady Dulcinea to help him, Don Quixote laid the Fellow flat and helpless at his Feet, and when another Carrier entered the Yard for the same Purpose treated him in like Fashion.

The other Carriers seeing their Comrades thus ill-us'd attacked the maddened Knight with a Volley of Stones, from which he sheltered himself as best he could, muttering out Curses and Threats the while with much Spirit and Undauntedness. The Inn-keeper to prevent further Mischief resolv'd to bestow on his Guest forthwith that unlucky Knighthood he so much desired. So, assuring him that he had already watch'd his Armour sufficiently long, the Master of the Inn fetched a Book, and with the Help of the two kind Females and a Boy who held a Bit of lighted Candle in his Hand, proceeded with the Ceremony. Pretending to mutter some pious Oration he gave the Knight a good blow on the Neck with the Flat of the Sword. "Heav'n make your worship a lucky Knight," cry'd one of the Ladies as she girded on his sword, "and prosper you wherever you go."

Aurora began to usher in the Morn as these extraordinary Ceremonies were ended, and with the most extravagant thanks for their great Kindnesses Don Quixote departed from the Inn, overjoy'd to find himself knighted. Calling to Mind the Admonitions of the Inn-keeper concerning the Provision of Money and other Necessaries, our hero resolved to return Home to furnish himself with these and likewise to provide himself with a Squire. As he rode along he now came upon a Country-Fellow who was unmercifully beating his Servant, a Lad, whom he accused of Carelessness in tending a Flock of Sheep. Frighten'd by this Apparition in Armour, the Farmer promised to loose the Boy and to pay him what he owed him. "But," said the Farmer, "I have no Money about me, let Andrew go Home with me, and I'll pay him every Piece out of Hand." And swearing by the Order of Knighthood, as Don Quixote bade him, the Fellow promised; however no sooner had the Knight pass'd out of Sight than the Farmer ty'd the Lad to the tree anew and beat him so unmercifully that scarce any Signs of Life were left in him, taunting him the while. But Don Quixote proceeded on his Way, well pleased with himself for what he thought a great Wrong righted.

Our Knight next perceived coming toward him a Company of Merchants of Toledo. Taking this to be some new Adventure he posted himself in the Middle of the Road, and challenged them as they approached that they should declare his Lady Dulcinea the most beautiful Damsel in the World. The Merchants perceived that the poor Gentleman had lost his Senses, and one of their Number undertook to talk with him but had the ill Fortune unwittingly to insult the fair Lady, whereat Don Quixote ran at him with Lance couch'd and had it not been that the Horse Rozinante stumbled and fell, leaving our Knight sprawled upon the Ground burdened with all his heavy Armour, the Merchant would have been a dead Man.

However, in this helpless Condition, the badly bruised Knight played the Hero with his Tongue; "Stay," cry'd he, "Cowards, Rascals, do not fly! 'Tis not through my Fault that I lie here, but through that of my Horse, ye Poltroons!" Hearing these Insults one of the Grooms came up to him and snatched his Lance. Having broken it to Pieces, he thrash'd soundly the helpless Knight until he had tir'd out his Passion and himself. Then the Company passed on, and Don Quixote trying in vain to rise to his Feet, nevertheless esteemed himself a happy Man although in such an unhappy State, persuaded that his Misfortune was one of those Accidents common in Knight-Errantry.

Musing thus, he bethought him what Passage he had read that might bring him Comfort in his Plight, and began to recite lustily the verses he called to Mind of the Story of Baldwin and the

Marquess of Mantua. At length, a Ploughman from the next Village with a Sack of Wheat from the Mill happen'd to pass by and espied him lying helpless on the Ground. To the Inquiries as to who he was and what was the Matter, Don Quixote reply'd only by reciting more Verses from the Romances he had read. In much Amazement the astonished Fellow presently lifted the Visor of the Knight's Helmet and recognized him to be Master Quixada, which was his proper Name before he imagined himself a Knight. Much astonish'd to find his Neighbor in such a State, but still learning Nothing from him but more extravagant passages from his Romances, the Fellow at last succeeded in setting Don Quixote upon his own Ass, and ascertaining that he had no serious wound, gather'd up all his Armour, and led him, Rozinante bearing the Armour, to his Home.

The Home of our Hero, when they reached it, they found in great Confusion. His Niece and the Curate and Barber had just decided to burn all his Books of Knight-Errantry on the Morrow, and now they were more than ever convinced that he had lost his Mind because of his Reading. His Friends could learn Nothing from the Knight of what had transpired, and at length comply'd with his desire that they should give him Something to eat and leave him to his Repose. And next Day came the Burning of the Books, superintended by the Curate and the Barber, though the Former resolv'd first to read at least the Title-page of every Book before it was consign'd to the Flames. He soon wearied of this however, and the last of the Books were given to the Bon-fire without Examination. Now they resolved to stop up the Door of the Room where the Books had been so that Don Quixote could not find it, and they told him that an Inchanter had carried away Study, Books and all.

Full fifteen Days did our Knight remain quietly at Home, but at the End of that Time he was ready for more Adventure. He had acquired a Squire, Sancho Panza, a poor but honest Country-Labourer, whom he lured on to accompany him by many Promises. To provide himself with Money this Time he sold some of his Property, and he and Sancho Panza departed by Stealth one Night, the Squire looking forward to the Island promised him of which he should be Governor. Sancho doubted however whether his wife could be Queen of the promised Island, "for", said he, "though it should rain down Kingdoms upon the Face of the Earth, not one of them would sit well upon Mary Gutierez's Head; for I must needs tell you, she's not worth two Brass Jacks to make a Queen of."

Soon they discovered in a Plain some thirty or forty Wind-mills, which Don Quixote took to be outrageous Giants ready for Combat. "Pray look better, Sir," quoth Sancho, "those Things yonder are no Giants, but Wind-mills, and the Arms you fancy are their Sails, which being whirled about by the Wind, make the Mill go." " 'Tis a Sign," cry'd Don Quixote, "thou art but little acquainted with Adventures! I tell thee, they are Giants, and I am resolv'd to engage in a dreadful unequal Combat with them all." Rushing with Rozinante's utmost Speed upon the first Wind-mill he could come at, the Wind at that Moment increased, the Arms of the Mill whirled round and broke his Lance in Pieces and hurled away both Knight and Horse into a Field.

Sancho ran to help his Master. "Did I not tell you they were Wind-mills, and that no Body could think otherwise, unless he had also Wind-mills in his Head?" "Peace, Friend Sancho," reply'd Don Quixote: "There is nothing so subject to the Inconstancy of Fortune as War."

The next Day's Adventure came when two Monks of the Order of St. Benedict approached them mounted on two Dromedaries, or so their high and stately Mules seemed to our Knight. Following them came a Coach carrying a Biscayan Lady to Seville. But to Don Quixote it seemed otherwise. "Without all Question those two black Things that move towards us must be some Necromancers, that are carrying away by Force some Princess in that Coach; and 'Tis my Duty to prevent so great an Injury." So saying, and against the Pleadings of his Squire, the Knight proceeded to meet the Monks, and addressing them as "Cursed Implements of Hell" demanded that they immediately release the high-born Princess in the Coach. Astonished both at the Figure and Expressions of the Speaker, the Monks protested mildly that they were religious Men travelling on their own Affairs. But not to be deceived by fair Words "I know you well enough, perfidious Caitiffs," reply'd Don Quixote, and rushed upon one of the Monks who saved himself by flinging himself off his Mule on the Ground. Poor Sancho had the worst of it then, for he considered the fallen Monk lawful Plunder, and nimbly skipp'd off his Ass, and running to the unlucky fellow began to strip him immediately. The two Muleteers who followed fell upon the poor Squire, thump'd and maul'd him in every Part of his Carcase and left him sprawling without Breath or Motion. This gave the second Monk a Chance to escape and join his Fellow, and the two proceeded on their Way.

By this time Don Quixote was engaged in conversation with the Lady in the Coach. "Lady," he cry'd, "your Discretion is now at liberty to dispose of your beautiful self as you please, for the presumptuous Arrogance of those who attempted to enslave your Person lies prostrate in the Dust, overthrown by this my strenuous Arm: And that you may not be at a Loss for the Name of your Deliverer, know I am call'd Don Quixote de la Mancha, by Profession a Knight-Errant and Adventurer, Captive to that peerless Beauty Donna Dulcinea del Toboso." Being about to turn the Coach back to Toboso so that the fair one therein might present herself to the Lady Dulcinea and inform her of the valorous Exploits of the Knight, the lady's Gentleman-Usher now interfered, and a furious Combat now ensued between these two. Don Quixote with Sword aloft was rushing upon the wary Biscayan, with a full Resolution to cleave him asunder, while he on his part resolv'd to face him with equal Bravery. The Lady in the Coach had made her Coachman drive out of Harm's-way, and she and her Women made many Vows and Offerings that Providence might deliver them.

And here we must deplore the abrupt End of this History, and the next Book will inform the Reader of the Outcome of this most terrible Combat, for the second Undertaker of this Work searched most diligently until he had found out the Continuation of this pleasant History.

GULLIVER'S TRAVELS

By

Jonathan Swift

JONATHAN SWIFT (*1667–1745*) was an Irish satirist and dean of St. Patrick's in Dublin, his birthplace. He became secretary to Sir William Temple in London in 1689 but returned to Ireland in 1694 to enter the priesthood. In 1699 he became secretary to Lord Berkeley of Ireland and soon began his career as a political pamphleteer. Swift became a Tory upon the party's return to power in 1710. He was made editor of the *Examiner* for two subsequent years when he issued a number of individual pamphlets. In 1713 he was appointed to the deanery of St. Patrick's and in Dublin completed *Gulliver's Travels* in 1776. This is hailed as one of the foremost satirical works of literature.

PART I

A VOYAGE TO LILLIPUT

THE *Antelope,* on which in 1699 I had a specially advantageous position as ship's surgeon, sailed for the South Sea and while making for the East Indies was driven by a violent storm to the northwest of Van Diemen's Land. Here the ship split upon a rock, six of the crew, myself included, getting clear of the sinking vessel in a small-boat, which in turn was spilled by the waves. What became of my companions I never knew, but I myself swam for shore, and being profoundly exhausted, slept above nine hours on some soft and very short grass.

When I attempted to rise, I was unable to stir; for, as I happened to lie on my back, I found my legs and arms were strongly fastened on each side to the ground; and my hair, which was long and thick, tied down in the same manner. I likewise felt several

slender ligatures across my body, from my armpits to my thighs.
I heard a confused noise about me; and in a little time felt something alive moving on my left leg, which, advancing gently over
my breast, came almost up to my chin. Bending my eyes downward as much as I could, I perceived it to be a human creature not
six inches high, with a bow and arrow in his hand and a quiver at
his back. In the meantime I felt some forty more of the same kind
following the first. I was in the utmost astonishment, and roared so
loud that they all ran back in a fright; and some of them, as I
learned afterward, were hurt by the falls they got by leaping from
my sides upon the ground. Being curious and audacious creatures,
the greater part of them soon returned.

In my great uneasiness, I struggled to get loose and had the
fortune to wrench my left arm free and loosen my hair a little.
There followed immediately a hundred stinging sensations in my
left arm and face—the little people had fired their arrows. Now I
thought it the most prudent method to lie still.

Soon I heard a knocking near my right ear, and perceived they
were building a platform. On this there mounted what seemed to
be a person of quality, who made a long speech which I could not
understand, but by signs I made him understand that I would be
submissive (though I knew that if once free I would be a match
for the greatest armies they had) and that I wanted food and
drink.

The *hurgo* (for so they call a great lord, as I later learnt) commanded ladders to be applied to my sides, on which hundreds of
the inhabitants mounted, bearing baskets full of meat. There were
shoulders, legs, and loins shaped like those of mutton, but smaller
than the wings of a lark. I ate them by two or three at a mouthful.
I took three loaves at a time, about the bigness of musket bullets.
They supplied me as they could, showing a thousand marks of
wonder and astonishment at my bulk and appetite.

For my drink, they slung up one of their largest hogsheads, which
I drank off at a draught, it holding not a half a pint. It tasted like
a small wine of Burgundy, but much more delicious. They brought
me a second hogshead, and I made signs for more, but they had
none to give me. When I had performed these wonders, they
shouted for joy, and danced upon my breast.

[323]

I was at moments much tempted to seize forty or fifty of them and dash them to the ground, but I felt myself bound by my honor —for so I interpreted my submissive behavior—also, by the laws of hospitality, they having fed me at such great cost; and besides, I admired the courage of these diminutive mortals who dared to mount and walk upon my body while one of my hands was at liberty.

They would not release me, but with great trouble raised and slung me on a machine of wood, some seven feet long and three inches from the ground and moving on twenty-two wheels. Fifteen hundred of the emperor's largest horses, each about four inches and a half high, were employed to draw me to the metropolis, some half a mile distant over flattish country.

Near the city gates there was an empty temple about the size of a large doghouse, unused for religious ceremonies because it had years before been defiled by an unnatural murder, and here it was determined I should live. They chained me there by uniting some four-score and eleven chains (like those for a lady's watch in Europe) and using six-and-thirty padlocks. Then they cut all the strings that bound me.

Now I was introduced to their emperor, a very handsome, strong and masculine person, plainly and simply clad. He gave orders that I be treated well; that the inhabitants cease from walking over me; and that I be taught their language through his scholars. Clothes and bedding were made for me by sewing together hundreds of their largest rolls of cloth.

After several weeks, when I had learned their language, I had many conversations with the great men of the country and learned their customs.

One of the most interesting of these was the filling of high offices by competitions in which the candidates jump on a tight-rope, he who dances thus without falling winning the coveted honor. Those in office often are commanded also to perform, to show they have not lost their skill. Flimnap, the treasurer, is by the far the best of them, tho' Reldresal, the principal secretary for private affairs, is a close second. These diversions are of course frequently attended by fatal accidents, and by broken limbs.

All of this, however, is somehow done despite a law that makes the acquirement of office a reward for great moral character, rather than for cleverness of any kind, including the intellectual variety. Another common affair of the country is the presence of two evils: both violent factions at home, and the danger of an invasion by a most potent enemy from abroad.

The present internal difficulty arose from a dispute as to whether eggs should be broken at the large end or the small; and while many scholars claimed there was no cause for a schism in religion on this ground, their holy book the Blundecral saying only that all true believers break their eggs at the convenient end, still the Bigendians had been exiled, and had found much favor in the court of the enemy people of Blefuscu.

Now the Lilliputians, taking me for a man of honor, and seeing that I might be useful in war, gave me my freedom after getting my signature to certain articles designed to protect their people and to provide for my keep. I was also to help them against the Blefuscu army, which, when the time came, I did by drawing half their battleships after me as I swam through the channel dividing their two kingdoms.

The emperor was so overjoyed that he ordered me to capture the rest of their navy, by which act that empire would be reduced to a province. But I plainly protested that I would never be an instrument of bringing a free and brave people into slavery; and when the matter was debated in council, the wisest part of the ministry were of my opinion.

This open, bold declaration of mine was so opposite to the schemes and politics of his imperial majesty, that he never forgave it. And certain of my secret enemies (especially the war admiral, who felt that my naval *coup* had deprived him of honor) helped to build up feeling against me. I learned in a very secret way through a friend at court that it was planned to put out my eyes and slowly to starve me to death. In the meantime I had the unwilling permission of his majesty to visit the kingdom of Blefuscu, a peace having been made with them. Now realizing my danger, I took my leave without a word of good-bye, and arriving at the capital across the channel, was roundly welcomed.

In a few days, the emperor of Lilliput sent ambassadors requesting my return, bound hand and foot, as a traitor.

The emperor of Blefuscu, having taken three days to consult, returned an answer consisting of many civilities and excuses. He said that, as for sending me bound, his brother emperor knew it was impossible; that tho' I had deprived him of his fleet, yet he owed me great obligations for many good offices. That, however, both their majesties would soon be made easy; for I had found a prodigious vessel on the shore, able to carry me to sea, which he had given orders to fit up, with my own assistance and direction, and he hoped, in a few weeks, both empires would be freed of so insupportable (financially and gustatorily speaking) an incumbrance.

And so it was. The boat was fitted, and stored with hundreds of carcases of oxen and sheep, with bread and drink proportionable. Also, I took a number of live cattle and sheep, and would gladly have taken a dozen of the natives, but this was forbidden me.

I was fortunate on my voyage in meeting an English merchantman and thus I was carried home; where I proved my unbelievable story by displaying the diminutive animals, which, by the way, multiplied and prospered, and the sheep are likely to prove a boon to woolen manufacturers by the fineness of their fleeces.

PART II

A VOYAGE TO BROBDINGNAG

Having been condemned by nature and fortune to an active and restless life, in ten months after my return I again took sail, on the *Adventure,* bound for Surat. Somewhere east of the Molucca Island, June 17th, 1703, we landed at an unknown island (or continent?) in search of water. I went ashore to do some exploring of my own, and of a sudden turning, I saw the others run for the boat and row as for life to the ship. Behind them came a huge creature, who walked in after them; but the sea being full of sharp rocks, he gave up, as for me, I ran in the opposite direction as fast as I could and coming to the top of a hill saw a vast country, with grass of an amazing height. I came upon a high road, for so I took it to be, though it served to the inhabitants only as a path through the barley. I was an hour walking to the end of this field, which was fenced in with a hedge of at least one hundred and twenty feet high, and the trees so lofty that I could make no computation of their altitude. Here was a stile, impossible for me to climb because every step was six feet high, and the top-stone above twenty.

Now I saw one of the inhabitants coming toward me, tall as an ordinary spire steeple, taking ten yards at every stride, and calling to some others in a voice many degrees louder than a speaking-trumpet; but the noise was so high in the air that at first I thought it to be thunder.

Being quite dispirited with toil, and wholly overcome by grief and despair, I lay down between two ridges. In my terrible state of mind I could not forbear thinking of Lilliput, whose inhabitants looked upon me as the greatest prodigy that ever appeared in the world; where I was able to draw a whole imperial fleet with my hand, and perform other actions which will be recorded forever in the chronicles of that empire. I reflected what a mortification it must prove to me to appear as inconsiderable in this nation, as one single Lilliputian would be amongst us—if indeed the first creature that seized me did not devour me.

The monsters began to mow the hay, and when I saw there was no escape from being trampled or cut to death, I screamed as loud as I might, until the man nearest heard, looked, and taking me between his fingers brought me within three yards of his eyes. All I ventured to do was to raise my eyes toward the sun, place my hands together in a supplicating posture, and speak some words in an humble, melancholy tone, suitable to the condition I then was in; for I apprehended every moment that he would dash me against the ground, as we usually do any hateful little animal which we have a mind to destroy. But my good star would have it, that he appeared pleased with my voice and gestures, and began to look upon me as a curiosity, much wondering to hear me pronounce articulate words, although he could not understand them. He did plainly apprehend my gestures desiring that he squeeze me less painfully between his thumb and forefinger, for he put me gently into his pocket and ran with me to his master.

By him I was taken home, and put into the care of his daughter, a girl of nine, some forty feet tall and small for her age. She named me Grildrig, which I learned, after she had taught me their language, imports what the Latins call *nanunculus,* the English *manni-kin.* She treated me with great care and affection, like a beloved pet, tenderly dressing and undressing me, seeing that I had all that I might require, and keeping me as much as she could out of the way of danger.

She made a cradle for me and hung it in the air to guard against the mice, which were about the size of myself, and one of which I had occasion to kill with my sword at great hazard to my life.

Another time I was nearly drowned by a frog, while rowing in a boat made by a native who had skill in the making of curios. The creature did not quite tip the vessel but climbed in, crawling back and forth over me and covering me with its horrid slime, till, banged over and over by one of my skulls it leaped into the water.

Another time I was vexatiously carried about by a monkey, who took me for one of its young, and forced into my mouth some disgusting victuals taken from one of his chaps.

My master the farmer soon saw how valuable I might prove to him, and carried me over the land as a show. He drove me so hard, requiring so unreasonably many performances and giving me so little rest, that I was like to die. Perceiving which, he was delighted when the queen, we having come to the capitol, offered to buy me.

To her majesty I made one petition, which was granted: that Glumdalcloth my nurse might remain with me. Here my life was on the whole pleasant, and certainly adventurous. I had many conversations with the king, a wise and good man, who asked me for a close account of the government and history of England.

I described our constitution and the Parliament; partly composed of an illustrious body called the House of Peers, persons of the noblest blood, of the most ancient and ample patrimonies, and given the most extraordinary care in their education that they might have a share in the legislature, to be members of the highest court of judicature, from whence there can be no appeal, and to be champions always ready for the defence of their prince and country, by their valor, conduct, and fidelity; the other part of Parliament consisting of an assembly, the House of Commons, who were all principal gentlemen, *freely* picked and culled by the people themselves, for their great abilities and love of their country, to represent the wisdom of the whole nation.

[328]

Then I recounted our history, showing my country to be far the greatest in Europe.

But the King, having taken careful notes, began to question me, and forced me to admit that the humor of the prince, or a sum of money to a court lady or a prime minister might make one a lord; that a stranger with a full purse might influence the vulgar voters to choose him for the Commons; that the courts might make a difference between a poor defendant and a rich one, and the lawyers draw out a case for years to their own benefit; that the bishops might not be appointed to that rank because of their knowledge of religion and their moral conscience but rather because they were the slavish chaplains of some ambitious nobleman.

All of this was highly shocking and foreign to this king, who likewise was perfectly astonished at the history of our country during the last century, protesting that it was only a heap of conspiracies, rebellions, murders, massacres, revolutions, and banishments. And when I offered to show his engineers how to make cannon which would batter down the strongest walls or destroy a whole metropolis, he was struck with horror, and was amazed how so impotent a grovelling an insect as I (these were his expressions) could entertain such inhuman ideas.

As for himself, he protested, although few things delighted him so much as new discoveries in art or in nature, yet he would rather lose half his kingdom than be privy to such a secret, which he commanded me, as I valued my life, never to mention any more.

A strange and narrow view! but the people of this country have not reduced politics to a science, as the more acute wits in Europe have done. This king rewarded the politicians but little, reserving his praise for those who made two ears of corn, or blades of grass, grow where only one had been before.

The learning of this whole people is very defective; consisting only in morality, history, poetry, and mathematics; but the last is wholly applied to what may be useful in life, and would by us be little esteemed. Of ideas, entities, abstractions, and transcendentals, I could never drive the least conception into their heads.

Thus I had not taught them much—though I had given their

scientists an example of what they called *relplum scalcath,* interpreted literally, *lusus naturae*—when by a happy accident I had my liberty. One day at the seashore I was carried off by an eagle (for which I think sorrowfully that my kind and innocent Glumdalclitch was both grieved and disgraced, who, pursued by others, let my box drop into the sea, whence as by a miracle I was rescued and returned to England.

CANDIDE

By

Voltaire

VOLTAIRE (*1694–1778*) was the assumed name of Jean François Marie Arouet, a French philosopher and author. He began writing satire and was thrown into the Bastille at the age of 23 on account of one of his lampoons. Released, he tried to advance himself at court until he was again incarcerated. He was released only upon condition that he flee to England where he became acquainted with Pope and his circle. In 1729 he returned to Paris and laid the foundation of what became great wealth, through lotteries and speculations. He was forced to retire to the country because of his continued lampooning but in 1745 he gained the patronage of Madame de Pompadour and was elected to the French Academy. In 1750, in Berlin, he became an intimate of Frederick the Great which friendship was disrupted three years later. After a few years of migratory life he settled near Geneva where he spent the last twenty years of his life, during which time he wrote *Candide.* The death of Louis XV made possible a visit of Voltaire to Paris after an absence of thirty-four years and he was welcomed enthusiastically.

IN THE WESTPHALIAN CASTLE of the baron Thunder-ten-tronck lived a youth of gentle disposition, good judgment, and unaffected simplicity, very aptly named Candide. The baroness, who weighed three hundred and fifty pounds, commanded considerable respect. Her daughter Cunégonde was a pretty, amiable girl of seventeen; her son seemed well worthy of his father. Pangloss, the preceptor, was the oracle of the family. He could prove admirably that there is no effect without a cause. He was also a profound optimist.

"It is demonstrable," he said, "that things cannot be otherwise than they are; since things have been created for a purpose, it must be for the best end. For instance, the nose is formed for spectacles; therefore we wear them. Stones were made to construct castles; therefore my lord has a magnificent castle. To say that everything is right is incorrect; everything is best."

One day the baron, catching Candide making love to Cunégonde, drove him out of doors with a few well placed kicks. Cunégonde, who had fainted, received a good box on the ears from the baroness as soon as she revived. Consternation reigned over this most beautiful and agreeable of castles.

Candide, driven from his paradise, plodded through the snow, passed the night in the fields, and the next day arrived half frozen in a nearby town. At the inn he met a man who assured him that if Candide came with him he would see that his way was paid and that he would be put to no expenditure whatsoever. "That is precisely the doctrine of Master Pangloss," said Candide. "I am convinced that everything is for the best."

He soon found himself in the Bulgarian army. His reward for his manœuvres of the first day was thirty blows with a cane. The next day he performed his exercises better and received only twenty; the following day ten. Then one day believing that men are free, he walked straight ahead, away from the army. He was overtaken two leagues distant and subjected to such a beating that he asked to be shot through the head. At that moment his Bulgarian majesty happened by, inquired into his crime, and realizing Candide's ignorance of the world, pardoned him. The army then departed to give battle to the king of the Abares.

Never was anything so glorious as these two armies. Their trumpets, drums, and cannon made such harmony as was never heard in hell itself. In the first discharge of cannon each side lost six thousand men. The bayonet was *sufficient reason* for several thousands. Passing over heaps of dead or dying men, Candide reached a neighboring village which the Bulgarians had burned to the ground. The butchery was horrible. Pursuing his way he finally arrived in Holland with scant provisions in his knapsack and Cunégonde's image in his heart. Asking charity of the good Christians he met, he was threatened with the house of correction. Appealing to an orator who had just harangued an assembly on the subject of charity, he was asked whether he was for the good cause. Candide answered: "There is no effect without cause, everything is necessarily arranged for the best." "Do you believe the Pope to be Antichrist?" asked the orator. "I don't know," answered Candide, "but I am very hungry." "You deserve nothing to eat," retorted the orator; "get out of my sight."

An unchristened Anabaptist, witnessing the scene, took Candide to his house, gave him meat and drink and two florins, whereupon Candide was convinced that everything was for the best in this world. About to give the two florins to a hideously scarred beggar, Candide was horrified to recognize Master Pangloss who told him that Cunégonde had been killed by the Bulgarians. Candide took Pangloss to the Anabaptist who made him his bookkeeper. After two months, obliged to go to Lisbon, the Anabaptist took the two philosophers with him. In sight of Lisbon, just as Pangloss was explaining how everything was for the best, their vessel was struck by a terrific storm.

The ship was totally wrecked, the Anabaptist drowned, but Candide and Pangloss reached shore to find thirty thousand inhabitants buried in the ruins resulting from the Lisbon earthquake. After the earthquake, the sages of the country decided to celebrate an *auto-da-fé* to preserve the country from future ruin. Candide was flogged and Pangloss hanged. After Candide's release an old woman took him to a house where, to his amazement, he found Cunégonde still alive. The three set out for Cadiz. During the trip they reflected upon Pangloss's philosophy and decided that now at last everything would be for the best.

From Cadiz they proceeded to Buenos Aires, Candide taking with him a valet named Cacambo. Here they left Cunégonde who was held captive by the Governor who had determined to marry her. Then Candide and Cacambo set out for Paraguay. When they reached the first barrier they were stopped and conducted to the Jesuit commandant. Great was the astonishment of Candide to recognize in him Cunégonde's brother, the baron's son, who had managed to escape from the Bulgarians; but greater, perhaps, were the joy and surprise of the reverend father when Candide told him that Cunégonde was still alive. The reverend father related to Candide how he had been left for dead after the massacre by the Bulgarians; how a Jesuit, sprinkling holy water upon his face, noticed that he was alive and rescued him. As a result the young noble-man had joined the order and eventually also became a colonel in the Paraguayan army. The baron embraced Candide and suggested that they go back, sword in hand, to deliver Cunégonde; but when Candide, agreeing, told him that he intended to marry Cunégonde, the baron became enraged and struck Candide across the face with the flat of his sword. Candide drew his rapier and ran him through. Immediate flight became essential. Candide donned the priest's robes and hat and off they rode in the direction of Cayenne.

The way was rough; their horses died of fatigue; they themselves subsisted for a whole month on wild fruit. At length they discovered a canoe beside a river bank. Entering it they paddled down stream until they reached a country where along the roads rolled glittering carriages drawn by huge red sheep. Noticing some children playing a game with rings of sparkling yellow, red, and green, Candide examined the disks and discovered them to be of gold and of immense rubies, emeralds, and diamonds. After the children departed Candide collected the precious playthings and he and Cacambo proceeded to the nearest village. Having dined at a tavern, Candide attempted to pay the innkeeper with two of the pieces of gold; but mine host burst into laughter, explaining that the gold pieces were common roadside pebbles in this country and that at the inns, maintained by the government for the convenience of travellers, no charge was made.

They soon discovered that they were in the land of El Dorado. The doors of the houses were of silver, the ceilings of beaten gold. Rubies and emeralds encrusted the walls. The inhabitants of El Dorado did not pray to God. God having given them everything they desired, they had nothing to ask of Him; and so they gave Him thanks incessantly.

Proceeding to the court, Candide and Cacambo were received by twenty beautiful maidens who conducted them to the bath and clad them in robes woven of the down of humming birds. His majesty ordered that before supper the two foreigners be shown the sights of the city. They beheld fountains of spring water, of rose water, and of liquors drawn from sugar cane, flowing in large public squares paved with precious stones emitting an odor

similar to that of cloves and cinnamon. There were no law courts
for the reason that law suits were unknown; nor were there any
prisons. After their tour of inspection the visitors returned to
the palace and partook of a magnificent repast.

They spent a whole month in this country and could have remained indefinitely; but Candide reflected that if he returned
to Europe with only a dozen sheep laden with the common pebbles
of El Dorado, he and Cacambo would be richer than all the
monarchs of Europe.

The king had a special machine constructed to carry the visitors
across the precipitous country surrounding El Dorado. In the
machine were placed two sheep upon which they would ride after
crossing the mountainous frontier, twenty sheep laden with provisions, and fifty carrying gold, diamonds, and other precious
stones.

The first part of the journey was very pleasant; but as the
days went by, some sheep sank in swamps, others perished of
hunger in the desert, others fell down precipices. At length the
travellers were reduced to two sheep laden with treasures when
they arrived at Surinam, a town belonging to the Dutch.

As they drew near the town they saw a mutilated negro who,
upon being questioned, revealed that he had lost his hand in a
sugar mill and had had his leg cut off by his master when he
attempted to run away. "It is at this expense," he said, "that you
eat sugar in Europe."

"O Pangloss! I am obliged to renounce optimism," declared
Candide. "Optimism," questioned Cacambo, "what is that?"
"Alas!" replied Candide, "it is the obstinacy of maintaining that
everything is best when it is worst."

It was decided between Candide and Cacambo that the latter
would go to Buenos Aires to ransom Cunégonde from the Governor; meanwhile Candide would go with his two sheep to Venice
where Cacambo would join him. Candide made his arrangements
with a sea-captain who put the sheep on his vessel and then, before Candide could get aboard, hoisted his sails and abandoned
him.

At length Candide fell in with an old philosopher named
Martin and they booked passage for Bordeaux where they de-

layed only long enough to exchange some of the remaining El
Dorado pebbles for cash and then left for Paris. Here, in a tavern,
Candide fell ill. The doctors took a great deal of his money and
during his convalescence some newly acquired friends played
cards with him for heavy stakes. Candide was surprised that he
invariably lost, but Martin was not in the least astonished; for
not only then but later, wherever they went in Paris, they became
victims of sharpers.

From Paris they went to Dieppe and caught a vessel bound for
Portsmouth, England. At this time England and France were at
war over a few acres of barren land in Canada, which seemed
very foolish to Candide. In Portsmouth they made a bargain with
a Dutch sea-captain to take them to Venice. "God be praised,"
exclaimed Candide upon their arrival in Italy; "it is here in Venice
that I shall meet my beloved Cunégonde. All is well; all is very
well; all is the best it could be."

But in Venice they found no trace of Cacambo. Candide was
thus forced to the conclusion that Cacambo had deserted and
pocketed his fortune. In Venice he visited the palace of a nobleman named Procurante who had a fine art collection which he
could not appreciate and a splendid library filled with books he
neither understood nor enjoyed. Finally Cacambo arrived but informed Candide that Cunégonde was now a slave in the household
of an exiled Transylvanian sovereign named Ragotski, residing in
Constantinople, who was receiving a meager pension from the
Sultan. Cacambo had paid the Governor of Buenos Aires two millions for the release of Cunégonde. A pirate stripped him of nearly
all the rest, taking him and Cunégonde to Constantinople; but
worst of all, Cunégonde had grown very ugly.

Naturally Candide and Cacambo and Martin immediately departed for Constantinople. Arriving there they hired a galley to
search for Cunégonde on the shores of the Propontis. Marvelous
to relate, in two of the galley slaves they recognized Pangloss and
the baron Jesuit. "Am I dreaming," exclaimed Candide; "is this
my lord baron whom I killed and is this Pangloss whom I saw
hanged?" Candide speedily ransomed his friends and off they
went to deliver Cunégonde from slavery.

The baron related to Candide his experiences. He had been

treated for the wound inflicted upon him by Candide, had fully
recovered, and had been appointed chaplain to the French ambassador at Constantinople. Pangloss's story was even more
extraordinary. After the hanging, which had been done very improperly, a surgeon purchased his body and commenced to
dissect it. At the first incision Pangloss screamed, the surgeon
sewed up the wound, and in a short while the philosopher was on
his feet again. He entered the service of a Venetian merchant and
accompanied him to Constantinople.

"And after all your experiences," remarked Candide, "do you
still believe that everything in this world happens for the best?"
"I have always abided by my first opinion," answered Pangloss,
"and it would not become me to retract my sentiments."

In the midst of their discussion they arrived at the house of the
Transylvanian prince on the shores of the Propontis and there
they beheld Cunégonde and the old woman hanging napkins to
dry on a line. Candide started back in horror upon seeing Cunégonde all sunburned, with bleary eyes, a withered neck, wrinkled
face and arms all covered with a red scurf. She embraced Candide
and her brother; they embraced the old woman; and Candide
ransomed them both. Cunégonde, unaware of her ugliness, reminded Candide of his promise of marriage, but her brother
interposed. Turning to Candide he declared: "You may kill me
again, but I shall never permit my sister to marry any person
below the rank of baron."

In truth Candide no longer had any great desire to marry Cunégonde, but the impertinence of the baron decided him to conclude
the match. They arranged the abduction of the baron and had
him carried by the first ship to the Father-General at Rome.
Candide, of course, married Cunégonde, and with the little money
now left in his possession he purchased a farm upon which they
lived with Pangloss, Martin, Cacambo, and the old woman.
Cacambo worked the garden and carried produce into Constantinople, all the while cursing his fate. Pangloss despaired of ever
returning to a German university to shine as a brilliant scholar.
Martin, persuaded that things are equally bad everywhere, assumed an attitude of patience. "Work," he maintained, "is the
only thing that renders life endurable."

The little group, following his advice, set themselves to exert their various talents. The little farm yielded a plentiful crop. Cunégonde, though ugly, was an excellent cook. And now and then Pangloss would say to Candide: "There is a linking of events in the best possible of worlds; for, after all, if you had not been kicked out of a fine castle for the love of Miss Cunégonde, if you had not suffered under the Inquisition, if you had not travelled on foot in America, if you had not impaled the baron with your sword, if you had not lost all the sheep you brought from the good country of El Dorado, you would not be here eating preserved citrons and pistachio-nuts." "That is a correct observation," replied Candide, "but we must cultivate our garden."

THE TRAGEDY OF FAUST

By

Johann Wolfgang von Goethe

JOHANN WOLFGANG VON GOETHE (*1749–1832*) was a German poet who was born at Frankfort-on-the-Main. He entered the University of Leipzig in 1765 where he received important intellectual gains from the director of the Academy of Arts. He studied drawing, etching and painting, published a play and wrote music. After a serious illness in 1768 he completed his studies at the University of Strassburg where he became acquainted with old ballad poetry as well as with contemporary English writers. In 1770 he met the beautiful Friederike who was the inspiration of some of Goethe's loveliest lyrics. Soon he felt a rivalry for Shakespeare which aroused his creative genius. From 1770 on he was continually writing. In 1776 he became a member of the privy-council and in 1782 he received a patent of nobility. His most fruitful period of production was his two year visit in Italy in 1786. *Faust* did not appear complete until 1808. In 1791 he was made director of the court theater at Weimar and the next year went into battle in the disastrous campaign against the French to study his own sensations under fire. His friendship with Schiller dates from 1794 to the latter's death in 1805 during which time they worked happily together. Goethe died after a short illness and he was buried near Schiller in the ducal vault at Weimar.

IN THE BRIGHT DAY OF HEAVEN three angels are chanting the glory of God manifested in His works. Raphael raises his voice to glorify the whole realm of Creation; Gabriel praises the earth as it revolves from night to day; Michael mentions the storms that on earth surge in conflict on the land and sea but predicts the gentle coming of God's day. Although these angels cannot comprehend Creation they feel that they can contemplate God's glory in it.

[339]

Mephistopheles now appears and since the Lord has asked Him how it fares on earth he will say nothing about suns and worlds; he will report that there is trouble on earth because men in trying to make use of reason abuse this divine gift to their own hurt. The one who most thoroughly abuses this gift is Faust, who suffers from the insatiable desire to discover the mysteries of the stars and the ecstasies of the earth. Now the Lord has hopes for Faust whom He is sure He can lead in the right way, but Mephistopheles believes that he can lead Faust along his road and makes a wager with the Lord to that effect. He has had enough of dead souls and wishes now to deal with a live one.

On earth it is night and in a lofty-arched, narrow Gothic room Faust sits restlessly at his desk. Long has he studied philosophy and law, medicine and theology and for a decade has been a teacher, yet with all such learning he feels himself a fool. In his pathetic ignorance he turns to a book on magic which is supposed to give one a view of the world as a whole, but it yields him only a shadowy picture of nature, not the reality—

> *A spectacle but yet a show I see;*
> *O endless Nature! I'd lay hold on thee!*

Impatiently turning the leaves of the magic-book Faust comes to the sign of the Earth Spirit and as he invokes it the Spirit appears in a ruddy flame and asks, "who calls me?" The Spirit then reveals itself as an impersonal force so different from Faust that he can never comprehend it even if he is a Superman. The Spirit's nature and work are different from his—

> *Here at the whirring loom of time I plod*
> *To weave the living garments of the God.*

And having thus spoken the Spirit disappears and a knock is heard at the door.

As Faust turns impatiently toward the door Wagner in dressing gown and night-cap and lamp in hand appears and wants to know if the dialogue he has just heard was not from some old Greek tragedy. It is difficult for this pair to come to an understanding with each other, since Wagner expects to find his knowledge in the parchments of the past while Faust is convinced that these avail nought unless one by immediate feeling can comprehend the spirit which once was in them. Alone again, Faust contemplates suicide, pours poison into a crystal cup but as he puts it to his mouth the chime of Easter bells and choral songs stay his hand—

> *How clear the tone, the murmuring how deep*
> *That draws me from the everlasting sleep!*

Faust now mingles with a group of town's people making merry on Easter Sunday and feels that while he has been trying in vain to solve the riddle of the universe these merely human beings have given themselves up to frivolity and sensuality. They seem to know that which has ever escaped him—the secret of happiness on earth. The people gather around him to pay tribute to Doctor Faust but impressed with the vanity of his life he feels that this is mere mockery. To Wagner whose soul is quite simple the condition of Faust is a mystery which is far from being cleared up when Faust says—

> *There dwell, alas! two souls within my breast,*
> *Each draws apart nor gives the other rest.*

Faust now spies a dog racing about madly and what for Wagner is but a poodle trying to scent out its master is for him a most mysterious creature. Now parting with Wagner Faust re-enters his study leading the poodle with him.

In his desire to penetrate to the depth of things Faust now opens the Bible at the beginning of the Gospel according to Saint John and reads, "In the beginning was the Word." But behind the word, he thinks, must be the Thought, deeper down the Power and at the very depth it seems to be written, "In the beginning was the Deed!" Now the poodle which has been restless during this reading seems to be undergoing various transmigrations into a terrible hippopotamus, an elephant and then a kind of space-filling shape. Finally it goes up in smoke and from the cloud emerges a creature in the costume of a travelling scholar. Faust asks his name but is reminded that he has just abjured faith in the "word," but then is informed that this being, although not the Devil is a part of the Satanic power which wills the bad but works the good and is in reality "the spirit that ever denies." It seems to Faust that this modified Devil plans the ruin of things on a small scale and he is wary of him, although he does consent to have him as a sort of companion to afford him recreations. The odd creature is Mephistopheles; he commences his work by calling up fair spirits who lull Faust into slumber by singing a soothing song.

Mephistopheles puts in an appearance a second time and knowing that Faust despairs of happiness as well as of knowledge agrees to give him enjoyment at least. According to the compact between the two, Mephistopheles will become Faust's slave during his life in the "Here" if Faust will be the same to Mephistopheles in the "There," or the Hereafter. In this manner Faust seems to put his soul in forfeit for the sake of obtaining happiness on earth but is skeptical about the possibility of a permanent satisfaction in life. He bets that Mephistopheles cannot make him so happy that there will come a moment in his life which he will be willing to prolong indefinitely. If and when he says, "O moment linger on, so fair thou art," Mephistopheles may have his soul, the clock may stop and time come to an end. The bet is taken and the compact made; now they are ready to start on the path of pleasure.

The program which Faust's diabolical guide has arranged begins with a visit to Auerbach's Wine Cellar in Leipzig. There Faust is introduced into a scene of debauchery and coarse levity but in this place redolent with the fumes of tobacco and wine and resounding with vulgar carousals the man of intellect cannot find his happiness. The effort of Mephistopheles to grant him his permanent pleasure is as thoroughly balked in a visit to the Witches' Kitchen where the chief entertainment is provided by a pair of apes with their spiritual vulgarity. The Witch brews a mysterious potion and bids Faust imbibe. The effect of the beverage is to rejuvenate the middle-aged scholar, inflame him with new desires and create the illusion that the first woman he meets will be a veritable Helen of Troy.

Faust is now in the power of Mephistopheles who, according to his part of the compact, stands ready to serve him. At this significant moment in his career he meets a beautiful maiden but when he approaches her offering to be her escort in the street she flees from him in fear. Faust now calls upon Mephistopheles to give him possession of the maiden who has enchanted him and would have her that very night but his crafty servant warns him that with such a timid maiden he must use more strategy than speed. They will begin by presenting her with costly gifts in the form of jewelry which Mephistopheles by means of his diabolical power knows how to unearth. With a casket full of these treasures the two make their way secretly into the room of the maid, Margaret, and after inspecting the cosy little place deposit the casket in a closet and depart. Now enters Margaret and begins to undress; as she is putting her garments away she discovers the casket of jewels and at once begins to adorn herself with them. But as the prying Mephistopheles discovers, the girl's mother sees the jewels and makes her daughter turn them over to the priest at the church. Faust's diabolical slave must get the girl another set of jewels so that the maiden's sorrow over the loss of these may be assuaged. To this plan Mephistopheles grudgingly consents.

Margaret now visits her neighbor, Martha, and in great agitation tells how she has found another box of jewels resembling the first one only finer, and is advised by Martha to keep the secret from her mother lest she lose this one also. Margaret came upon her friend just as she was grieving over her absent husband and now Mephistopheles enters to inform Martha that her husband is dead and buried in Padua. He flatters the widow by suggesting that she should have another marriage-offer and, turning to Margaret, adds that she should have a lover to caress and ends by asking her how fares the heart within her breast. Mephistopheles now returns to Faust and tells him how they can make use of Martha at whose house Faust will meet the object of his love. Faust must play his part by sanctioning the lie about the death of Martha's husband.

In the garden we see Margaret on Faust's arm, Martha and Mephistopheles walking up and down. Faust kisses Margaret's hand which act embarrasses her and makes her feel very humble. She tells him about her home, her widowed mother and soldier-brother and confesses a part of her feeling toward Faust. She recalls that he accosted her when she was coming out of church when she felt that he did not realize what kind of a girl she was or he would not have taken such a liberty. She tried to be angry with him but really could not. Margaret now plucks a star-flower and as one by one she picks off the leaves murmurs, "He loves, he loves me not." They are now in the garden arbor where the roguish Martha has concealed herself to spy upon the love-pair. Faust kisses Margaret who clasps him and as she returns the kiss confesses her deep love for him. Mephistopheles reappears, tells Faust 'tis time to go and leads him away leaving Margaret to wonder how such a man as Faust could ever find anything of interest in her.

Faust now appears alone in a forest by a cavern. Having left Margaret and with his tempter away, his better nature returns and he reveals his true self as that of one who adores nature and feels pure love for the young maiden he has met. Mephistopheles now reappears, quarrels with Faust and so goads him on that he yields to his lower nature and resolves to seduce Margaret—

> *She, her innocence I must undermine;*
> *Thou, Hell! demands this sacrifice as thine.*

In her room, at her spinning wheel, Margaret sings a ditty in which she confesses her love for Faust and complains that peace has departed from her heart to leave it sore.

Faust and Margaret meet in Martha's garden where the maiden asks her lover to declare his faith in things divine and asks him plainly whether he believes in God. Faust replies to her direct question in an indirect way—

> *Be not misled, thou Lovely Countenance!*
> *Who can God name, what creed his name enhance?*
> *Godhead is endless and doth all enfold;*
> *Godhead is mighty and doth all uphold.*
> *Holds and upholds He not thy soul and mine,*
> *Embracing all within the soul divine?*

Margaret feels that this is about what the preacher says only in slightly different words. Apparently reassured by Faust's confession of faith Margaret listens to Faust's wish that in some fond hour they might be plighted breast to breast, and would have her lover come to her but that she fears her mother might awaken. Faust now produces a phial containing a sleeping potion which Margaret agrees to administer to her mother. The rash scheme is carried out and she becomes his.

Margaret now appears before a shrine where, as she places flowers in the flower-pot, she pours out her soul to the *mater dolorosa* praying that the Virgin may hear her prayer and save her from disgrace and death. Valentine, her brother, now returns from war, learns his sister's secret and confronts Faust and a duel ensues. Faust is protected by Mephistopheles who parries his adversary's thrusts and when at length Valentine's hand grows lame Faust thrusts the sword home and Valentine falls and after cursing his sister dies.

Margaret now appears in the Cathedral where an Evil Spirit standing behind her taunts her by relating how when she used to come to the altar she merely prattled her prayers, but now must come and plead for mercy while the choir chants the *dies irae*. The Evil Spirit chides the choir chants and Margaret falls in a swoon. In harsh contrast with this deep mystical element in the tragedy we have the display of hideous witchcraft on Walpurgis Night in the Hartz Mountains.

Faust and Mephistopheles are now in a wild, rocky region, deep gorges about them and high in the background the Brocken-top appears shrouded in a lurid glare. Mephistopheles begins to talk witchcraft and attempts to lead his pupil to the heights but finally appeals to a Will-o'-the-Wisp as their guide. As they ascend the trees dance, the cliffs nod, the rocks snore and mountain torrents gush through the stones and grasses, all to the great bewilderment of poor Faust. Above them are heard the voices of witches while below the half-witches call out complaining that long as they have struggled to attain the heights, that is, the depths of spiritual depravity they have no hope of arriving there. Apparently they, while not good enough for the world are not bad enough for the deep summits of such spiritual wickedness in high places. On a plateau on one side is a group, a general and a minister, an author and a huckster, whose social depravity incline them toward the devilry of Brocken. While Mephistopheles is dancing with an Old Witch whose language is vile, Faust dances with a Young Witch from whose mouth there comes forth obscenity in the form of a red mouse which so disgusts him that he turns away from her and entertains a vision of Margaret.

But Margaret, as Faust now learns, is in prison having slain the child she bore her lover. Faust now turns upon Mephistopheles and curses him for having led him into wretched dissipations while his beloved was in such dire misery. Margaret, as the miserable Mephistopheles suggests, is not the first to have died for such a crime and, besides, why did Faust enter into his compact with him if he was not able to play his part to the end? Faust, trusting in the power of this evil spirit, now demands that he rescue Margaret only to learn that Mephistopheles cannot loosen the bonds of the Avenger; and then after all, it was Faust himself who was responsible for the maiden's ruin. Yet Mephistopheles will do all in his power and may be able to deliver Margaret from prison.

The power of Mephistopheles is such that he does get possession of the jailor's keys and Faust enters Margaret's cell. The maiden lies on a bed of straw where she sings a ribald ballad and from this as well as from her inability to recognize Faust it is evident that her reason has left her. As Faust calls her passionately by name, "Margaret, Margaret," she seems again to hear her lover's voice. She knows that loving tone, she will fly to him and seek refuge in his embrace. Faust bids her flee with him but she, thinking she is with him in the garden, bids him kiss her and hasten not away. If she will only come now he will press her to his heart with a thousandfold warmth. Now she takes his hand but finds it wet as though there were blood on it. She cannot be saved by flight, must stay and meet her death. Faust, whom she calls "Henry," will survive her and must arrange the graves. Her mother must have the best place, her brother close by and she herself shall lie a little on one side but not too far away. At her breast must be her babe, for no one else may lie with her in death. Faust pleads with her to go with him out into the free air but she will go with him only to the grave, not a step farther. Now she calls on Faust to save their child.

"Quick, quick! Save thy poor child! Away, away! Keep to the path by the brook, over the bridge, into the wood, to the left where the plank is in the pond. Be quick, catch hold of it! It strives to rise and struggles still. Help, O help!"

Faust tries to calm Margaret and tells her to come for the day is dawning. Yes, the day does dawn and it was to have been her wedding-day. But now the bell is tolling and the streets are thronged and soon they will have her blood. Faust must leave her and as she says, "must tell no one he has been with Margaret," Mephistopheles comes in and drags Faust away and as they are departing a voice from within the dungeon cries, "Henry, Henry," and then dies away.

THE NIBELUNGEN RING

By

Richard Wagner

WILHELM RICHARD WAGNER (*1813–1883*) was a German composer, born in Leipzig. Beethoven's music was his inspiration. When he was 20 years old he began his long career as an operatic composer with *Die Feen*. He tried his fortunes in Heidelberg, Konigsberg, Riga, Paris and Dresden. In Dresden he became a modest success. In 1845 his first opera *Tannhäuser* was considered a failure at first. Due to his revolutionary ideas he was forced to flee from Saxony in 1848 and was in exile for nearly 12 years. The poem of the *Nibelungen Ring* trilogy was finished in 1852. The king of Bavaria erected an opera house for him at Bayreuth in 1864, where festivals in his honor are still held. Wagner was his own librettist and was the first to make "leitmotiv" the outstanding feature in operatic works. His music was remarkably original and he was a master of orchestration.

RHINE GOLD

AT THE BOTTOM OF THE RHINE there appears a greenish twilight, lighter above and darker below. The upper part of the scene is filled with flowing water which streams restlessly from right to left. Towards the background the waters seem to melt into a fine mist so that the space to a man's height from the stage appears free from water, which flows like a train of clouds over the sombre depths. Everywhere appear sharp points of rocks jutting up from the depths and enclosing the whole stage so that nowhere is there any level spot while on all sides the thick darkness indicates still other deep fissures. In the centre of the stage, round a rock whose sharp peak rises into the sparkling water, one of the Rhine Maidens is seen gaily swimming.

While this Rhine Maiden Woglinde is warbling to the waters,

the voice of her sister, Wellgunde, is heard asking, "dost thou watch alone?" Wellgunde dives down to the rock, attempts to seize her sister, and then the two attempt playfully to catch each other. The pair is now joined by Flosshilde who rebukes her sisters for such play when they should be guarding the hoard of slumbering gold in the Rhine. At this moment appears Alberich, the Nibelung, who approaches the Rhine Maidens causing them to abandon their play and inquire both who the stranger is and what he wants. The Maidens coquette with the dwarf who endeavors to seize and embrace first one, then another of them until finally he holds Flosshilde in his arms. In a moment she has darted away from him and rejoins her sisters whereupon all three give vent to a shout of triumph and a song in praise of the Rhine Gold they are guarding. Alberich is fascinated by the gleam of the metal but knows not what the Rhine Gold means. From Wellgunde he learns that he who from the gold can shape a ring will thus secure immeasurable power, but that this can come only as one renounces love. Alberich accepts the conditions, forswears love, seizes the gold and makes way with it, followed by the Rhine Maidens who try to stop the robber and save the gold.

Gradually the waves of the Rhine give place to clouds which little by little fade out into a fine mist through which can be seen an open space on a mountain peak. As the day dawns there appears a gleaming castle on a cliff in the background while in the foreground the Rhine seems to flow. At one side in a flowery meadow Wotan and Fricka lie sleeping. Now Fricka awakens, her gaze falls on the castle, she starts in surprise and calls upon Wotan, who is still dreaming about the wondrous mansion, to awaken. The eternal work of rearing this structure to the skies as it was envisioned by Wotan is now ended; but, as Fricka observes, it is still to be paid for, and she trembles for Freia who is being held by the builders as a bond. For Wotan in a fatuous moment had pledged the goddess of joy to the grim builders of the castle. While Wotan and Fricka are arguing the wisdom of such a compact, Freia, who has escaped from the giant builders, rushes in and calls upon Wotan to save her.

Freia is followed by Fasolt and Fafner, men of gigantic stature whom Wotan had engaged to build the palace. They remind

Wotan that, while soft sleep was sealing his eyes, they had labored piling stone upon stone to build the great palace and must now be paid in terms of Freia. Much to the astonishment of the giants this pay is refused. While Fasolt and Fafner are arguing between themselves whether after all a woman's wonder and worth has the value of the castle, Wotan is gazing up the Rhine for Loge whom he thinks able to extricate him from this predicament. Just as the giants are about to take Freia away by force, Loge appears upon the scene. He has been away on a double errand—to examine the castle in its every detail of building to see whether the giants have fulfilled their part of the bargain, as also to discover some substitute for Freia, or what in the world is more precious than a woman's wonder and worth. His report is that the castle has been built that each stone stands where it should and that in the mind of man nothing can take the place of woman's charms. Wotan's plight would have been fatal had not Loge added that in the solitary case of the Nibelung, Alberich, he had found a man who would relinquish love for gold, but that he had robbed the Rhine of its treasure whereupon the Rhine Maidens had entreated Loge to appeal to Wotan for them that the gold might be restored to the Rhine. This gold, he suggests, might be paid the giants for their work and the release of Freia.

The idea of the gold from which the magic ring may be made appeals to the giants, but to obtain it for them Wotan must renounce love or take the gold by theft, and both ideas are abhorrent to him. While he is debating within himself the outraged giants attempt to settle the matter by carrying Freia away. The effect of her departure is to deprive all the gods save Loge of their bloom and brightness; the color leaves their cheeks the sparks expire in their eyes and gray gloom envelops them. Suddenly Wotan starts up with a resolution and calls Loge to his side. The two must go to Alberich's haunt in Nibelheim and seize the gold from the dwarf. Bidding the other gods wait, Wotan and Loge disappear down a crevice, make their way through the sulphurous vapor and descend to a gloomy, rocky chasm in the depths of the earth.

In a subterranean cavern from which a ruddy light gleams, the Nibelung Alberich drags his brother Mime by the ear and demands he produce the work he had been commanded to finish. Alberich lets Mime go and as he threatens again to seize him causes Mime to drop the desired piece of work which he was concealing. It is the Magic Helmet, the Tarnhelm! Alberich at once fits this to his head, conjures it to render him invisible and vanishes in a column of smoke. Mime, the poor smith, can no longer see his brother but he can feel him, since Alberich now whales him with an invisible scourge and warns the Nibelung elves who work at their anvils that now he has complete power over them. The vapor-column shrouding Alberich disappears leaving Mime nursing his wounds.

Loge, followed by Wotan, now emerges from a cleft and the side, accosts Mime and inquires into the cause of his groanings. Mime's story is to the effect that Alberich had wrought from the Rhine Gold a magic ring with which he had gained power over all the Nibelungen race, who now, instead of working at their anvils in making little ornaments for their wives, were now compelled to toil for Alberich alone. Mime continues to relate that he himself had fashioned a helmet whose magic he could not comprehend only to have it taken from him by this task-master.

As Alberich's threats and scourgings are approaching again Wotan takes a seat on a stone with Loge at his side. Alberich appears carrying the Tarnhelm in his girdle and driving before him a crowd of Nibelungs laden with gold and silver ornaments which they pile up in the form of a heap or hoard. Perceiving Wotan and Loge with Mime, Alberich drives Mime away into the crowd of Nibelungs all of whom now slip into the crevices and sink down to the shafts again; then he inquires what these visitors from the world above are seeking. Wotan answers him saying they have heard wonderful things about Nibelheim and have come to behold them. After various boastings on the part of Alberich and taunts from Loge, the dwarf begins to display the magic of the Tarnhelm by making it turn him into a dragon, at which Loge affects great fear. You have made your being wax great in this monster, suggests Loge, but can you make it so wane that you will appear as a toad? Alberich accepts the challenge, and turns himself into a toad upon which Wotan promptly plants his foot and makes the dwarf a prisoner.

Again the scene is an open space on a mountain-top still veiled in mist because of Freia's departure. Wotan and Loge leading the pinioned Alberich with them mount up from the cleft. Alberich may regain his freedom only at the price of the vast hoard of sparkling gold which Wotan has seen in Nibelheim. His hand now untied, Alberich touches the magic ring to his lips and summons the gold which is brought up from the crevice by the host of Nibelung gnomes. Alberich is forced to relinquish the magic helmet as also the ring upon which he pronounces a curse and then vanishes into the crevice. The gods, Fricka, Donner and Froh, now return and Loge summons the giants to come and receive the gold as the price of Freia's redemption. But the pile of gold must be arranged in such a way as to hide the heavenly maiden from the sight of her captors, hence Freia is placed in the middle of the scene between the staves of the giants and the mass of gold heaped up in front of her. Yet even with such a mass of gold in front of her Freia can still be seen, for golden hair is still visible. To cover this it is necessary for Loge to cast the Tarnhelm upon the pile but even then the brightness of Freia's eyes can be seen through a rift in the precious metal. To fill this fatal gap the golden ring is required but Wotan is loath to part with such a treasure and will not do so until finally he is warned by the goddess Erda, who rises from the earth, that he must surrender the ring or meet his downfall. Wotan finally throws the ring on the pile of gold where the giants struggle for the possession of it. Fasolt wrests the ring from Fafner who retaliates by felling Fasolt and wresting the ring from his hand as he lies dying and makes off with the booty.

Wotan is shocked by all that has happened and feels that he has paid a shameful price for his castle. The whole scene is veiled in mist but Donner climbs up to an over-hanging rock and summons the clouds to his side. Once they are gathered round him, Donner smites the rock with his hammer whereupon the lightning flashes and a peal of thunder is heard, the storm being followed by a rainbow which stretches like a bridge across the valley to the castle. After contemplating the castle, Wotan starts across the rainbow-bridge leading Fricka by the hand toward the castle, which from now on shall be called "Valhalla," a

THE NIBELUNGEN RING

mysterious name whose meaning will appear in time. As Wotan sets his foot upon the bridge he hears the Rhine Maidens praising the Rhine Gold and lamenting its loss.

THE VALKYRIES

In order to redeem himself and deliver the world from the power of gold, symbolized by the ring, Wotan is compelled to reinforce himself by begetting through Erda the Valkyries, or godlike daughters whose mission it is to bring to Valhalla the bodies of the heroes who fall fighting in Wotan's cause. These heroes are the Volsungs and among them are Siegmund and Sieglinda, born of an earthly mother. The Volsungs are now at war with the Neidings and Siegmund, worn out in the strife, seeks refuge inside a vast hut built about the roots of a mighty ash tree and throws himself down upon the hearth. Sieglinda enters, perceives the worn out warrior and in response to his plea gives him water to drink which refreshes him. He is so further refreshed by a drink of mead that he is about to depart, but at Sieglinda's request he remains.

Hunding now enters and, perceiving Siegmund, gives Sieglinda an inquiring look and learns from her how Siegmund had sank exhausted to the hearth and how she had given him nourishment. Hunding although somewhat suspicious of Siegmund, who seems to resemble his wife, grants him a temporary haven and requests him reveal his name. Siegmund replies saying that he cannot be called "Peaceful" and while he would like the name of "Joyful" he is forced to call himself "Woeful," since ill fortune has been his lot in life. Just now he is a victim of the Neidings. Unfortunately for him, Hunding is a member of that race and with vehemence he tells Siegmund that he has justly earned their hatred. He may remain for the night but on the morrow they will engage in mortal combat. Having sent Sieglinda from the room, Hunding taking his weapons with him follows her into the bedchamber and bolts the door.

Siegmund is now alone and as he reclines on the hearth he is agitated by the thought that he has no sword with which to defend himself on the morrow. But now for a moment the fire glows

[353]

and reveals the hilt of a sword buried in the ash tree. As the fire goes out the door of the bed-chamber opens, Sieglinda in a white robe emerges and glides over to the hearth. Hunding is now sleeping heavily since she mixed a drug with his drink and now Siegmund may depart safely. He may go armed too, since a magic sword which a stranger once drove into the ash tree may be drawn forth for his defence. Siegmund now embraces Sieglinda and lays claim to her as well as to the sword, to both weapon and wife. In the love songs which follow it is revealed that both are Volsungs and that the hero named "Siegmund" shall have the power to draw the sword from the tree. In wrenching the sword from the ash tree the hero becomes known as Siegmund, the woman at his side as Sieglinda, and in the wild intoxication of love they fly from the hut, Siegmund with his sister and bride.

The tidings of this elopement having come up to Valhalla, Wotan fully armed and with his spear appears upon the scene with Brunhilde, chief among the Valkyries, whom he bids make ready for the impending duel between Siegmund and Hunding. As Brunhilde disappears, Fricka drives up in a tiny car drawn by a pair of rams, rebukes Wotan for siding with the adulterous, incestuous Siegmund and calls upon him to throw the weight of his divine influence upon the side of the outraged husband. Further he is to remove the magic from the sword Siegmund found, and recall Brunhilde that she may not give him her aid. Brunhilde returns and finds Wotan in dire distress because he is no longer free to do as he would but is bound by the moral law which Fricka represents. At great length he unfolds to Brunhilde the story of his life with an account of its various defeats, and tells her further of his constant fear that Alberich will regain that which both of them lost to the giant, Fafner. He can never be free from fear and care until there comes the hero who, while fighting against the gods, will yet contend for Wotan's own cause. As for Brunhilde, she can accomplish her Valkyrie-work by assigning the victory to Hunding letting Siegmund fall in the fray.

Siegmund and Sieglinda now appear fleeing from the wrath of Hunding. The exhausted woman sinks down and bids her lover leave her and save himself, but he remains by her side trusting to the magic of his sword, "Needfull." At this juncture, while Hunding's horn is resounding, Brunhilde appears and solemnly announces to Siegmund that, according to Wotan's will, he must fall in battle and be conveyed to Valhalla; but since he cannot rejoin his wife there among the gods, Siegmund declines to go. Nevertheless, as she tells him, Hunding will overcome him, since Wotan has withdrawn the charm from the sword Needfull. But now deeply impressed by the love between Siegmund and Sieglinda and pitying them in their plight, Brunhilde resolves to disobey Wotan's command and thus she assures Siegmund that when the duel begins she will be at his side to aid him.

Siegmund now bids Sieglinda farewell for the time and hastens toward Hunding. In a moment the rival warriors are in mortal combat. Sieglinda calls out to them to stay their hands and take her own life while Brunhilde with her shield is seen protecting Siegmund from Hunding's furious blows. Siegmund, thus aided, is about to deal his adversary a deadly blow when Wotan who has rushed to the scene interposes his spear on which the magic sword of Siegmund is broken and he falls a victim to Hunding. Sieglinda, hearing Siegmund's dying sigh sinks down as if lifeless; Brunhilde lifts her upon her own horse and rides away with her. Wotan commands his servant to go to Fricka and inform her that his spear has been the means of carrying out her command and then with a contemptuous wave of his hand he strikes Hunding dead.

The Valkyries now on horse-back ride furiously to the scene of battle, two of them each bearing a dead body over his saddle turn and gallop toward Valhalla where they encounter Brunhilde who has brought Sieglinda with her. The safest place for her, they decide, is the tangled forest where Fafner guards his hoard of gold, for that is a spot which Wotan abhors. The fragments of Siegmund's sword are given her and she is bidden to keep them as a heritage for her son Siegfried who in a while will be born. Wotan now approaches the Valkyries who group about Brunhilde and attempt to conceal her, but Wotan seeks her out and in spite of the expostulations of the other Valkyrie daughters he proceeds to punish the one who has disobeyed his mandate. She is to be expelled from Valhalla and must become a mortal woman.

Brunhilde's own defense is that, although she crossed Wotan's will she carried out his wish and really did as he would have liked her to do. Because of this Wotan consents to her request that when she becomes a mortal woman she shall be surrounded by a fence of flames which no coward but a hero only shall dare penetrate. After a majestic song of farewell, Wotan places Brunhilde upon a huge rock and calls upon Loge to conjure up fire to encircle it. As the flames spring up Wotan guides the fire with his spear until the rock is wholly surrounded and concludes with the warning that he who fears the point of his spear will never stride through the fire.

SIEGFRIED

The hero whom Wotan has been awaiting is now born. His mother, Sieglinda, died as she brought him into the world; he has been brought up my Mime, brother of the envious Alberich, who had stationed him near the cave where Fafner guards the hoard of gold. Siegfried's heritage is the broken sword left him by his father, Siegmund. It is now Mime's task to mend the broken sword with which Siegfried will be able to slay Fafner and get possession of the gold. All of Mime's effort at the forge has thus far been in vain, for as often as he mends the weapon Siegfried breaks it again. While the dwarf is still at work, Siegfried romps in from the forest accompanied by a bear whom he bids ask Mime for the sword, much to the dwarf's sense of fear. Siegfried now seizes the sword and smashes it upon the anvil and refuses the food Mime offers him thus causing the dwarf to complain that he is an ungrateful son.

This rebuke suggests a question to the young hero. In the woods he has noticed that beasts and birds go in pairs and that they have young when they mate. Where, then, is Mime's minikin mate, or his own mother? He is enraged when Mime insists that he is Siegfried's father and mother together and moreover can perceive no sort of likeness between himself and the dwarf. After Siegfried has choked the dwarf he wrings from him the story of how his mother as she lay dying at his birth confided the babe to his care. Her name, said he, was Sieglinda and of Siegfried's father he knew nought save that he was slain in battle. The sword had been wielded by his father in the conflict wherein he was slain. Since he has learned that Mime is not his father, Siegfried decides to flee from him and thus wanders away into the woods.

Wotan, who had encountered catastrophe in economic and moral matters, now appears upon the scene as The Wanderer. He hails Mime and after a preliminary parley challenges him to engage in a battle of wits each contestant staking his head as the price of losing the tilt. Thereupon Mime asks Wotan to name the race who dwell in the depths of the earth and receives the answer, the Nibelungs. Asked who are they who sojourn upon the back of the earth, Wotan names Fafner and Fasolt, the giants; and asked, finally, who are they who dwell in the heights of the welkin he promptly mentions the gods who live in Valhalla. It is now Wotan's turn to propose questions. What is the race which Wotan has treated so harshly even when they are dear to him? They are the Volsungs, replies Mime. Now, what is the name of the sword with which Siegfried will slay Fafner in order to regain the ring? Mime replies that it is called "Needfull," and is pleased that a second time he has saved his head. But who, asks Wotan of the would-be weapon-smith, will mend that sword? In great terror Mime replies that he does not know so that, if he will, his questioner may demand his head as a forfeit. But Wotan is content with warning him and informing him that only he who has never felt fear will be able to make the sword new.

Siegfried now reappears and finds the dwarfish smith crouching in terror behind the anvil. Mime now informs Siegfried that the sword can be repaired only by him who has never felt fear, and finds it impossible to convey to the young hero's mind what fear can be. But if Siegfried really wishes to learn the lesson of terror he will bring him to Fafner who will duly teach him. Now it is urgent to repair the sword and Siegfried goes to work upon it by kindling a great fire and grinding the sword to powder instead of attempting to solder the broken parts together. While the hero is thus at work Mime is planning how he himself can gain possession of the ring and the great hoard of gold in the dragon's cave, for it is into such a creature that Fafner by means of the magic helmet has transformed himself. While Siegfried is using the fire to mold the powdered sword into a new weapon, Mime is busy with a pot in which he is preparing a poisoned broth. The sword is now properly molded and Siegfried is ready for the dragon, and in order to test his new weapon he smites it on the anvil which is thus rent asunder.

In the depth of the forest appears the opening of a dark cave haunted by the dragon. Nearby is Alberich brooding over the loss of the Rhine Gold. He is joined by Wotan, The Wanderer, who has come to do nothing but survey the scene. Wotan informs Alberich that his brother will bring to the place a hero who will slay Fafner, and goes so far as to tell the dragon himself of the danger in store for him only to have Fafner reply that he is in possession of the gold and desires to sleep. At day-break Mime and Siegfried appear, the hero ready for his lesson in fear from a creature which, as Mime informs him, has a terrible maw, poisonous spittle, venomous tail and the like, as also a heart although a hard and cruel one. At a gesture of impatience from Siegfried, Mime departs expressing the silent hope that Fafner and Siegfried will kill each other.

While Siegfried waits for the dragon to awaken he seats himself under a great linden tree and falls to musing first about the miserable dwarf and then about his lovely mother. Now a bird calls to him and, cutting a reed with his sword, he tries to answer it and when this fails he blows his horn to see what that will do. The effect of the horn-call is to bring forth the dragon, whom Siegfried regards as a rather odd mate for him. After a preliminary challenge, Siegfried confronts Fafner, avoids his slashing tail on which he inflicts a wound. The dragon withdraws his tail and rears up so as to expose his breast into which Siegfried plunges his sword. As the dragon rolls over dying, Siegfried withdraws his sword thereby smearing the dragon's blood on his hand where it burns like fire. As he puts his finger to his mouth to suck the burning blood off when, behold! it seems to render the song of the bird intelligible to him so that from its warbling he learns of the Nibelungen's hoard of gold, of the tarnhelm and the ring. Thus advised Siegfried proceeds to explore the dragon's cavern and before long he emerges with the tarnhelm and the ring. Again the bird in the linden tree calls to him this time telling him to beware of Mime so that when the dwarf offers him something to drink he promptly slays him with his sword and casts his little body into the cave, closing the mouth of it with the dragon's corpse.

Stretched forth again under the linden tree, Siegfried hears once more the voice of the bird who tells him of the wondrous wife which may be his if he will stride through the fire which encircles the couch where she sleeps. With the bird guiding him Siegfried makes his way to the path leading up to the rock where Brunhilde lies sleeping. At the foot of this rocky mount Wotan awaits the coming of Siegfried and in his anxiety lest the reign of the gods may give place to the rule of the heroes, he awakens Erda to inquire how he can stop the wheel of fate which is now rolling. The goddess of earth can divine nothing and advises Wotan to seek counsel of the Wish Maiden, Brunhilde, child of Wotan and Erda only to learn that Wotan had banished the Valkyrie from Valhalla and cast a deep sleep upon her. Such shall be the fate of Erda also and since her wisdom has wilted Wotan consigns her to eternal slumber. Soon after Erda vanishes, Siegfried appears. The bird which with fluttering wing and sweet song has brought him hither has now flown away leaving it to him to find the path in the faint light of the moon.

Siegfried now hears a voice and wonders whether it will tell the way to the rock where Brunhilde lies sleeping. It is the voice of Wotan, who blocks the path and challenges him to enter it. Siegfried now swiftly relates the story of how he had mended the sword, slain the dragon and killed Mime and had then been told by the bird of Brunhilde's fiery couch. With his spear Wotan points to the place where Brunhilde is sleeping but warns Siegfried against the fire which encircles her. Nothing daunted Siegfried attempts to ascend the mount but now finds the path blocked by the spear that had broken his father's sword. Drawing the sword which he himself had mended he smashes the spear of the god who now tells him that nothing can prevent him from reaching Brunhilde.

As Siegfried ascends the path the fires start up but with a sharp blast of his horn he plunges into the flames, which soon begin to subside, fading away into a light, transparent veil. There on her couch of stone lies Brunhilde in full armor. Siegfried removes her helmet and long, waving locks break forth. With his sword he gently cuts through the coat of mail and beholds Brunhilde in delicate female attire. This is no man but a woman enfolded in sleep and the sight of her beauty awakens within the heart of the hero a feeling he had never felt before—fear! Brunhilde awakens, perceives that her hero has consummated his various exploits by plunging through the fire and breaks forth into song of love triumphant in which she is joined by Siegfried.

TWILIGHT OF THE GODS

Erda has sunk into the earth for her everlasting sleep. Wotan in Valhalla is but a memory or a name. The norns with their runes are trying to decipher the riddle of fate. They wind their cord round the rocks and in their endeavor to untangle it the cord breaks and the norns make their way to mother Erda. The future is all uncertainty.

Siegfried and Brunhilde now enter, he in full armor and she with her steed, Grane. They renew their pledges of love, he bestows the Nibelungen ring upon her and receives her horse that he may fare forth to still other deeds of prowess. Apart, who can divide them; separated they are still one. As Siegfried rides away the sound of his horn is heard in the valley.

In the hall of the Gibichungs on the Rhine Gunther and Gutrune, brother and sister, are on their throne with Hagen, son of Alberich, sitting before them. Hagen tells his sovereigns that their kingdom is a glorious one but without a future since neither Gunther nor Gutrune is married. Gunther, he continues, should woo Brunhilde but that right is reserved for Siegfried, the hero of many exploits. And yet by Siegfried's aid Gunther might win Brunhilde while it is possible that Siegfried himself might woo Gutrune. Such is Hagen's plan but naturally it depends for its completion upon whether Siegfried comes their way. Just then a horn-call is heard in the distance and down the Rhine can be seen a vessel bearing hero and horse. The craft approaches smoothly and swiftly for the hand at the great oar is the one which slew the dragon. Siegfried lands his horse and now stands quietly leaning on him.

[360]

Siegfried inquires for Gibich's son and when he learns that he is addressing him in the person of Gunther demands that he fight him or be his friend. In place of war Gunther offers welcome. Hagen then leads Siegfried's horse away and Gunther conducts Siegfried in the hall of the Gibichungs. The inquisitive Hagen now asks Siegfried about the vast hoard of gold only to learn that the hero, despising it, left the treasure in the dragon's cavern retaining only the tarn helmet which he cannot use and the ring which is now worn by a noble woman. Gunther, to whom Siegfried appears to be offering these treasures, insists that he will serve his new friend without any reward from him.

Gutrune bearing a full drinking horn bids Siegfried welcome and offers him the libation. The effect of the potion is to arouse within Siegfried's heart a sudden love for Gutrune and to extinguish his memory of Brunhilde; hence when Gunther laments his own lack of a wife suggests that for Gunther's sake he will break through the fire round Brunhilde's abode and bring her forth as Gunther's bride. Immediately the men enter into a covenant of blood-brotherhood together drinking a horn of wine in which drops of their blood have been mixed. The compact accomplished, Siegfried sailed away in quest of Brunhilde.

On the Valkyries' rock at the entrance of the cave sits Brunhilde fondly gazing upon Siegfried's ring. Valtrauta, her sister Valkyrie, enters hastily with tidings from their father, Wotan. His spear was broken by Siegfried's sword and now, having caused the timbers of the world-ash tree to be piled up about Valhalla he has sent forth his ravens to bring him tidings of the world. Wotan's judgment is the redemption of gods and men cannot come until the accursed ring has been restored to the maidens in the Rhine. Yet although all world sorrow hangs upon the ring, Brunhilde will not part with the ring even though the splendor of Valhalla be annihilated. Valtrauta gallops away singing a song of woe.

Siegfried's horn is heard resounding in the valley and the enraptured Brunhilde awaits his coming. When Siegfried appears, however, he has used the tarn helmet to give him Gunther's form but still uses his power as the hero to carry him through the fire and take possession of Brunhilde although he places the sword between them that it may separate him from Gunther's bride.

When morning comes Siegfried, now wearing the ring he has wrenched from Brunhilde's hand, tells Hagen of his exploit, advises him that Gunther is coming with his bride, and inquires for Gutrune.

Gunther and Brunhilde now appear in the boat and in a moment Gunther has led her ashore. Brunhilde, pale and with her gaze fixed on the ground, suddenly perceives Siegfried and recoils in horror as she learns that he is mated with Gutrune as is she with Gunther. Her anguish is even worse when she observes the ring on his finger. Siegfried seeks to defend himself against any charge of deceitfulness by insisting that his worthy sword, Needfull, had sundered him from Gunther's bride. More than that Siegfried swears on Hagen's spear bidding the steel strike him if he has wronged either Brunhilde or Gunther. After this bit of self-justification, Siegfried gives vent to joy and putting his arm about Gutrune leads her away into the hall. Brunhilde and Gunther feel that they have been wronged and listen to Hagen's plan to bring about Siegfried's death whereby Hagen himself will, as he thinks, secure possession of the gold and the ring.

From a cliff on the Rhine the three Rhine Maidens rise to the surface of the stream and renew their plaintive song over the loss of the Rhine Gold. Siegfried now appears and taunts them for the way they lost the gold to Alberich. When they plead with him to return the ring to them and threaten him with the fate in store for him if he keeps it, he replies jauntily by saying that he might give them the ring for their love but will not surrender it because of their threat. Siegfried is now accosted by Gunther and Hagen with the vassals of the realm who have come forth hunting. Drinking horns are filled and Siegfried empties both his own and Gunther's. The drink inspires him to song and he relates the story of his valorous deeds including the tidings he gleaned from the bird which finally led him to Brunhilde's fiery rock. Two of Wotan's ravens now start up from the bush, circle over Siegfried's head and then put to flight over the Rhine to Valhalla. Siegfried is now awakened to his former self and as he turns to watch the ravens' flight Hagen thrusts his spear into his back. In his dying moments he recalls Brunhilde and sings in praise of her.

When the body of Siegfried is brought back to the hall of the Gibichungs Gutrune upbraids Hagen for the murder of her hero and when Gunther takes her part Hagen slays him also. Brunhilde now asserts herself with her former majesty. She sends other ravens to Valhalla bidding Wotan seek eternal rest. She commands the vassals to build a great pyre and place Siegfried's body upon it. She removes the fatal ring from Siegfried's finger and mounts her horse, Grane. As the flames of far-off Valhalla are seen, Brunhilde applies the torch to the pyre, and as she drives into the flames she casts the ring back into the Rhine. Hagen leaps in after it but is overcome by the Rhine Maidens who, once more in possession of their treasure sing a song of triumph. The end of the gods has come but the gold has been restored to the Rhine.

IDYLS OF THE KING

By

Alfred Lord Tennyson

ALFRED, FIRST BARON TENNYSON (*1809–1892*) was the poet of
Queen Victoria. After leaving Cambridge and a trip on the
Continent, he published his first volume when he was 21.
When he was 31 he published two volumes containing some
works which he never surpassed, such as *The Lady of Shalott,
Sir Galahad, Ulysses.* In 1850 he married and published his
In Memoriam. He loved the freedom and peace of country
life and moved to the Isle of Wight in 1853 where he re-
maimed until 1870. Queen Victoria created a barony for him
in 1884. He was buried in Westminster Abbey.

ENID

GERAINT, a knight of Arthur's court, had married Enid, a lady
whom he loved exceedingly. Enid was fond of Guinevere, Arthur's
beautiful wife, and spent much time in her company. When scandal linked Guinevere's name with that of Sir Lancelot, Geraint
begged leave of Arthur to return to his own estates to destroy bandits and caitiff knights who lived on the borders, hoping in this
manner to be able to take his wife from all corrupting influences. Arthur gave leave and Geraint and Enid departed for their
home.

So much did Prince Geraint love his beauteous wife that for
her sake he ceased from all knightly pastimes, that he might be
with her the longer. All who knew him bemoaned the loss of his
manhood and when these complaints reached the ears of the lady
Enid she grieved to think that she was the cause of her husband's unmanly actions. One morning as he slept she wept over

him, lamenting that he had become thus effeminate and saying that she was no true wife. Geraint awakened just as his wife uttered the last words and, seeing her in tears, thought that she was weeping for some knight at Arthur's court. Arising in haste he donned his clothes and bade his wife put on her meanest dress that they might ride into the wilderness together. Obediently she went to her closet and took therefrom the dress she had been wearing when first Geraint laid eyes on her.

Then she bethought herself of their young love. It chanced some years before that a young knight was riding past a hill on which were Guinevere and Prince Geraint. And Guinevere sent her maid to inquire the knight's name, who rode with a mis-shapen dwarf as servant. The dwarf lashed the poor maid with his whip and answered not, whereon Geraint swore an oath that he would follow them and avenge the queen's honor. So he rode in pursuit till those in front entered a city. Within Geraint, who rode unarmed, asked for arms and armor but the next day there was to be a tournament and arms could not be had. In search of lodging the prince came to the castle of the earl, Yniol, which castle had fallen to decay. Within the gates he saw the maid, Enid, daughter to Yniol, and swore that never had he seen thing so beautiful.

Yniol offered the knight his hospitality and his rusty armor and explained to him who was the knight he pursued. He was Yniol's nephew, arrogant and rude, who courted Enid. He was known as the sparrow-hawk since he had always won the tournament, like to the one on the morrow, in which a golden sparrow-hawk was given to the winner for his lady. But Geraint would not be suf-fered to enter the tournament, for all contestants must have their ladies present in the audience. So Geraint asked leave to take the lady Enid, saying that never had he seen any one whom he would prefer to champion.

And when the time had come for the tournament, Geraint de-feated the arrogant knight and made him tell his name and bade him ride to Arthur's court to crave the pardon of the queen and also to return the earldom he had wrested from Yniol. Then Geraint wished to take Enid for his bride and from the goods that had been stolen from her house, she took a golden dress and rode with him. But ever had she kept the faded dress she wore when first she saw her lord.

This dress she donned and they rode forth. Three knights came forth to slay Geraint but they themselves were slain, and then three more. And Geraint bade Enid ride before him, driving the dead men's horses and their arms. They rested near the chambers of an earl, who came to greet them and who knew Enid, for he, Limours, had been her suitor when she dwelt at home. While Geraint was drinking, the earl told Enid that in the early morning he would steal her away. This she imparted to her husband and they rode forth to the waste earldom of another earl, Doorm, whom his vassals called the Bull. Limours rode after them but was overthrown by Geraint. In the battle Geraint was wounded but, saying naught about it, rode on until he fell from his horse.

While Enid was weeping over her lord, Doorm rode by and told his followers to take the body to his castle. There, while she wept over him, Geraint returned to consciousness but feigned he still was unconscious, thinking that the manner in which he had treated his lady was unkind for now he knew she loved him. Doorm bade Enid eat and drink but she said she would not, until her lord were well enough to eat and drink. In anger, Doorm struck her, whereat she cried out and Geraint, rising with lightning speed, slew Doorm. Swiftly the knight and his lady fled the hall and mounted the one horse, hoping the load would not be so great that their enemies would capture them.

Suddenly in front of them was Edryn, he who had been known as the sparrow-hawk. Enid cried out, for her knight was weak and could not endure a struggle. But Edryn soothed her. He had become one of Arthur's knights and would not harm them. Arthur himself was near. And Edryn led them to the king. And when Geraint was recovered, they resumed their old places in the court. Nor did Geraint doubt his lady more but lived in happiness for many years

> *"till he crown'd*
> *A happy life with a fair death, and fell*
> *Against the heathen of the Northern Sea*
> *In battle, fighting for the blameless king."*

[366]

VIVIEN

The wily Vivien, scorned by Arthur's court, planned long to gain revenge. One day the king, unhappy at some rumor touching his wife, had walked apart with gloomy mien. Vivien, seeking to find favor in his eyes hinted to him that he was not appreciated and that there were others who appreciated him more than did Guinevere. Arthur had stared blankly at the girl and then walked on. But one had heard and told and the court laughed at any who had thought to tempt their blameless king.

And so to gain revenge Vivien had tried to snare old Merlin, mightiest of wizards, in the net of her bright hair. He had paid but scant attention to her, yet smiled occasionally at her pranks, for he was old and loved all youthful things. One day he dreamed a wave had swept him out of the world and that the wave was Vivien. In a black mood he took a boat and sailed to the wild woods of Broceliande, not knowing that Vivien had followed him.

Now they stood in the woods together and a great storm was coming on. Once he had told her, the girl reminded him, of a mighty charm, the victim of which felt as though he were encased within four walls and indeed could never escape. None could see him and none could he see save that one being who was his captor. This charm she wanted him to tell her as proof that he trusted her, for she loved him beyond belief. Merlin refused, saying that she might, some day, in anger, desire to work the spell on him; whereat she seemed aggrieved and said she loved him and could not do aught save try to make him happy.

Merlin then thought perhaps the girl might want to use the charm on some knight of the Table Round because she thought they talked unkindly of her. At this Vivien broke into such abuse of all the goodly knights and even of the saintly Arthur that Merlin murmured: "harlot," thinking this the rage of a woman scorned where she desires. She swore then that if she aimed at Merlin's peace of mind in asking for the charm, she wished lightning to strike her. And at that moment the storm broke and lightning struck a tree nearby. Vivien, thinking that it would strike her also for her oath, flung herself on the sage, protesting that she loved him more than life and that she was terrified of the storm and needed him to save her. Merlin, exhausted by her talk, told her the charm; and then, the storm subsiding, lay down to sleep. In a trice Vivien had woven the spell over the old magician.

> *"Then crying, 'I have made his glory mine,'*
> *And shrieking out, 'O fool!' the harlot leapt*
> *Adown the forest and the thicket clos'd*
> *Behind her, and the forest echo'd 'fool.'"*

ELAINE

Once, before he was king, had Arthur found on the armor of a long-dead king nine beauteous diamonds. When he ascended to the throne of England he had decreed that each year a tournament should be held, the winner of which should receive one diamond as his prize.

Eight years had Lancelot won the diamond and, this being the ninth and last tournament, had set his heart on winning the last diamond, largest and most beautiful of the lot. When he had all he intended them as a gift for Guinevere, whom he loved, and whose love made him happy and yet miserable, for he loved Arthur and knew that he injured him by loving his wife.

Guinevere was ill and could not attend the tourney. Lancelot, thinking to stay with her and cheer her, told Arthur that an old wound kept him from attending. Guinevere chided her lover, saying that there was enough talk about them already without his absenting himself to stay by her side. Let him, therefore, come to the tourney arrayed as an unknown knight and, when the fray is over, he can explain to the king that he had not intended to remain behind but had wanted to be unrecognized for he knew that half his battles were won in advance when he fought as Lancelot, so terrifying was his reputation in the field.

So Lancelot rode forth till he came to the castle of Astolat. There he asked the lord of the domain if he could lend him a shield, saying that he was a knight of the Round Table who wished to enter the tournament unknown. Although he refused to divulge his name the old man offered him the shield of a son,

Sir Torre, who had been injured at his first encounter and so had nothing emblazoned on it. His other son, Sir Lavaine, offered to accompany the stranger to the tourney, and to him in secret Lancelot told his name. Elaine, daughter of the lord of Astolat, fell in love with the great warrior at first sight and asked him to wear a favor of hers in the fight. Never had Lancelot worn a lady's favor but this he took the better to disguise himself, for none would suspect that Lancelot would wear a lady's sleeve in his helm.

At the tournament Lancelot performed so many feats of valor that the knights were saying that this was a hero fully as great as Lancelot himself. Lancelot's kith and kin, jealous for the reputation of their idol, bore down upon the stranger en masse, severely wounding him. He continued, however, until he won the diamond and then rode off without it, thinking that his death was upon him. Lavaine helped him to the home of a hermit who immediately cared for the stricken man. Arthur, meantime, sent the princely Sir Gawaine in pursuit of the victor to give him the diamond.

When Gawaine came to Astolat he was told of the stranger knight who had left his shield and was invited to wait till he returned for it. One look at Elaine and Gawaine consented. He made love to her but she told him that she loved the knight he was seeking and showed him the shield that had been left behind. Gawaine recognized the shield and told Elaine it was Lancelot's. Then, giving the diamond into the girl's keeping, he departed.

Elaine thereon went in search for Lancelot and, finding him, nursed him back to health. She told her love but Lancelot loved only Guinevere. To make her wroth with him, he departed without bidding her good-bye.

When Gawaine returned and told the court it was Lancelot who had put them all to shame and that he was loved by the lady Elaine, the queen grew sad. When Lancelot returned she was angry with him, thinking him unfaithful to her and flung the diamonds into the river. At that moment they were startled by sight of a barge bearing the beautiful, dead body of Elaine. In Elaine's hand was a letter telling of her unrequited love for Lancelot. The maid of Astolat was buried with all honor and the queen forgave her lover but he was unhappy, thinking how much better it would have been had he been able to love the maid Elaine.

GUINEVERE

Sir Modred, nephew to the king, desirous of replacing his royal master on the throne, began to spy on Guinevere that he might learn some scandal. Once as he hid upon a wall, looking on the queen and her servitors, Sir Lancelot saw and threw him off as one might fling some loathed worm. Yet he persisted and the queen, in fright, told Lancelot that he must away to his own realm, lest Modred find them together.

They sat one night to speak a last farewell, the king being gone from the palace, and Modred and his men came on them. Lancelot hurled the spying knight with such force that he stunned him and his men had to carry him off. Then Guinevere and Lancelot fled, he to his land beyond the sea, she to a convent in Almesbury where, not giving her name, she sought refuge.

News came to the little house in Almesbury. The king had followed Lancelot to make war upon him, leaving Modred to rule in his place and Modred had usurped the throne. Poor Guinevere was tormented by an artless maid who, not knowing her, was constantly in talk about the wicked queen.

And then one day Arthur found her. He had ceased the struggle with Lancelot and was returned to fight with Modred for his lawful throne. His end had been foretold; this war would be his last. But he wanted to leave some men-at-arms to guard his queen lest harm should come to her. She had destroyed the purpose of his life. England was ravaged with internal strife and was easy prey for the heathen of the north. Yet with it all he loved her, in a way. Perhaps when they both came before the throne of God, he said, she would call him husband and think not of another.

Speaking thus, he left; and she, who had not dared to look at him knew full well that it was her king she loved and that when they were in a purer world she would have another chance to tell him. He loved her; and great bitterness lifted from her heart.

And so she dwelt at Almesbury until the Abbess died.

"*Then she, for her good deeds and her pure life,*
And for the power of ministration in her,
And likewise for the high rank she had borne,
Was chosen Abbess, there, an Abbess lived
For three brief years, and there, an Abbess, pass'd
To where beyond these voices there is peace."

THE RING AND THE BOOK

By

Robert Browning

ROBERT BROWNING (*1812–1889*) was an English poet. He was born in a suburb of London, the son of a man of education and of scholarly tastes who was a clerk in the Bank of England. His mother was the daughter of a Hamburg ship-owner. Browning's poetical tastes developed early with Byron's works his favorite. He wrote a volume of verse at the age of 12 but fortunately he failed to find a publisher. Soon he came under the influence of Shelley and Keats. He was for a time a student at London University but his education was somewhat desultory as he preferred the study of life, languages and literature which he gained by an extensive continental trip. In 1835 he published a metaphysical drama, *Paracelsus,* which was recognized as the work of genius and brought him a prominent place among the literary men of his day. In 1846 he married Elizabeth Barrett, also a poet, and from that time they resided chiefly in Italy until her death in 1861 when Browning returned to England and spent his final days mainly in London. He died in Venice and was buried in Westminster Abbey. Among his more noted works are the *Ring and the Book, Pippa Passes, The Lost Leader* and *Cavalier Tunes.*

THERE LIVED IN ROME in 1679 Pietro and Violante Comparini, an elderly, bourgeois couple, fond of show and good living, who had run considerably into debt. At this period, they were in receipt of a papal bounty granted to the needy who did not like to beg. Creditors were insistent and the only way out of the situation would have been to have an heir so that they could draw on their capital which was tied up for the benefit of an unknown heir-at-law. Violante, realizing that at her age it was less than likely she would have a child, conceived the plan of securing the baby of a poor prostitute and then announced to the world that she had become the mother of a girl, Francesca Pompilia. Pietro, the husband, accepted his fatherhood as a stroke of good luck and did not think to question his wife's veracity.

The couple, indeed, grew more than fond of the girl who with the years grew more lovely and virtuous. At the time Pompilia became thirteen, there was in Rome a Count Guido Franceschini, an impoverished, fifty-year-old nobleman of Arezzo who for some time had been seeking preferment in the priesthood, where he held a minor rank, but without success. At this age, it became clear that the only means of building up the family fortunes in his own person, since he was the eldest of three brothers, was a moneyed marriage. As he was personally unattractive, being short, thin, pale and with a bulbous nose, it was not likely that any but a very obscure heiress might be satisfied with the one thing he had to offer —his rank. He heard about the beauteous child Pompilia at the local centre of gossip, the barber's shop, and received an exaggerated estimate of her dowry. He immediately asked for her hand, using his brother, a churchman, the Abate Paul, as his chief ambassador. The brothers did not hesitate to lie concerning their fortunes and poor, foolish Violante was soon dazzled into consenting to the match. Pietro, with some cupidity, however, inquired into the state of the Count's affairs and finding his income had been exaggerated declined, under plea of Pompilia's extreme youth, to consent.

Violante, not to be denied of the splendor she wished for herself and her dear Pompilia, pretended submission but secretly led Pompilia to the church of San Lorenzo in Lucina and there married her to the decrepit Guido. Pietro when confronted with the facts had to resign himself to the situation and paid down an instalment on Pompilia's dowry; he also transferred to the newly married pair all that he actually possessed. Thus the old couple had nowhere to live but under the roof of the Franceschini at Arezzo. Here not only Violante and Pietro but also the child-wife were subjected to the most petty cruelties and privations by the half-mad mother of Count Guido and the other brother who looked down upon them for their humble lineage. Finally, the old couple could bear the indignities no longer and they returned to Rome, penniless, and on money lent them for the journey by Count Guido.

In Rome, the Pope had proclaimed a jubilee in honor of his eightieth birthday, and absolution was to be had for the asking. It now occurred to Violante to cast off the burden of her sin by confession. Unfortunately, the Church decreed that for Violante absolution must be preceded by atonement and that she restore to her legal heirs that of which her pretended motherhood had robbed them. First, she had to reveal the fraud to her husband and Pietro lost no time in making use of the revelation. He repudiated Pompilia and with her all claims on her husband's part. The case was taken to court and the court decreed a compromise. Pietro appealed the decree and the case remained unsettled.

Naturally, it was the unhappy Pompilia who suffered most from these proceedings. She dreaded Guido as a lustful tyrant who held that "Husbands were God's representatives" and also because she knew that his discovery of her base birth could only result in an aversion towards her. She was right; for from this moment, Guido's one aim was to get rid of his wife, but in such a manner as not to forfeit any financial gains he might still derive from their union. He began a persistent and cunning campaign in order to be able to convict her of infidelity. To this end he dinned into her ears complaints about a certain Canon Guiseppe Caponsacchi and the attachment which she supposedly entertained for him. So deeply and desperately laid were Guido's plans, that he even composed, or had composed, false communications from Pompilia to Caponsacchi imploring the latter to help her escape from the clutches of her cruel husband and avowing her feeling for him. As it happened, Pompilia had appealed for protection against her husband's violence to the Archbishop and the Governor, but without success. She had even implored a priest, in confession, to write her parents and ask them to take her away, for like most women of her breeding and time she was unable to read or write. But the whole town was subservient to her husband's house, either through custom or fear. Almost without realizing it, her hopes finally centred on Caponsacchi. Her husband's false but insidious accusations, the fact that the Canon had a reputation for virtue and courage, all this served to point to him as the last straw to be clutched at in her desperate plight. What made the

plan more possible was that she knew he was contemplating a journey to Rome and thus, when an opportunity arose one night to
address him from her balcony, she made a fervent plea that he
assist her to escape and accompany her to her parents. Caponsacchi
was reluctant but, touched by the situation, he consented and on
a given night she slipped away from Guido and joined the
Canon where he awaited her with a carriage. They travelled day
and night till they reached Castelnuovo, a village four hours from
their destination. There they were compelled to rest and there the
wily and ever watchful Guido overtook them. They were not together at the time but the evidence of an "elopement" seemed
incontrovertible. On this charge with the added insult of adultery,
Guido had Pompilia and Caponsacchi arrested. The couple were
taken to the New Prisons in Rome and here ensued a famous
trial on the subject of which all Rome took sides.

One half of Rome, by definition suspicious of woman and her
cunning nature, inclined toward a definite conviction of Pompilia
as guilty. The other half of Rome, the more refined and reasoned
opinion, felt that Violante's original falsity engendered a chain
of events in which Pompilia was the feeble and saintly tool of
circumstance and her husband's machinations. A few of the most
distinguished but conservative citizens inclined toward a safely
neutral view of the case impugning an equal share of guilt to all
parties in the case.

But Pompilia and Caponsacchi answered all the questions put to
them simply and firmly; and although their statement on small
facts did not always coincide (as what two persons will?) on the
whole they created a general moral conviction of their innocence. Nevertheless, moral conviction was not interpreted as legal
proof and so the Court, finding itself in a dilemma, decreed that
for his complicity in the flight of Pompilia and too great intimacy
with her, Caponsacchi be banished for three years to Civita
Vecchia; and that Pompilia should be relegated, for the time being, to a convent. In other words, the prisoners were pronounced
guilty but a merely nominal punishment was inflicted.

Naturally, Guido was not satisfied with the outcome. He wanted
a divorce and continued to sue for it through his brother, the
Abate Paul, but before very long he learned that Pompilia was

about to become a mother and that, because of her condition, she had been removed from the convent to her parents' home to be more or less in their custody as a prisoner. In the small villa her parents occupied in a suburb of Rome, Pompilia gave birth to a son whom her parents had conveyed to a place of safety and concealment. Guido oppressed by hate, a desire for revenge and the delusion that the child was Caponsacchi's bastard devised a plan for killing Pompilia and her foster-parents. He employed four ruffians to assist him in his enterprise and secretly took up lodgings near the Comparini villa so that, hawk-like, he could watch their movements before making the final attack on his prey.

Meanwhile Pompilia was happy in her motherhood. The gossip over her flight with Caponsacchi had not troubled her. He had saved her in her hour of need and the sudden revelation of a possible ideal in the person of this virtuous and handsome man had sustained her through the trying months that followed. She even grows to love him in a way which she conceives to be her duty as a lover of the good. She saw in this brave man an embodiment of virtue and, being truly religious, with all the intensity of her simple child-like nature she loved him as a visible symbol of the good. The thought of an earthly fulfillment of her love for Caponsacchi never suggested itself to her; the only consummation she wished for was a union of souls in heaven. Pompilia even understood the evil she suffered at the hands of her enemy to be part of a larger pattern of all-redeeming good. Guido with all his rapacious brutality and materialism had sensed this powerful spiritual force in her and hated her for it all the more since he felt his own weapons blunted before it.

Thus, the dark deed was inevitable and past midnight on the second day of January he secured entrance into the Comparini villa by a ruse. He utilized one of his hired thugs to present a letter supposedly from the Canon Caponsacchi. Once the door was open Guido and his band forced their way in. Old Violante, since she came first to hand, was the first victim of his cold-blooded fury and she was quickly murdered. Pompilia, recognizing the desperate nature of the situation, extinguished the light thinking this would enable her to escape her assassins. She ran screaming for help toward a neighboring blacksmith but before she could leave the villa, Guido's lanterns had discovered her. Desperately, she attempted to hide under a bed from which Guido shortly dragged her forth. Then with barbarous frenzy he inflicted twenty-two wounds with a dagger and thinking the job fatal he dragged the bleeding woman into the room where both the Comparini lay dead hoping her dying glance would behold this last deed in anguish.

Meanwhile, the noise of this horrible massacre had attracted many citizens to the place and the murderers made a hasty escape, one of them unwittingly leaving his cloak behind and Guido, an incriminating cap. Pompilia, having implored of the Holy Virgin the grace of being allowed to confess, miraculously survived several days after the atrocious attack. Shortly thereafter the assassins were apprehended at an inn and Guido, more than the others, was both terrified and wondering that his wife could have lived to tell the horrible tale. Nevertheless, he continued to protest his innocence in vigorous and mock-manly terms. The assistants to this dire deed, all but one, confessed and Guido like a beast of the jungle attempted every ruse, wile, and evasion to save his skin. Finally, the last of the thugs confessed since Guido had not kept his promise of paying them the moment when they left Rome, as he had promised before the crime was committed. Guido, then, more frantic than ever grasped at the excuse that Pompilia had always been an unwilling and ineffectual mate:

> "... What you call my wife
> I call a nullity in female shape,
> Vapid disgust, soon to be pungent,
> When mixed with, made confusion and a curse
> By two abominable nondescripts,
> That father and that mother ...
> I still declare—life without absolute use
> Of the actual sweet therein, is death, not life."

Pompilia meanwhile lingering those miraculous four days had displayed so much wisdom, forbearance and charity against her evil-doers that almost all Rome was won to believe in the original innocence of this lovely child who was doomed to die before her seventeenth birthday. Her departure from this life was preceded

by a tale so sincere in its presentation that all suspicion of a possible affair with Caponsacchi vanished from even the most worldly
and cynical minds. Her final words were addressed to the imprisoned Canon and revealed, more than any evidence could have,
the quality of her love for this man:

> "O lover of my life, O soldier-saint,
> No work begun shall ever pause for death!
> Love will be helpful to me more and more
> I' the coming course, the new path I must tread—
> My weak hand in thy strong hand, strong for that!
> Tell him that if I seem without him now,
> That's the world's insight! Oh, he understands!
> He is at Civita—do I once doubt
> The world again is holding us apart?
> He had been here, displayed in my behalf
> The broad brow that reverberates the truth,
> And flashed the word God gave him, back to man!
> I know where the free soul is flown! My fate
> Will have been hard for even him to bear:
> Let it confirm him in the trust of God,
> Showing how holily he dared the deed!
> And, for the rest, say, from the deed, no touch
> Of harm came, but all good, all happiness,
> Not one faint fleck of failure! . . .
> . . . . He is a priest;
> He cannot marry therefor, which is right:
> I think he would not marry if he could.
> Marriage on earth seems such a counterfeit,
> Mere imitation of the inimitable:
> In heaven we have the real and true and sure.
>
> . . . .
>
> So let him wait God's instant men call years;
> Meantime hold hard by truth and his great soul,
> Do out the duty! Through such souls alone
> God stooping shows sufficient of His light
> For us i' the dark to rise by. And I rise."

As for Caponsacchi the anguish of Pompilia's death intensifies his love for her and he makes a dramatic and brilliant vindication of the beautiful girl at Guido's trial. He inhibits all expression of his love for her, however, lest it might detract from the perfect sum of her purity. And at the end, torn by sorrow and the genuine desire to keep his priesthood unsullied, he yet cannot escape the agonizing cry of a poor human in torture:

"O great, just, good God! Miserable me!"

For Caponsacchi had wrestled with temptation, had conquered it, but in doing so had suffered more severely than even the unfaltering but simpler soul, Pompilia.

Guido, now learning of Pompilia's death feels instinctively that all is up and abandons all his former rationalizations, appealing to the class prejudices and social snobberies of the Court. But when this and even flattery have failed, he resigns himself to the inevitable with bravado claiming that he lived and died a man and took a man's chances, "honest and bold." But at the very end as the hangmen and the priests descend into his cell he loses courage and cries out the truth for the first time:

> *"Sirs, have I spoken one word all this while*
> *Out of the world of words I had to say?*
> *Not one word! All was folly—I laughed and mocked!*
> *Sirs, my first true word, all truth and no lie,*
> *Is—save me notwithstanding! Life is all!*
> *I was just stark mad,—let the madman live*
> *Pressed by as many chains as you please pile!*
>
> . . . .
>
> *Abate,—Cardinal,—Christ,—Maria,—God, . . .*
> *Pompilia will you let them murder me?"*

This last appeal to Pompilia as the final judge indicates that at last the wretched Guido has perceived the power of human goodness and its power to triumph over human evil.

THE PICTURE OF DORIAN GRAY

By

Oscar Wilde

OSCAR WILDE (*1856–1900*) was an Irish author and poet who was born in Dublin and educated at Oxford. In 1882 he gave an extensive lecture tour in America and produced his play *Vera* and two years later *The Duchess of Padua*. In 1896 he served a two years' prison sentence at hard labor for vicious practices and upon his release published his *A Ballad of Reading Gaol*. His best works include *The Picture of Dorian Gray* and *The Importance of Being Earnest*.

BASIL HALLWARD'S STUDIO was full of the odor of roses and the murmur of the bees in the garden outside the window. Stretched on a divan, Lord Henry Wotton savored the summer day as he gazed at the easel before which his friend stood. On the easel was the full-length portrait of a young man of extraordinary physical beauty. Lord Henry was trying to persuade Basil to send the picture to the next year's exhibition at the Grosvenor Gallery. Basil refused, saying he had put too much of himself into the picture. Only because of a slip of the tongue did he tell his friend the name of the model, Dorian Gray. When he liked people immensely, he never told their names to anyone, as it seemed like surrendering a part of them. This secrecy seemed to make life more mysterious and marvelous to him. Henry answered that as a married man, he understood the value of secrecy, even of deception. When Basil charged him with posing as a cynic, Lord Henry answered that being natural was only a pose, the most irritating he knew. Being pressed, Basil told his friend of his first meeting with Dorian Gray. When he had first seen the boy at Lady Brandon's, he had felt a curious sensation of terror and tried to avoid meeting him. Basil had always been very independent by nature, and he felt

[380]

that this new personality was so fascinating that it would absorb his whole nature. He was, however, introduced to Dorian, who became so necessary to him that he saw him every day. Somehow the boy suggested to him an entirely new manner in art, so that Basil saw things and recreated them differently from the way in which he had done before.

Lord Henry expressed a desire to meet Dorian. As Basil answered that he did not want the two to meet, a servant announced that Dorian had arrived. Basil had only time to tell Lord Henry not to try to influence the boy, not to try to spoil him. Lord Henry saw that he was wonderfully handsome, with his frank blue eyes, his crisp gold hair, and the candor and passionate purity of youth in his face. Dorian took an instant liking to Lord Henry because he had such a beautiful voice and because he was such a delightful contrast to Basil, and insisted that he stay during the sitting. As Basil painted, Lord Henry chatted on in his cynical vein about one of his favorite topics—the need of self-development. Each one of us is here to realize one's nature perfectly, he believed, and were one man to live out his life completely, were he to give form to every feeling and expression to every thought, the world would gain a fresh impulse to joy. We are afraid of ourselves. The only way to get rid of a temptation is to yield to it.

As he spoke, Dorian felt new influences at work within him; the words touched a secret chord which had not stirred before. Lord Henry spoke to him of his beauty—told him Beauty is a form of Genius. When the boy laughed, he told him he would not laugh at the idea when his beauty had fled, that he must remember youth would last such a little time, and then come no more—that there is absolutely nothing in the world but youth.

That afternoon Basil finished the portrait. When he saw it, Dorian flushed with pleasure. He had never believed Basil's compliments, but Lord Henry's panegyric and his warning of the brevity of youth had stirred him, and he saw at last how beautiful he was. He envied the picture, for it would never be any older. "If it were I who was to be always young, and the picture that was to grow old! I would give my soul for that!" he cried. "Some day the picture will mock me!" and he burst into tears. Basil, seeing his friend's anguish, picked up a knife to destroy the picture, but the boy rushed at him: "I am in love with it, Basil! It is part of myself." Basil told him that he could have the picture. Then Dorian went off to the theater with Lord Harry, despite Basil's invitation to stay and dine with him.

The next day Lord Henry went to call on his uncle, Lord Fermor, who knew everybody and everything, to ask him about Dorian. His uncle told him that the boy's mother, the daughter of Lord Kelso, had been an extraordinarily beautiful girl who had run away with a penniless young nobody in a foot regiment who had been killed in a duel a few months after the marriage. An ugly rumor said that Kelso had got some adventurer to insult his son-in-law and kill him; certainly it was known that his daughter never spoke to him again, and died soon after her child was born. The boy was supposed to have inherited a large fortune. The romance of the story appealed to Lord Henry, and made him more interested than ever in Dorian. Talking to the boy was like playing on a violin—there was something enthralling in exercising influence upon him. He would try to make that wonderful spirit his own. That day he met Dorian at a luncheon party. Dorian was fascinated anew at his friend's conversation. Taking the idea that the only things one does not regret are one's mistakes, he played with it, until praise of folly soared into a philosophy, and his listeners were charmed out of themselves. Dorian sat like one in a spell, never taking his eyes off him. That afternoon he did not go to see Basil, as he had promised, but went walking with Lord Henry.

A month after that, as Dorian was waiting for his host in Lord Henry's Mayfair flat, Lady Henry fluttered in to talk to him. She was a silly, sentimental woman. As she went out, Lord Henry told Dorian never to marry, since marriage was only a disappointment. Dorian, blushing, told him that he was in love with an actress, Sibyl Vane. Three weeks before, filled with the desire Lord Henry had given him to know everything about life, he had been wandering about London at night. Losing his way in grimy streets, he had come upon a shabby little theater and had gone in. The play was *Romeo and Juliet,* and at first he had been annoyed at the idea of seeing such a play in such a tawdry place, but when he saw Juliet, he was lost. She was hardly seventeen, with a little flower-like face, and the loveiest voice in the world. After that he went to see her night after night; she was everything in life to him. He wanted Lord Henry and Basil to see her act. He had not seen Basil for a long time—had, in fact, been rather bored by his good advice—but he did want him to see the girl act.

That night, Dorian became engaged to Sibyl Vane. Sibyl's mother, a shallow, theatrical woman, was pleased that her daughter was sought after by the handsome young man. But Sibyl's brother James, who was just going off to the colonies, was bothered by the news that a gentleman was calling to see his sister every night after the theater. James was a rough, rather harsh lad; but he loved his sister, and somehow feared that this young dandy who was making love to her could mean her no good. He told his sister that if her Prince Charming (she knew Dorian by no other name) did her any wrong, he would kill him.

Before they went to the theater, Basil, Lord Henry and Dorian dined together. Dorian was full of his love. He said that when he was with her, he forgot all Lord Henry's fascinating, poisonous, delightful theories. Lord Henry took pleasure in watching the lad's enthusiasm; he took pleasure in watching people's emotions. Basil felt sorry to lose his friend, but felt that this marriage was better than many other things that might have happened to the boy. When the curtain rose, and Sibyl Vane stepped on the stage as Juliet, even Lord Henry was forced to say that the girl was one of the loveliest creatures he had ever seen. But she was curiously listless; her speeches, though the voice was exquisite, were delivered in a thoroughly artificial manner. She seemed to be absolutely incompetent. Dorian's friends were horribly disappointed. The staginess of the girl's acting grew worse as she went on. Dorian grew more and more pale. Sibyl was a complete failure. Even the pit and gallery lost interest in the play and began to hiss. Basil and Lord Henry left after the second act, but Dorian remained to the end.

As soon as it was over, Dorian rushed to the greenroom. To his amazement, he found Sibyl pleased that she had been so bad. In him she had at last found reality. Before, she had felt that the theater and acting were the one reality, but now that she knew love, she saw how silly and hollow they were. She knew now something higher, something of which all art is only a reflection, and she knew she could never act well again. Dorian went to the door. "You have killed my love," he said. "I loved you because you were marvelous; I would have made you magnificent. Now you are only a third-rate actress with a pretty face. I can't see you again." And though she wept bitterly, he went out into the night. It was dawn when he arrived home. As he went into his library, his eye fell upon the portrait Basil had painted of him, and he started. Around the mouth were clearly drawn lines of cruelty. He picked up a mirror and examined his face, but no line warped his lips. He looked again at the painting; there was no doubt that the whole expression had altered. Suddenly he remembered what he had said that day in Basil Hallward's studio—he had wished that he himself might remain young, and the portrait grow old. Surely this wish had not been fulfilled? He was overcome with remorse. He would not sin; no longer would he listen to Lord Henry's wicked words; he would make amends to Sibyl for the wrong he had done her. Thinking that, he drew a screen before the portrait and went to bed, dreaming of Sibyl.

When he awoke, he went to look at the portrait again. It was true—it had changed. He saw more than ever how he had injured the girl. Leaving his morning mail unread, he covered pages of letter-paper with a letter of self-reproach, asking her to forgive him. He was interrupted by Lord Henry, who came to tell him that the girl had committed suicide. After his first outburst of pained surprise, Dorian wondered that he could not feel the tragedy as much as he wanted to; it all seemed like a wonderful play in which he had taken a great part, but by which he had not been wounded. Lord Henry consoled him with facile and cynical words, until he ceased regretting even the marring of the beautiful portrait, and took pleasure in thinking that it would bear his sins, while his own beauty would not fade. When Basil came the next day, sad because of the girl's death, he was horrified at Dorian's indifference at the whole tragedy. But he could not long reproach Dorian; there was so much of good in the boy that he had great hope for him. Before he left, he asked Dorian to let him see the portrait, which was still covered by the screen. He was amazed when the boy, white with rage, told him that if he looked at the portrait, their friendship would be over. He said that he had wanted to exhibit the picture in Paris, and asked Dorian if he had noticed anything strange about the picture. Dorian was terrified, but learned that Basil wanted to know if he had painted into it his own adoration of the boy. When Dorian said that there was something curious about the picture, Basil thought that his own secret was shown there, and agreed that the picture should not be exhibited. After he went, Dorian, fearing that others might ask questions, had the picture borne away to his old schoolroom, which was never opened, and covered it with a great piece of embroidered satin.

Downstairs again, Dorian found that Lord Henry had sent him a book. It was a psychological study of a young Parisian, who spent his life trying to realize in the nineteenth century all the passions and modes of thought that belonged to every century except his own. It was a poisonous book. For years, he could not free himself from its influence. Strange rumors about him floated around London, but in the face of his wonderful, changeless beauty one could not help believing in his purity. But upstairs in the schoolroom, the evil and aging face of the portrait showed what was happening to his soul. At times, he felt a selfish pity for himself, but these moments were brief, for the more he fed his mad hunger for life, the more it grew. Society knew him as a charming host, as a collector of all beautiful objects; it knew nothing of the nights he spent in sordid little ill-famed taverns near the docks. On his return, he would sit in front of the picture, partly loathing it, partly smiling with secret pleasure on the misshapen shadow that had to bear the burden that should have been his own.

After a few years, he could not endure to be long out of England, or even out of London, lest in his absence someone gain access to the room where the portrait was. He feared that it might be stolen, and that the world would know his secret. Perhaps it was already suspected. Curious stories became current about him, and his strange absences from society became notorious. It was remarked that some of those who had been most intimate with him appeared after a time to shun him. Yet these whispers only increased his charm, in the eyes of many.

On the eve of his thirty-eighth birthday, as he was walking home late in the evening, Dorian met Basil Hallward. Basil was taking a train shortly after midnight, and was to be out of England for six months, but before he went he wanted a talk with Dorian. He thought Dorian should know the dreadful things that were being said about him in London. Basil did not believe them, for he knew a man's vices are written on his face, but people were whispering hideous things about Dorian. Why was it that so many gentlemen would not go to his house or invite him to theirs? Why was his friendship fatal to young men? Dorian replied that in England it was enough for a man to have distinction and brains for every tongue to wag about him. But Basil was not to be turned thus lightly aside. It was said that Dorian corrupted everyone with whom he became intimate. To one terrible charge against his friend, Basil had answered that it was impossible, that he knew Dorian thoroughly. But now he wondered if he did know him; to be sure of this, he would have to see his soul.

"You shall see it tonight!" cried Dorian. Leading his friend upstairs, he took him into the old school-room and flung aside the cover of the painting. An exclamation of horror burst from the painter's lips. The hideous face on the canvas filled him with loathing and disgust. He knew that Dorian must be even worse than those who talked against him fancied him to be. He flung himself into a chair, begging Dorian to repent, to ask God for forgiveness, before it was too late. Suddenly an uncontrollable feeling of hatred came over Dorian, and seizing a knife which lay on a chest, he stabbed his friend behind the ear, stabbed him again and again.

Strangely calm, he went downstairs and hid Basil's hat and coat. After a night of dreamless sleep, he arose and sent a letter to Mr. Alan Campbell, asking him to come to see him at once. Campbell was a young scientist devoted to chemistry. He and Dorian had been great friends, but for many months now they had not spoken to one another. As Dorian waited, he became more and more anxious, until by the time Campbell arrived he was in a horror of fear. Then his fear passed, and quite coolly he demanded that Campbell, with his scientific knowledge, destroy the body in the room above. Campbell refused, but he was trapped, for Dorian had information about him which he threatened to make known unless his request was obeyed. Campbell sent home for his materials, and was escorted upstairs by Dorian. As Dorian opened the door of the school-room, he saw that on one of the hands of the portrait a loathsome red dew gleamed. Hastily he covered the picture. A few hours later, the grisly occupant of the room had disappeared.

That night, Dorian's soul was sick to death. Remembering Lord Henry's words, "To cure the soul by means of the senses, and the senses by means of the soul!" he drove to a horrid little tavern near the docks, to seek relief in opium. He was followed from the place by a sailor who heard him called Prince Charming by a woman he had long ago cast off. The sailor was Sibyl Vane's brother, who had searched long years for the man who had caused his sister's death. He was about to send a bullet through Dorian's head when he decided that this youth could not be the criminal he was seeking. By the time he learned from the woman who had followed him that Dorian was no youth, his enemy had slipped away in the night.

A week later Dorian was with his guests at Selby Royal, his country house. But James Vane had followed him there, and he fainted in terror when he saw Vane's face peering through a window at him. Very fortunately for Dorian, Vane was killed in the hunt next day; he had enlisted as a beater, and had accidentally got in the way of the shooting. Dorian could breathe again; he was safe.

Soon Dorian went back to town, vowing to reform. He was pleased with himself, for he had at first planned to run away with a village maiden, but had then decided to leave her innocent. He found people in town talking about Basil's disappearance. Basil had often gone away quietly before—he disliked telling people where he was going—but now he seemed to have disappeared completely. Sadness gradually came upon Dorian, not for Basil, nor for James Vane, nor for Alan Campbell, who had shot himself one night in his laboratory, but for himself, for the living death of his own soul.

But he had spared the girl in the country; perhaps the portrait was not so ugly as it had been. He went to look at it, and found no change, save that in the eyes there was a look of cunning, and in the mouth the curve of the hypocrite. Was the red stain larger than before? Had it dripped on the feet? If he could kill the picture, he could kill the past, he could be free. Seizing a knife, he stabbed the picture. There was a cry of agony, and a crash. When the servants finally broke in, they found upon the wall a splendid portrait of their master in all his youth and beauty, and lying on the floor, with a knife in his heart, a loathsome, withered, wrinkled old man.

RIP VAN WINKLE

A Posthumous Writing of Diedrich Knickerbocker

By

Washington Irving

WASHINGTON IRVING (*1783–1859*) was born in New York City. He was a sickly lad and his education was curtailed. He began to study law when he was 19 but two years later his brothers sent him to Europe for his health. Improved, he returned home and was admitted to the bar. With some friends he started a magazine which published twenty numbers and abruptly stopped. By 1809 he had published the first of his burlesques on the old Dutch settlers of Manhattan Island. By 1820 he was universally known in the United States through his *Rip Van Winkle* and *The Legend of Sleepy Hollow* which have since become classics in American literature. He passed a few years in Europe and returned home to write more books. He went to Spain in 1826 for historical material. Learning that Prescott was working on a history of Mexico Irving deferred the idea to him. He established his residence at Tarrytown near the scene of his legend of Sleepy Hollow but his retirement was postponed by his appointment in 1842 as minister to Spain for four years. Returning home he completed his five volume *Life of George Washington* which was his final work. He never married, remaining faithful to the memory of his fiancée who died shortly after their bethrothal.

WHOEVER has made a voyage up the Hudson must remember the Kattskill mountains. They are a dismembered branch of the great Appalachian family, rising to a noble height away off to the west of the river, and every change of weather and of season produces its change in the magic of their hues and shapes.

Back in the days when this country was yet a province of Great Britain, at the foot of these fairy mountains there was a little village which had been settled by Dutch colonists about the beginning of the government of Peter Stuyvesant. In one of the weather-beaten houses of this village lived a simple, good-natured fellow of the name of Rip Van Winkle.

Rip was a kind neighbor, and an obedient, hen-pecked husband. The good wives of the village took his part in all the family squabbles, of which there were many, and they laid the blame on Dame Winkle and her sharp tongue which was going incessantly day and night and railing at Rip because of his idleness and carelessness. But his wife had reason to complain of his idleness, for Rip had an insuperable aversion to all kinds of profitable labor. He could be assiduous enough in unprofitable work, such as fishing all day without getting a single nibble, or assisting the neighbors with odd jobs, or shooting squirrels, and was always ready to attend to anybody's business but his own.

His farm, which he declared it was of no use for him to work, was the worst conditioned farm in the neighborhood, his children ran ragged and wild, and his son Rip promised to inherit the habits of his father along with his old clothes that he wore. In spite of all this Rip would have whistled life away in cheerful contentment if the scoldings of his wife's tongue had not been continually dinned into his ears.

To escape her tirades Rip was wont to betake himself either to the woods with a gun or to a kind of club which met on a bench before the inn for endless conversation, some of it profound but most of it gossip. His faithful dog, Wolf, was his companion in exile on all these trips.

One fine day in autumn, Rip and his dog had unconsciously wandered away to one of the highest parts of the Kattskill mountains. Panting and fatigued after his climbing and squirrel-hunting, Rip threw himself down to rest on a grassy knoll on the top of a precipice. Far in the distance he could see the lordly Hudson, and as he mused there and dreaded the return to his wife's sharp tongue, he thought he heard some one call from a distance, "Rip Van Winkle! Rip Van Winkle!"

He saw no one at first, and then as Wolf uttered a low growl he looked down into the glen beneath him and saw a strange figure slowly toiling up the rocks, a burden on its back. As he came nearer, Rip saw that the figure was short and square-built with thick bushy hair. His dress was of the antique Dutch fashion, and the burden on his shoulder was a stout keg that seemed to be full of liquor. The figure beckoned to Rip to help him, and as they ascended the path together, long, rolling peals, as of distant thunder, were heard.

Soon they came to a hollow like a small amphitheater, where was seen a strange sight. A company of odd-looking personages were playing at nine-pins. They were dressed in the same queer, outlandish fashion as Rip's companion. They all had beards of various shapes and colors, and their visages were peculiar. As they played their game, all of them maintained grave faces and a mysterious silence, while the sound of the balls echoed through the mountains and made the noise that had sounded to Rip like thunder.

The fellow who had toiled up the mountain with the keg now emptied its contents into large flagons and made signs to Rip to wait on the company. He obeyed fearfully, and they returned to their game. As his apprehensions gradually died down, he ventured to taste of the liquor himself, and finding it excellent he drank again and again, and soon fell into a deep sleep.

When he woke, Rip found himself on the grassy knoll atop the precipice from which he had first seen the man with the keg. It was a bright summer morning. He rubbed his eyes and slowly recalled the events before he slept. On looking for his gun, instead of his well-oiled fowling-piece, he found beside him an old firelock encrusted with rust. Wolf had disappeared, and though he whistled and called for him the dog was nowhere to be seen.

As he rose to walk Rip found that he was stiff in the joints, and he descended to the glen with some difficulty. He tried to find the amphitheater where he had had his adventure with the players at nine-pins, but it was not to be discovered. Moreover, the gully up which he and his odd companion had ascended with the keg of liquor was now a rushing mountain torrent. Troubled and perplexed, Rip decided to give up for lost his dog and gun and turn his footsteps homewards.

As he approached the village he met a number of people whom he had never seen before, and the manner of their dress was different from that to which he was accustomed. They all stared at him, and because they invariably stroked their chins when they looked at him, he did the same and found that his beard was a foot long! The children hooted at him and the long beard, and the dogs barked in an unfriendly fashion. In the village he saw rows of houses he had never seen before, while many of his familiar landmarks had disappeared.

Rip drew near to his own house, dreading the scolding of his wife. The roof had fallen in and the doors were off the hinges. A half-starved dog that resembled Wolf snarled at him. He entered the house, but it was deserted. More perplexed than ever he turned to the location of the inn. It, too, was gone, and a rickety building which a sign proclaimed to be "The Union Hotel" stood in its place, the windows of which were broken. The ruby face of King George on the sign was singularly altered, and the figure now wore a blue and buff instead of a red coat, held a sword instead of a scepter in its hand, wore a cocked hat, and was inscribed "General Washington."

The busy crowd around the door were all new faces to Rip, as strange as the incomprehensible flag fluttering from the flag-pole with its assemblage of stars and stripes. Strange also was their talk of Congress, liberty, Bunker Hill.

The attention of the tavern politicians was attracted to this uncouth newcomer with the long beard, and he was challenged. As Rip declared himself a native of the place and a loyal subject of the King, the crowd shouted "a Tory! a spy! away with him!" Inquiring for his neighbors by name, the unhappy man learned that many of them were dead. "Does nobody here know Rip Van Winkle," he finally cried in despair, and the crowd pointed to a counterpart of himself, ragged and lazy, leaning against a tree.

Doubtful of his own identity at this point, the poor man told of having fallen asleep on the mountain, whereupon the bystanders winked significantly at each other. When a young woman with a child in her arms spoke to the infant calling him Rip, the returned wanderer found by questioning her that this was his daughter and that when she was a little girl her father had disappeared from home and never returned.

Catching his daughter and her child in his arms he cried, "I am your father—young Rip Van Winkle once—old Rip Van Winkle now—does nobody here know poor Rip Van Winkle?" And all stood amazed, until an old woman, tottering out from among the crowd peered at him for a moment and then exclaimed, "Sure enough! it is Rip Van Winkle. Welcome home, old neighbor—why, where have you been these twenty long years?"

It was true. Rip had left his home for the trip to the mountains twenty years ago. The neighbors stared when they heard his story, but old Peter Vanderdonk, the most ancient inhabitant of the village corroborated it, and asserted that it had long been known that the Kattskill mountains were haunted by strange beings, and that the great Hendrick Hudson himself kept vigil there every twenty years with his crew of the Half Moon, as they all played at nine-pins in their old Dutch costumes.

Rip went home to live with his daughter, who was married to a stout cheery farmer, one of the urchins that used to climb upon his back, the old man remembered. Rip's son and heir was employed to work on the farm, but showed the same distaste for labor that his father had. It was a long time before the old man who had slept so long upon the mountainside fully understood the events that had taken place since he left the village, and that he was now a free citizen of the United States. It meant more to him that he was at last free of the tyranny of Dame Van Winkle, who had died a short time since.

He told his tale to all comers, and soon every one knew it by heart. Some doubted, but most accepted it, and to this day when rumbles of thunder are heard among the Kattskill mountains they say Hendrick Hudson and his crew are at their game of nine-pins, and all hen-pecked husbands wish for a quieting draught out of Rip Van Winkle's flagon.

PEER GYNT

By

Henrik Ibsen

HENRIK IBSEN (*1828–1906*) was a Norwegian poet and
dramatist. He was a journalist until he was appointed director
of a theater at Bergen. In this post he wrote five romantic
dramas followed by others later. He was granted a pension
by the Norwegian parliament in 1866 and in the following
year he published the lyric drama *Peer Gynt*. His works include such popular plays as *A Doll's House, The Wild Duck,
Hedda Gabler* and *When We Dead Awaken*.

PART ONE

ON A PATH through a wooded hillside comes Peer Gynt, a strongly-
built youth of twenty, followed by his mother, Ase, a slightly-built
woman, who is scolding him for his shiftlessness. He has been relating a marvellous story of riding on the back of a reindeer, but
to his mother he is only a liar, a devil's story-teller.

Bang! Peer fired and dropped the reindeer buck, but when he
mounted its back and tried to knife it in the neck, the beast pinioned him with its horns and set flight along the Gendin Edge,
sharp as a scythe. Along the Edge they rode until they seemed to
cleave a passage through the air and with eagles in flight gazed
upon glittering suns. Then the buck turned downward and with
its rider plunged into the depths of a calm mountain lake. Peer
swam ashore and came home, but as for the buck, it is still there,
and Mother Ase is welcome to it.

In carrying out these imaginary escapades, Peer has let the Gynt
farm decay; hedge and fence are down, the meadow lies fallow
and the window panes of the farm house are stuffed with clouts.
A dreamer, he is also a brawler who fought the blacksmith and

PEER GYNT

broke his brawny arm. When he is not hunting and brawling, he is dreaming that some day he will be a king, a kaiser.

Something might have come of Peer Gynt, says his mother, if his head had not been stuffed with lies and dreams. He might have been the one to marry Ingrid, the belle of Hegstad, a golden girl, an heiress. No, it's too late to woo her now for she's to be married this day to Mads Moen. But Peer will go to the wedding and his mother must intercede for him that he may be the chosen bridegroom. But Ase will rather go and tell the bride's father how worthless is her son, and to forestall this move Peer seizes his mother, carries her up a ladder to the mill-house roof where he maroons her and makes his way alone to Hegstad. Will he meet the bride, Ingrid, alone in the house? No, rather a swarm of rural wedding guests who titter and sneer at the sight of Peer Gynt. And there is the blacksmith with whom he fought and who now taunts him with having been jilted by the bride. From afar he can hear the sound of music and can even see the girls dancing, six or eight to a man. He must join the frolic.

There is silence as Peer Gynt enters the farm house but now comes Solveig who says, "Are you not the lad that was wanting to dance?" But when he tells her that he is Peer Gynt she draws back in dismay at that name. Peer now turns to the crowd of guests some of whom taunt him while one offers him brandy to drink. When Solveig returns Peer seizes hold of her, whirls her wildly in the dance and in harsh tones tells her he can turn himself into a Troll and come to her bedside at midnight only to receive her mild rebuke. Now, the bridegroom is having trouble for his bride has locked herself in and refuses to come forth whereupon he appeals to Peer Gynt for aid offering him an ox for his help in getting the bride. Peer agrees but having broken into the room he carries off the bride for himself and now, Ingrid in his arms, he can be seen on the sheer slope of the hill-side climbing up like a goat and shouldering the bride like a pig.

The next morning, on a high and narrow mountain path, Peer Gynt moves hastily and sullenly along while Ingrid in tears tries to hold him back. They must part, he tells her, and go their own ways even though sin has united them, for he is done with women, done with all but one—Solveig. In the valley on the marshy ground

[395]

near a mountain lake is Peer Gynt's mother, Ase, gazing and calling out in every direction. When she is joined by Solveig, her parents and little sister, Helga, she tears her hair, waves her arms and gives vent to cries of horror at what her son has done. But now she turns from this lament and begins to tell them of Peer's prowess and how he rode through the air on a buck reindeer, a tale which enchants Solveig so that she bids Ase say on and tell her everything that's to be told of this Peer.

But Peer Gynt with all the parish at his heels is now running full speed across the mountain moorlands. There he senses reality and a life of action in stemming the rush of the cataract and wrenching fir trees from their roots, which is better for him than a life of lies and dreams. And now, screaming and singing, three herd-girls rush across his path and invite him to sleep with them in their mountain hut. Each wench has lost her lover, one married a widow, and another eloped with a gypsy and the other was killed for the murder of his bastard child. But Peer is a three-headed troll, a boy for three girls and will sleep tonight in their arms.

The garish night followed by a day of drunken sleep is passed, and now it is sunset on the shining snow-peaks of Rondë Mountains. Peer Gynt sinks down and reflects. That flight o'er the Gendin Edge, the rush up hill with the bride and this sporting with crazy wenches—all lies and accursed stuff! While he stumbles and splashes in the quagmire's filth yonder soar eagles, and he too will fly and as young maidens gaze upward at him he will swoop down on them. He will build a new farm for the race of the Gynts for he is come of great ones and great things shall come of him.

Now he is resting on the hill-side and through the great trees can catch the gleaming of the stars. A Green Clad Woman glides past him whereupon he follows her with various lover-antics. Is it true that he loves her and will treat her well and that he is the son of a king? She is the Dovrë-King's daughter, her father is king of the Hill Trolls. She seems to be clad in rags but rightly viewed her gown is all silk and gold and once in the hall of Rondë's Castle he will view all things like a Troll. They are wedded and now, in the form of a gigantic pig, comes the bridal steed on which they gallop into the hall in the hill-side.

Here is a great assembly of Troll courtiers, gnomes and brown-
ies surrounding the Troll King on his throne. The angry Trolls
threaten to bite and scratch, and even to boil or roast the miserable
Christian who has seduced the princess, but her father thinks it
better to make a Troll of him. The difference between trolls and
men, he says, is that out in the shining world the saying goes,
"Man, be thyself!" while with the tribe of Trolls, it is "Troll, to
thyself be enough!" To become a Troll, Peer Gynt must drink
their vile mead, have a tail nailed to his back and have his eyes slit
so that what's foul shall look fair. Peer swallows the mead, submits to the tail but balks at distortion of vision which will make
him a Troll forever. Peer is now attacked on all sides by the Trolls
and buried in a heap of imps when church bells sound in the
distance and all Trolls take to flight.

Now, in the outer darkness, Peer Gynt is challenged by a Voice,
the Boyg, who identifies himself as one who is Himself. Can Peer
say as much? He seizes a huge bough and tries to beat his way
through but his slashes strike nothing for the Boyg conquers without battling. The whirring of bird-wings and bird-cries are heard.
A prayer-book is hurled into the creature's eyes, the sound of bells
and of psalm-singing is heard far away and as the Boyg shrinks
to nothing it gasps, "He was too strong. There were women behind
him." Peer Gynt awakes from this mad dream and spits. What
would he not give for a pickled herring! But now appears little
Helga with a basket of food for him. In the distance is Solveig who
calls out, "If you come nearer, I'll run away." Helga must tell
Solveig not to forget Peer Gynt.

The outlaw is now in the woods hewing timber for the house he
is building. Shall it be a castle with tower and vane and glittering
with metal and glass? That were the Devil's own lie again; a
thatched hovel is shelter enough in rain or snow. The hut is done
and around it lies deep snow over which on snow-shoes comes
Solveig. She had received the message sent by little Helga, then
others came in the storm and the stillness, still others in darkness
and dreams. Now, loosed from father and mother and alone in
God's wide earth, she comes to him who shall be all to her. And
here in his hut with the fir-branches soughing over head she is
home, she is his. But the place must be warmed and Peer must

go fetch fuel. In the woods he is encountered by his former Troll-bride who leads their child after her, lame in his shank as Peer Gynt is lame in his soul. Can he go into Solveig now? To conceal, to confess? No, that were a sacrilege. He is coming but it's dark and he has a burden to bear and must bear it alone. She must be patient and wait, be his way short or long, she must wait. Yes, Solveig will wait!

In her room, tossing about restlessly in her bed, Ase is waiting for Peer Gynt to return. The time drags drearily and her life is ebbing. Peer Gynt, a price on his head and now in full flight from trouble, has come to bid his mother farewell and when he sees her eyes glazing he must close them forever. They will play horse once more as they did when he was a child. Peer throws a string round the back of the chair on which the cat is lying, takes up a stick, seats himself at the end of the bed and begins to drive with the black cat as their steed. Now, there's a ringing in the dying woman's ears but 'tis but the sound of sleigh-bells; now, a rumbling as though they drove over a fiord. This sparkling and gleaming in the dying mother's eyes is the light in the celestial castle they're approaching and St. Peter who's there will welcome them in. O, what a frolic for poor dying Ase, but she will lie back and trust all to her boy.

Come, gee-up, Granë, thou trotter and bring us right to the gate. Peer Gynt and his mother have come and Master Saint Peter must let mother enter, her son can turn off at the gate. Saint Peter is far too officious, he'll catch it when God comes along, and now God the Father has come here and Ase will enter scot free. But why are her eyes so glassy in her silent stare? The driver drops the reins, releases the steed and presses his cheek against the dead mother's lips. That was the driver's fare. Now he is going? Seaward, so far? Aye, further still.

PART TWO

On the south-west coast of Morocco under an awning under a palm-grove gentlemen of various nations sit at a table as the guests of the middle-aged Peer Gynt. His yacht is anchored off shore and the jolly-boat is drawn up on the beach. The guests propose a toast to their genial host who then proceeds to explain his bachelordom. He could have married a princess but his would-be father-in-law demanded that he change his station in life and undergo ennoblement which he found distasteful. He is a self-taught man, has taken his religion intermittently and may have engaged in some doubtful businesses. If he did bring black slaves into Carolina and sell idol-images to China he was careful to send missionaries to the heathen and exchange Bibles for the rum he imported. He has always guarded himself against the viper of the Irretrieveable by leaving a way open for retreat. Yes, of course, in all these things he has had a goal—the Gyntish Self, the world behind his forehead's arch, the emperor of his existence.

But now comes startling news—the Greeks have risen against the Turks. His guests may side with the men of Hellas but for himself he sides with the stronger and will lend money to the Turks. The shore-party breaks up, the guests put off in the jolly-boat and, having taken possession of Peer Gynt's yacht, are now standing out to sea. Peer Gynt now prays, bids God let other folks' business lie over and attend to him. In answer to his prayer, the vessel takes fire, the boiler bursts and the craft with all on board goes to the bottom. Peer Gynt's Providence has looked out for his welfare but in no very economical way.

Bereft of his yacht and alone at nightfall in Africa, the timid Peer takes refuge from lions that may be prowling about by climbing a palm tree where he spends the night. At daybreak he is awake but now with a branch of the tree must defend himself against a swarm of monkeys. Now he descends the tree, dismisses his fears and, lighting a cigar, contemplates the Sahara desert and plans in imagination to cut a canal through to the Mediterranean to turn the desert into a sea with islands at the oases. There he would build his land of Gyntiana with Peeropolis as its capital. His meditations are broken by the neighing of a horse, the Emperor's milk-white charger, as also his robes and jewels which have been stolen and put in hiding. Now, bedecked in royal raiment and astride his steed Peer Gynt rides away and is mistaken by the dancing girls for a Mohammedan prophet. One in particular, Anitra, beguiles him with her dancing but in the end this gay deceiver takes his jewels and his horse and rides away.

Once more in European dress, Peer Gynt decides that the time has come for the business of being one's self. Many paths lie before him. He has been a gold-digger ego, a pelt-hunter and slave-dealer, but now he will turn archaeologist and Egyptologist ransacking the ruins of Assyria, Babylon, Troy and Greece. But here is Egypt and how much the statue of Memnon resembles the Troll King! Here, also, the Sphinx when after all 'tis but the Boyg and here a human being, Begriffenfeldt, who'd have Peer Gynt as Kaiser of those who are thoroughly themselves, themselves to the spring-board's utmost verge. It is the lunatic asylum in Cairo. What Kaiser Peer beholds there all but makes him like all the other inmates and, sinking down in the dirt with a wreath of straw on his head, Selfhood's Kaiser is in a sorry plight and one from which he is thankful to escape.

PART THREE

The aged Peer Gynt is now homeward bound after fifty years' absence from Norway. It is sunset and stormy weather off the Norwegian coast. The storm breaks upon the vessel and up from the hold comes the Strange Passenger whose interest in medical science is so great he begs Peer Gynt to promise him his much esteemed carcase for anatomical research but especially to bring to light the centre of Peer's dreams. The ship is now wrecked on the sunken rocks. Peer Gynt and the cook are clinging to the overturned jolly-boat and since it can support but one Peer casts the cook off but then pulls him up by the hair that he may repeat the Lord's Prayer. When the cook remembers only "give us this day our daily bread," Peer observes that to the end he was himself, a cook, and saves him. Now re-appears the Strange Passenger who identifies himself as Dread but glides away as soon as Peer reaches the shore.

Peer reaches the Gynt homestead where his household goods are being sold at auction. A young lad of twenty buys Peer's casting ladle with which he made silver buttons. There are no bids for the skull of the reindeer on which Peer rode over the Gendin Edge. A button is bid for the palace he built in Rondë but no bidders appear for Granë, his horse. Peer himself offers his Cairo Kaiserdom including the crown of straw and tries to justify his whole life by

a fable from Aesop. Wandering away from the crowd he comes
to the hut he built on the heath long ago, but when he hears a
voice singing softly—

> —*Comest thou soon?*
> *Is thy burden heavy,*
> *Take time, take time;*
> *I will await thee;*
> *I promised of old—*

He rushes off along the wood-path saying, "Oh, Dread—here was
my Kaiserdom."

Now he is upon the heath whose fir trees stretching for miles
have been charred by fire while mists envelop the scene and balls
of fog and scud cling to the earth. They are his thoughts and
should have soared upward, but here they must trundle like white
woolen thread-balls. Withered leaves fly before him in the wind
as the watch-words he should have proclaimed but long have been
gnawed by the worm. Dewdrops dripping from the black branches
are the tears unshed forever but now they are frozen and their
power forever ended. Broken straws in his path are the deeds he
should have achieved but here they are throttled by doubt. Peer
Gynt hastens away from all these.

On another part of the heath, Peer Gynt encounters the Button
Moulder coming from a side path and carrying a large casting
ladle. Is this old gaffer named Peer? If so he must go into the
casting ladle of the Button Moulder whose business it is to gather
up scraps of button-personalities, melt them down and make complete buttons of them. Peer protests that after all he has not been
such a great sinner and thus deserves a better fate than this, but
his fault, according to the Button Moulder, is that he has been no
sinner at all in the higher sense, for he took his sin too lightly
and wasn't even middling bad. The sulphurous pit is no place
for one who has but splashed in the mire, and Peer who has failed
to sin on the heroic scale of the old Norsemen, the Berserkers, must
go into the casting ladle and be melted up with Tom, Dick and
Harry.

Now, Peer, dreading such an ignominious fate as the Gynt-cessa-
tion, declares that, if the Button Moulder will grant him a loan

of himself, he will produce witnesses to testify that he has been himself all his days. This is agreed and they separate to meet again at the next crossroads. Now running hard, Peer encounters an old man, bent with age and trudging on staff in hand. It is the King of the Trolls who is now so down in the world as to be reduced to begging. Peer reminds the King, or Old Man of the Rondë, how he came to Rondë a-wooing but finally refused to be a mere Troll because they wished to slit his eyes to make him see awry. Did he not stand out against that and renounce all love and power for the sake of remaining himself? The Old Man of the Rondë must remember that and must so testify in court. But this he cannot do truthfully since, when Peer left Rondë's Hall, he inscribed its motto upon his escutcheon—Troll! to thyself be enough!

With the judgment of the Trolls' Enoughness passed on him Peer now comes to the crossroads where the Button Moulder is waiting for him and his witness. The Old Man of the Rondë is not far off but no, protests Peer, don't call him. Instead let the threatening Button Moulder answer one question, just one—what is it, at bottom, this 'being one's self?' The obvious answer will doubtless be lost on such a man as Peer Gynt but it is this—To be one's self is to slay one's self! But another respite is granted and another crossroad appointed.

Peer now encounters A Lean Person in a priest's cassock and carrying a fowling net over his shoulder, but it turns out that this odd personage is a tramping photographer who is applying the newly discovered art of Daguerre. He listens to Peer's story of how he has trafficked in slaves, dealt in idols, played the part of a prophet and the like but considers this "what the Swedes call 'Mighty poor sport' indeed." In Paris, he goes on to say, they take sun-portraits of a man; these are either positive or negative, white as a ptarmigan or black as a raven, but Peer's picture is neither for he has simply smudged himself out hence the photographer cannot testify for him.

Shall Peer now try a third crossroads? No, it is too far and he would go home, hence he runs towards his old hut and flings himself down on the threshold just as Solveig, dressed for church and carrying a psalm-book, appears in the doorway. In her blindness,

Solveig gropes about until finally her hands rest on the aged Peer Gynt's head. "He is here, God be praised! He is here." From behind the hut the Button Moulder calls for Peer Gynt's sin-list and his crime is about to cry out when Solveig says, "Thou hast made all my life like a beautiful song."

But the soul of Peer Gynt will be lost unless Solveig can answer a riddle and tell where he has been in all his wanderings since they parted years before. To Solveig the riddle of the wandering is easy to solve; Peer Gynt has been in her heart all the time, in her faith, in her hope, in her love. Clinging to Solveig, Peer hides his face in her lap. There is a long silence, then the sun rises and Solveig sings softly—•

> *Sleep thou, dearest boy of mine!*
> *I will cradle thee, I will watch thee.*

From behind the hut the voice of the Button Moulder is heard—

> *At the last cross-road we will meet again, Peer;*
> *And then we shall see whether——; I say no more.*

It is now full daylight and Solveig sings louder—

> *I will cradle thee, I will watch thee;*
> *Sleep and dream thou, dear my boy!*

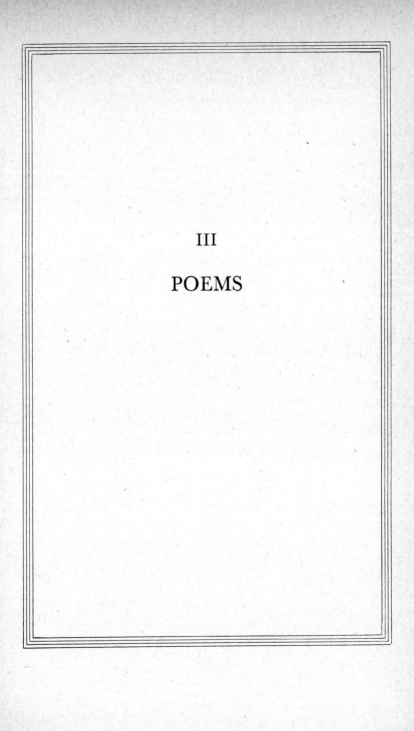

III

POEMS

PROTHALAMION

By

Edmund Spenser

EDMUND SPENSER (*1552–1599*) was an English poet, born near
the Tower of London. When he was 26 he gained a position
in the household of the Earl of Leicester. In 1580 he was
appointed secretary to Lord Grey, the new Lord Deputy of
Ireland and from that time on spent most of his life in Ireland where he finished *The Faerie Queene* which he had
begun earlier. In 1591 Kilcolman Castle and its extensive
lands were legally transferred to him. In 1589 he accompanied
Raleigh to London and was welcomed at court. Expecting
high honors he returned to Ireland disappointed, where he
married. *Epithalamion,* which is probably the richest nuptial
hymn in the English language, celebrates his marriage. In
1596 he wrote his masterful poem *Prothalamion* for a double
marriage at Essex House. His castle was sacked and burned
by Irish rebels in 1598 and he fled to England where he died
at a London inn three months later. He lies buried near
Chaucer in Westminster Abbey.

CALM was the day, and through the trembling air
   Sweet-breathing Zephyrus did softly play—
   A gentle spirit that lightly did delay
Hot Titan's beams, which then did glister fair;
    When I (whom sullen care,
Through discontent of my long fruitless stay
   In princes's court, and expectation vain
Of idle hopes, which still do fly away
   Like empty shadows, did afflict my brain)
    Walk'd forth to ease my pain
Along the shore of silver-streaming Thames;
Whose rutty bank, the which his river hems,

Was painted all with variable flowers,
And all the meads adorn'd with dainty gems
    Fit to bedeck maidens's bowers,
    And crown their paramours
Against the bridal day, which is not long:
Sweet Thames! run softly, till I end my song.

There is a meadow by the river's side
    A flock of nymphs I chancéd to espy,
    All lovely daughters of the flood thereby,
With goodly greenish locks all loose untied
    As each had been a bride;
And each one had a little wicker basket
    Made of fine twigs, entrailéd curiously,
In which they gathered flowers to fill their flasket,
    And with fine fingers cropt full feateously
    The tender stalks on high.
Of every sort which in that meadow grew
They gathered some; the violet, pallid blue,
    The little daisy that at evening closes,
The virgin lily and the primrose true,
    With store of vermeil roses,
    To deck their bridegrooms' posies
Against the bridal day, which was not long:
Sweet Thames! run softly, till I end my song.

With that I saw two swans of goodly hue
    Come softly swimming down along the lee;
    Two fairer birds I yet did never see;
The snow which doth the top of Pindus strow
    Did never whiter show,
Nor Jove himself, when he a swan would be
    For love of Leda, whiter did appear;
Yet Leda was (they say) as white as he,
    Yet not so white as these, nor nothing near;
    So purely white they were,
That even the gentle stream, the which them bare,
Seem'd foul to them, and bade his billows spare

To wet their silken feathers, lest they might
Soil their fair plumes with water not so fair
 And mar their beauties bright,
 That shone as Heaven's light
Against their bridal day, which was not long:
Sweet Thames! run softly, till I end my song.

Eftsoons the nymphs, which now had flowers their fill,
 Ran all in haste to see that silver brood
 As they came floating on the crystal flood;
Whom when they saw they stood amazed still
 Their wondering eyes to fill;
Them seem'd they never saw a sight so fair
 Of fowls, so lovely, that they sure did deem
Them heavenly born, or to be that same pair
 Which through the sky draw Venus's silver team;
 For sure they did not seem
To be begot of any earthly seed,
But rather angels, or of angels' breed;
 Yet were they bred of summer's heat, they say,
In sweetest season, when each flower and weed
 The earth did fresh array;
 So fresh they seem'd as day,
Even as their bridal day, which was not long:
Sweet Thames! run softly, till I end my song.

Then forth they all out of their baskets drew
 Great store of flowers, the honour of the field,
 That to the sense did fragrant odours yield
All which upon those goodly birds they threw
 And all the waves did strew
That like old Peneus' waters they did seem
 When down along by pleasant Tempe's shore
Scatter'd with flowers, through Thessaly they stream,
 That they appear, through lilies' plenteous store
 Like a bride's chamber-floor.
Two of those nymphs meanwhile two garlands bound
Of freshest flowers which in that meed they found,

[409]

The which presenting all in trim array,
Their snowy foreheads wherewithal they crowned;
    Whilst one did sing this lay
    Prepared against that day,
Against their bridal day, which was not long:
Sweet Thames! run softly, till I end my song.

'Ye gentle birds! the world's fair ornament,
  And Heaven's glory, whom this happy hour
  Doth lead unto your lovers' blissful bower,
Joy you may have, and gentle heart's content
    Of your love's couplement;
And let fair Venus, that is queen of love,
  With her heart-quelling sun upon you smile,
Whose smile, they say, hath virtue to remove
  All love's dislike, and friendship's faulty guile
    For ever to assoil.
Let endless peace your steadfast hearts accord,
And blessed plenty wait upon your board;
  And let your bed with pleasures chaste abound,
That fruitful issue may to you afford
    Which may your foes confound
    And make your joys redound
Upon your bridal day, which is not long:
Sweet Thames! run softly, till I end my song.'

So ended she; and all the rest around
  To her redoubled that her undersong,
  Which said their bridal day should not be long:
And gentle Echo from the neighboring ground
    Their accents did resound.
So forth these joyous birds did pass along
  Adown the lee that to them murmur'd low,
As he would speak but that he lack'd a tongue,
  Yet did by signs his glad affection show
    Making his stream run slow.
And all the fowl which in his flood did dwell
'Gan flock about these twain, that did excell

The rest, so far as Cynthia doth shend
The lesser stars. So they, enrangéd well,
   Did on those two attend,
   And their best service lend
Against their wedding day, which was not long:
Sweet Thames! run softly, till I end my song.

At length they all to merry London came,
  To merry London, my most friendly nurse
  That to me gave this life's first native source,
Though from another place I take my name,
   And house of ancient fame:
There when they came whereas those bricky towers
  To which on Thames's broad aged back do ride,
Where now the studious lawyers have their bowers,
  There whilome wont the Templar-knights to bide,
   Till they decayed through pride;
Next whereunto there stands a stately place,
Where oft I gainéd gifts and goodly grace
  Of that great lord which therein wont to dwell,
Whose want too well now feels my friendless case;
   But ah! here fits not well
   Old woes, but joys, to tell
Against the bridal day, which is not long:
Sweet Thames! run softly, till I end my song.

Yet therein now doth lodge a noble peer,
  Great England's glory and the world's wide wonder,
  Whose dreadful name late through all Spain did thunder,
And Hercules' two pillars standing near
   Did make to quake and fear:
Fair branch of honour, flower of chivalry!
  That fillest England with thy triumphs' fame,
Joy have thou of thy noble victory
  And endless happiness of thine own name
   That promiseth the same;
That through thy prowess and victorious arms
Thy country may be freed from foreign harms

And great Eliza's glorious name may ring
Through all the world, fill'd with thy wide alarms,
    Which some brave muse may sing
    To ages following,
Upon the bridal day, which is not long:
Sweet Thames! run softly, till I end my song.

From those high towers this noble lord issúing
    Like radiant Hesper, when his golden hair
    In th' ocean billows he had bathéd fair,
Descended to the river's open viewing
    With a great train ensuing.
Above the rest were goodly to be seen
    Two gentle knights of lovely face and feature,
Beseeming well the bower of any queen,
    With gifts of wit and ornaments of nature,
    Fit for so goodly stature,
That like the twins of Jove they seem'd in sight
Which deck the baldrick of the Heavens bright;
    They two, forth pacing to the river's side
Received those to fair brides, their love's delight;
    Which at th' appointed tide,
    Each one did make his bride
Against their bridal day, which is not long:
Sweet Thames! run softly, till I end my song.

THE PASSIONATE SHEPHERD
TO HIS LOVE

By

Christopher Marlowe

CHRISTOPHER MARLOWE (*1564–1593*) was Shakespeare's great predecessor in the English drama. A shoemaker's son, he was educated at Cambridge University. The earliest of his extant plays was first printed when he was 26. The feature of the work was the introduction of blank verse. His *The Jew of Malta* is important chiefly for its relation to Shakespeare's *Merchant of Venice*. Marlowe met an untimely and violent death in a tavern quarrel at the age of 29.

COME live with me and be my Love,
And we will all the pleasures prove
That hills and valleys, dale and field,
And all the craggy mountains yield.

There will we sit upon the rocks
And see the shepherds feed their flocks,
By shallow rivers, to whose falls
Melodious birds sing madrigals.

There will I make thee beds of roses
And a thousand fragrant posies,
A cap of flowers and a kirtle
Embroider'd all with leaves of myrtle.

A gown made of the finest wool,
Which from our pretty lambs we pull,
Fair linéd slippers for the cold,
With buckles of the purest gold.

A belt of straw and ivy buds
With coral clasps and amber studs:
And if these pleasures may thee move,
Come live with me and be my Love.

Thy silver dishes for thy meat
As precious as the gods do eat,
Shall on an ivory table be
Prepared each day for thee and me.

The shepherd swains shall dance and sing
For thy delights each May morning:
If these delights thy mind may move,
Then live with me and be my Love.

TO THE MEMORY OF MY BELOVED MASTER WILLIAM SHAKESPEARE

By

Ben Jonson

BEN JONSON (*?1573–1637*) was an English dramatist about whose early life little is definitely known. He served in the English army. Upon his retirement he journeyed abroad for a short stay and upon returning became an actor and dramatist. In his later life he was a good friend of both Shakespeare and Bacon. Shakespeare even played one of the characters in his *Every Man in his Humor* which was produced in 1598. He wrote tragedies as well as comedies in addition to many elegies, epistles, love-poems, epigrams and epitaphs. Of his songs the most famous is *Drink to Me Only with Thine Eyes*. He prefixed a memorial poem to the collected edition of Shakespeare's works, which was published in 1623. He was buried in Westminster Abbey.

TO DRAW NO ENVY, Shakespeare, on thy name,
Am I thus ample to thy book and fame;
While I confess thy writings to be such
As neither man nor muse can praise too much.
'Tis true, and all men's suffrage. But these ways
Were not the paths I meant unto thy praise;
For silliest ignorance on these may light,
Which, when it sounds at best, but echoes right;
Or blind affection, which doth ne'er advance
The truth, but gropes and urges all by chance;
Or crafty malice might pretend this praise,
And think to ruin where it seemed to raise.

These are as some infamous bawd or whore
Should praise a matron. What could hurt her more?
But thou art proof against them and, indeed,
Above the ill fortune of them, or the need,
I, therefore, will begin. Soul of the age!
The applause, delight, the wonder of our stage.
My Shakespeare, rise! I will not lodge thee by
Chaucer or Spenser, or bid Beaumont lie
A little further to make thee a room:
Thou art a monument without a tomb,
And art alive still while thy book doth live
And we have wits to read and praise to give.
That I not mix thee so my brain excuses,
I mean with great but disproportioned Muses;
For if I thought my judgment were of years,
I should commit thee surely with thy peers,
And tell how far thou didst our Lyly outshine,
Or sporting Kyd, or Marlowe's mighty line.
And though thou hadst small Latin and less Greek,
From thence to honor thee I would not seek
For names, but call forth thundering Aeschylus,
Euripides and Sophocles to us;
Pacuvius, Accius, him of Cordova dead,
To life again to hear thy buskin tread,
And shake a stage; or, when thy socks were on,
Leave thee alone for the comparison
Of all that insolent Greece or haughty Rome
Sent forth, or since did from their ashes come.
Triumph, my Britain, thou hast one to show
To whom all scenes of Europe homage owe.
He was not of an age but for all time!
And all the muses still were in their prime,
When, like Apollo, he came forth to warm
Our ears, or like a Mercury to charm!
Nature herself was proud of his designs
And joyed to wear the dressing of his lines,
Which were so richly spun and woven so fit
As since she will vouchsafe no other wit.

The merry Greek, tart Aristophanes,
Neat Terence, witty Plautus now not please,
But antiquated and deserted lie,
As they were not of Nature's family.
Yet must I not give Nature all; thy art,
My gentle Shakespeare, must enjoy a part.
For though the poet's matter Nature be,
His art doth give the fashion, and that he
Who casts to write a living line must sweat,
(Such as thine are) and strike the second heat
Upon the Muses' anvil; turn the same
(And himself with it) that he thinks to frame,
Or for the laurel he may gain a scorn;
For a good poet's made as well as born.
And such wert thou! Look how the father's face
Lives in his issue, even so the race
Of Shakespeare's mind and manners brightly shines
In his well turnéd and true filéd lines;
In each of which he seems to shake a lance,
As brandished at the eyes of ignorance.
Sweet Swan of Avon! What a sight it were
To see thee in our waters yet appear,
And make those flights upon the banks of Thames
That so did take Eliza and our James!
But stay, I see thee in the hemisphere
Advanced, and made a constellation there!
Shine forth, thou star of poets, and with rage
Or influence chide or cheer the drooping stage,
Which since thy flight from hence hath mourned like night,
And despairs day, but for thy volume's light.

ELEGY WRITTEN IN
A COUNTRY CHURCHYARD

By

Thomas Gray

THOMAS GRAY (*1716–1771*) was an English poet, born in London. From Eton he went to Cambridge from where he left for a Continental tour and returned to take his degree. After graduation he continued Cambridge as his place of residence. When he was 41 he was offered the laureateship but declined it. When he was 52 he was appointed professor of history and modern languages at Cambridge which post he retained until his death. His most famous work, *Elegy Written in a Country Churchyard,* was begun in 1742 and was not finished until 1750.

THE CURFEW TOLLS the knell of parting day,
   The lowing herd winds slowly o'er the lea,
The ploughman homeward plods his weary way,
   And leaves the world to darkness and to me.

Now fades the glimmering landscape on the sight,
   And all the air a solemn stillness holds,
Save where the beetle wheels his droning flight,
   And drowsy tinklings lull the distant folds:

Save that from yonder ivy-mantled tow'r,
   The mopeing owl does to the moon complain
Of such as, wandering near her secret bow'r,
   Molest her ancient solitary reign.

Beneath those rugged elms, that yew-tree's shade,
   Where heaves the turf in many a moldering heap,
Each in his narrow cell forever laid,
   The rude forefathers of the hamlet sleep.

The breezy call of incense-breathing Morn,
  The swallow twittering from the straw-built shed,
The cock's shrill clarion, or the echoing horn,
  No more shall rouse them from their lowly bed.

For them no more the blazing hearth shall burn,
  Or busy housewife ply her evening care:
No children run to lisp their sire's return,
  Or climb his knees the envied kiss to share.

Oft did the harvest to their sickle yield,
  Their furrow oft the stubborn glebe has broke:
How jocund did they drive their team afield!
  How bow'd the woods beneath their sturdy stroke!

Let not Ambition mock their useful toil,
  Their homely joys, and destiny obscure;
Nor Grandeur hear with a disdainful smile
  The short and simple annals of the poor.

The boast of heraldry, the pomp of pow'r,
  And all that beauty, all that wealth e'er gave,
Awaits alike th' inevitable hour.
  The paths of glory lead but to the grave.

Nor you, ye Proud, impute to These the fault,
  If Mem'ry o'er their Tomb no Trophies raise,
Where through the long-drawn aisle and fretted vault
  The pealing anthem swells the note of praise.

Can storied urn or animated bust
  Back to its mansion call the fleeting breath?
Can Honour's voice provoke the silent dust,
  Or Flatt'ry soothe the dull cold ear of death?

Perhaps in this neglected spot is laid
  Some heart once pregnant with celestial fire;
Hands, that the rod of empire might have sway'd,
  Or wak'd to ecstasy the living lyre.

[419]

But Knowledge to their eyes her ample page
    Rich with the spoils of time did ne'er unroll;
Chill Penury repress'd their noble rage,
    And froze the genial current of the soul.

Full many a gem of purest ray serene,
    The dark unfathom'd caves of ocean bear:
Full many a flower is born to blush unseen,
    And waste its sweetness on the desert air.

Some village-Hampden, that with dauntless breast
    The little Tyrant of his fields withstood,
Some mute inglorious Milton here may rest,
    Some Cromwell guiltless of his country's blood.

Th' applause of list'ning senates to command,
    The threats of pain and ruin to despise,
To scatter plenty o'er a smiling land,
    And read their hist'ry in a nation's eyes,

Their lot forbad: nor circumscrib'd alone
    Their growing virtues, but their crimes confin'd;
Forbad to wade through slaughter to a throne,
    And shut the gates of mercy on mankind,

The struggling pangs of conscious truth to hide,
    To quench the blushes of ingenuous shame,
Or heap the shrine of Luxury and Pride
    With incense kindled at the Muse's flame.

Far from the madding crowd's ignoble strife,
    Their sober wishes never learned to stray;
Along the cool sequester'd vale of life
    They kept the noiseless tenor of their way.

Yet ev'n these bones from insult to protect
    Some frail memorial still erected nigh,
With uncouth rhimes and shapeless sculpture deck'd
    Implores the passing tribute of a sigh.

[420]

Their names, their years, spelt by th' unlettered muse,
  The place of fame and elegy supply:
And many a holy text around she strews,
  That teach the rustic moralist to die.

For who, to dumb Forgetfulness a prey,
  This pleasing anxious being e'er resign'd,
Left the warm precincts of the cheerful day,
  Nor cast one longing lingering look behind?

On some fond breast the parting soul relies,
  Some pious drops the closing eye requires;
E'en from the tomb the voice of Nature cries,
  E'en in our ashes live their wonted Fires.

For thee, who mindful of th' unhonor'd Dead,
  Dost in these lines their artless tale relate;
If chance, by lonely contemplation led,
  Some kindred spirit shall inquire thy fate—

Haply some hoary-headed Swain may say,
  "Oft have we seen him at the peep of dawn
Brushing with hasty steps the dews away,
  To meet the sun upon the upland lawn.

"There at the foot of yonder nodding beech
  That wreathes its old fantastic roots so high,
His listless length at noontide would he stretch,
  And pore upon the brook that babbles by.

"Hard by yon wood, now smiling as in scorn,
  Mutt'ring his wayward fancies he would rove,
Now drooping, woeful—wan, like one forlorn,
  Or craz'd with care, or cross'd with hopeless love.

"One morn I miss'd him on the custom'd hill,
  Along the heath, and near his fav'rite tree;
Another came; nor yet beside the rill,
  Nor up the lawn, nor at the wood was he:

"The next, with dirges due in sad array
  Slow thro the church-way path we saw him borne.—
Approach and read (for thou can'st read) the lay,
  Grav'd on the stone beneath yon aged thorn."

THE EPITAPH

Here rests his head upon the lap of Earth
  A Youth to Fortune and to Fame unknown.
Fair Science frown'd not on his humble birth,
  And Melancholy mark'd him for her own.

Large was his bounty, and his soul sincere,
  Heaven did a recompence as largely send:
He gave to Mis'ry (all he had) a tear,
  He gain'd from Heaven ('twas all he wish'd) a friend.

No farther seek his merits to disclose,
  Or draw his frailties from their dread abode,
(There they alike in trembling hope repose,)
  The bosom of his Father and his God.

THE MENTAL TRAVELLER

By

William Blake

WILLIAM BLAKE (*1757–1827*) was an English engraver and
poet. In 1789, and five years later, he published two books
showing contrary states of the human soul illustrated with
about 60 engravings which gained wide repute for their
unique and original style. He designed numerous other works
chiefly based upon religious and philosophical topics among
the best of which are his *Inventions to the Book of Job* and
the illustrations of Blair's *Grave*. He died in poverty and
obscurity but he has since been the subject of study and
appraisal by many essayists.

I TRAVELLED through a land of men,
   A land of men and women, too;
And heard and saw such dreadful things
   As cold earth-wanderers never knew.

For there a babe is born in joy
   That was begotten in dire woe;
Just as we reap in joy the fruit
   Which we in bitter tears did sow.

And if the babe is born a boy
   He's given to a woman old,
Who nails him down upon a rock,
   Catches his shrieks in cups of gold.

She binds iron thorns around his head,
   She pierces both his hands and feet,
She cuts his heart out at his side,
   To make it feel both cold and heat.

Her fingers number every nerve
  Just as a miser counts his gold;
She lives upon his shrieks and cries
  And she grows young as he grows old.

Till he becomes a bleeding youth,
  And she becomes a virgin bright;
Then he rends up his manacles,
  And binds her down for his delight.

He plants himself in all her nerves
  Just as a husbandman his mould,
And she becomes his dwelling-place
  And garden fruitful seventyfold.

An aged shadow soon he fades,
  Wandering round an earthly,
Full-filled all with gems and gold
  Which he by industry had got.

And these are the gems of the human soul,
  The rubies and pearls of a lovesick eye,
The countless gold of the aching heart,
  The martyr's groan and the lover's sigh.

They are his meat, they are his drink;
  He feeds the beggar and the poor;
To the wayfaring traveller
  For ever open is his door.

His grief is their eternal joy,
  They make the roofs and walls to ring;
Till from the fire upon the hearth
  A little female babe doth spring.

And she is all of solid fire
  And gems and gold, that none has had
Dares stretch to touch her baby form,
  Or wrap her in his swaddling-band.

But she comes to the man she loves,
　　If young or old or rich or poor;
They soon drive out the aged host,
　　A beggar at another's door.

He wanders weeping far away,
　　Until some other take him in;
Oft blind and age-bent, sore distressed,
　　Until he can a maiden win.

And to allay his freezing age,
　　The poor man takes her in his arms;
The cottage fades before his sight,
　　The garden and its lovely charms.

The guests are scattered through the land;
　　For the eye altering alters all;
The senses roll themselves in fear,
　　And the flat earth becomes a ball.

The stars, sun, moon all shrink away,
　　A desert vast without a bound,
And nothing left to eat or drink,
　　And a dark desert all around.

The honey of her infant lips,
　　The bread and wine of her sweet smile,
The wild game of her roving eye,
　　Do him to infancy beguile.

For as he eats and drinks he grows
　　Younger and younger every day,
And on the desert wild they both
Wander in terror and dismay.

Like the wild stag she flees away;
　　Her fear plants many a thicket wild,
While he pursues her night and day,
　　By various arts of love beguiled;

By various arts of love and hate,
  Till the wild desert's planted o'er
With labyrinths of wayward love,
  Where roam the lion, wolf and bear.

Till he becomes a wayward babe,
  And she a weeping woman old;
Then many a lover wanders there,
  The sun and stars are nearer rolled;

The trees bring forth sweet ecstasy
  To all who in the desert roam;
Till many a city there is built,
  And many a pleasant shepherd's home.

But, when they find the frowning babe,
  Terror strikes through the region wide:
They cry—"The babe—the babe is born!"
  And flee away on every side.

For who dare touch the frowning form
  Except it be a woman old;
She nails him down upon the rock,
  And all is done as I have told.

"The 'Mental Traveller' indicates an explorer of mental phenomena. The mental phenomenon symbolized here seems to be the career of any great Idea or intellectual movement—as, for instance, Christianity, chivalry, art, etc., represented as going through the stages of 1, birth; 2, adversity and persecution; 3, triumph and maturity; 4, decadence through over-ripeness; 5, gradual transformation under new conditions into another renovated Idea, which again has to pass through all the same stages. In other words, the poem represents the action and reaction of Ideas upon society, and of society upon Ideas."

ALGERNON CHARLES SWINBURNE

INTIMATIONS OF IMMORTALITY
From Recollections of Early Childhood

By

William Wordsworth

WILLIAM WORDSWORTH (*1770–1850*) was an English poet, born in Cumberland. Twice during his scholarship at Cambridge he took continental tours, embracing the principles of the Revolution in 1791 only to eventually become a Conservative. He published his first books in England when he was 23 years old. In 1798 he and Coleridge jointly published a memorable volume, *Lyrical Ballads*. It was severely criticized by reviewers and was unaccepted by the public but marks an epoch in the history of English poetry. Wordsworth and his sister were enabled to travel extensively through an endowment by the Wedgwoods and in 1802 the Earl of Lonsdale's death gave him a competency which enabled him to marry his "phantom of delight." Thereafter for nearly fifty years Wordsworth's life flowed on tranquilly. He became the center of a group of distinguished literary men and in 1843 he was appointed Laureate of England.

I

THERE WAS A TIME when meadow, grove and stream
The earth and every common sight,
    To me did seem
     Apparelled in celestial light,
The glory and the freshness of a dream.
It is not now as it hath been of yore;—
     Turn wheresoe'er I may
      By night or day,
The things which I have seen I now can see no more.

II

The Rainbow comes and goes,
    And lovely is the rose,
    The Moon doth with delight
Look round her when the heavens are bare.
    Waters on a starry night
    Are beautiful and fair;
    The sunshine is a glorious birth;
    But yet I know where'er I go
That there hath passed away a glory from the earth.

III

Now, while the birds thus sing a joyous song,
    And while the young lambs bound,
    As to the tabor's sound
To me alone there came a thought of grief;
A timely utterance gave that thought relief,
    And I again am strong:
The cataracts blow their trumpets from the steep;
No more shall grief of mine the seasons wrong;
I hear the Echoes through the mountains throng
The winds come to me from the fields of sleep,
    And all the earth is gay;
    Land and sea
    Give themselves up to jollity,
    And with the heart of May
Doth every beast keep holiday;--
    Thou Child of Joy,
Shout round me, let me hear thy shouts, thou happy
    Shepherd-boy!

IV

Ye blessèd creatures, I have heard the call
    Ye to each other make; I see

The heavens laugh with you in your jubilee;
   My heart is at your festival,
   My head hath its coronal,
The fulness of your bliss I feel—I feel it all.
   Oh evil day! if I were sullen
   While earth herself is adorning,
    This sweet May-morning,
   And the children are culling
    On every side,
  In a thousand valleys far and wide,
Fresh flowers; while the earth shines warm,
And the babe leaps up on his mother's arm:—
   I hear, I hear, with joy I hear!
  —But there's a Tree, of many, one,
  A single field which I have looked upon,
Both of them speak of something that is gone:
   The Pansy at my feet
   Doth the same tale repeat:
Whither is fled the visionary gleam?
Where is it now, the glory and the dream?

        v

Our birth is but a sleep and a forgetting.
The Soul that rises with us, our life's Star,
   Hath had elsewhere its setting,
   And cometh from afar:
   Not in entire forgetfulness,
   And not in utter nakedness,
But trailing clouds of glory do we come
   From God, who is our home:
Heaven lies about us in our infancy!
Shades of the prison-house begin to close
   Upon the growing Boy,
But he beholds the light, and whence it flows,
   He sees in it his joy;
The youth who daily farther from the east
   Must travel, still is Nature's Priest,

And by the vision splendid
Is on his way attended;
At length the Man perceives it die away,
And fade into the light of common day.

VI

Earth fills her lap with pleasures of her own;
Yearnings she hath in her own natural kind,
And, even with something of a mother's mind,
  And no unworthy aim,
   The homely Nurse doth all she can
To make her foster-child, her Inmate Man,
  Forget the glories he hath known,
And that imperial palace whence he came.
Behold the child among his new-born blisses,
A six year's Darling of a pigmy size!
See, where 'mid work of his own hand he lies,
Fretted by sallies of his mother's kisses,
With light upon him from his father's eyes!
See, at his feet, some little plan or chart,
Some fragment from his dream of human life,
Shaped by himself with newly learned art;
  A wedding or a festival,
  A mourning or a funeral;
   And this hath now his heart,
  And unto this he frames his song:
   Then will he fit his tongue
To dialogues of business, love or strife;
  But it will not be long
  Ere this be thrown aside,
  And with new joy and pride
The little Actor cons another part;
Filling from time to time his "humorous stage"
With all the Persons down to palsied Age,
That Life brings with her in her equipage;
  As if his whole vocation
  Were endless imitation.

     .   .   .

VIII

Thou, whose exterior semblance doth belie
　　Thy Soul's immensity;
Thou best philosopher, who yet dost keep
Thy heritage, thou Eye among the blind,
That, deaf and silent, read'st the eternal deep,
Haunted forever by the eternal mind,—
　　Mighty Prophet! Seer blest!
　　On whom those truths do rest,
Which we are toiling all our lives to find,
In darkness lost, the darkness of the grave;
Thou, over whom thy Immortality
Broods like the Day, a Master o'er a Slave,
A Presence which is not to be put by;
Thou little Child, yet glorious in the might
Of heaven-born freedom on thy being's height,
Why with such earnest pains dost thou provoke
The years to bring the inevitable yoke,
Thus blindly with thy blessedness at strife?
Full soon thy Soul shall have her earthly freight,
And custom lie upon thee with a weight,
Heavy as frost, and deep almost as life!

IX

　　O joy! that in our members
　　Is something that doth live,
　　That nature yet remembers
　　What was so fugitive!
The thought of our past years in me doth breed
Perpetual benediction: not indeed
For that which is most worthy to be blest—
Delight and liberty, the simple creed
Of Childhood, whether busy or at rest,
With new-fledged hopes still fluttering in the breast:—
　　Not for these I raise
　　The song of thanks and praise;

[431]

But for those obstinate questionings
Of sense and outward things,
Falling from us, vanishings;
Blank misgivings of a Creature
Moving about in worlds not realized,
High instincts before which our mortal nature
Did tremble like a guilty Thing surprised:
But for those first affections,
Those shadowy recollections,
Which, be they what they may,
Are yet the fountain light of all our day,
Are yet a master light of all our seeing;
Uphold us, cherish and have power to make
Our noisy years seem moments in the being
Of the eternal Silence: truths that wake,
To perish never;
Which neither listlessness nor mad endeavor,
Nor Man nor Boy,
Nor all that is with enmity with joy,
Can utterly abolish or destroy!
Hence in a season of calm weather
Though inland far we be,
Our Souls have sight of that immortal sea
Which brought us hither,
Can in a moment travel thither,
And see the Children sport upon the shore
And hear the mighty waters rolling evermore.

X

Then sing, ye Birds, sing, sing a joyous song!
And let the young Lambs bound
As to the tabor's sound!
We in thought will join your throng,
Ye that pipe and ye that play,
Ye that through your hearts today
Feel the gladness of the May!
What though the radiance which was once so bright

Be now forever taken from my sight,
   Though nothing can bring back the hour
Of splendor in the grass, of glory in the flower;
   We will not grieve, rather find
   Strength in what remains behind;
   In the primal sympathy
   Which having been must ever be;
   In the soothing thoughts that spring
   Out of human suffering;
   In the faith that looks through death
In years that bring the philosophic mind.

XI

And O, ye Fountains, Meadows, Hills and Groves,
Forebode not any severing of our loves!
Yet in my heart of hearts I feel your might;
I only have relinquished one delight
To live beneath your more habitual sway.
I love the brooks which down their channels fret,
Even more than when I tripped lightly as they;
The innocent brightness of a new-born Day
   Is lovely yet;
The Clouds that gather round the setting sun
Do take a sober coloring from an eye
That hath kept watch o'er man's mortality;
Another race hath been, and other palms are won,
Thanks to the human heart by which we live,
Thanks to its tenderness, its joys and fears,
To me the meanest flower that blows can give
Thoughts that do often lie too deep for tears.

THE COTTER'S SATURDAY NIGHT

By

Robert Burns

ROBERT BURNS (*1759–1796*) was one of the most celebrated of
Scotch poets. His father was a gardener and the son was
brought up in poverty with a limited education but learned
French and a smattering of Latin. He began writing poetry at
the age of 17 and the next year he was sent away to study
surveying where he began a course of dissipation that was the
cause of life-long misery and misfortune. When he was 25
years old he became a farmer again and then he wrote some
of his best known poems. In 1786 he published a collection of
his works which won him great favor and he was invited to
Edinburgh by the better known Scotch writers. In 1791 he gave
up his farm and settled in Dumfries where he received a salary
as exciseman of about $350 a year. His closing years were a
period of misfortune and he died at the age of 37 although his
writing activities continued to the end and he indignantly refused offers of a regular salary for contributions to the London
papers. Some of his best known poems include the *Jolly
Beggars, The Cotter's Saturday Night, Flow Gently Sweet
Afton, To a Mouse,* and *Highland Mary.*

MY LOVED, my honored, much respected friend,
   No mercenary bard his homage pays:
With honest pride I scorn each selfish end,
   My dearest meed a friend's esteem and praise:
To you I sing, in simple Scottish lays,
   The lowly train in life's sequestered scene;
The native feelings strong, the guileless ways;
   What Aiken in a cottage would have been—
Ah! tho' his worth unknown, far happier there, I ween.

November chill blaws loud wi' angry sough,
    The short'ning winter day is near a close;
The miry beasts retreating frae the pleugh;
    The black'ning trains o' craws to their repose:
    The toil-worn cotter frae his labor goes,
This night his weekly moil is at an end,
    Collects his spades, his mattocks and his hoes,
Hoping the morn in ease and rest to spend,
And weary, o'er the moor, his course does hameward bend.

At length his lonely cot appears in view,
    Beneath the shelter of an aged tree;
Th' expectant wee-things, toddlin, stacher through
    To meet their dad, wi' flichterin noise an' glee.
    His wee bit ingle, blinkin bonnilie,
His clean hearth-stane, his thrifty wifie's smile,
    The lisping infant prattling on his knee,
Does a' his weary kiaugh and care beguile,
An' makes him quite forget his labor an' his toil.

Belyve, the elder bairns come drapping in,
    At service out, amang the farmer roun';
Some ca' the pleugh, some herd, some tentie rin
    A cannie errand to a neibor town:
    Their eldest hope, their Jenny, woman-grown,
In youthfu' bloom, love sparkling in her e'e,
    Comes hame, perhaps to show a braw new gown,
Or deposite her sair-won penny-fee,
To help her parents dear, if they in hardship be.

With joy unfeigned brothers and sisters meet,
    An' each for other's weelfare kindly spiers:
The social hours, swift-winged, unnoticed fleet;
    Each tells the uncos that he sees or hears;
    The parents, partial, eye their hopeful years;
Anticipation forward points the view.
    The mother, wi' her needle an' her sheers,
Gars auld claes look amaist as weel's the new;
The father mixes a' wi' admonition due.

Their master's an' their mistress's command,
   The younkers a' are warned to obey;
An' mind their labors wi' an eyedent hand,
   An' ne'er, tho' out o' sight, to jauk or play:
   "And O! be sure to fear the Lord alway,
An' mind your duty, duly, morn an' night!
   Lest in temptation's path ye gang astray,
Implore His counsel and assisting might:
They never sought in vain that sought the Lord aright!"

But hark! a rap comes gently to the door;
   Jenny, wha' kens the meaning o' the same,
Tells how a neibor lad cam o'er the moor,
   To do some errands, and convoy her hame.
   The wily mother sees the conscious flame
Sparkle in Jenny's e'e, and flush her cheek;
   Wi' heart-struck anxious care, inquires his name,
While Jenny hafflins is afraid to speak;
Weel pleased the mother hears it's nae wild worthless rake.

Wi' kindly welcome, Jenny brings him ben;
   A strappin' youth; he takes the mother's eye;
Blithe Jenny sees the visit's no ill ta'en;
   The father cracks of horses, pleughs, and kye.
   The youngster's artless heart o'erflows wi' joy,
But blate and laithfu', scarce can weel behave;
   The mother, wi' a woman's wiles, can spy
What makes the youth sae bashfu' and sae grave;
Weel pleased to think her bairn's respected like the lave.

O happy love! where love like this is found;
   O heart-felt rapture, bliss beyond compare!
I've paced much this weary mortal round,
   And sage experience bids me this declare—
   "If Heaven a draught of heavenly pleasure spare,
One cordial in this melancholy vale,
   'Tis when a youthful, loving, modest pair
In other's arms breathe out the tender tale,
Beneath the milk-white thorn that scents the evening gale."

THE COTTER'S SATURDAY NIGHT

Is there, in human form, that bears a heart—
A wretch, a villain, lost to love and truth—
That can with studied, sly, ensnaring art,
Betray sweet Jenny's unsuspecting youth?
Curse on his perjured arts, dissembling smooth!
Are honor, virtue, conscience, all exiled?
Is there no pity, no relenting ruth,
Points to the parents fondling o'er their child?
Then paints the ruined maid, and their distraction wild?

But now the supper crowns their simple board
The halesome parritch, chief of Scotia's food:
The sowpe their only hawkie does afford,
That 'yont the hallan snugly chows her cood;
The dame brings forth in complimental mood,
To grace the lad, her weel-hain'd kebbuck, fell;
And aft he's pressed, and aft he ca's it good;
The frugal wifie, garrulous, will tell
How 'twas a towmond auld sin' lint was i' the bell.

The cheerfu' supper done, wi' serious face
They round the ingle form a circle wide;
The sire turns o'er, wi' patriarchal grace,
The big ha'-Bible, ance his father's pride:
His bonnet rev'rently is laid aside,
His lyart haffets wearing thin and bare;
Those strains that once did sweet in Zion glide—
He wales a portion with judicious care,
And "Let us worship God!" he says with solemn air.

They chant their artless notes in simple guise;
They tune their hearts, by far the noblest aim;
Perhaps *Dundee's* wild warbling measures rise,
Or plaintive *Martyrs,* worthy of the name;
Or noble *Elgin* beets the heav'nward flame,
The sweetest far of Scotia's holy lays:
Compared with these, Italian trills are tame;
The tickled ears no heartfelt raptures raise;
Nae unison hae they with our Creator's praise.

[437]

The priest-like father reads the sacred page
   How Abram was the friend of God on high;
Or Moses bade eternal warfare rage,
   With Amalek's ungracious progeny;
   Or how the royal bard did groaning lie
Beneath the stroke of Heaven's avenging ire;
   Or Job's pathetic plaint, and wailing cry;
   Or rapt Isaiah's wild seraphic fire;
Or other holy seers that tune the sacred lyre.

Perhaps the Christian volume is the theme,
   How guiltless blood for guilty man was shed;
How He who bore in Heaven the second name
   Had not on earth whereon to lay His head;
   How His first followers and servants sped;
The precepts sage they wrote to many a land:
   How he, who lone in Patmos banished,
Saw in the sun a mighty angel stand,
And heard great Bab'lon's doom pronounced by Heaven's command.

Then kneeling down to Heaven's Eternal King
   The saint, the father, and the husband prays:
Hope "springs exulting on triumphant wing"
   That thus they all shall meet in future days:
   There ever bask in uncreated rays
No more to sigh or shed the bitter tear,
   Together hymning their Creator's praise
In such society, yet still more dear;
While circling Time moves round in an eternal sphere.

Compared with this, how poor Religion's pride,
   In all the pomp of method and of art,
When men display to congregations wide
   Devotion's every grace, except the heart!
   The Power, incensed, the pageant will desert,
The pompous strain, the sacerdotal stole;
   But haply, in some cottage far apart,
May hear, well pleased, the language of the soul;
And in His Book of Life the inmates poor enroll.

[438]

Then homeward all take off their several way;
   The youngling cottagers retire to rest:
The parent-pair their secret homage pay,
   And proffer up to Heaven the warm request,
   That He who stills the raven's clamorous nest,
And decks the lily fair in flowery pride,
   Would, in the way His wisdom sees the best,
For them and for their little ones provide;
But chiefly in their hearts with grace divine preside.

From scenes like these old Scotia's grandeur springs,
   That makes her loved at home, revered abroad;
Princes and lords are but the breath of kings,
   "An honest man's the noblest work of God;"
   And, certes, in fair virtue's heavenly road,
The cottage leaves the palace far behind;
   What is a lordling's pomp? A cumbrous load,
Disguising oft the wretch of humankind,
Studied in arts of hell, in wickedness refined!

O Scotia! my dear, my native soil!
   For whom my warmest wish to Heaven is sent!
Long may thy hardy sons of rustic toil
   Be blest with health, and peace, and sweet content!
   And O may Heaven their simple lives prevent
From luxury's contagion weak and vile;
   Then, howe'er crowns and coronets be rent,
A virtuous populace may rise the while,
And stand a wall of fire around their much loved isle.

O Thou! who poured the patriotic tide
   That streamed through Wallace's undaunted heart,
Who dared to nobly stem tyrannic pride,
   Or nobly die—the second glorious part,
   (The patriot's God, peculiarly thou art,
His friend, inspirer, guardian, and reward!)
   O never, never, Scotia's realm desert;
But still the patriot, and the patriot bard,
In bright succession raise, her ornament and guard!

KUBLA KHAN

By

Samuel Taylor Coleridge

SAMUEL TAYLOR COLERIDGE (*1772–1834*) the English poet and
philosopher was the son of a learned clergyman. During his
early years he gained friendships with Lamb and Southey
and he became imbued with the revolutionary principles then
in vogue. With his friends he dreamed of a communistic
literary settlement in America. He started a short-lived paper
in 1796 and then retired to the country. He exercised a
marvelous personal attraction over men and friends conferred
an annuity upon him. In 1798 Wordsworth and he published
the epoch-making *Lyrical Ballads*. From then on he wrote
almost constantly. Acute rheumatism caused him to take up
the opium habit which estranged him from his wife and
caused him much misery in his later years. Coleridge is held
to be the founder of modern Shakespearian criticism. His
Kubla Khan is credited by critics as being unrivaled in the
English language for imagery as well as for melody and power
of poetic diction. Among his other works are *Christabel, The
Ancient Mariner* and *The Nightingale*.

IN XANADU did Kubla Khan
  A stately pleasure-dome decree:
Where Alph, the sacred river, ran
Through caverns measureless to man
  Down to a sunless sea.
So twice five miles of fertile ground
With walls and towers were girdled round:
And here were gardens bright with sinuous rills
Where blossomed many an incense-bearing tree,
And here were forests ancient as the hills,
Enfolding sunny spots of greenery.

But oh! that deep romantic chasm which slanted
Down the green hill athwart a cedarn cover!
A savage place! As holy and enchanted
As e'er beneath a waning moon was haunted
By woman waiting for her demon-lover!
And from this chasm, with ceaseless turmoil seething,
As if this earth in fast thick pants were breathing,
A mighty fountain momently was forced,
Amid whose swift half-intermitted burst,
Huge fragments vaulted like rebounding hail,
Or chaffy grain beneath the thresher's flail:
And 'mid these dancing rocks at once and ever
It flung up momently the sacred river.
Five miles meandering with a mazy motion
Through wood and dale the sacred river ran,
Then reached the caverns measureless to man,
And sank in tumult to a lifeless ocean:
And 'mid this tumult Kubla hear'd from far
Ancestral voices prophesying war!

  The shadow of the dome of pleasure
  Floated midway on the waves;
  Where was heard with mingled measure
  From the fountain and the caves.
It was a miracle of rare device,
A sunny pleasure-dome with caves of ice!
  A damsel with a dulcimer
  In a vision once I saw:
  It was an Abyssinian maid,
  And on her dulcimer she played,
  Singing of Mount Abora.
  Could I revive within me
  Her symphony and song,
  To such a deep delight 'twould win me,
That with music loud and long,
I would build that dome in air,
That sunny dome! those caves of ice!
And all who heard should see them there,

And all should cry, Beware! Beware!
His flashing eyes, his floating hair!
Weave a circle round him thrice,
And close your eyes with holy dread,
For he on honey-dew hath fed,
And drunk the milk of Paradise.

ODE TO THE WEST WIND

By

Percy Bysshe Shelley

PERCY BYSSHE SHELLEY (*1792–1822*) was an English poet. He was a student at Oxford until a small pamphlet, *The Necessity of Atheism* which he printed, caused his expulsion. He married in 1811 but was separated from his wife three years later and ran away with Mary Godwin. They journeyed from place to place in Europe and finally at Geneva he met Byron. Their friendship was broken before Byron left on his ill-fated trip to the Greek Revolution. Upon learning of the death of his wife in 1816 Shelley married Mary Godwin. Two years later he contracted a pulmonary ailment and took his family to Italy to regain his health. Here he met Keats. Four years later Shelley was drowned when a squall upset his boat. His ashes were buried in Rome. During the year 1819 he wrote some of his best works including his classical lyrical poem *Ode to the West Wind.*

I

O, WILD WEST WIND, thou breath of Autumn's being,
Thou, from whose unseen presence the leaves dead
Are driven, like ghosts from an enchanter fleeing,

Yellow, and black, and pale, and hectic red,
Pestilence-stricken multitudes: O, thou,
Who chariotest to their dark wintry bed

The winged seeds, where they lie cold and low,
Each like a corpse within its grave, until
Thine azure sister of the Spring shall blow

Her clarion o'er the dreaming earth, and fill
(Driving sweet buds like flocks to feed in air)
With living hues and odors plain and hill:

Wild Spirit, which art moving everywhere;
Destroyer and preserver; hear, O, hear!

II

Thou, on whose stream, 'mid the steep sky's commotion
Loose clouds like earth's decaying leaves are shed,
Shook from the tangled boughs of Heaven and Ocean,

Angels of rain and lightning: there are spread
On the blue surface of thine airy surge,
Like the bright hair uplifted from the head

Of some fierce Mænad, even from the dim verge
Of the horizon to the zenith's height
The locks of the approaching storm. Thou dirge

Of the dying year, to which this closing night
Will be the dome of a vast sepulchre,
Vaulted with all thy congregate might

Of vapors, from whose solid atmosphere
Black rain, and fire, and hail will burst; O, hear!

III

Thou who didst waken from his summer dreams
The blue Mediterranean where he lay,
Lulled by the coil of his crystalline streams,

Beside a pumice isle in Baiae's bay,
And saw in sleep old palaces and towers
Quivering within the wave's intenser day,

All overgrown with azure moss and flowers
So sweet, the sense faints picturing them! Thou
For whose path the Atlantic's level powers

Cleave themselves into chasms, while far below
The sea-blooms and the oozy woods which wear
The sapless foliage of the ocean, know

Thy voice, and suddenly grow gray with fear,
And tremble and despoil themselves: O, hear!

IV

If I were a dead leaf though mightest hear;
If I were a swift cloud to fly with thee;
A wave to pant beneath thy power, and share

The impulse of thy strength, only less free
Than thou, O, uncontrollable! If even
I were as in my boyhood, and could be

The comrade of thy wanderings over heaven,
As then, when to outstrip thy skyey speed
Scarce seemed a vision; I would ne'er have striven

As thus with thee in prayer in my sore need.
Oh, lift me as a wave, a leaf, a cloud!
I fall upon the thorns of life! I bleed!

A heavy weight of hours has chained and bowed
One too like thee: tameless, and swift, and proud.

V

Make me thy lyre, even as the forest is:
What if my leaves are falling like its own!
The tumult of thy mighty harmonies

Will take from both a deep, autumnal tone,
Sweet though in sadness. Be thou, spirit fierce,
My spirit! Be thou me, impetuous one!

Drive my dead thoughts over the universe
Like withered leaves to quicken a new birth!
And, by the incantation of this verse,

Scatter, as from an unextinguished hearth,
Ashes and sparks, my words among mankind!
Be through my lips to unawakened earth.

The trumpet of a prophecy! O, wind,
If winter comes, can Spring be far behind?

ODE ON A GRECIAN URN

By

John Keats

JOHN KEATS (*1795–1821*) was the son of a livery-stable keeper. He was early apprenticed to a surgeon and continued his medical studies in London. His first published poem appeared in Leigh Hunt's magazine when he was 21 years old. His first published volume of verse the next year was a failure. When he was 23 he made a tour through Scotland where he contracted throat trouble which soon developed into consumption. Keats continued to write through his failing health. He died in Rome and was buried there near Shelley. Although his life was short he produced several famous poems like *Ode on a Grecian Urn, To a Nightingale* and *To Autumn*.

I

THOU still unravished bride of quietness,
  Thou foster-child of silence and slow time,
Sylvan historian, who canst thus express
  A flowery tale more sweetly than our rhyme:
What leaf-fringed legend haunts about thy shape
  Of deities or mortals, or of both,
    In Tempé or the dales of Arcady?
  What men or gods are these? What maidens loth?
What mad pursuit? What struggle to escape?
  What pipes and timbrels? What wild ecstasy?

II

Heard melodies are sweet, but those unheard
  Are sweeter; therefore, ye soft pipes play on;
Not to the sensual ear, but, more endeared,
  Pipe to the spirit ditties of no tone!

Fair youth, beneath the trees, thou canst not leave
  Thy song, nor ever can those trees be bare,
Bold lover, never, never canst thou kiss,
  Though winning near the goal—yet, do not grieve;
She cannot fade, though thou has not thy bliss,
  For ever wilt thou love, and she be fair!

III

Ah, happy, happy boughs! that cannot shed
  Your leaves, nor ever bid the spring adieu;
And, happy melodist, unwearied,
  For ever piping songs for ever new;
More happy love! More happy, happy love!
  For ever warm and still to be enjoyed,
For ever panting, and for ever young;
  All breathing human passion far above,
That leaves a heart high-sorrowful and cloyed,
  A burning forehead and a parching tongue.

IV

Who are these coming to the sacrifice?
  To what green altar, O mysterious priest,
Leadest thou that heifer lowing at the skies,
  And all her silken flanks with garlands drest?
What little town by river or sea shore,
  Or mountain-built with peaceful citadel,
Is emptied of this folk, this pious morn?
  And, little town, thy streets for evermore
Will silent be; and not a soul to tell
  Why thou art desolate, can e'er return.

V

O Attic shape! Fair attitude! with brede
  Of marble men and maidens overwrought,
With forest branches and the trodden weed;
  Thou, silent form, dost tease us out of thought

As doth eternity: Cold Pastoral!
When old age shall this generation waste,
  Thou shalt remain in midst of other woe
Than ours, a friend to man, to whom thou sayest,
  "Beauty is truth, truth beauty"—that is all
Ye know on earth, and all ye need to know.

OH ROME! MY COUNTRY! CITY OF THE SOUL!

By

Lord Byron

GEORGE GORDON, LORD BYRON (*1788–1824*) the English poet,
was the son of a Captain of the Guards. His mother's fortune
was squandered by his father, and mother and son retired to
Aberdeen, Scotland, on a small income. At the age of 11 he
succeeded to the title of his grand-uncle and moved to the
ancestral home of the family. Byron was born with malformed
feet which probably affected his disposition. His young manhood was consumed in heavy dissipation. The book of poems
which he wrote when he was 19 was criticized by the *Edinburgh Review* and he replied with sharp satire. He married in
1815 and after the birth of his daughter, Lady Byron returned
to her father's house. Popular judgment so condemned him
for this that he left England and wandered about Europe. In
1822 he started publication of a journal in company with
Shelley and Leigh Hunt, which collapsed upon the death of
Shelley. When the Greeks arose against the Turks he sailed
for the scene of rebellion, was appointed a commander-in-
chief but died soon after a brief illness. Among his chief
writings are *Childe Harold, The Prisoner of Chillon* and
Don Juan.

OH ROME, my country! City of the soul!
The orphans of the heart must turn to thee,
Lone mother of dead empires! and control
In their shut breasts their petty misery.
What are our woes and suffrance? Come and see
The cypress, hear the owl, and plod your way
O'er steps of broken thrones and temples, Ye!
Whose agonies are evils of a day—
A world is at our feet as fragile as our clay.

OH ROME! MY COUNTRY! CITY OF THE SOUL!

The Niobe of nations! there she stands
Childless and crownless, in her voiceless woe;
An empty urn within her withered hands,
Whose holy dust was scattered long ago;
The Scipios' tomb contains no ashes now;
The very sepulchers lie tenantless
Of their heroic dwellers: dost thou flow,
Old Tiber! through a marble wilderness?
Rise with thy yellow waves, and mantle her distress.

The Goth, the Christian, Time, War, Flood, and Fire,
Have dealt upon the seven-hilled city's pride;
She saw·her glories star by star expire,
And up the steep barbarian monarchs ride,
Where the car climbed the Capitol; far and wide
Temple and tower went down, nor left a site:
Chaos of ruins! who shall trace the void,
O'er the dim fragments cast a lunar light,
And say, "here was, or is," where all is doubly night?

The double night of ages, and of her,
Night's daughter, Ignorance, hath wrapt and wrap
All round us; we but feel our way to err:
The ocean hath his chart, the stars their map,
And Knowledge spreads them on her ample lap;
But Rome is as the desert, where we steer
Stumbling o'er recollection; now we clap
Our hands, and cry "Eureka!" it is clear—
When but some false mirage of ruin rises near.

Alas! the lofty city! and alas!
The trebly hundred triumphs! and the day
When Brutus made the dagger's edge surpass
The conqueror's sword in bearing fame away!
Alas for Tully's voice, and Virgil's lay,
And Livy's pictured page! but these shall be
Her resurrection; all beside—decay
Alas, for Earth, for never shall we see
That brightness in her eye she bore when **Rome** was free!

Oh thou, whose chariot rolled on Fortune's wheel,
Triumphant Sylla! Thou who didst subdue
Thy country's foes ere thou wouldst pause to feel
The wrath of thy own wrongs, or reap the due
Of hoarded vengeance till thy eagles flew
O'er prostate Asia;—thou who with thy frown
Annihilated senates—Roman, too,
With all thy vices, for thou didst lay down
With an atoning smile a more than earthly crown—

The dictatorial wreath—couldst thou divine
To what would one day dwindle that which made
Thee more than mortal? and that so supine
By aught than Romans, Rome should thus be laid?
She who was named eternal, and arrayed
Her warriors but to conquer—she who veiled
Earth with her haughty shadow, and displayed,
Until the o'er-canopied horizon failed,
Her rushing wings—Oh! she who was Almighty hailed.

Sylla was first of victors; but our own,
The sagest of usurpers, Cromwell!—he
Too swept off Senates while he hewed the throne
Down to a block—immortal rebel! See
What crimes it costs to be a moment free,
And famous through all ages! but beneath
His fate the moral lurks of destiny;
His day of double victory and death
Beheld him win two realms, and happier, yield his breath.

The third of the same moon whose former course
Had all but crowned him, on the selfsame day
Deposed him gently from his throne of force,
And laid him with the earth's preceding clay.
And showed not Fortune thus how fame and sway,
And all we deem delightful, and consume
Our souls to compass through each arduous way,

Are in her eyes less happy than the tomb?
Were they but so in man's, how different were his doom!

.   .   .

I see before me the Gladiator lie:
He leans upon his hand—his manly brow
Consents to death, but conquers agony,
And his drooped head sinks gradually low—
And through his side the last drops, ebbing slow
From the red gash, fall heavy, one by one,
Like the first of a thunder-shower; and now
The arena swims around him—he is gone,
Ere ceased the inhuman shout which hailed the wretch who won.

He heard it, but he heeded not—his eyes
Were with his heart, and that was far away;
He recked not of the life he lost nor prize,
But where his rude hut by the Danube lay,
There were his young barbarians all at play,
There was their Dacian mother—he, their sire,
Butchered to make a Roman holiday—
All this rushed with his blood—Shall he expire
And unavenged? Arise! ye Goths, and glut your ire!

But here, where Murder breathed her bloody stream;
And here, where buzzing nations choked the ways,
And roared or murmured like a mountain stream
Dashing or winding as its torrent strays;
Here, where the Roman millions' blame or praise
Was death or life, the playthings of a crowd,
My voice sounds much—and fall the stars' faint rays
On the arena void—seats crushed—walls bowed—
And galleries, where my steps seem echoes strangely loud.

A ruin—yet what ruin!—from its mass
Walls, palaces, half-cities, have been reared;
Yet oft the enormous skeleton ye pass,
And marvel where the spoil could have appeared.

[453]

Hath it indeed been plundered, or but cleared?
Alas! developed, opens the decay,
When the colossal fabric's form is neared:
It will not bear the brightness of the day,
Which streams too much on all, years, man have reft away.

But when the rising moon begins to climb
Its topmost arch, and gently pauses there;
When the stars twinkle through the loops of time,
And the low night-breeze waves along the air
The garland-forest, which the gray walls wear,
Like laurels on the bald first Caesar's head;
When the light shines serene but doth not glare,
Then in this magic circle raise the dead:
Heroes have trod this spot—'tis on their dust ye tread.

'While stands the Coliseum, Rome shall stand;
When falls the Coliseum, Rome shall fall,
And when Rome falls—the World.' From our own land
Thus spake the pilgrims o'er this mighty wall
In Saxon times, which we are wont to call
Ancient; and these three mortal things are still
On their foundations, and unaltered all;
Rome and her Ruin past Redemption's skill,
The world, the same wide den—of thieves, or what ye will.

THE HOUND OF HEAVEN

By

Francis Joseph Thompson

FRANCIS JOSEPH THOMPSON (*1860–1907*) the English poet, was born at Ashton, Lancashire. His father, a doctor, became a convert to Roman Catholicism, therefore Francis was educated at Ushaw College, near Durham. Subsequently he studied medicine at Owens College in Manchester but he took no interest in the profession and was bent on literary production. A period of friendlessness and failure followed in which he became a solitary character who yet turned his visions of beauty into unrecognized verse. After years of destitution his poetic genius was recognized. The Meynells befriended him and in 1893 his first book of poetry was published. For glory of inspiration and natural magnificence of utterance he is unique among the poets of his time.

I FLED HIM, down the nights and down the days;
   I fled Him, down the arches of the years;
I fled Him, down the labyrinthine ways
    Of my own mind; and in the midst of tears
I hid from Him, and under running laughter.
    Up vistaed hopes, I sped;
    And shot, precipitated,
Adown Titanic glooms of chasmèd fears,
 From those strong Feet that followed, followed after.
    But with unhurrying chase,
      And unperturbed pace
Deliberate speed, majestic instancy,
    They beat—and a Voice beat
    More instant than the Feet—
    "All things betray thee, who betrayest Me."
    I pleaded, outlaw-wise,

By many a hearted casement, curtained red,
Trellised with intertwining charities;
(For, though I knew His love who followèd
Yet I was sore adread
Lest, having Him, I must have naught beside);
But, if one little casement parted wide,
The gust of His approach would clash it to.
Fear wist not to evade, as Love wist to pursue.
Across the margent of the world I fled,
And troubled the gold gateways of the stars,
Smiting for shelter on their clangèd bars;
Fretted to dulcet jars
And silvern chatter the pale ports o' the moon.
I said to dawn, Be sudden; to eve, Be soon;
With thy young skiey blossoms heap me over
From this tremendous Lover!
Float thy vague veil about me, lest He see!
I tempted all His servitors, but to find
My own betrayal in their constancy,
In faith to Him their fickleness to me,
Their traitorous trueness, and their loyal deceit.
To all swift things for swiftness did I sue;
Clung to the whistling mane of every wind.
But whether they swept, smoothly fleet,
The long savannahs of the blue;
Or whether, thunder-driven,
They clanged his chariot 'thwart a heaven
Plashy with flying lightnings round the spurn o' their feet;—
Fear wist not to evade as Love wist to pursue.
Still with unhurrying chase,
And unperturbed pace,
Deliberate speed, majestic instancy,
Came on the following Feet,
And a Voice above their beat—
"Naught shelters thee, who wilt not shelter me."

I sought no more that after which I strayed
In face of man or maid;

But still within the little children's eyes
  Seems something, something that replies;
They at least are for me, surely for me!
I turned me to them very wistfully;
But, just as their young eyes grew sudden fair
  With dawning answers there,
Their angel plucked them from me by the hair.
"Come, then, ye other children, Nature's—share
With me" (said I) "your delicate fellowship;
  Let me greet you lip to lip,
  Let me twine you with caresses,
    Wantoning
  With our Lady-Mother's vagrant tresses,
    Banqueting
  With her in her wind-walled palace,
  Underneath her azured dais,
  Quaffing, as your taintless way is,
    From a chalice
Lucent weeping out of the dayspring."
    So it was done;
I in their delicate fellowship was one—
Drew the bolt of Nature's secrecies.
I knew all the swift importings
  On the wilful face of skies;
  I knew how the clouds arise
  Spumèd of the wild sea-snortings;
    All that's born or dies
  Rose and drooped with—made them shapers
Of mine own moods, or wailful or divine—
  With them joyed and was bereaven.
  I was heavy with the even,
  When she lit her glimmering tapers
  Round the day's dead sanctities.
  I laughed in the morning's eyes.
I triumphed and I saddened with all weather,
  Heaven and I wept together,
And its sweet tears were salt with mortal mine;
Against the red throb of its sunset-heart

I laid my own to beat,
And share commingling heat;
But not by that, by that, was eased my human smart
In vain my tears were wet on Heaven's gray cheek.
For ah! we know not what each other says,
These things and I; in sound I speak—
Their sound is but their stir, they speak by silences.
Nature, poor stepdame, cannot slake my drought;
Let her, if she would own me,
Drop yon blue bosom-veil of sky, and show me
The breasts o' her tenderness:
Never did any milk of hers once bless
My thirsting mouth.
Nigh and nigh draws the chase,
With unperturbed pace,
Deliberate speed, majestic instancy;
And past those noisèd Feet
A voice comes yet more fleet—
"Lo! naught contents thee, who conten'st not Me."

Naked I wait Thy love's uplifted stroke!
My harness piece by piece Thou hast hewn from me,
And smitten me to my knee;
I am defenceless utterly.
I slept, methinks, and woke,
And, slowly gazing, find me stripped in sleep.
In the rash lustihead of my young powers,
I shook the pillaring hours
And pulled my life upon me; grimed with smears,
I stand amid the dust o' the mounded years—
My mangled youth lies dead beneath the heap.
My days have crackled and gone up in smoke,
Have puffed and burst as sun-starts on a stream.
Yea, faileth now even dream
The dreamer, and the lute the lutanist;
Even the linkèd fantasies, in whose blossomy twist
I swung the earth a trinket at my wrist,
Are yielding; cords of all too weak account

For earth with heavy grief so overplussed.
    Ah! is Thy love indeed
A weed, albeit an amaranthine weed,
Suffering no flowers except itself to mount?
      Ah! must—
      Designer infinite!—
Ah! must thou char the wood ere Thou canst limn with it?
My freshness spent its wavering shower i' the dust;
And now my heart is as a broken fount,
Wherein tear-drippings stagnate, spilt down ever
    From the dank thoughts that shiver
Upon the sightful branches of my mind.
    Such is; what is to be?
The pulp so bitter, how shall taste the rind?
I dimly guess that Time in mists confounds;
Yet ever and anon a trumpet sounds
From the hid battlements of Eternity;
Those shaken mists a space unsettle, then
Round the half-glimpsed turrets slowly wash again.
    But not ere him who summoneth
    I first have seen, enwound
With glooming robes purpureal, cypress-crowned;
His name I know, and what his trumpet saith.
Whether man's heart or life it be which yields
    Thee harvest, must Thy harvest fields
    Be dunged with rotten death?
      Now of that long pursuit
      Comes on at hand the bruit;
    That Voice is round me like a bursting sea.
    "And is thy earth so marred,
    Shattered in shard on shard?
    Lo, all things fly thee, for thou fliest Me!
    Strange, piteous, futile thing,
Wherefore should any set thee love apart?
Seeing none but I makes much of nought"
    (He said),
  "And human love needs human meriting:
    How hast thou merited—

Of all man's clotted clay the dingiest clot?
　Alack, thou knowest not
How little worthy of any love thou art!
Whom wilt thou find to love ignoble thee
　Save Me, save only Me?
All which I took from thee I did but take,
　Not for thy harms,
But just that thou might'st seek it in My arms.
　All which thy child's mistake
Fancies as lost, I have stored for thee at home:
　Rise, clasp My hand and come!"

　　Halts by me that footfall:
　　Is my gloom, after all,
Shade of His hand, outstretched caressingly?
　"Ah, fondest, blindest, weakest,
　I am he Whom thou seekest!
Thou dravest love from thee, who dravest Me."

THE GARDEN OF PROSERPINE

By

Algernon Charles Swinburne

ALGERNON CHARLES SWINBURNE (*1837–1909*) was an English poet, born in London. His second published volume, when he was 27, gained him considerable recognition and his output continued rather stable thereafter. He tried the drama in 1871 and three years later he took up dramatic criticism. Among his works are included *Essays and Studies, Astrophel and Other Poems* and *A Study of Shakespeare.*

HERE, where the world is quiet;
   Here, where all trouble seems
Dead winds' and spent waves' riot
   In doubtful dreams of dreaming;
I watch the green field growing
For reaping folk and sowing,
For harvest-time and mowing,
   A sleepy world of streams.

I am tired of tears and laughter,
   And men that laugh and weep;
Of what may come hereafter
   For men that sow and reap:
I am weary of days and hours,
Blown buds of barren flowers,
Desires and dreams and powers
   And everything but sleep.

Here life hath death for neighbor
   And far from eye ear
Wan waves and wet winds labour,
   Weak ships and spirits steer;

They drive adrift, and whither
They wot not who make thither;
But no such winds blow hither,
   And no such things grow here.

No growth of moor or coppice,
   No heather-flower or vine,
But bloomless buds of poppies
   Green grapes of Proserpine,
Pale beds of blowing rushes,
Where no leaf blooms or blushes
Save this whereout she crushes
   For dead men deadly wine.

Pale, without name or number,
   In fruitless fields of corn,
They bow themselves and slumber
   All night till light is born;
And like a soul belated,
In hell and heaven unmated,
By cloud and mist abated
   Comes out of darkness morn.

Though one were strong as seven,
   He too with death shall dwell,
Nor wake with wings in heaven,
   Nor weep for pains in hell;
Though one were fair as roses,
His beauty clouds and closes;
And well though love reposes,
   In the end it is not well.

Pale, beyond porch and portal,
   Crowned with calm leaves, she stands
Who gathers all things mortal
   With cold immortal hands;

THE GARDEN OF PROSERPINE

Her languid lips are sweeter
Than love's who fears to greet her
To men that mix and meet her
    From many times and lands.

She waits for each and other,
    She waits for all men born;
Forgets the earth her mother,
    The life of fruits and corn;
And spring and seed and swallow
Take wing for her and follow
Where summer song rings hollow
    And flowers are put to scorn.

There go the loves that wither,
    The old loves with wearier wings;
And all dead years draw thither,
    And all disastrous things;
Dead dreams of days forsaken,
Blind buds that snows have shaken,
Wild leaves that winds have taken,
    Red strays of ruined springs.

We are not sure of sorrow,
    And joy was never sure;
To-day will die tomorrow;
    Time stoops to no man's lure;
And love, grown faint and fretful,
With lips but half regretful
Sighs, and with eyes forgetful
    Weeps that no loves endure.

From too much love of living,
    From hope and fear set free,
We thank with brief thanksgiving
    Whatever gods may be

That no life lives for ever;
That dead men rise up never;
That even the weariest river
   Winds somewhere safe to sea.

Then star nor sun shall waken,
   Nor any change of light:
Nor sound of waters shaken,
   Nor any sound or sight:
Nor wintry leaves nor vernal,
Nor days nor things diurnal;
Only the sleep eternal
   In an eternal night.

THANATOPSIS

By

William Cullen Bryant

WILLIAM CULLEN BRYANT (*1794–1878*) was an American poet
and journalist, born at Cummington, Mass. He was admitted
to the bar at the age of 21 and practised law for 9 years,
whereupon he moved to New York and in 1829 became
editor, and later joint-proprietor, of the New York *Evening
Post* which position he retained until his death. As a journalist he was a strenuous abolitionist. His poetical life forms
a separate story as his most famous poem *Thanatopsis* was
written while he was still a boy. At the age of 70 he took up
the translation of *Homer* and published a complete *Iliad*. He
was much in demand as a public speaker. He collapsed during
a speech, at the age of 84, and died two weeks later. Among
his better known poems are *Lines to a Waterfowl*, *The
Fringed Gentian* and *The Crowded Street*.

To HIM who in the love of Nature holds
Communion with her visible forms, she speaks
A various language: for his gayer hours
She has a voice of gladness, and a smile
And eloquence of beauty, and she glides
Into his darker musings, with a mild
And healing sympathy, that steals away
Their sharpness, ere he is aware. When thoughts
Of the last bitter hour come like a blight
Over thy spirit, and sad images
Of the stern agony, and shroud, and pall,
And breathless darkness, and the narrow house
Make thee to shudder, and grow sick at heart;—
Go forth, under the open sky, and list
To Nature's teaching, while from all around—

Earth and her waters, and the depths of air—
Comes a still voice:—Yet a few days, and thee
The all-beholding sun shall see no more
In all his course; nor yet in the cold ground,
Where thy pale form was laid, with many tears,
Nor in the embrace of ocean, shall exist
Thy image. Earth that nourished thee,
Thy growth, to be resolved to earth again,
And, lost each human trace, surrendering up
Thine individual being, shalt thou go
To mix forever with the elements,
To be a brother to the insensible rock
And to the sluggish clod, which the rude swain
Turns with his share, and treads upon. The oak
Shall send his roots abroad, and pierce thy mould.

Yet not to thine eternal resting-place
Shalt thou retire alone, nor couldst thou wish
Couch more magnificent. Thou shalt lie down
With patriarchs of the infant world—with kings,
The powerful of the earth—the wise, the good,
Fair forms, and hoary seers of ages past,
All in one mighty sepulchre. The hills
Rock-ribbed and ancient as the sun,—the vales
Stretching in pensive quietness between;
The venerable woods—rivers that move
In majesty, and the complaining brooks
That make the meadows green; and, poured round all,
Old Ocean's gray and melancholy waste,—
Are both the solemn decorations all
Of the great tomb of man. The golden sun,
The planets, all the infinite host of heaven,
Are shining on the sad abodes of death,
Through the still lapse of ages. All that tread
The globe are but a handful to the tribes
That slumber in its bosom.—Take the wings
Of morning, pierce the Barcan wilderness,
Or lose thyself in the continuous woods

Where rolls the Oregon, and hears no sound,
Save his own dashings—yet the dead are there;
And millions in those solitudes, since first
The flight of years began, have laid them down
In their last sleep—the dead reign there alone.
So shalt thou rest, and what if thou withdraw
In silence from the living, and no friend
Take note of thy departure? All that breathe
Will share thy destiny. The gay will laugh
When thou art gone, the solemn brood of care
Plod on, and each one as before will chase
His favorite phantom; yet all these shall leave
Their mirth and their employments, and shall come
And make their bed with thee. As the long train
Of ages glides away, the sons of men,
The youth in life's green spring, and he who goes
In the full strength of years, matron and maid,
The speechless babe, and the gray-headed man—
Shall one by one be gathered to thy side,
By those, who in their turn shall follow them.
So live, that when thy summons comes to join
The innumerable caravan, which moves
To that mysterious realm, where each shall take
His chamber in the silent halls of death,
Thou go not, like the quarry-slave at night,
Scourged to his dungeon, but, sustained and soothed
By an unfaltering trust, approach thy grave,
Like one who wraps the drapery of his couch
About him, and lies down to pleasant dreams.

WHEN LILACS LAST IN THE DOORYARD BLOOMED

By

Walt Whitman

WALT (originally Walter) WHITMAN (*1819–1892*) was an
American poet, born on Long Island. He was educated in
the public schools at Brooklyn and New York. When he was
17 he became a teacher on Long Island while writing for
newspapers and magazines at the same time. He edited the
Brooklyn Eagle for a year and then started a wandering trip
through the South. He published the first collection of *Leaves
of Grass* in 1855 and devoted the remainder of his life to
the elaboration of this book. He was a volunteer army nurse
during the Civil War which brought on a serious illness from
which it is believed he never recovered fully. He was given
a clerkship in the Treasury Department after having been
dismissed by the Interior Department on account of his *Leaves
of Grass*. He never married. The works of his later period
were incorporated in successive editions of the *Leaves*.

I

WHEN LILACS LAST in the dooryard bloomed,
And the great star early drooped in the western sky at night,
I mourned, and yet shall mourn with ever-returning spring.
Ever-returning spring, trinity sure to me you bring,
Lilac blooming perennial and drooping star in the west,
And thought of him I love.

II

O powerful western fallen star!
O shades of night—O moody, tearful night!
O great star disappeared—O the black murk that hides the star!

O cruel hands that hold me powerless—O helpless soul of me!
O harsh surrounding cloud that will not free my soul.

III

In the dooryard fronting the old farmhouse near the white-washed
  palings,
Stands the lilac bush tall growing with heart-shaped leaves of
  rich green,
With many a pointed blossom rising delicate, with the perfume
  strong I love,
With every leaf a miracle—and from this bush in the dooryard,
With delicate-colored blossoms and heart-shaped leaves of rich
  green,
A sprig with its flower I break.

IV

In the swamp in secluded recesses,
A shy and hidden bird is warbling a song.
Solitary the thrush,
The hermit withdrawn to himself, avoiding the settlements,
Sings by himself a song
Song of the bleeding throat,
Death's outlet song of life (for well dear brother I know
If thou wast not granted to sing thou wouldst surely die).

V

Over the breast of the spring, the land, amid cities,
Amid lanes and through old woods, where lately the violets peeped
  from the ground, spotting the gray débris,
Amid the grass in the fields each side of the lanes, passing the end-
  less grass,
Passing the yellow-speared wheat, every grain from its shroud in
  the dark-brown fields uprisen,
Passing the apple-tree blows of white and pink in the orchards,
Carrying a corpse to where it shall rest in the grave,
Night and day journeys a coffin.

VI

Coffin that passes through lanes and streets,
Through day and night with the great cloud darkening the land,
With the pomp of the inlooped flags with the cities draped in
  black,
With the show of the States themselves as of crape-veiled women
  standing,
With processions long and winding and the flambeaus of the night,
With the countless torches lit, with the silent sea of faces and
  the unbared heads,
With the waiting depot, the arriving coffin and the somber faces,
With dirges through the night, with the thousand voices rising
  strong and solemn,
With all the mournful voices of the dirges poured around the
  coffin,
The dim-lit churches and the shuddering organs—where amid
  these you journey,
With the tolling, tolling bells' perpetual clang,
Here, the coffin slowly passes,
I give you my sprig of lilac.

VIII

O western orb sailing the heaven,
Now I know what you must have meant as a month since I
  walked,
As I walked in silence the transparent shadowy night,
As I saw you had something to tell as you bent to me night after
  night,
As you drooped from the sky low down as if to my side (while
  the other stars all looked on),
As we wandered together the solemn night (for something, I know
  not what, kept me from sleep),
As the night advanced, and I saw on the rim of the west how
  full you were of woe,
As I stood on the rising ground in the breeze in the cool transparent night,

As my soul in its trouble dissatisfied sank, as where you, sad orb,
Concluded, dropped in the night, and was gone.

.   .   .

XI

O what shall I hang on the chamber walls?
And what shall the picture be that I hang on the walls,
To adorn the burial house of him I love?
Pictures of growing spring and farms and homes,
With the Fourth-month eve at sundown, and the gray smoke lucid
    and bright,
With floods of the yellow gold of the gorgeous, indolent, sinking
    sun, burning, expanding the air,
With the fresh sweet herbage under foot, and the pale green leaves
    of the trees prolific,
In the distance the flowing glaze, the breast of the river, with
    a wind-dapple here and there,
With ranging hills on the banks, with many a line against the
    sky, and the shadows,
And the city at hand with dwellings so dense, and stacks of
    chimneys,
And all the scenes of life, and the workshops, and the workmen
    homeward returning.

XII

Lo, body and soul—this land,
My own Manhattan with spires, and the sparkling and hurrying
    tides, and the ships,
The varied and ample land, the South and the North in the light,
    Ohio's shores and flashing Missouri,
And ever the far-spreading prairies covered with grass and corn.
Lo, the most excellent sun so calm and haughty,
The violet and purple morn with just-felt breezes,
The gentle soft-born measureless light,
The miracle spreading, bathing all, the fulfilled noon,
The coming eve delicious, the welcome night and the stars,
Over my cities shining all, enveloping man and land.

.   .   .

XIV

Now while I sat in the day, and looked forth,
In the close of the day with its light and the fields of spring, and
the farmers preparing their crops,
In the large unconscious scenery of my land with its lakes and
forests,
In the heavenly aerial beauty (after the perturbed winds and the
storms),
Under the arching heavens of the afternoon swift passing, and
the voices of children and women,
The many-moving sea-tides, and I saw ships how they sailed,
And the summer approaching with richness, and the fields all
busy with labor,
And the infinite separate houses, how they all went on, each with
its meals and the minutiæ of daily usages,
And the streets how their throbbings throbbed, and the cities
pent—lo, then and there,
Falling upon them all and among them all, enveloping me with
the rest,
Appeared the cloud, appeared the long black trail,
And I knew death, its thought, and the sacred knowledge of
death.

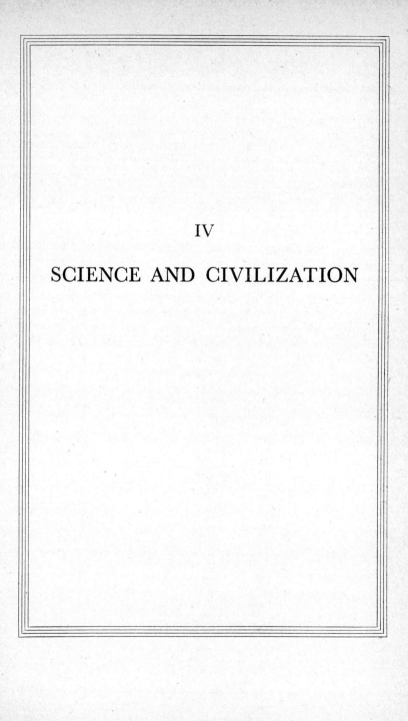

IV

SCIENCE AND CIVILIZATION

THE CYCLES OF HISTORY

By

Polybius

POLYBIUS (*204–122* B.C.) the Greek historian was born in
Arcadia. He was one of the 1000 nobles among his countrymen who were sent to Rome as hostages after the conquest
of Macedonia in 168 B.C. He was permitted by the Roman
senate to return to Greece 16 years later. He was soon joined
by Scipio and, following the General in his African campaign,
was present at the destruction of Carthage in 146 B.C. Of his
forty books only five are preserved complete. But the plan of
his whole work is fully known. His history was designed
mainly to show how and why all of the civilized countries of
the world fell under the dominion of Rome.

IN EVERY PRACTICAL UNDERTAKING by a state we must regard as the
most powerful agent of success or failure the form of its constitution, for from this as from a fountain-head all conceptions
and plans of action not only proceed but attain their consummation. Most of those who profess to give us authoritative instruc-
tion on this subject distinguish three kinds of constitutions, which
they designate as Kingship, Aristocracy and Democracy. But we
must regard the best constitution as that which partakes of all
these elements. This assertion has been proved by the example of
Lycurgus who was the first to construct a constitution on this principle, that of Sparta. As for the Roman constitution, it had three
elements each of them possessing sovereign powers, and their
respective share of power in the whole state had been regulated
with such a scrupulous regard to quality and equilibrium that no
one could say for certain, not even a native, whether the constitution as a whole was an aristocracy or democracy or despotism.

[475]

We cannot hold every absolute government to be a kingship, but only that which is accepted voluntarily and is directed by an appeal to reason rather than to fear and force. Nor is every oligarchy to be regarded as an aristocracy, which exists only when the power is wielded by the justest and wisest men selected on their merits. In like manner it is not enough to constitute a democracy that the whole crowd of citizens should have the right to do whatever they wish or purpose. For we have had examples of tyrannical forms of government which, differing as widely as possible from kingship bear some points of resemblance to it. Again, there have been many instances of oligarchical governments analogous to aristocracies, but as different from them as could possibly be. The same holds true of democracy, which by its violence can become mere mob-rule.

No clearer proof of the truth of what I say could be obtained than by a careful observation of the natural origin, genesis and decadence of these several forms of government. For it is only by seeing distinctly how each of them is produced that a distinct view can be obtained of its growth, zenith and decadence, as also the time, circumstance and place in which each of these may be expected to recur. For there are natural laws which regulate the merging of one form of government into another, as there is a natural cycle of the three forms of polity.

What is the origin of a constitution and how is it produced? Suppose that the race of men is reduced almost to extinction by floods, pestilences, failure of crops and like causes, for such things have happened and it is likely that they will happen again. Suppose, further, that from the survivors as from seeds the race of men to have multiplied again. In such a case they would herd together like animals, for in their condition of weakness they would seek those of their own kind to herd with. Now, in such a case, as with animals, he who was superior to the rest in strength of body or courage of soul would lead and rule them. This happens with animals which are without the faculty of reason, as with bulls, goats and cocks where the strongest take the lead, and this fact we must regard as in the truest sense the teaching of nature. Originally it is probable that the condition of life among men was this herding like animals and following the strongest and bravest as leaders. The limit of such authority would be physical strength and the name we should give to it would be despotism. But as soon as the idea of family ties and social relations has arisen amongst such an agglomeration of men there is born also the idea of kingship, and then for the first time mankind conceives the notion of goodness and justice, or their reverse. This is the origin of the social compact among men, as also the origin of morality.

The way in which such conceptions originate is like this—the intercourse of the sexes is an instinct of nature whose result is the birth of children. Now, if any one of these children when arrived at maturity is ungrateful and makes no return to those by whom he was nurtured, it is plain he will probably offend and annoy such as are present who have seen the trouble bestowed by the parents on the nurture of their children. Such a difference in conduct is not likely to escape observation, for men will observe it and express their displeasure on the spot. Or, if a man who has been rescued or helped in the hour of danger, instead of showing gratitude toward his preserver, seeks to do him harm, it is obvious that the rest will be displeased and offended with him, since they sympathize with their neighbor imagining how they would feel in his case. Hence arises in every breast a notion of the meaning of duty which is in fact the beginning and end of justice.

On the other hand when any one man stands out as the champion of all in a time of danger and with firm courage braves the onslaught of wild beasts, it is probable that such a man would meet with marks of favor and pre-eminence from the common people, while he who acted in a contrary way would fall under their contempt and dislike. From this would arise a theory of the disgraceful and the honorable and the difference between them, and how one should be sought and the other shunned. When, therefore, the leading and most powerful man among his people ever encourages such persons in accordance with the popular sentiment, and thereby assumes in the eyes of his subjects the appearance of being the distributer to each man according to his deserts, they no longer obey him and support his rule from fear of violence but rather from the conviction of its utility. In this way he becomes a king instead of a despot, reason having ousted brute courage and bodily strength from their supremacy. This is the natural process of the notion of goodness and justice in mankind, as this is also the origin and genesis of genuine kingship. And men do not keep up the government of such men personally but for their descendants also, from the conviction that those who are born from and educated by such men will have principles like theirs. If later they become displeased with these descendants it is not on the basis of physical strength and brute courage but by reason of their intellectual and moral faculties.

In olden times those who were selected and continued in office grew old in their royal functions, made magnificent strongholds and extended their frontiers partly for the security of their subjects and partly to provide them with abundance of the necessities of life. While engaged in these works they were exempt from all vituperation and jealousy because they did not make their distinctive dress, food or drink at all conspicuous, but lived very much like the rest and joined in the everyday employments of the common people. But when their royal power became hereditary and their descendants found every necessity for security ready to their hands, as well as more than was necessary for their personal support, they gave rein to their appetites, imagined that rulers must wear different clothes from those of the subjects, have different and elaborate luxuries for the table and must seek even sensual indulgence however unlawful. Then the kingship became a tyranny and the first step in distintegration was taken. Plots began to be formed against the government, but these did not proceed from the worst men but from the noblest, most high-minded and courageous, since these are the men who can least submit to the tyrannical acts of their rulers.

As soon as the people got leaders, they co-operated with them against the dynasty, so that both kingship and despotism alike were abolished, and aristocracy once more began to revive and start afresh. For in their immediate gratitude to those who had deposed the despots the people employed them as leaders entrusting their interests to them. These leaders looked upon their office as a great privilege, made the public advantage their chief concern and conducted all kinds of business, public or private, with diligence and caution. But when the sons of these men received the same position of authority from their fathers, having been bred from the first under the shadow of their fathers' authority and lofty position and having had no experience of misfortune and none at all of civil equality and freedom of speech, they fell into bad ways. Some gave themselves up to avarice and the unscrupulous love of money, others to drinking and boundless debauchery. Thus they turned an aristocracy into an oligarchy.

But it was not long before these oligarchs aroused in the minds of the people the same feelings they had had before, so that their fall was very like the disaster which had befallen the tyrants. The knowledge of the jealousy and hatred now existing among the citizens emboldened some one to oppose the government by word or deed, and such a one was thus sure of finding the whole people ready and prepared to take his side. Having gotten rid of these rulers either by assassination or exile, the people do not venture to set up the kingship again being still in fear of the injustice to which this had formerly led. Nor do they dare intrust their common interests again to a group of rulers, since they have just had an example of their misconduct. Therefore the only sound hope left them is that which depends upon themselves and in that they are driven to take refuge. This changes the constitution from an oligarchy to a democracy, wherein the people themselves took upon themselves the superintendence and charge of the state.

Now as long as any who have had experience of oligarchal supremacy and domination survive they regard their present constitution as a blessing, and hold equality and freedom as of the utmost value. But as soon as a new generation has arisen and the democracy has descended to their children's children, long association weakens their value for equality and freedom, hence some seek to become more powerful than the ordinary citizen. Those most liable to this temptation are the rich. When they begin to be fond of office and find themselves unable to obtain it by their own unassisted efforts and their own merits, they entice and corrupt the common people in every possible way. When in their senseless mania for reputation they have made the populace ready and greedy to receive bribes, the virtue of democracy is destroyed, for it is transformed into a government of violence and the strong hand. Then the constitution of the state becomes mob-rule in which there is violence and contempt for law.

For the mob, in the habit of feeding at the expense of others, and having its hopes of a livelihood in the property of its neighbors, produces a reign of mere violence as soon as it has got a leader sufficiently ambitious and daring. Then come tumultuous assemblies, massacres, banishments, and re-divisions of the land until the state loses all trace of civilization. Then, as at the beginning, there appears the strong and courageous man who takes charge of the affairs of state only to become a master and despot.

This is the regular cycle of constitutional revolutions and the natural order in which constitutions change, are transformed and then return to their original stage. If a man have a clear grasp of these principles he may perhaps make a mistake as to the dates on which this or that will happen, but rarely will he be entirely mistaken as to the stage of growth or decay at which a state has arrived, or as to the point at which it will undergo some revolutionary change. It is in the case of the Roman constitution that this method of inquiry fully teaches us its formation, growth and zenith. For if any constitution ever owed its original foundation and growth to natural causes it was this one, and to natural causes will it owe its decay.

Lycurgus recognized these truths and legislated accordingly. That statesman was fully aware that all these changes come about by an undeviating law of nature. He reflected that every form of government which is unmixed and rests on one species of power is unstable, because it is swiftly perverted into that particular form of evil peculiar to it. For just as rust is the natural dissolvent of iron, wood-worms and grubs to timber, by which they are destroyed without any external injury but by that which is engendered within themselves, so in each constitution there is naturally engendered a particular vice inseparable from it. In kingship it is absolutism, in aristocracy oligarchy, in democracy lawless ferocity and violence; and to these vicious states are all these forms of government inevitably transformed.

THE PRINCE

By

Machiavelli

Niccolo di Bernardo dei Machiavelli (*1469–1527*) was an Italian author, born in Florence. When he was 29 he entered statecraft culminating a career as a diplomatist by a mission to Caesar Borgia. Upon the restoration of Medici in 1512 he was involved in the downfall of his patron and was arrested a year later. He retired to devote himself to literature after he was pardoned. He aroused the citizens of Florence to attack the French in 1525 after their disastrous defeat at Pavia. After the sack of Rome two years later and the imprisonment of Pope Clement VII, the Florentines again drove out the Medicis. His writings fill six volumes, the greatest source of his reputation being the celebrated book *De Principatibus* or as it has been called since, *The Prince* which was published in Rome in 1532, after the author's death.

A prince ought to direct all his thoughts and faculties in the direction of war, for it is the only profession worthy of his pursuit. If he leads a soft and delicate life instead of being hardened to war, he is likely to be stripped of his dominions. If he is ignorant of the art of war, he is likely to appear contemptible to his soldiers, and as they lack esteem for him he will be wanting in his confidence in them. In his warlike operations, a prince must be more assiduous in times of peace than in those of war, and to this end must employ both his bodily and mental faculties. As to bodily affairs, he must keep his troops under discipline and by hunting inure himself to hardship and fatigue. His mind he must exercise by reading history wherein he will find some illustrious model to imitate, as Alexander took Achilles, Caesar Alexander and Scipio Cyrus. Never should a prince be idle in times of peace.

In considering the things which enhance or diminish the reputation of a prince, we must avoid the models of visionary republics which never did nor can exist, and consider that the manner in which men live is so different from that in which they ought to live that if a prince endeavors to do what he thinks he ought to do he is on the high road to ruin. If, then, we lay aside all the imaginary schemes for the education of a prince we can appreciate that all men, especially princes, are distinguished by some quality likely to give them a reputation—liberal or sparing, cruel or merciful, pusillanimous or courageous, courteous or haughty, chaste or lascivious and so on. Now such is the frailty and perverseness of human nature that some things having the appearance of virtue would prove the ruin of a prince, while others seemingly bad are such that on them his welfare and security may depend.

It is to the interest of a prince to be accounted liberal, but in gaining such a reputation he must be careful not to squander his revenue to such a degree that he will need to have recourse to confiscations and extortions, which in time will make him odious. If he cannot show his liberality without injuring his State, he need not trouble himself about being thought parsimonious, since in time his real liberality will be appreciated. It is wiser, therefore, to submit to the imputation of covetousness than by liberality to reduce oneself to tyranny which will create both infamy and hatred. A prince should desire, likewise, to appear merciful yet he should be careful how he extends his clemency, and should not fear to be thought cruel if by making a few examples he keeps his subjects obedient and united, for thereby will he prove himself more merciful in the end. Caesar Borgia was accounted cruel, but his cruelty reformed and united Romagna and settled it in peace. Should a prince desire to be loved or feared? He should desire both, although it is safer to be feared than to be loved, but whereas a prince has it in his power to make his subjects fear him, it depends upon his subjects whether they will love him or not, yet he can conduct himself in such a manner as to avoid their hatred.

Naturally every one feels that a prince should act in good faith, yet experience shows that those princes who have made the least account of their word have often done the greatest things. A contest may be decided by either law or force, by the way of men or the way of beasts. Since law is not always sufficient and force is made necessary, a prince should know how to resemble a beast as well as a man. Herein he should take the lion and the fox as his examples; a fox to find out the snares, a lion to terrify the wolves. A wise prince ought not to keep his word when this will injure him; since the generality of mankind will not keep their promises to him he need not keep his promises with them. But such craftiness must be practiced with both simulation and dissimulation with the confidence that a prince will always find dupes to his hypocrisy among the vulgar mass, who have eyes for appearances but no gift of penetration whereby they might discern the heart.

In a more general way it may be said that a prince should avoid doing those things which may make him appear odious or contemptible, which if he can do he will fill his part pretty well and need not be under any apprehension of danger from the infamy of other vices. A prince becomes odious to his subjects when he usurps their rights or debauches theirs wives and daughters; contemptible when he is fickle, full of levity, effeminate and the like. If we consider various Roman Emperors we see that they had to choose between pleasing the soldiery or the people, which turned to their advantage or disadvantage according to the degree of reputation they had among them. Marcus Aurelius, who succeeded to the Empire by right of inheritance, was obliged to neither of these parties so that he lived and died in peace and honor. On the other hand, Severus committed every kind of outrage and violence on the people in order to feed the avarice of the soldiers, and yet his reign was a happy one for he was admired by the people and beloved by the soldiery. Various other emperors were ruined by making themselves either odious or contemptible. A new prince cannot come up to the example of Marcus Aurelius nor will he have in all respects to follow that of Severus. Once his dominion is established, he may imitate the former but, while he is establishing himself in it, the latter may be his guide.

Some princes in order to secure themselves in their dominions have built fortresses, others have demolished them, but no rule concerning such things can be laid down without knowledge of the respective States where they are put into practice. However it may be said that no new prince ever disarmed his subjects but, upon finding them disarmed, put arms into their hands, whereby he gets his soldiers entirely at his service making those that were suspicious faithful, those that were faithful still more so. Princes, particularly new ones, have generally found that those whom they suspected at the beginning were more faithful to them than those whom they had trusted from the first. Now when a prince has more reason to fear his own subjects than foreign enemies, he ought to build fortresses but if he is more afraid of foreigners than of his own subjects, he ought to let fortresses alone. He is much to be blamed who confides in such things and pays no attention to the affection of his subjects.

In order to gain reputation, a prince may well engage in great enterprises and extraordinary actions, and it is of great service to him when he affords rare examples of civil administration, especially when there is occasion to reward one person for the good, and punish another for the evil he has done. A prince should likewise encourage the arts and sciences and honor such as excell therein by giving them rewards. Then, at the proper seasons, he should take the opportunity to entertain his people with feasts, public spectacles and rejoicings of every sort in order to divert them and keep them in good humor. It is important for the prince to choose the right kind of ministers, or secretaries, since the first opinion that will be formed of his capacity will be from the persons he has about him. But how can a prince tell whether his minister is a good one or not? The infallible rule is that when a minister thinks more of himself than of his prince, so that all his actions tend toward his private interest, he is a bad minister. But the prince, in order to keep his minister attached to him, should consider his services and heap honors, riches, and other favors upon him so that he will be satisfied with his office. When prince and minister are on such a footing, they may safely confide in each other; otherwise events will prove fatal to one of them.

A pest which infects all Courts is flattery, yet it is hard for a prince to avoid this contagion, since all men are so fond of their own actions and are apt to deceive themselves in such matters. Now the defence against flatterers consists in letting people know that you are not offended at truth, and yet if you should indulge every one in such a privilege you would soon lose the respect due you. A wise prince should take a middle ground and thus grant to some discreet men the liberty of telling him the truth in such things as he may demand, forbidding them to meddle in anything else. They may speak freely and he should often consult their opinions and then listen to nobody else. But these opinions should be given only when they are asked for, since good counsel proceeds from the wisdom of the prince, not the wisdom of the prince from good counsel.

If a new prince will observe such rules as have been laid down here they will make him appear like an hereditary one and render his dominion more secure than if he were so. Men are more affected by the present than by the past and when they find themselves happy and at ease, they will support the new prince with all their might provided he is not wanting in other things. Thus he will reap the glory, not only of having founded a new principality but of having fortified and adorned it with wholesome laws, a good army, firm alliances and good examples.

There are many who think that the affairs of this world are governed either by Divine Providence or Fortune in such a manner that human wisdom has no share in them, hence we should let everything take its natural course. But it would seem as if Fortune had reserved but one half of our actions for herself and left the other in great measure to our own free-will and management. He that relies solely upon Fortune must inevitably be ruined, while he succeeds who accommodates himself to the nature of the times. No person however wise can accommodate himself perfectly to all changes, so that it is often necessary to proceed with vigor rather than to be cool and deliberate. It is better to be bold than to be bashful, since Fortune is like a woman who is more liberal with her favors to those who attack her with warmth and vigor than to such as are timid and respectful. Fortune is partial to young men because they are frank and forward, and seems to think they have a right to her embrace.

OF THE NATURALL CONDITION
OF MANKIND

(From the *Leviathan*)

By

Thomas Hobbes

THOMAS HOBBES (*1588–1679*) was an English philosopher. Graduating from Oxford at twenty he became the tutor of the son of the Earl of Devonshire with whom he toured the Continent. Subsequent to this he spent all of his time in philosophical studies. He published a defense of the royal prerogative in 1640 and fled to Paris to escape the possible wrath of Parliament. In 1647 he was appointed mathematical tutor to the Prince of Wales who afterward became Charles II. Several of his books he was obliged to leave unpublished and one was issued surreptitiously from the press just before his death. At the age of 84 Hobbes amused himself by writing his autobiography in Latin verse. When he was 87 he had completed a verse translation of the *Iliad* and the *Odyssey*. Hobbes is commonly regarded as the "father of associational psychology."

IN THE NATURE OF MAN we find three principall causes of quarrell. First, Competition; Secondly, Diffidence; Thirdly, Glory.

The first maketh men to invade for Gain; the second, for Safety; and the third for Reputation. The first use Violence to make themselves Masters of other men's persons, wives, children, and cattell; the second, to defend them; the third, for trifles, as a word, a smile, a different opinion, and any other signe of under-value, either direct in their Persons, or by reflexion in their Kindred, their Friends, their Nation, their Profession, or their Name.

Hereby it is manifest, that during the time men live without a common Power to keep them all in awe, they are in that condition which is called Warre; and such a warre, as is of every man, against every man. For WARRE, consisteth not in Battell onely, or the act of fighting; but in a tract of time, wherein the Will to contend by Battell is sufficiently known: and therefore the notion of *Time,* is to be considered in the nature of Warre; as it is in the nature of Weather. For as the nature of Foule weather, leyeth not in a showre or two of rain; but in an inclination thereto of many dayes together; So the nature of War, consisteth not in actuall fighting; but in the known disposition thereto, during all the time there is no assurance to the contrary. All other time is PEACE.

It may seem strange to some man, that has not well weighed these things; that Nature should thus dissociate, and render men apt to invade, and destroy one another: and he may therefore, not trusting to this Inference, made from the Passions, desire perhaps to have the same confirmed by Experience. Let him therefore consider with himselfe, when taking a journey, he armes himselfe, and seeks to go well accompanied; when going to sleep, he locks his dores; when even in his house he locks his chests; and this when he knowes there bee Lawes, and publike Officers, armed, to revenge all injuries shall bee done him; what opinion he has of his fellow subjects, when he rides armed; of his fellow Citizens, when he locks his dores; and of his children, and servants, when he locks his chests. Does he not there as much accuse mankind by his actions, as I do by my words? But neither of us accuse mans nature in it. The Desires, and other Passions of man, are in themselves no Sin. No more are the Actions, that proceed from those Passions, till they know a Law that forbids them: which till Lawes be made they cannot know: nor can any Law be made, till they have agreed upon the Person that shall make it.

And because the condition of Man is a condition of Warre of every one against every one; in which case every one is governed by his own Reason; and there is nothing he can make use of, that may not be a help unto him, in preserving his life against his enemyes; It followeth, that in such a condition, every man has a Right to every thing; even to one anothers body. And therefore, as long as this naturall Right of every man to every thing endureth, there can be no security to any man, (how strong or wise soever he be) of living out the time which Nature ordinarily alloweth men to live. And consequently it is a precept, or generall rule of Reason, *That every man ought to endeavour Peace, as farre as he has hope of obtaining it; and when he cannot obtain it, that he may seek and use all helps and advantages of Warre.* The first branche of which rule containeth and fundamental Law of Nature; which is to seek Peace and follow it. The Second, the summe of the Right of Nature; which is, by all means we can, to defend ourselves.

From this Fundamentall Law of Nature, by which men are commanded to endeavour Peace, is derived this second Law; *That a man be willing, when others are so too, as farre-forth, as for Peace, and defence of himselfe he shall think it necessary, to lay down this right to all things; and be contented with so much liberty against other men as he would allow other men against himself.* For as long as every man holdeth this right of doing anything he liketh, so long are all men in the condition of Warre. But if other men will not lay down their right as well as he, then there is no Reason for any one to devest himselfe of his; For that were to expose himselfe to Prey, (which no man is bound to) rather than to dispose himselfe to Peace. This is that Law of the Gospell; *Whatsoever you require that others should do to you, that do ye to them.*

To *lay downe* a mans *Right* to anything, is to devest himselfe of the Liberty of hindering another of the benefit of his own Right to the same. The mutuall transferring of Right is that which men call CONTRACT.

THE SOCIAL CONTRACT

By

Jean Jacques Rousseau

JEAN JACQUES ROUSSEAU (*1712–1778*) was a French philosopher, writer and musician, who was born in Switzerland. At the age of 16 he became an adventurer and vagabond. His first notable contribution to literature was in 1749. Four years later he wrote an opera which was produced in Paris and in the same year he wrote *Discourse on the Origin of Inequality*. In 1762 he published his great work on political science, *Social Contract*. His revolutionary views aroused a furore and he was forced to flee from Paris to England where he settled until 1770 when he returned to resume his old life as a musical copyist.

MAN IS BORN FREE and everywhere he is in chains. One thinks himself the master of others and still remains a greater slave than they. How did this change come about? I do not know. What can make it legitimate? That question I think I can answer. If I took into account only force, I should say, 'as long as a people is compelled to obey and does obey, it does well; but as soon as it can shake off the yoke and does so, it does better. For, regaining its liberty by the very right that took it away, either it is justified in using it or there was no justification for those who took it away.' Nevertheless, this right does not come from nature and must therefore be founded on conventions, for the social order is a sacred right which is the basis of all other rights.

The most ancient of all societies and the only one that is natural is the family, yet even there the children remain attached to the father only so long as they need him for their preservation, for as soon as this need ceases the natural bond is dissolved. The children are released from the obedience they owed their father and the father is released from the care he owed his children. The

[489]

difference between the family and the State is that, in the family, the love of the father for his children repays him for the care he takes of them while in the State the pleasure of commanding takes the place of the love which the chief cannot have for the people under him.

Now, since no man has a natural authority over his fellow, for force creates no right, we must conclude that conventions form the basis of all legitimate authority among men. There will always be a great difference between subduing a multitude and ruling a society. Even if scattered individuals were successively enslaved by one man, I still see no more than a master and his slaves, certainly not a prince and his ruler. I see what may be termed an aggregation, not as association, for there is as yet neither public good nor body politic. We must always go back to the first convention by which society was formed. The problem is to find a form of association which will defend and protect the person and goods of each associate and in which each, while uniting himself with all, may still obey himself alone and remain as free as before. This is the fundamental problem for which the Social Contract provides the solution.

The ideas of this Contract, although perhaps they have never been set forth formally, are everywhere the same and everywhere tacitly admitted. They amount to saying that each man, in giving himself to all in general, gives himself to nobody in particular, for there is no associate over whom he does not acquire the same right as that which he yields to others over himself. He gains an equivalent for everything he loses and increase of force for the preservation of that which he himself has. Each person puts his person and all his power in common under the supreme direction of the general will, and in his corporate capacity each member is received as an indivisible part of the whole. At once, in place of the individual personality of each contracting party, this act of association creates a moral and collective body composed of as many members as the assembly contains votes, and receiving from this act its unity, its common self (*moi commun*), its life and its will. This public person thus formed by the union of all other persons formerly took the name of city, but now takes that of Republic or body politic. When it is passive it is called State, when it is active it is Sovereign while compared with others it is called a Power. Those who are associated in it take the name of People; severally they are called citizens who share in the sovereign power and under the laws of the State they are subjects.

This act of association, or Contract, consists of a mutual undertaking between the public and the individuals comprising it, so that each individual makes as it were a contract with both himself and the Sovereign State. As member of this Sovereign he is bound to the individuals in it, and as a member of the State he is bound to the Sovereign. The body politic, or Sovereign, drawing its being from the sanctity of the Contract can never bind itself to do anything derogatory to the original act of Contract as, for instance, to alienate any part of itself or to submit to another "Sovereign." This does not mean that the body politic, or Sovereign, cannot enter into undertakings with others provided the contract is not infringed by them. The Sovereign is a simple being, an individual in comparison to what is external to it. Violation of the act by which it exists would be self-annihilation.

As soon as the multitude is united in one body, it is impossible to offend against one of its members without attacking the whole body, or to attack the whole body without offending against the members who comprise it. Duty and interest, therefore, oblige the two contracting to give each other help, hence men should seek in their double capacity as individuals and citizens to combine all the advantages involved in that capacity. Each individual as a man may have a particular will contrary to the general will. His particular interest may be quite different from the common interest, so that he may regard what he owes to the common cause as a gratuitous contribution. He may wish to enjoy the rights of citizenship without being ready to fulfill the duties of a subject. But this would prove the undoing of the body politic.

Now in order that the Social Compact may not be an empty formula, it involves the principle that whoever refuses to obey the general will shall be compelled to do so. This means that the individual as a citizen will be forced to be free, for it is only by such means that he can secure his personal independence. In this principle lies the key to the working of the political machine; this alone renders legitimate those civil undertakings which without it would be absurd, tyrannical and liable to frightful abuses. It is thus by means of the Social Contract that men pass from the State of Nature to the Civil State.

The passage from the State of Nature to the Civil State produces a remarkable change in man, for it substitutes justice for instinct, right for might. Then only, when the voice of duty take the place of physical impulses, does man find that instead of considering himself alone that he is being forced to act upon different principles and to consult his reason before listening to his inclinations. Although in this Civil State man may deprive himself of some of the advantages he enjoyed in the State of Nature, he gains others so great that he is bound to bless the happy moment which took him away from his natural condition, for instead of being a stupid and unimaginative animal he is now an intelligent being and a man.

What a man loses by the Social Contract is his natural liberty, his unlimited right to everything. What he gains is civil liberty and the proprietorship of all he now possesses. Here we must be careful to distinguish between natural liberty, which is bounded only by the strength of the individual, and that civil liberty which is limited by the general will. We must distinguish, also, between mere possession, based upon force or original occupancy, and property which is based upon a positive title. For the State in relation to its members is the master of all their goods by virtue of the Social Contract. However the acquisition of property may be achieved, whether by first occupancy or cultivation in the case of land, the right which each individual has to his own estate is ever subordinate to the right which the community has over all. In taking over the goods of individuals, the community does not despoil them of their property but only assures them legitimate possession of the same. The community changes mere usurpation into the true right of proprietorship. Instead of destroying natural inequality among men, the Social Contract substitutes for such physical inequality as nature may have set up among men, an equality that is moral and legitimate; hence men who are unequal in strength and intelligence become equal by convention and legal right.

Sovereignty is inalienable. The general will alone can direct the State according to the object for which it was instituted—the common good. For if the clashing of particular interests made the establishment of societies necessary, the agreement of these very interests made it possible. The common element in these different interests is what forms the social tie, and if there were no point of agreement among them all no society could exist. The Sovereignty being nothing less than the general will can never be alienated, and the Sovereign who is no less than a collective being cannot be represented except by himself. The power may be transmitted but not the will. The particular will may agree with the general will or it may not, for the particular will tends toward partiality, the general will toward equality. The Sovereign may say, 'I now will what this man wills,' but it cannot say, 'what he wills tomorrow I also shall will,' since it is absurd for the will to bind itself for the future or to consent to anything that is not for the good of the being who wills.

For the same reason that Sovereignty is inalienable, it is indivisible, also. But our political theorists being unable to divide Sovereignty in principle attempt to divide it according to its object; that is, into legislative and executive power; into rights of taxation, justice and war; into internal administration and power of foreign treaty. Sometimes they confuse all these sections and sometimes they distinguish them thus turning the Sovereign into a fantastic being composed of several connected pieces, as if they were making man of several bodies, one with eyes, one with arms, another with feet and each with nothing besides. This error is due to a lack of exact notions concerning the Sovereign authority, due also to taking for parts of it what are only emanations of it. Thus, for example, the acts of declaring war and making peace have been regarded as acts of Sovereignty, but this is not the case, since these do not constitute law but merely the application of it. It is a particular act which decides how the law applies. If we were to examine other divisions in the same manner, we should find that whenever Sovereignty seems to be divided, there is an illusion.

The general will is always right and tends to the public advantage, but it does not follow from this that the deliberations of the people are always equally correct. Our will is always for our own good but we do not always see what that is. The people is never corrupted but it is often deceived, and it is on such occasions only does it seem to will what is bad. There is often a great deal of difference between the will of all and the general will. The general will considers only the common interest while the will of all takes private interest into account and is itself no more than a sum of particular wills. Take away from these same wills the pluses and minuses which cancel one another and the general will remains as the sum of the differences.

If, when the people, being furnished with adequate information, were holding its deliberations and the citizens had no communication with one another, the grand total of the small differences would always give the general will and the decision would always be good. But when factions arise and partial associations are formed at the expense of the great association, the will of each of these associations becomes general in relation to its members but remains particular in relation to the State. Then it may be said that there are no longer as many votes as there are men, but only as many as there are associations. It is essential, therefore, if the general will is to be able to express itself, that there should be no partial society within the State but that each citizen should think only his own thoughts.

If the State is a moral person whose life is the union of its members, and if the most important of its cares is the care for its own preservation, it must have a universal and compelling force in order to move and dispose each part as may be most advantageous to the whole. As nature gives each man absolute power over all his members, the Social Compact gives the body politic absolute power over all its members also. Now it is this power which, under the direction of the general will, bears the name of Sovereignty. But there are limits to the Sovereign power; for, in addition to the public person we have to consider the private persons composing it, and their life and liberty are naturally independent of it. Hence we are bound to distinguish clearly between the respective rights of the citizens and the Sovereign, as we must distinguish also between the natural rights private persons enjoy as men and the duties they have to fulfill as subjects. Each man alienates by the Social Compact only such part of his powers, goods and liberty as it may be important for the community to control, although the Sovereign is sole judge of what is important.

[494]

There is really no contradiction in these statements; for, while every citizen ought to render his service to the State as soon as the Sovereign demands it, the Sovereign itself cannot impose upon its subjects any fetters which are useless to the community, nor can it even wish to do so. For neither by the law of reason nor the law of nature can anything occur without a cause. The undertakings which bind us to the social body are obligatory only because they are mutual, and their nature such that in fulfilling them we cannot work for others without working for ourselves. Why is it that the general will is always in the right and that all continually will the happiness of each one, unless it is because there is not a man who does not think of "each" as meaning him, and consider himself in voting for all? This proves that equality of rights and the idea of justice which such equality creates originate in the preference each man gives to himself, and accordingly in the very nature of man. It proves that the general will must be general in its object as well as in its essence, must come from all and apply to all.

From whatever side we approach our principle, we reach the same conclusion—that the Social Compact sets up among the citizens an equality of such a kind that all bind themselves to observe the same conditions and enjoy the same rights. Thus from the very nature of the Compact every act of Sovereignty, *i. e.* every authentic act of the general will, binds or favors all the citizens equally, so that the Sovereign recognizes only the body of the nation and draws no distinctions among those of whom it is made up. The act of Sovereignty is not a convention between a superior and an inferior, but a convention between the body and its members. It is legitimate because it is based on the Social Contract, equitable because common to all and useful because it can have no other object than the general good.

The general will is indestructible; it is always constant, unalterable and pure. As long as several men in assembly regard themselves as a single body they have only a single will which is concerned with their common preservation and general well-being. In this case all the springs of the State are vigorous and simple, its rules clear and luminous. There are no embroilments or conflicts of interest; the common good is everywhere apparent and only good sense is needed to perceive it. Peace, unity and equality are the foes of political subtleties. Men who are upright and simple are difficult to deceive because of their simplicity and thus lures and ingenious pretexts fail to impose on them for they are not subtle enough to be dupes. When, among the happiest people in the world, bands of peasants are seen regulating affairs of State under an oak and always acting wisely, can we help scorning the ingenious methods of other nations which make themselves illustrious and wretched with so much art and mystery?

THE WEALTH OF NATIONS

By

Adam Smith

ADAM SMITH (*1723–1790*) was a Scottish political economist, who was educated at Glasgow and Oxford universities. He became a professor of logic at his Alma Mater in 1751 and professor of moral philosophy the next year. Smith's *Wealth of Nations* was published in 1776 and ranks foremost on all works of political economy.

IT IS NOT from the benevolence of the butcher, the brewer, or the baker, that we expect our dinner, but from their regard to their self-interest. We do not approach them on humanitarian grounds for if we did our needs would never be satisfied. We never besiege them with our necessities, but always try to convince them of the advantages they may gain. A puppy fawns upon its dam, and a spaniel endeavors to attract the attention of its master when he is at dinner. Occasionally, men resort to the same tactics, but in a civilized society they must rely for the most part not so much on the kindness of their fellows as on their willingness to co-operate to the advantage of their own interests. Most of the things we need we obtain by barter and purchase, and it is this tendency of men to exchange things with one another which gives rise to the division of labor.

In the tribal organization of society the man who was dexterous in the manufacture of weapons exchanged them with his neighbors for cattle. If he found it advantageous to his self-interest to continue bartering weapons for cattle he made the manufacture of weapons his main occupation. For the same reason another man became a smith or a tanner of hides. The certainty of being able to exchange their surplus products for the surpluses of other men encouraged them to perfect themselves in their particular occupations. Thus the widely different talents of men complement one another, and result in an increase of productivity far greater than would be the case if men produced only to satisfy their own needs.

In a small market the incentive to apply oneself to a single occupation is limited inasmuch as the surplus products of the labor applied to a single occupation are not readily exchangeable. As the market widens the opportunities for the exchange of surpluses grow larger. In lone houses and small villages, for instance, families must perform a great many tasks which in a large town would be left to the talents of workmen who specialize in various of these tasks. Even country workmen are expected to apply themselves to different occupations which in the towns would be divided among a number of workmen. A country carpenter is not only a joiner and a cabinet maker, but also a cart and wagon maker. As the market grows in size with the introduction of carriage by water the industries along the sea coast grow, divide, and subdivide, under the stimulus of cheaper transportation costs. A broad-wheeled wagon attended by two men can transport four ton weight of goods between London and Edinburgh in about six weeks. In about the same time a ship with a crew of eight men can carry two hundred ton weight of goods between the ports of London and Leith. A cargo of this size would require fifty wagons, four hundred horses, and a hundred men. Without the advantage of water carriage commerce and industry would only be a small part of what they are at present, and the market would be greatly limited. Exchange too would be limited, and the division of labor would hardly progress very far.

The effects of the division of labor are more clearly understood after examining a manufacturing industry of even little importance. In the trade of pin making an inexperienced workman could not himself make more than a few pins a day. Without the division of labor, even though he applied himself to the utmost, the number of pins he could produce would be trifling. The production of a pin is divided into a number of branches, each of which is a special process in itself. Special machinery and special skills are necessary for most of these processes, and in each of them a number of men apply themselves to a particular operation. One man draws out the wire, another cuts it, and a third sharpens the sections. Even the head of the pin requires two or three men to perform separate tasks before the head is fastened to the pin. Whitening the pin is a distinct operation, and inserting the pins in paper is a trade by itself. Eighteen separate operations are necessary to complete the pin, and even in those plants which are so small and poorly equipped that workers are forced to double on some of the processes it is not unusual to turn out twelve pounds of pins in a day. But if all these men were to work independently and without any previous knowledge of pin making they could produce only a fraction of what they are at present capable of producing with a proper division and combination of their different operations.

In every field of manufacture the division of labor results in an increase of the productive powers of labor. Various trades and employments have divided and subdivided under the stimulus of the advantages to be gained from the division of labor. This division of labor is carried farthest in those countries where industries have reached a high state of development. The work of one man in a rude state of society is the work of several in an improved one. Where society has advanced the farmer applies himself to farming and the manufacturer to manufacturing, and the labor employed in manufacturing is divided among a great number of hands. Although in agriculture many different tasks arise they are apt to be performed by the individual farmer. The plowman, the harrower, the sower, and the harvester, are usually the same person, for these varying tasks are seasonal and there would be small profit for the farmer if each one of them were performed by different men. The impossibility of a complete division of labor in agriculture accounts for the fact that the productivity of agriculture often lags behind that of industry.

The increased quantity of goods which is the result of the division of labor is due to the dexterity arising from continual application to a single task, the time saved in confining the labor of the workman to one occupation, and the invention of specialized machinery which reduces the amount of labor necessary to produce a commodity. The invention of labor-saving machinery apparently has its source in the division of labor. Men who are employed in an unchanging occupation are very likely to discover easier methods of performing their own particular work. Most of the machines used in industries where the division of labor is intensive are the inventions of common workmen who turned their thoughts towards making their work easier. For instance, it was customary to employ boys on the early steam engines to open and shut alternately the communication between the boiler and the cylinder as the piston rose and fell. One of these boys found that by connecting the handle of the valve to another part of the engine with a piece of string the valve would open and shut automatically, and leave him free to play with his fellows. Thus one of the greatest improvements of the steam engine since its invention was the result of a boy's desire to play.

Without mutual assistance and co-operation not only would the division of labor be impossible, but the members of society would be deprived of the meanest comforts. The wide variations of productive employments, and the increase of the supply of goods resulting from them confer a universal opulence upon all ranks of society. Under the system of the division of labor even the lowest workmen are enabled to produce great surpluses of their own products which they can exchange for other surpluses. The simplest woolen coat, for instance, which the common laborer wears is the result of the joint labor of a great number of workmen. The shepherd, the sorter of the wool, the combers and carders, the dyers, the spinners, the weavers, the fullers, and many others all contribute their labor to the production of the coat. Furthermore, there are the merchants, the carriers of the raw wool on land and sea, the shipbuilders, the navigators, the sailors, and the rope makers who play their part in gathering the materials for the coat. And then there is the complicated machinery which weaves the woolen cloth. Before the machine could be constructed the work of miners, the builders of furnaces, the forgers, and the brick makers was necessary. The list is interminable even for an article as simple as a woolen coat. It is evident that to produce the most trifling comforts there must be a vast and unending co-operation between all the members of society.

How may we know the value of the products of industry and agriculture? First we must distinguish sharply between value in use, or utility, and value in exchange. The utility of a thing may be very great, but almost of no value in exchange. The utility of water, while it is great, will bring nothing in exchange. A diamond has scarcely any value in use, but it may command a great quantity of goods in exchange. Thus, many things which are very useful have frequently little or no value in exchange, and many things which have the greatest value in exchange have frequently little or no value in use. Value in exchange and value in use are separate categories. The real source of the value of a commodity in exchange is the amount of labor that is necessary for its production. The real price of everything is measured by the toil and trouble that go into its production. In order to measure the value of different commodities the amount of labor that goes into their production must be reduced to a common unit. It is not sufficient to measure the labor cost of commodities by the time spent in producing them because the amount of labor applied to one commodity in an hour might far exceed the amount of labor applied to the production of another commodity in two hours. The different degrees of hardship endured or ingenuity exercised may not be comparable on any basis. How then are commodities requiring varying intensities of labor and skill for their production to be placed on an exchange basis? The mechanism of the market solves this problem for us. The exchange values expressed by the market prices of different commodities are brought into adjustment by the bargaining of individuals in the market. The result is a rough equality. This means that the exchange of goods is an exchange of things of equal value, and that this value arises from equal quantities of labor in the commodities exchanged.

But the labor cost of production alone is not sufficient to account for the value of a commodity. Other factors besides labor are necessary for its production. These other factors, capital and land, along with labor, enter into the production of an article and determine its value. The three derivatives of land, labor, and capital are rent, wages, and interest. To the extent that they enter into the production of a commodity they determine its value.

Rent, wages, and interest make up the cost of production which, as the determinant of value, finds its clearest expression in the natural price of a commodity. When the quantity of goods brought to the market for sale just covers effectual demand, that is, the demand of those buyers whose price offers meet the cost of production, then market price coincides with natural price. When the supply of goods in the market exceeds the demand for them market price falls below natural price. When demand exceeds supply the market price rises above the natural price. Under the conditions of a competitive market the tendency of prices is always toward the natural price. A fall in the market price below natural price resulting from an excess of supply over demand leads producers to restrict supply, and the reduction in the supply of goods tends to raise prices toward their natural price. This movement toward an equilibrium price, when either demand or supply exceed each other, is the salient characteristic of the competitive market. The increase in market price when the demand for goods is greater than their supply cannot continue indefinitely. An influx of producers into the market, who seek to profit by these higher prices, forces the market price down to its natural level. This spontaneous adjustment to equilibrium is stimulated by the self-interest of buyers and sellers who bring demand and supply into close relationship by competing for the best price.

Interference with free competition, the most important force in a freely adjusting market, is disadvantageous to the public welfare. By pursuing the satisfaction of his own interests the individual frequently promotes the welfare of society more effectually than is his intention. The interests of the individual and of society are in most situations reconcilable in the field of production, but the theory of the continual adjustment and readjustment of conflicting demands is not meant to be applied to distribution, for in this field there exists too many inequalities. The social and economic gulf between workers and employers is a wide one indeed.

Spontaneity is not confined to the economic order. It also has a place in the social order, but too often it is restrained by the arbitrary actions of government. In the social order spontaneity assumes the form of natural liberty. Once the restraint of government is removed from society the simple system of natural liberty establishes itself. Every man, as long as he does not violate the laws of justice, remains perfectly free to pursue the satisfaction of his interests in his own way. A producer is free to place his industry in unobstructed competition with that of any other producer. It is not the part of government to supervise the activities of industry, nor to decide what activities are in the best interests of society. The government is always careless of its expenditures since the money it spends is earned by others. With a source of funds that is always available there is no reason why a government should be thrifty. Furthermore, no government can know what action on its part would be to the best interests of all the individuals in society. Only the individual is the proper judge of what is best for himself.

In a system of natural liberty there are three functions to which government can lay claim; first, the protection of the state against foreign invasion, second, the protection of every member of society against the injustice and oppression of his neighbors, and third, the erection and maintenance of necessary public works which do not come within the scope of private enterprise. Government must refrain from moving outside this sphere, otherwise the natural spontaneity of economic institutions will be hampered, and the well-being of society eventually destroyed.

Industrial development leaves many evils in its wake, chief among which is the almost perpetual dissension between master and workman. Occasionally it happens that a workman is able to purchase the materials of his work and maintain himself until he sells the product of his labor. But a case of this kind is rare, and for every workman who is independent there are twenty who serve under a master. The wages of labor depend on the contract between master and workman. Both master and workman are actuated by motives which are more often in conflict than in agreement. The workmen seek to get as much, the masters to give as little as possible. Workmen combine in order to raise their wages, and the masters combine in order to lower them. In almost all situations, however, the advantage in a labor dispute lies with the masters. They are fewer in number and can combine more easily. Moreover, they have the law on their side for while the law does not authorise masters to combine it does not prohibit them from doing so. But combinations of workmen are forbidden under the law. The attempts of workmen to combine and raise wages are made illegal under various acts of parliament, but there are no legal obstacles in the path of employers who wish to combine to lower wages. In all labor disputes an employer can hold out much longer than his workmen. A landlord, a farmer, a master manufacturer, or a merchant can live a year or two on the accumulations of the past. Most workmen cannot live a week on what they have been able to save over the necessary expenses of a bare living.

The fact that employers combine is rarely commented upon, but whoever imagines that it is uncommon for them to combine as a class are inadequately informed of the subject. Employers are always in a sort of tacit but none the less uniform agreement to keep wages at their existing level. The employer who is temerous enough to violate this agreement earns the opprobrium of his fellow employers. Sometimes employers combine not to keep wages at an existing level but to depress the wage level. Combinations of this sort are always conducted with the utmost secrecy, until the moment of execution. As a measure of protection workmen combine against employers either for the purpose of protecting their wages, or, as is sometimes the case, to raise the price of their labor. In justification they may claim that the costs of food and shelter are high, or that their employers are accumulating excessive profits. No matter what their reasons for combining, be they offensive or defensive, their actions are always publicized. They may be desperate, and act with the folly and extravagance of desperate men who have either to starve or to frighten their employers into an immediate compliance with their demands. The employers in turn clamor for legal remedy, and demand the strictest execution of those laws which have been enacted with so much severity against labor combinations in general. The position of the workers is such that their most desperate efforts to better their conditions usually end in disaster. Their failure is partly the result of the better bargaining position of their employers, and partly their own inability to refrain long from selling their labor. The demands of subsistence soon scatter their forces in retreat.

There is a natural level below which employers cannot depress wages, and this is the level of subsistence. The wages of a workman must be sufficient to purchase the necessities of life for himself and his family, otherwise the supply of workmen would rapidly diminish. Even in the lowest forms of labor a workman and his wife must earn something over and above their bare costs of subsistence in order to support a family. Under certain conditions workmen are at an advantage, and their wages are raised above a subsistence level through no effort of their own. Situations of this kind arise when the demand for the services of workmen exceed the supply of these services. The scarcity of workmen results in competition among employers for the available services of workmen, and the price of labor rises. But an increase of the demand for workmen is always proportionate to the increase of funds which can be distributed in the form of additional wages. An increase of the demand for workers is the direct result of an increase of national wealth. The wages of labor are always higher in those countries where the national wealth is increasing rapidly.

While England is much richer than North America wages are higher in North America. In the province of New York, for instance, common laborers, carpenters, bricklayers, and journeymen tailors, earn much more than they would in England. And the price of provisions in North America is everywhere much lower than it is in England. While North America is not yet as rich as England it is much more thriving, and is accumulating riches at a much more rapid rate than England. One of the most certain ways of determining the prosperity of a country is the speed with which population increases. In Great Britain population does not double in less than five hundred years while in North America the population doubles in about twenty-five years. This is due not to immigration but to the great multiplication of the species. It is not uncommon for those who reach old age to see from fifty to one hundred, and sometimes more, descendants from their own body. In North America labor is so well rewarded that a large family, instead of being a burden, is a blessing and a lucrative source of income to the parents. The labor of each child, even before it leaves the home, is valued at a hundred pounds. In Europe a young widow with four or five young children can little expect to marry again, but in North America she would be courted as a sort of fortune. It is no wonder that the people of North America marry at an early age. Yet, despite the rapid increase of population, there is a continual complaint of the scarcity of hands.

If the wealth of a country has been stationary for a long time the wages of labor will not be very high. The wage fund may be very large, but if it has remained constant for a number of centuries the workers available in any one year can easily supply the workers needed in the following year. There would be no scarcity of hands, and it would not be necessary for employers to compete with one another for the available supply of labor. In fact, the natural multiplication of workmen would produce a supply of labor in excess of demand. Employment would be scarce, and workmen would be forced to compete with one another for it. In a country of this sort if the wages of labor have never been more than just enough to maintain workmen, competition between them for employment would soon reduce wages to the lowest level of subsistence. China is such a country. It is rich, fertile, and populous, but it has long been stationary, and has changed little since Marco Polo visited it five hundred years ago. The accounts of all travellers agree that the wages of labor are very low in China. A laborer who digs the ground all day is contented with the payment of a little rice. In Europe artificers are satisfied to remain in their shops and await the call of a customer, but in China they run about the streets with the tools of their respective trades, and beg employment. Among the lower classes of China poverty far surpasses that of the poorest nations of Europe. In the neighborhood of Canton thousands of people live on boats, and consider as welcome fare the garbage of a European ship or the floating carcass of a dead dog.

Decent wages encourage the development of industry. A living wage not only increases the bodily strength of the worker, but also stimulates him to put forth greater effort in production with a view, perhaps, to ending his days in peace and plenty. Workers are more active and diligent when wages are high than when they are low. As a general rule when workers are paid by the piece they are apt to overwork themselves to the point of ruining their health. Almost every class of workers is subject to occupational diseases as a result of excessive application to their particular kinds of work. If employers would listen to the dictates of reason and humanity they would find it more to their interest to moderate production rather than to drive their workmen to the utmost. In every sort of trade the man who works at a moderate rate of speed will be more than likely able to work constantly over a longer period of time, and produce far more, than if he is driven to the point of exhaustion. For its progress the social order depends largely on a spirit of co-operation not only between members of the same class but also between those of different classes. The employer who fails to extend simple justice to his workers in his desire for wider profits is short-sightedly defeating his own interests. In the long run the well-being of society is bound to suffer if the well-being of the worker is treated with careless contempt.

CAPITAL

A Critique of Political Economy, Volume I

By

Karl Marx

KARL MARX (*1818–1883*) was a German economist and founder of international socialism. When he was 25 he went to the headquarters of revolutionary economics in Paris but was expelled from the country two years later. He took an active part in the revolutionary movement on the Rhine in 1848 and upon its failure the next year he settled in London. He studied diligently at the British Museum where he acquired his knowledge of economic literature and economic development of modern Europe. His theories are stated in *Das Kapital* which is one of the most important books ever written.

THE TYPE OF SOCIETY in which civilized man in Europe and America lives is capitalist society. This type is different from other societies in that its wealth consists almost entirely of what are called *commodities*. A commodity is not an object for self-use or self-consumption but is produced to be exchanged for other products. It gets its character as a commodity, not from its natural qualities, but from society, from social relations. Thus the honey of bees or the dress made by a peasant girl for her own use or the ornaments worn by savages are not commodities, even though they satisfy animal and human needs; they *only become* commodities when the honey, the dress, or the ornaments are produced for exchange with other articles or each other.

The process of exchange, however, involves a reciprocal relationship between men. Every article which enters into the process must satisfy some human need, real or imaginary. Otherwise an article, intended for exchange, will not be exchanged; it will not become a commodity. Thus every commodity must serve some useful purpose, not necessarily morally useful, but useful, in the sense, of satisfying a human desire, illicit or licit, moral or immoral, degrading or uplifting. This property of every article, so necessary in order that any exchange can occur, is called *Use value*.

Nevertheless, having use value, as already stated, does not make an article into a commodity. It is the property of being produced for exchange which makes it a commodity. The understanding of this exchange process is the essential key to an understanding of capitalist production and transforms empirical book-keeping and business into the science of political economy.

When society has developed to the point where the exchange of articles becomes a customary social operation, an interesting phenomenon is immediately observable. Every commodity is exchanged in a definite proportion with other commodities. At a given time, two pounds of salt can be exchanged for a quarter of a pound of tomatoes, which, in turn, is exchangeable for one pound of potatoes. Or, to put this in another way, if five cents is the price of two pounds of salt, one quarter of a pound of tomatoes and one pound of potatoes, then these articles are exchangeable with each other, in these exact proportions. The name for this property of commodities, this property of being exchangeable in certain definite proportion, is *Exchange value*. The essential question which demands an answer is: what constitutes the value of a commodity? What is the common element or elements in things as different in their essential characteristics as salt, tomatoes and potatoes, which makes it possible for them to be exchanged in these definite proportions?

One answer might be: their natural properties. But it is obvious that while these properties distinguish them and make possible the exchange, they do not determine how much of each should be exchanged for each other. While commodities differ in their natural properties, they are alike in one fundamental respect. They are the products of human labor. Thus a commodity possesses value only because human effort is embodied in it. And this value is directly proportional to the time expended in laboring, not by any particular individual, but by society in producing any particular commodity; i.e., it represents the amount of time, socially necessary, to produce a given use-value under normal conditions

[509]

of production, with average skill and speed. If the amount of labor-time expended by society to produce a particular commodity is decreased, due to better instruments of production, then the value is correspondingly decreased. Thus commodities are exchanged in certain proportions, due to the fact that they embody in these proportions equal amounts of socially-necessary labor.

This law for the exchange of commodities is modified by a variety of factors, like supply and demand, operating within capitalist society. Nevertheless, these factors do not nullify or destroy the law; they only modify its operation. The law of gravitation is not nullified or destroyed because lighter-than-atmosphere substances rise instead of falling; it is only modified.

Upon the basis of this law, that the value of commodity is determined by the amount of socially-necessary labor time, we can point out certain forms of exchange of commodities peculiar to different societies. Where exchange of commodities takes place only occasionally and accidentally, it takes the *elementary* or *accidental value-form;* i.e., one commodity is occasionally exchanged for another. Here, of course, socially necessary labor-time, as the determiner of value, operates very loosely and imperfectly. When the exchange of a particular commodity, say cattle, for other commodities becomes customary, then we have the *total or expanded form of value.* This type of exchange is found among the Homeric Greeks. A higher development of exchange occurs when a particular commodity comes to be used as the *general equivalent* in terms of which all commodities are expressed. This form is the *general form of value.* The *general equivalent* under this form of exchange itself undergoes a development. While at first women or cattle or any other article especially important to these societies is used as the general equivalent of value, as commodity production becomes more advanced, the precious metals, for a variety of reasons, take the place of the earlier and clumsier equivalents. But for the precious metals to replace the others, society will have to establish private property as the characteristic form of property. Only within a society where it is customary to produce a considerable part of the social wealth as commodities, and where a multiplicity of exchanges takes place between men who recognize each other as the owners of the various commodities offered for exchange, do the precious metals, gold, silver and electrum, become the general equivalent of value, or money.

With the appearance of money as the general equivalent of value, a new economic category makes its appearance, that of price. Price is simply the value of a commodity expressed in terms of money. Dependent upon the kind of commodity which functions as money, the value of commodities will have various prices. Thus commodities will have one price when expressed in terms of gold, and still another when expressed in terms of silver. The fact that price is the phenomenal expression of value, does not at all mean that price and value actually always coincide, for the price may be higher or lower than the value. A great many factors, which cannot be discussed here, enter partially to destroy this coincidence.

The appearance of money also means that society has developed from the stage of direct exchange or barter, to the *elementary circulation of commodities* or of *simple commodity production.* At this later stage, men no longer have to give one commodity in exchange for another, as in barter, but can sell their commodities for money, by means of which they can buy, at such time as they please, and where they please, other commodities.

Money now becomes extremely important. Exchange of commodities, as a whole, can no longer take place without it. Thus the eyes of men fix greedily upon gold; and everywhere frantic efforts are made to obtain it. It has become a social power, capable of buying anything and everything at any time. And it intensifies and expands the production and circulation of commodities so that more and more is produced, and greater and greater areas for circulation are included. As a consequence, money which previously operated to facilitate circulation, now becomes a means of payment for commodities bought long before. It transforms buyer and seller into creditor and debtor. Further to facilitate this twofold function, money which first exists as precious metals in the bulk, is transformed into coin, minted by powerful groups or states. Coin becomes insufficient to serve the needs of circulation and so paper money is printed. Finally, all kinds of credit facilities make their appearance. But these latter phenomena only find their fullest development under capitalism.

[511]

Simple commodity production operates primarily upon the principle that production is carried on in order to produce more commodities. And money serves simply to facilitate the process of selling commodities in order to buy other commodities. But money itself leads to a transformation of this process. As money becomes more and more important, it is gradually transferred into a means to buy other commodities in order to get more money; i.e., to increase the original amount of money; it becomes a means to get *surplus value,* the increment above and beyond the amount with which the money-owner began. When this stage is reached, money or commodities used for this purpose are transformed into *capital;* i.e., *value whose sole purpose is to produce surplus value.* In simple commodity production, the use of money did not increase at all the wealth of its owner, for nothing was gained by any transaction of exchange, except, of course, the satisfaction of some want. The commodity A was equivalent in value to the money B, and the money B bought another commodity C which was equivalent to the value of A. In other words, commodity circulation did not produce this increment, this surplus value so dear to the capitalist. Where surplus value was obtained, it was gotten by direct robbery or extortion; i.e., by violating the fundamental law of commodity exchange: that equals are exchanged for equals. But if extortion and robbery are not the means used, if the law of commodity-exchange is utilized, how can the capitalist obtain this surplus value?

There is only one way that surplus value can be produced without directly violating this law: by a commodity whose consumption will produce more value than the commodity itself costs. The only power, as was pointed out at the beginning, capable of producing value is labor. Thus if the ability to produce value, i.e., *labor power,* can be bought and sold, if it appears as a commodity on the market, then one has something capable of producing more than it itself is worth. Here is a commodity which can cost less than the commodity which it produces.

Two conditions must be historically fulfilled before labor-power can appear on the market as a commodity. First, the laborer must be a free man; otherwise he has no commodity to sell. He is a slave, a commodity himself, and has nothing to sell on the open market. Secondly, he must be in the position where his ability to work, i.e., his *labor power* is useless to him, because he does not own the necessary means of production, but is useful to the one who buys his labor power, because the latter owns the means of production.

As a commodity, labor power is no different from any other commodity. It sells on the market for its value, which is equivalent to the quantity of the means of life necessary to sustain the worker.

When money or commodities become capital, and labor-power appears as a commodity on the market, then the specific stage of *capitalist* production is achieved.

How does the capitalist use his capital and his labor-power to produce surplus value? The capitalist is interested in making a profit, in obtaining surplus value. For this purpose, he invests his money in machinery, a factory and raw material. But these things alone are insufficient. He needs man's labor upon these machines before they will begin producing for him. How can he get these men? He can only get them if men have been stripped of the means of production, i.e., of instruments of labor and the raw material, and are compelled to sell their skill, their ability to work on the labor market. But even if the capitalist is able to buy labor-power, this does not get him his surplus value. Suppose workers were given the fruits of their labor; suppose the products they produced during their day of work belonged to them? The capitalist would have invested his money in vain, for he would get back nothing more perhaps than his original investment, if he got that. Thus the worker must enter production, having a right to nothing but the wages offered him. What he produces does not belong to him, but to the capitalist who hired him. This is not the only difficulty, even though the capitalist has very early managed to separate the worker from the means of production; and organized society so that it recognizes his right to everything produced from his own property. There is the difficulty of getting surplus value from the worker. Suppose at the end of the day, what is produced is equivalent to the money invested in raw material, the wear and tear of machinery and the wages. The capitalist would still not make a profit. Fortunately, things work out differently for the capitalist. The value of labor-power is determined by the quantity of the necessities of life required to reproduce the worker and his family. Now the worker may need to work only four hours to reproduce the equivalent of his wages. But the capitalist does not hire the worker for four hours, he hires him for the day; he hires his labor-power and pays for it, but he does not pay the worker for what he produces. Thus if he sees to it that the worker works as hard as he can, after the first four hours, the worker will work only for the capitalist. What is produced during the remaining four hours will be the surplus value, so greedily desired by the capitalist, which he can transform into monetary profit by selling his products on the market.

The process can now be more abstractly described. The money in the hands of the capitalist is *money-capital.* He transforms the money-capital into two kinds, *constant capital, i.e.,* machinery, factory, raw material, and *variable capital,* i.e., labor-power. Both are necessary in order to produce surplus value. But constant capital is uncreative. It is only transferred by labor to the new products. Variable capital, however, is creative, for it not only recreates itself, but also creates new, additional value, which previously never existed. Thus by uniting variable capital, the creative force, with constant capital, the capitalist achieves a marriage, devoutly wished-for, a marriage which creates surplus value, without violating the fundamental law of commodity production.

Nevertheless, while the capitalist obtains surplus value by the above means, his concern is not with this general category, but with a specific form of it: profit. While profit is identical with surplus value, since it is surplus value, in relation to constant and variable capital both profit and surplus value express themselves differently. Their rates are different, because they are determined in different ways. The rate of surplus value is obtained by dividing the surplus value by the variable capital, or expressed as a fraction

$$\frac{\text{surplus value}}{\text{variable capital.}}$$ The constant capital is left out of consideration,

since it creates nothing, but is simply transferred over to the new commodity. The capitalist, however, since he is concerned only with the profit he makes upon his investment, includes the constant capital as well as the wages he pays as his investment and divides

his profit by these, or expressed as a fraction, he determines his
rate of profit by putting the surplus value over the constant and
variable capital, thus: $\dfrac{\text{surplus value}}{\text{constant capital} + \text{variable capital}} = \text{rate}$
of profit. The results will necessarily differ, even though the sur-
plus value remains the same. An example will illustrate this easily.
If the profit is $5,000, the wages paid $5,000 and the constant
capital expended $20,000, then the rate of surplus value will be
100% while the rate of profit only 20%.

There is another and very important respect in which the rate
of profit differs from surplus value. The constant capital can vary
as much as it pleases, without affecting in any way the rate of
surplus value, but the same variations in the constant capital will
make a corresponding difference in the rate of profit. The greater
the amount of constant capital over the variable capital, the ratio,
of course, between the variable capital and the surplus value remaining the same, the smaller the rate of profit and vice versa.
This law has a tremendous effect upon the investment of capital.
As a particular industry, under the conditions of competition, expands its *organic composition of capital,* i.e., introduces more and
more machinery in relation to the number of workers it employs,
its rate of profit will fall lower than other industries whose organic
composition of capital is less. Thus capital will tend to flow into
these industries, with the lower organic composition, until competition and the law of supply and demand reduces the rate of
profit to the rate common to other industries. This is how the
average rate of profit is produced.

Now the existence of an average rate of profit seems to contradict the law of the rate of profit, which is determined by this ratio:
$\dfrac{\text{surplus value}}{\text{constant capital} + \text{variable capital,}}$ for the rate of profit for an
industry whose organic composition is less, should be higher than
that of an industry whose organic composition is greater. This,
however, would only be true, if the average rate of profit did not
represent the rate of profit for the capitalist class as a whole, i.e., the
total surplus value over the total constant capital plus the total
variable capital of capitalist society. But it does. When all the sur-

plus value of the capitalist class is placed over the total constant and variable capital of capitalist society, the *average rate of profit* corresponds to the rate of profit determined by means of the law of value. What really happens is that the capitalists share the surplus value, among themselves, in the exact proportion of the extent of their investment. Each capitalist is simply a stock holder in the corporate capitalist society.

The average rate of profit also determines what is known as the *production price,* which is either always above or below the actual value price. (Market price constantly oscillates around this production price.) While the price of production is determined differently from the way in which the value price is determined, it nevertheless conforms to and operates within the general law of value. The capitalist determines his price of production by adding together the constant capital, the variable capital, and the amount obtained by multiplying the average rate of profit with the constant and variable capital. The price the capitalist arrives at in this way seems to him the *natural price.* In those industries, where the organic composition of capital is low, the price of production will be less than the value; in those industries where the organic composition of capital is average, the price will correspond to the value; and in those industries where the organic composition of capital is high, the price will be higher than the value price.

The capitalist, as we have seen, produces surplus value by exploiting labor-power or the laboring class. He is, therefore, under the nagging incentive, both as a result of competition from other capitalists and his own imperious desire to increase his capital and profits, to get more and more surplus labor from his workers. To increase the *mass of his surplus value,* he must employ one of three methods: 1) increase the number of hours of work absolutely, thus increase the *absolute* surplus value; 2) intensify the labor of the worker, thus making him produce more in the same time; and 3) increase the surplus value *relatively,* i.e., by improvements in the organization of work and the instruments of production. While the capitalist, in general, prefers lengthening the hours of work, there are definite limitations upon the continuation of this process. The first is the length of the day itself. The working-day cannot be made longer than twenty-four hours. The second is the physical endurance of the worker. While the capitalist has no interest in the human aspects of the life of his workers, he is interested in his workers as productive factors. If he works them too hard, he will not be able to get from them the maximum return in production. He may kill them too soon; and so have difficulty replacing them. The English capitalist class almost decimated its own working class by overwork, as the reports of factory inspectors, like Horner, show. The capitalist may overcome these difficulties in another way, by hiring more workers. The mass of surplus value is thereby increased. But the capitalist, in lengthening the working day, has still another object in view: that of increasing the rate of surplus value which will save him a pretty penny or two. Neither is accomplished by hiring more workers. But even this method has its definite limitations. To increase the mass of surplus value, the capitalist must have at hand a certain amount of capital in order to be able to pay the wages of the additional hired workers, to buy a sufficient quantity of raw material to keep the workers busy for the day or the week or the month, and sufficient tools or machinery. And it may take considerable time before he can raise sufficient capital for this purpose. He can use still another way: that of directly cutting wages. But this is, as a usual thing, extremely difficult. Therefore the second method comes in handy: that of intensifying the labor of his workers. While working them the same number of hours, he makes them increase the speed of their labor, use up energy. The capitalist, in this way, can get more surplus value and expend less in variable capital. For by increasing speed sufficiently, he can get the same mass of surplus value, as if he had hired more workers, without the disadvantage of having to pay for them. But this too has its limits in the endurance of his workers. They will not be able to maintain the pace, if increased too much; their speed will slacken and even the quality of the work fall.

Thus the capitalist is compelled at various stages to employ the third method: that of increasing the productivity of labor by improving its organization and introducing improved instruments of production. Their introduction has the effect of increasing the *surplus value relatively,* not *absolutely,* for value is determined by the amount of time socially necessary to produce a commodity. If the workers work the same number of hours, with the same degree of intensity, but now under better organization and improved instruments and so produce more commodities, the total value of these commodities is not increased. It remains the same. However, the value of each commodity falls, since less socially necessary labor-time has entered into its production. And this, in itself, other conditions remaining equal, has the effect of lowering the value of labor-power, since less time is now used up to reproduce the variable capital, and more time remains to the capitalist for the purpose of producing surplus value.

The above three factors, (1) length of working-day, (2) intensity of labor, and (3) productivity of labor, have definite effects upon the price of labor-power. Three types of effects can be indicated. (a) The length of the working day and the intensity of labor remain the same, but the productivity of labor increases, then the value of labor-power will fall. Depending upon the strength of the working class, it may or may not be followed by a fall in the price of labor-power. (b) If the length of the working day and the productivity of labor remain the same, but the intensity either increases or decreases, then the value of labor will correlatively increase or decrease. (c) If the productivity and intensity of labor remain the same, but the working day is either lengthened or shortened, then the value of labor-power is increased in the first case, without any necessary increase in wages, or in the latter case remains the same. The capitalist, however, loses part of his surplus value by shortening the day. He can regain it by depressing the price of labor-power below its value. The possibility of this depends once more upon the strength of the working class.

The development and expansion in the use of the third method of exploiting labor has tremendous consequences upon the whole of capitalist society. The earliest capitalist did not have the advantage of well developed scientific institutions and machinery at his disposal. He developed capitalist production upon the basis of the already existing elementary technic of production. The prevailing mode of production was the simple commodity economy, and its technic was primarily handicraft. The capitalist only organized it co-operatively by putting the artisans, now transformed into workers, under a single roof. At one stroke, this act cheapened the cost of production. One house is cheaper than many houses. It led to economies in the cost and use of raw materials. And it also heightened the productivity of labor, since workers work better in groups than in isolation.

Co-operation, as a method of organizing labor capitalistically, had other significant effects. It led to the further stage, known as manufacturing. The capitalist soon recognized that productivity could be enormously increased by making each worker perform only a particular function in the entire productive process. The worker naturally became much more proficient and efficient; and the tools, as a result, were variously altered until they were perfectly suited for that particular function. This process could be organized so that either all workers simultaneously produced a particular and different part which would be assembled together completely in another section of the factory; or there would be groups of workers each of whom performed his special function only when each object had reached a certain stage in the entire process of production, as instanced in the making of cloth. Manufacture is particularly important, since it reduces the differences between the skills and speed of labor to general uniformity. No worker can work faster or slower than his fellow worker, without halting the process of production or keeping some unnecessarily idle.

During the stage of manufacture, machinery played only a subordinate role. The skill of the various detail workers was most important; and it made the skilled workers extremely independent and self-willed. But the general competition of capitalists, and the high cost of skilled labor, both led to the more and more predominant use of machinery. The capitalist was interested in instruments of production, which saved not only human labor-power, and so increased their profits, but was emancipated from the organic limitations of the human being. Both characteristics belong to the machine. It saves human labor-power and can operate an indefinite number of tools at the same time, which is impossible to the human being. With the coming into predominance of machinery in production, production in other industries undergoes a revolution. The mechanization of one industry involves the mechanization of others, until every branch of production is mechanically transformed. At the same time, the predominance of machinery produces profound social effects upon the different economic classes. The peasant is uprooted from his land. Tremendous cities with enormous working class populations come into existence. The family of the worker disappears, for the housewife along with her children turn into factory workers. Unemployment becomes a normal feature of the social life. A labor movement comes into existence, demanding all kinds of reforms and revolutionary changes. All about one arises demands for a new type of social organization capable of utilizing fully the new and extraordinary benefits which science and machine production bring to mankind.

The capitalist mode of production, however, operates as a fetter upon the new, unleashed productive forces, for machine production demands the complete socialization and planning of production to satisfy the needs of society. And planned production is impossible under capitalism. This cannot be seen clearly, until capitalist reproduction, the way in which social wealth under capitalism is and must be accumulated, is understood.

Capitalist production is not merely production, but also reproduction. To keep capitalist society going from one year to the next, from one generation to the next, it must recreate the productive instruments which are used up in the process. These instruments for the capitalist are of two kinds, (1) the technical means of production:—machinery, tools, buildings, railroads, etc., and (2) labor. Labor is taken care of or takes care of itself through the wages it receives with which it buys back the commodities it produces during the week, year, or generation. But the technical means of production must be obtained by setting aside a definite proportion of what the capitalist considers his *revenue,* i.e., his income. We shall dwell upon the importance of this revenue later, but for the present it is important to point out that this very process of reproduction does something which is not emphasized in most text books of economics. Capitalist reproduction is a process which not only produces commodities, consumptive and productive, but reproduces as well the capitalist and the worker. The worker is reproduced through wages, which represent not the value of the products he produces but the value of his labor-power. The products produced belong to the capitalist from the beginning. Thus the working class remains, both at the beginning and at the end of the productive process, just the working class with nothing more to sell than its labor-power. The capitalist is reproduced at each stage of production by the commodities created for him by the worker, which not only bring back his original investment, but a handsome profit besides. This original investment of constant capital and variable capital is reproduced by the worker, but it is the means by which the capitalist returns again and again to reproduction and fetters the worker to the machine.

Continued capitalist reproduction has still another far-reaching consequence for the worker. At the beginning of the process of commodity production, the capitalist and the worker met each other with their respective commodities, which represented the results of the labor of each. Thus the principle of single commodity production that equals are exchanged for equals was realized. The worker selling his labor-power got in return wages; the capitalist got in return the products produced by the laborer, a part of which represented surplus value. But the continued reproduction of this process ultimately leads to a new situation. At the end of a certain number of reproductions, the capitalist will have consumed his original investment. What remains, while it belongs to him legally, is no longer the product of his own labor, but the product of the worker. Thus capitalist reproduction turns into actual robbery, a continual appropriation by the capitalist of what really belongs to the worker. This continual process of robbery is obscured by the laws of property and the forms of commodity-exchange, which maintain the illusory appearance that the capitalist gets what belongs to him, and that the worker is paid for his *labor,* i.e., *the products of his labor,* rather than for his *labor-power.*

We can now observe how the *revenue* of the capitalist functions. The revenue of the capitalist must inevitably be divided into two parts. One part goes back into production. The other part he uses for his own personal consumption. Depending upon the amount returned into production, we have either *simple* or *expanding* reproduction. In either case, we have the *accumulation of capital,* i.e., *the transformation of surplus value into capital.* The general process of the gradual transformation of *surplus value* into accumulated capital was revealed in the previous paragraph. Nevertheless, it takes two forms. In *simple reproduction,* the capitalist transforms sufficient surplus value into capital to replace the constant capital, raw material and variable capital to continue reproduction on the same basis as before. In expanding reproduction, the capitalist not only advances sufficient surplus value as capital to replace the old used-up capital, but additional sums to enlarge production. Thus begins the process of increasing the amount of capital expended in the form of constant capital over the variable capital, i.e., to a greater and greater concentration of capital. Improved machinery and organization is introduced, ultimately leading to science and technology becoming the obedient servants of the insatiable process of expanding accumulation. Every industry and every aspect of the social life undergo tremendous transformations. There is a search for new markets, new industries arise and expand rapidly, competition between capitalists sharpens; agriculture comes under the domination of the capitalist mode. But there are three aspects of this accumulation of capital upon an expanding basis which deserves special comment. One is the tremendous growth of enormous masses of capital in the hands of fewer and fewer capitalists, i.e., centralization and concentration of capital, and of a surplus labor population which operates to reduce the total working class population to a lower and lower standard of living for all sections of the working class. The second is the occurrence of periodic crises as a result of accumulation. The last is the historic tendency of the process of capitalist accumulation.

1) The very process of expanding reproduction involves an increase in the labor supply. Accumulation is impossible without an increase absolutely of the labor supply. At the same time, the process of accumulation is seriously affected by the labor supply. If accumulation grows too quickly for the available labor supply, wages rise sky high; and accumulation slows up the lags, until the labor market grows large enough to suit the needs of the capitalist. Nevertheless, accumulation is only seriously affected at specific periods by a scarcity of labor. In general, it has its own

safeguards against scarcity in its very development. The increase in the organic composition inevitably involves the creation of a surplus labor population, by including as useful for production a population previously unused: women and children, and by increasing the productivity of the worker so that fewer and fewer are needed relative to the technical composition, i.e., the instruments of labor. Thus accumulation involves, on the one hand, an absolute increase in the size of the working class, and, on the other hand, a relative decrease of that part of labor which enters into production over that part which remains either permanently or temporarily outside of production. The consequence: there is greater and greater competition between workers for jobs. The greater the competition for jobs, the lower falls, as a whole, the price of wages. This means the standard of living of the working class must fall relatively and absolutely. Of course, factors like trade unions and state intervention can modify the action of this law.

Accumulation affects the capitalist class differently. Whereas the working class increases absolutely, the capitalist class tends to decrease absolutely and relatively. One factor is the growth of enormous masses of capital, i.e., in the concentration and centralization of capital in the hands of single capitalists or groups. This gives them enormous power with which to wipe out smaller and weaker groups of capitalists. But the process of elimination of the weaker capitalists results either in the absorption of their capital or its destruction. Thus centralization of capital in the hands of fewer capitalists can be brought about without accumulation. But centralization of large masses of already existing capital in the hands of a few, leads to intensified accumulation; for the gathering together of small sums of existing capital into one great sum, makes possible a tremendous expansion of production. And this, in time, weeds out more capitalists. The decrease of the number of capitalists, of course, is the general tendency, but it is modified by a variety of factors, as, for example, the development of new industries.

2) Accumulation is not a continual unimpeded process. The expansion and growth of production have definite limits in the capacity of the market, i.e., the broad masses of the population to

consume what is produced, the amount of wages which is passed
on to the workers. The unrelenting competition of capitalists for
this market, their efforts at the same time continually to lower the
value of labor-power, thus to increase the amount of surplus value
which they can appropriate from the workers, leads ultimately to
a state where the capitalist class is producing more than can be
consumed by the market. The inevitable consequence is the
economic crisis, which occurs at stated intervals in the general
process of capitalist production. Production ceases in one factory
after another, in one industry after another. There seems to be
too much of everything: too much labor, too many commodities,
too many factories, too much raw material. The only thing of
which there seems an insufficiency is money, money to pay debts,
to buy articles of consumption, etc. Capitalism enters into a
period of panic, when everyone who can, begins to hoard money.

A crisis, of course, also works to concentrate and centralize
capital into the hands of fewer capitalists, to intensify the necessity of increasing the organic composition of capital, so that less
workers will be needed for production: thus, also to increase the
relative supply of unemployed labor.

3) The process described above, has, as we have seen, two
important consequences. It centralizes the means of production
and socializes the method of production by a tremendous division
and co-operation of labor. But both are achieved at the expense
of the vast majority of the population of society, particularly of
the working class. Instead of freeing mankind, these new resources
of production, chained down and imprisoned as it is by the
capitalist mode of production, lead to further degradation, misery,
and exploitation. But the incompatibility of these new resources
of production, of the highly centralized and socialized character
of machine production, with the capitalist mode of production,
must reach the point of explosion. The explosion occurs, ignited
by the revolutionary and organized energy of the working class.
The capitalist expropriations are expropriated; and the new
planned society completely socialized and centralized, appears
free of all exploiters, to begin the longed-for era of the freedom
of man!

THE ORIGIN OF SPECIES

By

Charles Darwin

CHARLES ROBERT DARWIN (*1809–1882*) was an English naturalist and the accredited discoverer of the principle of natural selection. His father was a doctor and a member of the Royal Society and his mother was a daughter of Josiah Wedgwood, the famous potterist. On leaving Cambridge in 1831 Darwin joined, as a naturalist, a government exploration expedition that circumnavigated the world and his work upon his observations were published by the government. When he was ready to publish his theory of evolution, he learned that a friend of his had developed substantially the same theory. He wanted to defer to his friend but was persuaded to have both papers read simultaneously before a learned society. He later developed his theory into a book *The Origin of Species,* in 1859, which created a wide and profound sensation.

THE ORIGIN OF SPECIES is by means of Natural Selection, or the preservation of favored races in the struggle for life. It is to be understood by the variation of plants and animals under domestication in the hands of man, and by analogous variations of organisms in a state of nature controlled by Natural Selection.

When we compare the individuals of the same variety among our older cultivated plants and animals, one of the first points which strikes us is that generally they differ more from one another than do the individuals of any one species in a state of nature. As we reflect upon this we are driven to conclude that this greater variability is due to the fact that our domestic productions have been raised under conditions different and less uniform than those to which the parent-species had been exposed under nature. Our oldest cultivated plants such as wheat still yield new varieties, and our oldest domesticated animals like our cattle are still capable of rapid improvement or modification. These modifications depend upon the nature of the organism and the nature of the conditions to which it is subjected.

Under domestication we observe much variability of a species caused or at least excited by changed conditions of life, but often in a manner so obscure that we are tempted to consider the variations as spontaneous. Variability is not caused by man, for he unintentionally exposes organic beings to new conditions of life leaving nature to act upon the organism and cause it to vary. One of the most remarkable features in our domesticated races is that we see in them adaptation to man's own use or fancy, not adaptations to the plant or animal's own good. In adapting plants or animals to his own pleasure or benefit, man may proceed methodically with the aim of improving the breed, or he may act unconsciously with no idea save that of preserving the breed that pleases him. Yet man's power of artificial selection, or breeding, often enables him to change the character of a species altogether, so that it would seem as if he had drawn the plant of a perfect species and then given it existence, so plastic is the organization of the animal.

There is no reason why the principles which have acted so efficiently with plants and animals under the domestication of man should not have acted analogously with species in nature under the law of Natural Selection. It may be doubted whether sudden and considerable deviations of structure such as we see in our domestic productions are ever permanently propagated in a state of nature. For almost every part of every organic being is so beautifully related to its complex conditions of life that it seems as improbable that any part should have been suddenly produced perfect, as that a complex machine should have been invented by man in a perfect state. Individual differences may be the first steps toward slight varieties; a well-marked variety may be called an incipient species.

Among organisms in the state of nature there is some individual variability yet this helps but little in understanding how species arise in nature. How have all these exquisite adaptations of one part of the organism to another, of one organism to another as also to the general conditions of life been perfected? How have the

varieties which I have called incipient species become converted
into good and distinct species? Such results follow from the
struggle for existence which follows inevitably from the high rate
at which all organic beings tend to increase. It is the doctrine
of Malthus applied with manifold force to the whole animal and
vegetable kingdoms. All plants and animals tend to increase in a
geometrical ratio; an annual plant producing only two seeds would
result in a million plants at the end of twenty years and even
slow-breeding man has doubled in twenty-five years. This natural
tendency to increase is checked in various ways—by lack of food,
change of climate with extreme cold and drought, epidemics and
the destruction of one species by another. Here we may console
ourselves with the thought that the war of nature is not incessant,
that death is prompt and that the happy and healthy survive and
multiply.

How does the struggle for existence act in regard to variation?
By the principle of selection, but does that which is so potent in
the hands of man apply as efficiently under nature? Neither man
nor nature can originate varieties; they can only preserve and
accumulate such as happen to occur. Since variations useful to man
occur it is reasonable to suppose that other variations in some
way useful in the great struggle for existence occur in the course
of many successive generations. In this manner, individuals having
even a slight advantage over others have the best chance of sur-
viving and procreating their kind while any variation in the least
degree injurious is rigidly destroyed. As man can produce great
results with his domestic animals and plants by adding up in any
given direction so can Natural Selection accomplish still greater
results because of the incomparably longer time for action involved
in the process. Nature can act on every internal organ, on every
shade of constitutional difference, on the whole machinery of
life; and while man selects for his own good alone, Natural Selection works in behalf of the good of the creature nature is developing. It is as though natural selection were daily and hourly
scrutinizing the slightest variations throughout the whole world
with the aim of rejecting the bad and preserving the good, working silently and insensibly whenever and wherever opportunity
offers. Of these slow and insensible changes we see nothing but

the resultant forms of life now so different from what they were.

With the changing conditions of life and the infinite complexity of organisms it would be an extraordinary fact if no variations useful to each being's own welfare had not occurred after the manner of the variations useful to man. But if such variations useful to any organic being do occur, those individuals thus characterized will have the best chance of being preserved in the struggle for life and these will tend to produce offspring similarly characterized. This is Natural Selection; it leads to the improvement of each creature in relation to both its organic and inorganic conditions of life.

Natural Selection leads to both divergence of character with the improvement of the species and the extinction of the less improved and intermediate forms of life. It is a truly wonderful fact that all animals and plants throughout all time and space should be related to one another in groups subordinate to groups, although these cannot be ranked in a single file but seem clustered round points and these around other points and so on in endless cycles. If species had been independently created there would be no explanation of this kind of classification, which is explicable through the complex character of Natural Selection and inheritance, entailing divergence of character and extinction.

The affinities of all beings of the same class may be likened to a great tree. At each period of growth all the budding twigs have tried to branch out on all sides and to overtop and kill the surrounding twigs and branches in the same manner as species and groups of species have at all times overmastered other species in the great battle of life. From the first growth of the tree many a limb and branch has decayed and dropped off so that now these fallen branches may represent those whole orders, families and genera which now have no living representatives and are known to us in only fossil states. As buds give rise to fresh buds, these overtop the feebler branches, and so it has been with the great Tree of Life which fills with its dead and broken branches the crust of the earth while it covers its surface with its ever-branching and beautiful ramifications.

Natural Selection and extinction go hand in hand. Natural Selection works for the preservation of profitable modifications in organisms, as also for the extermination of the less-favored forms with which it comes into competition. Hence if we look at each species as descended from some unknown form, we see that both the parent and all the transitional varieties have been exterminated by the very process of the formation and perfection of the new form. But if these innumerable transitional forms must have existed why do we not find them embedded in countless numbers in the crust of the earth? Since the process of extermination has acted on an enormous scale so must the number of intermediate varieties be enormous. Why is it, then, that not every geological formation and every stratum is full of them, for geology does not reveal any such finely graduated organic chain. This is perhaps the most obvious and serious objection which can be urged against the Theory of Natural Selection.

The explanation of the difficulty lies in the extreme imperfection of the geological record for when we turn to our richest geological museums we behold only a paltry display. But we have no right to expect to find in our geological formations an infinite number of fine transitional forms; we ought to look for only a few links, and such assuredly we do find. The abrupt manner in which whole groups of species suddenly appear in certain formations has been urged by several paleontologists as a fatal objection to the belief in the transmutation of species, and if such species have really started into life at once the fact would be fatal to the theory of evolution through Natural Selection. But we continually over-rate the perfection of the geological record and falsely infer that because certain genera have not been found beneath a certain stage they did not exist before that stage. As Natural Selection acts solely by accumulating slight, successive favorable variations, it can produce no great or sudden modifications; it can act only by short and slow steps. Hence the canon of *natura non facit saltum,* which every fresh addition to our knowledge tends to confirm, is on this theory intelligible. We can see why throughout nature the same general end is gained by an almost infinite diversity of means, for every peculiarity when once acquired is long inherited and structures already modified in many different ways have to be adapted for the same general purpose. We can see why nature is so prodigal in variety though niggard in invention, but why this should be a law of nature if each species has been independently created no man can explain.

Some of the difficulties in the way of the theory of Natural Selection are so serious that one can hardly reflect upon them without being staggered. Can we believe that Natural Selection could produce, on the one hand, an organ of trifling importance as the tail of a giraffe, which serves as a fly-flapper, and, on the other, an organ as wonderful as the eye?

To suppose that the eye with all its inimitable contrivances could have been formed by Natural Selection seems absurd in the highest degree. But when it was first said that the sun stood still and the world turned round it the common sense of mankind declared the doctrine false. Reason tells us that if numerous gradations from a simple and imperfect eye to one complex and perfect can be shown to exist, each grade being useful to its possessor, then the difficulty of believing that a perfect and complex eye could be formed by Natural Selection, though insuperable by our imagination, should not be considered as subversive of the theory. The simplest organ which can be called an eye consists of an optic nerve surrounded by pigment-cells and covered with translucent skin but without any lens or other refractive body. We may descend even a step lower and find aggregates of pigment cells without any nerves apparently serving as organs of vision. When we bear in mind how small the number of living forms must be in comparison with those which have become extinct, the difficulty in supposing that such a primitive organ developed into an optical instrument ceases to be so great. If one finds that large bodies of facts otherwise inexplicable can be explained by the theory of Natural Selection, he ought to admit that a structure even as perfect as an eagle's eye might thus be formed even though in this case he does not know the transitional states.

To arrive at a just conclusion regarding the formation of the eye it is indispensable that reason should conquer the imagination. We must suppose that there is a power represented by Natural Selection always intently watching each slight variation in the transparent layers and carefully preserving each which in any way or degree tends to produce a distincter image. We must suppose each new state of the instrument to be multiplied by the million, each to be preserved until a better one is produced and then the old ones to be destroyed. Let this process go on for millions of years and during each year millions of individuals of many kinds and may we not believe that a living optical instrument might thus be formed as superior to one of glass as the works of the Creator are to those of man?

Nothing at first can appear more difficult to believe than that the more complex organs and instincts have been perfected by the accumulation of innumerable slight variations each one good for the individual possessor. Nevertheless, this difficulty though appearing insuperably great to our imagination cannot be considered real if we admit the following propositions—that all parts of an organism offer individual variations, that there is a struggle for existence leading to profitable deviations of structure or instinct and that gradations in the state of perfection of each organ each good of its kind may have existed. There is no good reason why these views should shock the religious views of any one, for just as noble a conception of the Deity can be found in the idea that He created a few original forms capable of self-development into other and needful forms as to believe that He required a fresh act of creation to supply the voids caused by the action of His laws. The belief that species were immutable productions was almost unavoidable as long as the history of the world was thought to be of short duration, but now that we have acquired some idea of the lapse of time in geology that difficulty has been removed.

Authors of great eminence seem to be fully satisfied with the view that each species has been independently created, but it seems to accord better with what we know of the laws impressed on matter by the Creator that the production and extinction of the past and present inhabitants of the world should have been due to secondary causes like those determining the birth and death of the individual. There is grandeur in this view of life with its several powers having been breathed by the Creator into a few forms or into one so that, while this planet has gone cycling according to the fixed law of gravity, from a simple beginning endless forms most beautiful and wonderful have been and still are being evolved.

[531]

THE DECLINE OF THE WEST

By

Oswald Spengler

OSWALD SPENGLER (*1880–*   ) is a German social and political philosopher. He was born at Blankenburg, and he studied philosophy, mathematics, and art at the universities of Halle, Munich, and Berlin. He is best known for his philosophy of history, which he worked out in *The Decline of the West* (1918–1922). He expressed a belief that civilization moves in cycles and that Western culture has entered upon its period of decline. The World War gave him much ammunition for this viewpoint, which he was able to exploit quite successfully. In this book a fatalistic attitude toward the waxing and waning of civilizations is adopted.

THIS BOOK attempts to define various forms of national culture on the earth and to predetermine their course until they come to an end. Whether the culture with its subsequent civilization be Chinese or Classical or Modern it will be found to pass through successive stages of birth, youth, mature age and death: to have, also, its spring, summer, autumn and winter. The method of determining these periods is not that of mathematical law but analogy. To view these various cultures sidewise is to observe Caesar and Napoleon, Buddha and Christ, Athens and Florence, Christianity and modern Socialism side by side. In order to understand them we must distinguish between the World as Nature spread out in space and the World as History moving in time. This will give us an organic view of the problem and supply a morphology of world-history. The proper view of history is not a near-by or Ptolemaic but a far-off or Copernican one, hence we can gain no genuine view of history by taking our stand in Europe and following the conventional idea of "ancient, mediaeval and modern"; we must view all cultures in their own orbits.

Each culture has its own character gradually assumed from within not impressed on it from without; it must be viewed vitally in its own portraiture or physiognomic, not mechanically or according to a mere systematic. Each culture has a soul with a style of its own. That which controls the development and decay of a culture is the principle of destiny in the form of a vital necessity working in time. The control of a culture is not in the hands of causality operating in space. This is because a national culture has an irreversible direction and, like time itself, can be lived and experienced better than it can be thought of and defined. Each culture has its own destiny so that the fate of Sophocles' *Laocoön* is radically different from that of Shakespeare's *King Lear;* in one case it is the noble sorrow, in the other the noble deed. Modern culture is alive to time as the ancient culture was not, thinks of the present as something moving from past to future and stresses the importance of an event or incident rather than that of mere fate.

The character or physiognomy of a culture can be represented in the all-embracing symbolism of space, by which means our "here" as something proper to us in distinction from another's "there" which is alien. The world as it moves in time is a Becoming but when it stagnates in space, as a stream running into a land-locked lake, it is a Become, or something finished. Time is the life of space and space the death of time. The ancients thought of space as flat and limited while with the moderns it is full and unlimited. A modern painter gives space depth or third dimension. A modern philosopher like Kant renders it flexible and even mental. A modern mathematician like Gauss treats it as though it was capable of several geometries. The classical soul thought of space narrowly as something to be found in a body. The Arabian or Magian soul conceived of it more broadly as a cavern, while the modern or Faustian soul views it in the light of infinity. Thus we find three types of mathematics or conceptions of quantity—number as magnitude, as symbol, as function.

The Apollinian Soul, chiefly Grecian, was embodied in classical culture. The Faustian Soul expressed itself in European culture

after the year 1000. At the time of Augustus, in the land bounded
by Nile and Tigris, the Black Sea and South Arabia, appeared the
Magian Soul of the Arabian culture in the Persian, Jewish,
Christian and Manichean religions. The nude statue is Apollinian,
the fugue Faustian, the mosaic and arabesque Magian. Each was
independent of the others, since each had its own soul to express.
Since Europe has been dominated in turn by Classical and
Christian culture, and since there has long been a tendency on
the part of the modern to bow in adoration before Grecian culture, it is necessary to note the wide differences between these
two souls. The effects of the Magian Soul, filtering in here and
there must be observed separately.

The Doric architecture of the Apollinian soul came forth spon-
taneously in independence of the Egyptian style and in opposition
to the Minoan, in Crete. Its thick columns are set in the earth
and on them based a small, firm, trim temple whose significance,
with its frieze, is wholly exteriorizing. Its form is Euclidean and
flat in effect, its tone is earthly, its significance bodily. Faustian
architecture, beginning with the Romanesque as in the Cathedral
at Speyer, was equally original in source, equally significant in the
style of the Faustian Soul. It departs from the idea of building
by mere load and support introducing the ideal of mass and force
and developing a vast interior for the soul. In the still more
significant case of the Gothic, the Faustian soul increases the
proportions of the structure, while decreasing the heaviness, which
architecturo-engineering feat is accomplished by a system of thrust
and counter-thrust in the groined arch within and the flying
buttress on the outside. With windows in place of walls the
Gothic is enabled to express the Faustian striving outward toward
limitless space, upward toward a spiritual order.

In plastic art the Apollinian soul attained to its highest degree
of perfection in the form of the naked statue which, being expressive of only a soul-less body, made the body with its language
of muscles its sole spokesman. Although the classic artist perfected
or idealized the human body the effect of his noble work was only
pose, not character. It was lacking in soul-portraiture. The Faustian
plastic of the Gothic period developed a human tracery with a
web of innumerable figures in stone, which was required to present

a picture of the world from the Fall of Man to the Last Judgment. Michelangelo, moved in the anti-Gothic Renaissance to imitate the classical ideal, cannot help making the marble body the outer expression of an inward soul with its independent life of spirit. In such Faustian plastic we behold the human portraiture and spiritual character which was of no interest to classical man.

Classical painting did not develop an independent picture but was satisfied with fresco executed in the obvious colors of red and yellow, black and white. The painting, a part of the building, was executed in the form of exact imitation instead of in response to expression from within. The Faustian Soul expressed itself in painting as the Apollinian had done in sculpture. The lighter and more voluminous conception of nature has led the modern painter to develop his art in the form of an independent picture painted with oil on canvas and involving the third dimension whose perspective leads the gaze off into the limitless. The introduction of green made the painting look like nature, blue loaned it the impression of distance while the studio-brown of Rembrandt made it modern and Protestant.

The music of the classical man, in spite of Apollo's famous lyre, was not an independent art penetrating into a distinct tone-world outside the sight-world with its steely tyranny of light. Apollinian music was a kind of sculpture for the ear. In its naïve distrust of polyphonic music and harmony it was single-voiced and monophonic. Faustian music, which in the Gothic period discovered the free tone-world, considers its art a fluid, not a plastic one. It adopted polyphony as expressive of music's richness, developed in the sonata its independence and gave it adequate volume in the full orchestral symphony. It has reached its highest form in chamber music which expresses the Faustian idea of tone as something in itself, of music as something absolute. It is the dominant Faustian art to which the others are logically subordinate.

The classic drama of the Apollinian Soul was an open-air, day-light play as though a part of the world at large and was constructed in the tight form of unities—of time, place, action. Often it assumed the conventional form of contrast between nature and law, *phusis* and *nomos,* and as often indulged in presentations of ghastly scenes supposed to cleanse the soul of such emotions as fear and pity. The characters of the Greek play were not developed through events in their lives but were ruled by an outside fate so that their recitation and gesture were exterior to their souls. The plot was habitually the fate-plot, not the character-plot. Ajax is made mad before the play, Hamlet goes mad during the performance of it. Modern drama of the Faustian type is now presented in a closed theatre with its own lighting, is the drama of real character, moves by motivating events in the lives of the characters and in its range includes history and biography. In Shakespeare all classic limitations are rejected by the mighty will of the dramatist whose stage includes woods, seas, gardens, battle-fields which convey the impression of boundlessness in the scene and will-power in the character on the stage.

The calm Apollinian soul showed as little vigor in its ethical conceptions, was wanting in a moral sense and entertained no idea of pessimism. Its conceptions of virtue and pleasure were accorded no deep analysis, its cardinal virtues were put forth naturally and with an ease unknown to modern man in his ethical enterprise. It was not until the end when the Stoics and Epicureans appeared that there was any sharp distinction between virtue and pleasure and even with such rival views both alike sank into the quieting ideal of ataraxy and apathy, or *apatheia*. The chief moral problem consisted in knowing, not in doing, the Good hence it was a clear mind rather than a strong will which inspired their ethical systems. Their consummate aim was wisdom, their life ideal, galene, or calm at sea.

Faustian morals involve the will. They reach their climax in Kant's Categorical Imperative and involve the dynamic as also the idea of distance such as we find in our modern system of energy and in music. The moral ideal is something which is to be imposed upon others, upon all and those who proclaim it may otherwise be as unlike as Darwin and Nietzsche, the Popes and the Socialists. This has produced a long series of granite men wholly unlike the Grecians who were ever enamored of the True and Good and Beautiful and who were never able to produce, even in Alexander or Caesar, what we would call a man, *ein Mann*. Our modern struggle for existence, of which even Gothic architecture was symbolic, was unknown to Apollinian men to whom any sort of Protestantism or Storm and Stress was alien. Our moral system is an active, purposive one inclining toward a plebian morality of humanity, of sociality and the greatest happiness of the greatest number. In this the tragic morality of the great mind— Shakespeare, Bach, Kant, Goethe, is lost to view. Now all must obey the will of all.

The political conceptions peculiar to the Appollinian soul were in keeping with its views of man and the world according to which everything was viewed in now a solid then a corpuscular manner, or as bodies. The body politic of the Greeks was of the atomic sort, the political unit was the city-state, *polis,* and the political activity instead of being a confederation of such units was a conflict between them, as Athens versus Sparta. Although toward the close of the classic period Aristotle announced that man was a political animal, the organic conception of the State was wanting. No Greek possessed the notion of some historical evolution of the State toward something but looked upon his city-state in a timeless Now, or in the case of other cities as something that came into and then went out of being. If we compare the destinies of Athens after Themistocles and France after Louis XIV, we observe that the ancient State was not conducted according to the logical plan manifest in the modern one. Just as the Greek theatre lacked perspective and its drama anything more than a here-and-now, so its State was wanting in perspective and wide horizon.

In sharp contrast with this minuscular view of the State, we have the network of international politics with capital cities of countries and the system of cabinet diplomacy operating among them. We tend to look upon the State compositely as though it had been made by a social contract, had a long history behind and an indefinite future in front of it. Hence our political history is one of interminable connections while that of the ancients was simply a collection of biographies and anecdotes presented, as it were, as a row of statues viewed in the bright light of the beautiful present. Thus we find it difficult to credit Thucydides when he states that before his time, about 400 B.C., nothing great had happened in the world.

The Faustian soul is bound to consider the State in direct relation to history as something which has not been made but has grown. Such a history is not a systematic thing to be explained according to mechanical causation. It is something physiognomic, or characteristic, hence political history instead of looking upward toward a super-wise and super-just State, like Plato's Republic, must consider the birth, growth and decay of political forms as they really exist in the fact-world. History working in time produces the State as something in space, or the place where history halts. When the State is fully formed the history which produced it lies down to sleep and the men of history become plants again. Then re-appears the timeless village with its eternal peasant and in the midst of the land lie the old cities as empty receptacles of extinguished souls. Then there comes that peace on earth which historical men in their striving could never find and yet must ever seek.

The economic theory and practice of the classical man was an expression of that Apollinian soul-life which elsewhere expressed itself in the city-state, the small temple and the life sized statue. Wealth was of a distinctly bodily character. The source of classic economics was the age-old and ever-living idea of barter such as obtains even today in out of the way places removed from the urban market. With the Greeks it obtained classic form in the stamped coin invented by the Greeks about 650 B.C. and in economic history parallel with the invention of the credit-debit system, or double-entry book-keeping by Fra Luca Pacioli in 1494. Ancient money was thus thought of materially as magnitude; modern money is conceived and treated mentally or mathematically as function; then it was like stuff and form whereas now it is so much force and mass. Indeed the modern bookkeeping, clearing-house system of economics is comparable to the operation of positive and negative forces in magnetism.

The economics of modern man, European and American, is that of money as force and function, not as the measure of magnitudes in either things or works. In an age of energy and machinery the whole system of economics has been the creation of a number of superior minds able to make modern money function. The mental act of thinking in money as such operates in such a way that when a magnate writes down a million on paper that million begins to exist in the sense that it will enhance all economic energy in his particular field. Remove that mental force or substitute gold pieces for it and nothing would come to pass since wealth, credit and the like are but potential forces which can be put into operation. It is money-thought that counts, and the inventor of the steam-engine, not the stoker, is the important individual. Karl Marx as well as Adam Smith before him persisted in the classic idea that money was not function but magnitude hence he sought to means of production from these who discover methods and organize industries to carry them out. Under Capitalism, the "firm" is an impersonal, incorporeal center of force whence activities stream forth in all directions to indefinite distances. As a result, Faustian culture involves a maximum as Appollinian culture involved a minimum of organization.

But men are growing tired of money-economy and it is through money that democracy destroys itself after money has itself destroyed intellect. The old Gothic spirit awakens again and with its knights seeks to destroy the plunderous Vikingism of the present. Its upward striving and outward straining extended beyond the scope of the Cathedrals of the XIIIth century, passing on into long-range weapons, the extension of literature into printed books, the expanded earth of Columbus and broader sky of Copernicus, the telescope and microscope, the chemical elements, the steam-engine and now the gas-engine. Modern man's range is such that he can cross continents in days, fly over them in hours and send sounds with the speed of light to the far ends of the earth. These strivings with space and time are accompanied by such workings upon matter that modern man bores mountains, spans wide streams, constructs enormous ships and builds into the skies and is now under the intoxication of inventions poured out rapidly one after another. But all such Faustian activity puts man at the mercy of the machine and makes him the slave of his own creation.

This modern power over nature involves also a power over wealth and creates the dictatorship of money, but this is not lasting. If money were something tangible as it was with the Greeks it would be as imperishable as gold, but in the modern credit system in its independence of gold money has become only a form of thought and thus fades out as soon as it has thought its economic world through to finality. Now comes the battle between economics and politics, between Capitalism and Socialism, Democracy and Caesarism, the master-will and the plunder-will. The coming of Caesarism breaks the dictatorship of money and checks the course of democracy and it is only by blood that money can be overthrown. Money is now riotously celebrating its last victories at the approach of Caesarism which will take the affairs of the world in hand. In time the Fourth Estate or mass may be in power reducing all life to its own low level and bringing civilization to an end. Then will be realized the Decline of the West and the end of Faustian culture, which reaches its end in Socialism. The Buddhist withdrew from the presence of his former ideals into himself; the Stoic, or Apollinian nihilist, watched them crumble before his eyes; the Faustian nihilist shatters them with his will.

The end of a civilization is signalized by various phenomena, as megapolitanism, or the building of great cities with their enormous buildings. This megapolitan tendency is manifest in such great centres as Cnossus and Mycenae, Babylon and Thebes, Tenochtitlan and Samarra. This last-named city stretched for twenty miles along the Tigris. The Balkuwara Palace forms a square about three fourths of a mile on each side and one of the giant mosques measures, according to the plan, 858 x 594 feet. Further examples of meaningless, empty and pretentious architecture appear in the winter of a civilization in the gigantic buildings of Luxor and Karnak, in the vast fora and triumphal arches of the Romans, if not in American architecture of today. The city which comes at last in the winter of a civilization means intellect and money, or mind and money for their own sake. Here we find, also, factious art, luxury, sports, unnatural excitements and rapidly changing fashions. The body of a civilized people dissolves into a formless mass, devoid of culture and wanting in soul-life. It is the destiny of civilization to detach itself from its original culture-life and develop in its own way. Our modern, Faustian civilization having released itself from its original Gothic culture and having produced a thorough-bred civilization-form is now in the final stage of hardening. Time flows on forever and makes of any culture a mere incident in the endless geological and stellar histories of the world. In the grand almanac of nations with their spiritual, cultural and political epochs, Western Civilization, the Faustian Soul, is now well down in the third and last period and will come to its end in the year 2200.

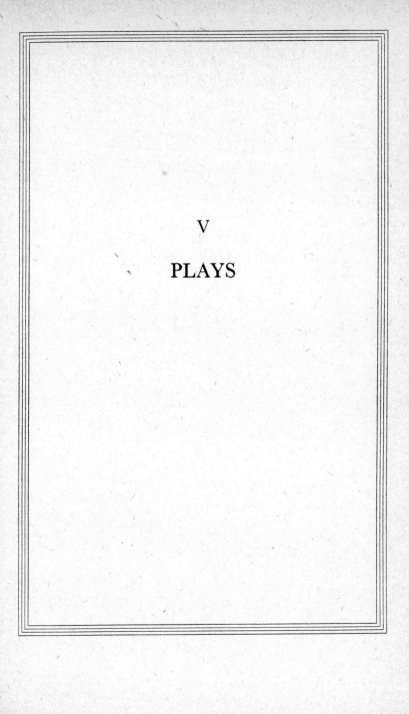

V

PLAYS

AGAMEMNON

By

Aeschylus

AESCHYLUS (525-456 B.C.) was one of the most prolific of
Greek dramatists, a son of Euphorion who is generally considered the father of Greek tragedy. Aeschylus was born near
Athens in the town of Mysteries and he fought at Marathon,
Salamis and Plataea when the Persians were repulsed by the
Greeks. When he was about 57 years old he retired to the
court of Hiero who was the king of Syracuse. Aeschylus is
reputed to have written over 70 tragedies but only 7 of them
remain. They include *Prometheus Bound,* the *Seven Against
Thebes* and *Agamemnon.* Aeschylus died in Sicily in 456 B.C.
where a monument was raised to his memory. He was the origi-
nator of dramatic dialogue and created many new forms in the
staging of the drama.

DRAMATIS PERSONAE

WATCHMAN	AGAMEMNON
CHORUS OF ARGIVE ELDERS	CASSANDRA
CLYTAEMNESTRA	AEGISTHUS
HERALD	

SCENE—Argos
TIME—The heroic age

WHEN HELEN had fled to Troy with Paris, a Greek army, led by
Agamemnon, her husband's brother, had sailed in pursuit. The
goddess, Artemis, had kept the Greek fleet in check by sending
adverse winds. In order to appease the goddess, Agamemnon had
enticed his daughter, Iphigenia, to the ships by promise of a
marriage with the hero, Achilles; and then, in accordance with
the words of a seer, had her killed as a sacrifice. The ships sailed,

Troy was taken after ten years, and the warriors embarked for home.

Upon the roof of the palace of Agamemnon in Argos a watch-man has kept watch every night for the beacon-fires that will signal the fall of Troy. At last the fires blaze forth in the distance and the watchman descends to tell the news to Clytaemnestra, Agamemnon's wife. The Chorus of Argive Elders enters and tells of the sacrifice of Iphigenia and the sailing of the Greek ships. These are old men, unfit for military service, who were left be-hind when their king went on his great adventure. Clytaemnestra comes to inform them of the capture of Troy. She explains that a series of signal-fires had been arranged, going from Troy itself to a point where it could be seen from Argos. The elders are sceptical of the good news and wish some form of confirmation. A herald rushes upon the scene with news: Troy has fallen and Agamemnon has hastened home.

The elders speak darkly of fears they will not divulge and question the herald about the war. He tells them that, when it came time to return to their native shores, the Greek host was caught in a storm so terrible that many perished and many more were borne far out to sea. The ship which Agamemnon had boarded was, however, unharmed, and they had thanked the gods for their mercy. Clytaemnestra bids the herald welcome and tells him that she has remained faithful to her departed king. The elders mutter ominously. Clytaemnestra departs and the Chorus tells of the doom that the beautiful Helen brought to Troy.

A procession enters, led by the returning hero, Agamemnon, and Cassandra, a beautiful young Trojan prophetess whom he has taken captive, ending the chastity of her holy life. The chorus welcomes him, protesting its devotion and saying that now he may learn for himself which of those he left behind have been loyal and which not. He replies that he is familiar with feigned loyalty and can discover it. Of those who sailed with him, only Odysseus was completely loyal. With these words he descends from his chariot and sees his wife coming, with her serving-women, to greet him. She speaks of the anxious years of waiting, of the rumors of his death, of the fear that, should he not return soon, the people would revolt. Because of her fear of rebellion, she sent her son, Orestes, away to visit a friend, which is the reason he is not present to greet his father. Then she orders her followers to strew her lord's path with purple, that he need not set his feet on common soil. He answers that only gods should be treated with such pomp. He will give thanks to the gods and walk upon the ground. Clytaemnestra protests too much. She insists and at last he removes his sandals and walks on the purple cloth, enjoining his wife to take care of Cassandra. The chorus is filled with forebodings since an evil destiny must await their master as a consequence of the shedding of his daughter's blood.

Clytaemnestra tells Cassandra that she will be well treated and must not be too proud to be a slave, as many great ones, even Heracles, were slaves at times. The proud captive does not respond and the chorus suggests that she needs an interpreter. Clytaemnestra says that the prophetess is simply in a wild mood at thus being taken from her own hearth and treated like a servant. However, she has no time to waste, for the feast in honor of Agamemnon is in preparation. Angrily she enters the house. The Chorus, pitying Cassandra, pleads gently with her to leave the chariot and go within.

CASSANDRA

Woe, woe, woe! O Apollo, O Apollo!

CHORUS

Wherefore thy cry of woe in Loxias' name? No god is he that hath to do with those who wail.

CASSANDRA

Woe, woe, woe! O Apollo, O Apollo!

CHORUS

Once more with ill-omened words she crieth upon the god when it beseems not to attend at time of lamentation.

CASSANDRA

Apollo, Apollo! God of the Ways, my destroyer! For thou hast destroyed me—and utterly—this second time.

CHORUS

She is about to prophesy, methinks, touching her own miseries. The gift divine still abides even in the soul of one enslaved.

CASSANDRA

Apollo, Apollo! God of the Ways, my destroyer! Ah, what way is this that thou hast brought me! To what a house!

CHORUS

To that of Atreus' sons. If thou dost not perceive this, I'll tell it thee. And thou shalt not say 'tis untrue.

CASSANDRA

Nay, nay, rather to a house of heaven loathed, a house that knoweth many a horrible butchery of kin, a human shambles and a floor swimming with blood.

CHORUS

Methinks the stranger is keen-scented as a hound; she is on the trail where she will discover blood.

CASSANDRA

Aye, here is the evidence wherein I put my trust! Behold yon babes bewailing their own butchery and their roasted flesh eaten by their sire.

CHORUS

Thy fame to read the future had reached our ears; but of prophets we are not in quest.

CASSANDRA

O God, what can it be she purposeth? What is this strange woe she purposeth here within, what monstrous, monstrous horror, beyond love's enduring, beyond all remedy? And help stands far away!

CHORUS

These prophesyings pass my comprehension.

CASSANDRA

Ah, fell woman, so thou wilt do this deed? Thy husband, the partner of thy bed, when thou hast cheered him with the bath, wilt thou—how shall I tell the end? Aye, soon it will be done. Now this hand, now that, she stretches forth!

CHORUS

Not yet do I comprehend; for now, after riddles, I am bewildered by dark oracles.

CASSANDRA

Ha! Ha! What apparition's this? Surely 'tis some net of death? But she is the snare, she who shares his bed, she who shares the guilt. Let the fatal pack, insatiable against the race, raise a shout of jubilance over a victim accursed!

CHORUS

What Spirit of Vengeance is this thou dost bid raise high its voice o'er this house? Thy utterance cheers me not. Back to my heart surge the drops of my pallid blood, even as when they drip from a mortal wound, ebbing away as life's beams sink low; and death cometh speedily.

CASSANDRA

Ha, ha, see there, see there! Keep the bull from his mate! She hath caught him in the robe and gores him with the crafty device of her black horn! 'Tis of doom wrought by guile in a murderous bath that I am telling thee.

CHORUS

Frenzied in soul thou art, by some god possessed, and dost wail in wild strains thine own fate, like some brown nightingale that never ceases making lament . . .

CASSANDRA

Ah, fate of the tuneful nightingale! The gods clothed her in winged form and gave to her a sweet life without tears. But for me waiteth destruction by the two-edged sword.

Cassandra becomes calmer and talks to the elders of herself. It is Apollo that had granted her the gift of prophecy and, because of it, she had been able to predict the fall of Troy. Now she can see the death of Agamemnon at the hands of his wife and can foretell also her own impending death. She tramples beneath her foot the wand and other insignia of her prophetic office, in order that her death be that of a common slave, not that of a priestess of Apollo. Then, proudly, the lovely girl enters the palace.

The Chorus starts to reflect on human destiny but is interrupted by a shriek from within.

AGAMEMNON

Ay me! I am smitten deep with a mortal blow!

CHORUS

Silence! Who is this that crieth out, wounded by a mortal blow?

AGAMEMNON

And once again, ay me! I am smitten by a second blow.

The elders recognize the voice of their king and realize that Cassandra's prophesy has come to pass. They fear that a tyranny will be established now that Agamemnon is dead, and they plan to resist it. Some, however, insist that they make sure the king is dead before they decide on the wisest course of action. This they agree upon.

On investigation, the elders discover the dead bodies of Agamemnon and Cassandra, with Clytaemnestra standing by their side. The queen confesses the double murder, nay, she glories in it. This man, her husband, had slain their own daughter and had brought home with him on his return a concubine to share his bed. The elders want to drive their queen forth from the city but she insists that she is not responsible for the deed; it is the grim destiny of the house of Atreus that has worked itself out on Agamemnon.

CHORUS

Alas, alas, my king, my king, how shall I bewail thee? How voice my heartfelt love for thee? To lie in this spider's web, breathing forth thy life in impious death! Ah, me, to lie on this ignoble bed, struck down in treacherous death wrought by a weapon of double edge wielded by the hand of thine own wife!

CLYTAEMNESTRA

Neither do I think he met an ignoble death. And did he not then by treachery bring ruin on his house? Yet, as he hath suffered —worthy meed of worthy deed—for what he did unto my sweet flower, shoot sprung from him, the sore-wept Iphigenia, let him make no high vaunt in the halls of Hades, since with death dealt him by the sword he hath paid for what he first began.

Aegisthus, nephew of Agamemnon, bursts upon the scene with an armed retinue and announces that he had planned the murder. Atreus, father of Agamemnon and Menelaus, had done him a great injury. It was Thyestes, Aegisthus' father and his own brother, whom Atreus had driven into exile. Then, when Thyestes had returned, a suppliant to his own hearth, Atreus had pretended to welcome him and had given him a banquet of the cooked flesh of his own children, excepting the third child, Aegisthus. After that, he had driven both of them out of Argos once more.

The elders curse Aegisthus, predicting his own evil end, and pray that Orestes, Agamemnon's son, may avenge his father's death. Aegisthus tells them that, with Agamemnon's gold and the force of his men-at-arms, he and Clytaemnestra will rule over them, and that the yoke will be heavy. As they continue to mutter against him, he orders his men to draw their swords and is about to start a massacre when Clytaemnestra intercedes, bidding the elders return to their homes and save their necks. Aegisthus angrily tells them he is their master.

CHORUS

It would not be like men of Argos to cringe before a knave.

AEGISTHUS

Ha! I'll visit thee with vengeance yet in days to come.

CHORUS

Not if fate shall guide Orestes to return home.

AEGISTHUS

Of myself I know that exiles feed on hope.

CHORUS

Keep on, grow thee fat, polluting justice, since thou canst.

AEGISTHUS

Know that thou shalt pay me the penalty to requite thy folly.

CHORUS

Brag in thy bravery like a cock beside his hen.

CLYTAEMNESTRA

Care not for their idle yelpings. I and thou will be masters of this house and order it aright.

ANTIGONE

By

Sophocles

SOPHOCLES (*496–405* B.C.), the Athenian tragic poet, at the age of 28 won a competition with Aeschylus whose eminence as a tragic poet had long been undisputed. The triumph had decisive influence on the future of all tragic art. Among Sophocles' great works are *Antigone, Ajax, Electra* and *Philoctetes.*

DRAMATIS PERSONAE

ANTIGONE ⎱ daughters of Oedipus and sisters of Polyneices
ISMENE ⎰ and Eteocles
CREON, King of Thebes
HAEMON, son of Creon, betrothed to Antigone
EURYDICE, wife of Creon
TEIRESIAS, the prophet
CHORUS, of Theban Elders
A WATCHMAN
A MESSENGER
A SECOND MESSENGER

ETEOCLES, one of the sons of Oedipus, former king of Thebes, had taken his father's place at the head of that state. His brother, Polyneices, desirous of the throne, had besieged Thebes with an army of Argives. In the fighting Eteocles and Polyneices killed each other and the Argives were put to route. A kinsman, Creon, was proclaimed ruler of Thebes, in which dwelt the bereaved daughters of Oedipus, Antigone and Ismene.

Antigone comes to her sister, Ismene, with fearful news. Creon, father of her betrothed, Haemon, has just pronounced Polyneices a traitor to the state. Although Eteocles has been buried with appropriate rites, Polyneices, as a traitor, must be left to rot on the field of battle. Any one daring to bury him will be stoned to death. Antigone asks her sister's help. Polyneices must be buried. Ismene answers that she will not break the laws of the state. To this Antigone replies that she must choose between the decrees of the state and the laws of God. As for herself, one course only is open: she alone will bury Polyneices though it cost her life.

Creon calls together the Chorus of Theban Elders and tells them of his edict, warning them that the state must be put before all claims of friendship or of blood. Guards have been posted at the corpse of Polyneices and death waits for any who dare to break the law. At this moment a guard enters to say that during the night some unknown person had covered with dust the body of Oedipus' son. Lots were drawn and he was chosen to bring the news to Creon. The king thunders that the guards were probably bribed. Unless they bring the culprit to him, he says, they shall all die on the cross.

The guard returns to the body and sweeps it clean of dust. Then he and his comrades keep a night-long vigil. Morning brings with it a whirlwind which veils the corpse. When the day once more is clear Antigone is seen burying the rotting body of her brother. The guards swoop down and seize her and the guard who had acted as messenger to Creon brings her before the king.

CREON

Speak, girl, with head bent low and downcast eyes,
Dost thou plead guilty or deny the deed?

ANTIGONE

Guilty. I did it, I deny it not.

CREON (*to Guard*)

Sirrah, begone whither thou wilt, and thank
Thy luck that thou hast 'scaped a heavy charge.

(*to Antigone*)

Now answer this plain question, yes or no,
Wast thou acquainted with the interdict?

[554]

ANTIGONE

I knew, all knew; how should I fail to know?

CREON

And yet wert bold enough to break the law?

ANTIGONE

Yea, for these laws were not ordained of Zeus,
And she who sits enthroned with gods below,
Justice, enacted not these human laws.
Nor did I deem that thou, a mortal man,
Could'st by a breath annul and override
The immutable unwritten laws of heaven.
They were not born to-day nor yesterday;
They die not; and none knoweth whence they sprang.
I was not like them, who feared no mortal's frown,
To disobey these laws and so provoke
The wrath of heaven. I knew that I must die,
E'en hadst thou not proclaimed it; and if death
Is thereby hastened, I shall count it gain.
For death is gain to him whose life, like mine,
Is full of misery. Thus my lot appears
Not sad, but blissful; for had I endured
To leave my mother's son unburied there,
I should have grieved with reason, but not now.
And if in this thou judgest me a fool,
Methinks the judge of folly's not acquit.

CHORUS

A stubborn daughter of a stubborn sire,
This ill-starred maiden kicks against the pricks.

CREON

Well, let her know the stubbornest of wills
Are soonest bended, as the hardest iron,
O'er-heated in the fire to brittleness,
Flies soonest into fragments, shivered through.
A snaffle curbs the fieriest steed, and he,

Who in subjection lives must needs be meek.
But this proud girl, in insolence well-schooled,
First overstepped the established law, and then—
A second and worse act of insolence—
She boasts and glories in her wickedness.
Now if she thus can flout authority
Unpunished, I am woman, she the man.
But though she be my sister's child or nearer
Of kin than all who worship at my hearth,
 Nor she nor yet her sister shall escape
The utmost penalty, for both I hold,
As Arch-conspirators, of equal guilt.
Bring forth the other; even now I saw her
Within the palace, frenzied and distraught.
The workings of the mind discover oft
Dark deeds in darkness schemed, before the act.
More hateful still the miscreant who seeks
When caught, to make a virtue of a crime.

Ismene is summoned and accused of aiding her sister. Though innocent, she desires to share Antigone's fate because she approves her action; therefore she confesses to a guilt she does not share. Antigone rejects her sister as one who opposed the holy action she has performed. Creon condemns Antigone to death saying that his son must sow his seed in other fields. Haemon, having heard the news, comes in haste to tell his father that he will hold duty more precious than love. However he must inform Creon that the people are muttering, protesting that for the noblest of deeds it is not fitting that the maid should suffer the worst of deaths. Haemon agrees with them and asks his father to think most carefully before he proceeds with his order. May he not be wrong in dealing so harshly with Antigone? Creon in anger brands his son a woman's slave. Haemon threatens to take his own life if Antigone dies. Creon is adamant and Haemon leaves saying that his father shall never again behold his face.

Unswerving from what he regards as duty, Creon commands that Antigone be taken to a rocky cave. There she shall be given a slight amount of food and the cave sealed up.

CHORUS

Love resistless in fight, all yield at a glance of thine eye,
Love who pillowed all night on a maiden's cheek dost lie,
Over the upland folds thou roamest, and the trackless sea,
Love the gods captive holds. Shall mortals not yield to thee?
Mad are thy subjects all, and even the wisest heart
Straight to folly will fall, at a touch of thy poisoned dart.
Thou didst kindle the strife, this feud of kinsman with kin,
By the eyes of a winsome wife, and the yearning her heart to win.
For as her consort still, enthroned with Justice above,
Thou bendest man to thy will, O all invincible Love.

Lo I myself am borne aside,
From Justice, as I view this bride.
(*O sigh an eye in tears to drown*)
Antigone, so young, so fair,
  Thus hurried down
Death's bower with the dead to share.

ANTIGONE

Friends, countrymen, my last farewell I make;
  My journey's done.
One last fond, lingering look I take
  At the bright sun.
For death who puts to sleep both young and old
  Hales my young life,
And beckons me to Acheron's dark fold
  An unwed wife.
No youths have sung the marriage song for me,
  My bridal bed
No maids have strewn with flowers from the lea,
  'Tis Death I wed.

CHORUS

But bethink thee, thou are sped,
Great and glorious, to the dead,
Thou the sword's edge hath not tasted,
No disease thy frame hath wasted.
Freely thou alone shalt go
Living to the dead below.

ANTIGONE

Nay, but the piteous tale I've heard men tell
  Of Tantalus' doomed child,
Chained upon Sipylus' high rock fell,
  That clung like ivy wild,
Drenched by the pelting rain and whirling snow,
  Left there to pine,
While on her frozen breast the tears aye flow—
  Her fate is mine.

CHORUS

She was sprung of gods, divine,
Mortals we of mortal line.
Like renown with gods to gain
Recompenses all thy pain.
Take this solace to thy tomb
Hers in life and death thy doom.

ANTIGONE

Alack, alack! Ye mock me. Is it meet
  Thus to insult me living, to my face?
Cease, by our country's altars I entreat,
  Ye lordly rulers of a lordly race.
O fount of Dirce, wood-embowered plain
  Where Theban chariots to victory speed,
Mark ye the cruel laws that now have wrought my bane,
  The friends who show no pity in my need!
Was ever fate like mine? O monstrous doom,
  Within a rock-built prison sepulchered,
To fade and wither in a living tomb,
  An alien midst the living and the dead.

CHORUS

In thy boldness over-rash
Madly thou thy foot didst dash
'Gainst high Justice' altar stair.
Thou a father's guilt dost bear.

[558]

ANTIGONE

At this thou touchest my most poignant pain,
  My ill-starred father's piteous disgrace,
The taint of blood, the hereditary stain,
  That clings to all of Labdacus' famed race.
Woe worth the monstrous marriage-bed where lay
  A mother with the one her womb had borne;
Therein I was conceived, woe worth the day,
  Fruit of incestuous sheets, a maid forlorn,
And now I pass, accursed and unwed,
  To meet them as an alien there below;
And thee, O brother, in marriage ill-bestead,
  'Twas thy dead hand that dealt me this death-blow.

CHORUS

Religion has her claims, 'tis true,
Let rites be paid when rites are due.
Yet is it ill to disobey
The powers who hold by might the sway.
Thou hast withstood authority,
A self-willed rebel, thou must die.

ANTIGONE

Unwept, unwed, unfriended, hence I go,
  No longer may I see the day's bright eye;
Not one friend left to share my bitter woe,
  And o'er my ashes heave one passing sigh.

Creon, not wanting the blood of Antigone to stain the honor of Thebes, tells her she will have sufficient food to keep her alive in her dark tomb. Thus she is at liberty either to die or to live but never may she see again the earth or sky. Antigone is led away.

The great blind seer of Thebes, Teiresias, whom Odysseus later consulted among the shades, has himself led into the presence of his country's ruler. Creon, who was in the habit of consulting the prophet on matters of importance to the state, has never found this living oracle to be wrong. Hence he is frightened when

Teiresias tells him that he hovers on the edge of peril. Dogs and crows, the sage tells him, have gorged themselves on the flesh of Polyneices. The Gods are angered and disdain the burnt offerings at the altars. Let Creon quickly order burial for the son of Oedipus. Once more the king is angered and hotly accuses Teiresias of accepting a bribe to give him such advice. The prophet, hurt by such justice, says he will reveal a mystery he had not thought to speak. Creon has wronged the Gods by sending below the earth a living creature and by leaving a dead one upon it. Such sin will only end by taking the life of a child of his. In addition, the neighboring states, some of whose warriors followed Polyneices to the walls of Thebes, will be enraged that those who died were not given burial. They will band together to avenge such insult to their honor.

The Chorus of Theban Elders, accustomed for many years to heed the words of Teiresias, is aroused to a clamor of protest against their king. Creon, shaken by Teiresias' prophecy, is now quick to yield. What advice have they to offer? he asks. He will follow it implicitly. The Chorus urges him to free Antigone and to bury her brother. But he should trust no one else to do this. He must go himself. Ordering his men to arm themselves with axes and to hasten to the living tomb of Antigone, where he will join them, Creon leaves at once.

The old men of the Chorus, fearful lest tragedy may not be averted, pray to Dionysus, patron God of Thebes, to aid them in their need. A messenger enters and brings them fresh fears by saying that, of all men, Creon seemed the most to be envied but now he is doomed to a living death, for a life without joy cannot be called by any other name. Haemon is dead, slain by his own hand.

Eurydice, wife of Creon, is attracted by the loud talking and catching something of its import, comes to ask the messenger for his tale. He tells of how he went with Creon to the poor, mangled body of Polyneices, which, with appropriate rights, they placed upon a funeral pyre. This done they hastened to the cave to which Antigone had been consigned to keep a tryst with death. As they approached they met a guard who, hearing from within the cave a wail, had run to inform his lord that all was not well. Hastening to the cavern's entrance, they heard Haemon's voice raised in lamentation and saw that the rocks sealing the tomb had been partially removed. Within, through semi-darkness, they beheld the body of Antigone, dead, a noose of linen about her neck. Clasping the cold form close to his breast, Haemon lay, weeping for his bride and cursing his father's cruelty. The king rushed to his son crying to him to come forth. Haemon, glaring at him, spat in his face and, drawing his sword, struck fiercely at his father. Creon jumped backwards and the blow flew wide of its mark. Then the boy, turning the sword upon himself, thrust it deep into his side, and, with choking breath, clasped Antigone in his arms, the red stream from his mouth pouring over her cheek as he expired. And there they lay, two corpses, their marriage rites consummated in the halls of death. The messenger stops and, without a word, Eurydice walks away.

At first, the Elders are amazed at the Queen's silence; then the messenger hopes it merely means she is too proud to weep in public. The elders have misgivings still and are about to hurry after her when Creon returns. Heavy with sorrow, he laments the death of his son, saying that the blame for all this tragedy lies on his own shoulders. A second messenger rushes in, announcing that Creon has not yet known the full cup of pain; another dear one waits for him at home, lying cold in death. Eurydice had returned to the palace and slain herself. Close to the altar she had thrust herself upon a keen-edged sword and, lying wounded, had wept for her dead son. Then, with dying breath, she had cursed her husband, murderer of her son.

Creon, overcome by the doom he has unleashed, says he is guilty of these three deaths. He can ask for but one thing: a two-edged sword with which he can imitate his wife and son.

CREON

Away with me, a worthless wretch who slew
Unwitting thee, my son, thy mother too.
Whither to turn I know not; every way
  Leads but astray,
And on my head I feel the heavy weight
  Of crushing fate.

CHORUS

Of happiness the chiefest part
  Is a wise heart:
And to defraud the gods in aught
  With peril's fraught.
Swelling words of high-flown might
Mightily the gods do smite.
Chastisement for errors past
Wisdom brings to age at last.

MEDEA

By

Euripides

EURIPIDES (*480–406* B.C.), a Greek tragedian, was born at
Salamis the year the Persian fleet was defeated. Although his
parents were poor he gained a good education and he produced his first play *The Daughters of Peleus* at the age of 25.
He gained his first prize as a playwright after fourteen years of
disappointment. He was a friend of Socrates and of other great
Greek thinkers and artists. But, morbidly sensitive, he felt he
was misunderstood by his fellow Athenians. He lived in a library
and his views on life and religion were generally skeptical.
After his death a cenotaph was erected to him at Athens
upon which it was declared that all Greece was his monument. In sharp contrast to his two great predecessors,
Aeschylus and Sophocles, Euripides portrayed the new moral,
social and political movements which were transforming
Athens late in the 5th century B.C. He was the most modern
of the Greek dramatists and in some plays he appears as the
precursor of the modern romantic school. His popularity increased after his death and he exercised a profound influence
on the Roman and Byzantine periods, also influencing modern
English, German and especially French dramatists. His great
play *Medea* (one of the ninety he wrote) was produced 431 B.C.

DRAMATIS PERSONAE

NURSE OF MEDEA'S CHILDREN	JASON
CHILDREN'S GUARDIAN	AEGEUS, KING OF ATHENS
MEDEA	MESSENGER
CHORUS OF CORINTHIAN LADIES	CHILDREN OF MEDEA
CREON, KING OF CORINTH	

SCENE: In front of Jason's House at Corinth.

THE NURSE who cares for Medea's children stand at the gates of
her mistress' home bemoaning the evils that the years have

[563]

wrought. Since Medea aided Jason in his famous quest of the Golden Fleece she has lived happily with him and their children, even though she was a foreigner and he a Greek. Now, however, in Corinth, Jason has expressed a desire to leave Medea and to marry a daughter of Creon, king of the realm. Medea, who loved her lord utterly, is tormented with anguish, crying out that this is her payment for the many things she has done for Jason. At times her mood is so grim that the Nurse is frightened for her young charges, whom Medea now seems to loathe.

The Children's Guardian, seeing the Nurse lost in revery, asks her of what she thinks. When she tells him, he informs her that Medea's ills have but begun. There is a rumor, he says, that Creon may banish the foreign woman and her children. Jason is so enamored of Creon's daughter that he will probably do nothing to alter the sentence, if it be pronounced. The children enter the house and the voice of their mother rings out from inside.

MEDEA

Woe! I have suffered, have suffered foul wrongs that may waken,
  may waken
Mighty lamentings full well! O ye children accursed from the
  womb,
Hence to destruction, ye brood of a loved one forsaken, forsaken!
Hence with your father, and perish our home in the blackness of
  doom!

NURSE

Ah me, in the father's offences
  What part have the babes, that thine hate
Should blast them?—forlorn innocences,
  How sorely I fear for your fate!
How terrible princes' moods are!—
  Long ruling, unschooled to obey,—
Unforgiving, unsleeping their feuds are:
  Better life's level way.

Be it mine, if in greatness I may not,
  In quiet and peace to grow old.

Sweeter name than "The Mean" shall ye say not,
 And to taste it is sweetness untold.
But to men never weal above measure
 Availed: on its perilous height
The Gods in their hour of displeasure
 The heavier smite.

The Chorus of Corinthian Ladies enters and asks the Nurse why Medea is heard wailing. Medea's voice is heard again, protesting that for love of Jason she slew her own brother but that now she will not be satisfied until he and his bride are ruined. The Chorus asks the Nurse to tell Medea that they are her friends and want to see her. The Nurse enters the house and Medea comes forth. Impassionedly she addresses the assembled women, trying to show them that her own troubles are really the result of the social position of woman.

MEDEA

Of all things upon earth that bleed and grow
A herb most bruised is woman. We must pay
Our store of gold, hoarded for that one day,
To buy us some man's love, and lo, they bring
A master of our flesh! There comes the sting
Of the whole shame. And then the jeopardy,
For good or ill what shall that master be;
Reject she cannot: and if he but stays
His suit, 'tis shame on all that woman's days.
So thrown amid new laws, new places, why,
'Tis magic she must have, or prophecy—
Home never taught her that—how best to guide
Toward peace this thing that sleepeth at her side.
And she who, laboring long, shall find some way
Whereby her lord may bear with her, nor fray
His yoke too fiercely, blessed is the breath
That woman draws! Else, let her pray for death.
Her lord, if he be wearied of the face
Withindoors, gets him forth; some merrier place

Will ease his heart: but she waits on, her whole
Vision enchained on a single soul.
And then, forsooth, 'tis they that face the call
Of war, while we sit sheltered, hid from all
Peril!—False mocking! Sooner would I stand
Three times to face their battles, shield in hand,
Than bear one child.

Creon enters the scene and tells Medea that she and her two
sons are now exiles and must leave Corinth at once. Medea demands to be told the reason for this drastic measure. The answer
is that it is known that she has been threatening terrible things
and that Creon would fear for his daughter's safety if he permitted
Medea to remain. She answers that his daughter has done no
wrong; it is Jason who has committed the injury and whom she
hates. However, if she can stay in Corinth she will be quiet and do
nothing about her wrongs. Creon is adamant and insists that she
must go. Finally, she asks permission to remain but one more
day in order to find a refuge for her children. To this he agrees,
though with misgivings, adding that if she is in the city at the next
sunrise, she will be killed. He leaves and Medea quickly shows
her reasons for requesting the one day in Corinth. She will kill
Creon, his daughter, and Jason. Her chief problem is to determine
how she can effect the three deaths without being caught.

Jason comes to see Medea and tells her that he did not want
her to be banished. It was her own threatening words which
frightened the king. Jason contends that he has no ill-feeling
toward her. He merely was in love with another woman and
wanted to marry her. As for Medea and his children—he had
come to give them money and anything else they might need.
Medea rails at him and asks where she shall go. Did she not save
his life? Did she not bear his children? Now where can she go,
having made enemies of her own people for his sake. Jason replies that in return for what she did he has given her a home in
Greece where she could know justice and respect of law. He is
not marrying the king's daughter because he is tired of Medea. He
is attempting to find peace, honor, and wealth, so that Medea
and the children as well as he could find a home and cease to be

wanderers, struggling with poverty. The Chorus thinks the words hypocritical and Medea says that he was hiding his forthcoming marriage. Jason departs, saying that he would do all he could but that Medea's pride will prove her undoing.

Aegeus, king of Athens, enters and greets Medea. He had made a pilgrimage to the oracle of Phoebus because he was childless. The oracle had spoken thus: "Loose not the wine-skin's forward-jutting foot till to the hearth ancestral back thou come." Now he is traveling to his friend, Pittheus, king of Troezen, a man renowned for his wisdom, to ask him to explain the words. Medea tells him of Jason's coming marriage and of her banishment. If he will give her refuge in Athens she will make charms so that he can have children. Aegeus tells her that he will welcome her to Athens but that he cannot escort her there. If she can come there safely he will assure her that no one will harm her so long as she cares to stay. At her request he swears that, once she comes to Athens, he will not give her up to her enemies, if they desire to take her away. Whereupon he departs.

Now that she can escape the vengeance of the Corinthians, Medea lays her plans. She will send some one to ask Jason to come to her and when he arrives she will say that she knows now that she was wrong and, although she is willing to go into exile she would like her children to remain behind. Then she will send the king's daughter a robe and a golden diadem so poisoned that the wearer of them will die instantly. When this has come to pass she will slay both her sons and flee to Athens. The chorus attempts to dissuade her but she is firm and sends the Nurse for Jason.

When Jason comes Medea addresses him as she had planned. He is happy at her sudden change and promises to plead that his sons may stay in Corinth. When he speaks of their future Medea weeps but does not alter her purpose. She sends the poisoned gifts to Jason's future bride, saying that these may move her to beg her father that Jason's sons may remain. The children take the gifts and go off with their father to deliver them. Shortly thereafter they return with their Guardian who tells Medea that her request is granted; the children may stay. This touches her so deeply that she forswears her vow to kill them or

to do their father any more harm but then, steeling herself, she
says she must go on as she had planned.

A messenger rushes in, crying to Medea to flee. The princess
died when she put on the robe and diadem and her old father,
clasping the dead body in his grief, was also killed. There is no
time to waste. Medea must go at once or she cannot escape.

MEDEA

Friends, my resolve is taken, with all speed
To slay my children, and to flee this land,
And not to linger and to yield my sons
To death by other hands more merciless.
They needs must die: and, since it needs must be,
Even I will give them death, who gave them life.
Up, gird thee for the fray, mine heart! Why loiter
To do the dread ill deeds that must be done?
Come, wretched hand of mine, grasp thou the sword;
Grasp!—on to the starting-point of a blasted life!
Oh, turn not craven!—think not on thy babes,
How dear they are, how thou didst bear them: nay,
For this short day do thou forget thy sons,
Thereafter mourn them. For, although thou slay,
Yet dear they are, and I—am wretched, wretched.

She enters the house.

CHORUS

O Earth, O all-revealing splendor
    Of the Sun, look down on a woman accurst,
    Or ever she slake the murder-thirst
Of a mother whose hands would smite the tender
        Fruit of her womb.
Look down, for she sprang of thy lineage golden:
Man's vengeance threatens—thy seed are holden
        'Neath the shadow of doom!
But thou, O heaven-begotten glory,
Restrain her, refrain her: the wretched, the gory
Erinys by demons dogged, we implore thee,
        Snatch thou from yon home!

For naught was the childbirth-travail wasted;
  For naught didst thou bear them, the near and the dear,
  O thou who hast fled through the Pass of Fear,
From the dark-blue Clashing Crags who hast hasted
      Speeding thy flight!
Alas for her!—wherefore hath grim wrath stirred her
Through depths of her soul, that ruthless murderer
      Her wrongs must requite?
For stern upon mortals the vengeance falleth
For kin's blood spilt; from the earth it calleth,
A voice from the Gods, and the slayers appalleth
      On whose homes it shall light.

From inside the house children's cries can be heard.

FIRST CHILD

What shall I do?—how flee my mother's hands?

SECOND CHILD

I know not, dearest brother. Death is here.

CHORUS

Ah the cry!—dost thou hear it?—the children's cry!
Wretch!—Woman of cursed destiny!
Shall I enter? My heart crieth, "Rescue the children from murder
nigh!"

The women beat at the barred doors.

FIRST CHILD

Help!—for the Gods' sake help! Sore is our need!

SECOND CHILD

The swords' death-net is closing round us now!

Silence follows. And from beneath the door blood starts to flow.

As the women shrink back Jason enters, followed by servants.
He has come in haste lest the Corinthians, in their anger, take

vengeance on his guiltless children. The Chorus tells Jason that his sons are dead, slain by their mother's hand. He orders his followers to break down the doors and avenge him in Medea's blood. At that moment Medea appears above the palace roof in a chariot drawn by dragons. She is a descendant of the Sun-God and he has sent the chariot, she says, to protect her. At first Jason curses her; then, thinking of his dead sons, he asks that she at least allow him to give them proper burial. This she refuses, saying that she will bury them herself where no foe can rifle the graves. Finally, distraught, he pleads to kiss their dead lips, but this, too, she refuses him.

CHORUS

Great treasure halls hath Zeus in heaven,
From whence to man strange dooms be given,
Past hope or fear.
And the end men looked for cometh not,
And a path is there where no man thought:
So hath it fallen here.

HAMLET
Prince of Denmark

By

William Shakespeare

WILLIAM SHAKESPEARE (*1564–1616*) is considered the greatest of dramatic poets. He was born in Stratford-on-Avon, England, the third child of a wealthy family. He received an education at his home school but when he was 14 his father's fortunes failed and he became a butcher boy to aid his family. When he was 19 he married Anne Hathaway, eight years his senior. About four years after his marriage Shakespeare left Stratford, allegedly for deer-stealing, and went to London. In the metropolis he earned his living by holding horses at the door of the Globe Theater also getting employment as a prompter and call boy. When he was 29 he published his first narrative poem, *Venus and Adonis,* which was quickly followed by his earlier experiments in comedy such as *Love's Labour's Lost.* This was later presented before Queen Elizabeth. When he was 35 he became connected with the new "Globe" playhouse near London Bridge and with the Blackfriars Theater where his dramas were presented. During the opening years of the 17th century he ceased for a time to write comedy and engaged upon his great series of tragedies. In 1608 he was again writing comedies, and romances. He died in March 1616, which is supposed to be the anniversary of his fifty-second birthday.

AT ELSINORE on a platform before the castle stands Franciscon, a soldier keeping guard. The clock strikes twelve in the cold night air and the chilled and anxious guard is glad to be relieved by an officer, Bernardo. A moment later appears Marcellus, who is accompanied by Horatio, a visitor at the castle. Marcellus asks Bernardo whether a certain dreadful apparition has appeared again or is it, as Horatio has suggested, a frightened soldier's fantasy? While they are arguing, the Ghost appears and at the instigation of Marcellus, Horatio addresses it—

HORATIO

What art thou that usurp'st this time of night,
Together with that fair and warlike form
In which the majesty of buried Denmark
Did sometimes march? by heaven I charge thee speak!

It was the very figure of the king in armor that he wore when he fought Norway and killed King Fortinbras, and now is Norway up in arms again as young Fortinbras threatens Denmark. The state is rotten and ominous are the times even as they were when Julius Caesar fell. Again the Ghost appears but when conjured to speak of his sad country's fate, it stands and stares in silence. It was about to speak but the cock crowed and heralded the dawn, whereupon the Ghost faded away. Horatio and Marcellus leave the platform resolved to impart to young Hamlet what they have seen.

HORATIO

But, look, the morn in russet mantle clad,
Walks o'er the dew of yon high eastern hill.
Break we our watch up, and, by my advice,
Let us impart what we have seen to-night
Unto young Hamlet; for, upon my life,
This spirit, dumb to us, will speak to him.

Marcellus agrees to this and the two depart knowing where they can find the young prince.

King Claudius, holding court, bids his subjects lament the loss of their late king and yet rejoice in the reign of his brother now the husband of his widow, Queen Gertrude, that there may be mirth in funeral and dirge in matrimony. The king dispatches emissaries to Norway, conveying Denmark's greetings and warnings, gives Laertes, son of the Lord Chamberlain Polonius, leave to return to Paris whence he had come for the coronation, and then turns his attention to Hamlet—

HAMLET

KING

But now, my cousin Hamlet, and my son—
How is it that the clouds still hang on you?

HAMLET

Not so, my lord; I am too much i' the sun.

QUEEN

Good Hamlet, cast thy nighted color off,
And let thine eye look like a friend on Denmark.
Do not forever with thy veiled lids
Seek for thy noble father in the dust.
Thou know'st 'tis common; all that live must die,
Passing through nature to eternity.

HAMLET

Ay, madam, it is common.

QUEEN

          If it be,
Why seems it so particular with thee?

HAMLET

Seems, madam! nay, it is; I know not 'seems.'
'Tis not alone my inky cloak, good mother,
Nor customary suits of solemn black,
Nor windy suspiration of forc'd breath,
No, nor the fruitful river in the eye,
Nor the dejected haviour of the visage,
Together with all forms, moods, and shows of grief,
That can denote me truly; these indeed seem,
For they are actions that a man might play:
But I have that within which passeth show;
These but the trappings and the suits of woe.

King Claudius rebukes Hamlet for his excessive grief over
his father's death to which he would fain have him reconciled; Queen Gertrude begs him not to return to the university at

Wittenberg but remain in Denmark and after he gives his consent to her plea King and Queen and court exeunt from the stage leaving Hamlet alone—

HAMLET

O that this too, too solid flesh would melt,
Thaw, and resolve itself into a dew!
Or that the Everlasting had not fix'd
His canon 'gainst self-slaughter! O God! O God!
How weary, stale, flat, and unprofitable
Seem to me all the uses of this world!

Although as yet Hamlet knows not the manner of his father's death, he contemplates suicide as an escape from a situation which causes him so much grief over his father's death and his mother's hasty marriage with his uncle.

Now enter Horatio, Marcellus and Bernardo who come upon Hamlet brooding over his father's funeral and his mother's wedding. He tells them he can still see his father in his mind's eye whereupon Horatio tells him about the vision they had had of a kingly figure fully armed and greatly resembling Hamlet's father. They wished Hamlet to know of this and would have him watch with them.

HAMLET

Indeed, indeed, sirs, but this troubles me. Hold you the watch to-night?

MARCELLUS AND BERNARDO

We do, my lord.

HAMLET

Arm'd, say you?

MARCELLUS AND BERNARDO

Arm'd, my lord.

HAMLET

From top to toe?

[574]

MARCELLUS AND BERNARDO

My lord, from head to foot.

HAMLET

Then saw you not his face?

HORATIO

O, yes, my lord; he wore his beaver up.

HAMLET

What looked he, frowningly?

HORATIO

A countenance more in sorrow than in anger.

Hamlet decides to watch with the others that very night with the hope that the Ghost will walk again, and if it resembles his father he will speak to it though all Hell should bid him hold his peace.

Laertes, having obtained the King's permission to return to Paris, takes leave of his sister, Ophelia, bidding her beware of Hamlet's attentions for, while he may profess to love her he as a prince is not free to marry whom he would. Ophelia, although reluctantly, promises to heed her brother's advice, whereupon Polonius enters, chides Laertes for tarrying and then dismisses him with fatherly advice—

And these precepts in thy memory
See thou character. Give thy thoughts no tongue,
Nor any unproportion'd thought his act,
Be thou familiar, but by no means vulgar,
Those friends thou hast, and their adoption tried,
Grapple them to thy soul with hoops of steel;
But do not dull thy palm with entertainment
Of each new-hatch'd, unfledg'd comrade. Beware
Of entrance to a quarrel, but, being in,
Bear 't that the opposed may beware of thee.
Give every man thy ear, but few thy voice;
Take each man's censure, but reserve thy judgment.

.   .   .

[575]

Neither a borrower nor a lender be;
For loan oft loses both itself and friend,
And borrowing dulls the edge of husbandry,
This above all: to thine own self be true,
And it must follow, as the night the day,
Thou canst not then be false to any man.

Laertes gone, Polonius rebukes Ophelia for having been too much in Hamlet's company, assures her that his protestations of love mean nothing, and commands her to shut herself from the prince's presence. As Ophelia had promised her brother to heed his advice, so she assures her father she will obey his command.

Hamlet, with Horatio and Marcellus, is upon the platform. The air is nipping and bites shrewdly. The bell tolls twelve. There is a flourish of trumpets and the boom of a small cannon as King celebrates his nocturnal revel. Then the Ghost appears.

HAMLET
What may this mean
That thou, dead corpse, again in complete steel
Revisit'st thus the glimpses of the moon,
Making night hideous; and we fools of nature
So horridly to shake our disposition
With thoughts beyond the reaches of our souls?
Say, why is this? wherefore? what should we do?

The Ghost draws away beckoning Hamlet to follow him, which he does in spite of his friends' attempts to hold him back. Once they are far removed the Ghost speaks—

GHOST
I am thy father's spirit,
Doom'd for a certain term to walk the night,
And for the day confin'd to fast in fires,
Till the foul crimes done in my days of nature
Are burnt and purg'd away.

[576]

Now, Hamlet hear:
'Tis given out that, sleeping in my orchard,
A serpent stung me; so the whole ear of Denmark
Is by a forged process of my death
Rankly abus'd; but know, thou noble youth,
The serpent that did sting thy father's life
Now wears his crown.

HAMLET

O my prophetic soul!
My uncle!

After bidding Hamlet remember him and avenge his death, the
Ghost departs. Hamlet's friends now come upon him and im-
portune him to disclose what he has learned. He gives them to
understand that the King is guilty of his father's murder and
makes them swear upon his sword that they will in no wise reveal what they this night have seen. He proposes the oath of
silence and the Ghost from beneath the earth gives the sepulchral
command "swear." As they leave the watch and return to the
castle, Hamlet voices the peculiar plight he is in by saying—

The time is out of joint;—O cursed spite,
That ever I was born to set it right.

Hamlet, having warned his friends that he intended to feign
madness, or "put an antic disposition on," now appears before
Ophelia in dirty and dishevelled garb, with pale face and trembling
knees and carrying himself in a most extraordinary manner. This
the maiden reports to her father who takes it to be the "very
ecstasy of love" and decides to convey the matter, along with
Hamlet's letters to Ophelia, to the King and Queen. The sympathetic Queen is disposed to credit the idea that Hamlet is
mad for love, but the guilty king is suspicious, whereupon Polonius
suggests that they contrive to release the maiden in Hamlet's
presence to observe his attitude when alone with her, the king
and Polonius to be in hiding.
Meanwhile, Hamlet's school-mates, Guildenstern and Rosencrantz, have arrived at the castle having been sent for to spy

upon Hamlet and learn the cause of his lunacy. Hamlet greets
them warmly although he is suspicious of their errand at Elsinore
and finally makes them confess they were sent for on his account,
as he explains to them—

I will tell you why; so shall my anticipation prevent your discovery. . . . I have of late—but wherefore I know not—lost all
my mirth, forgone all custom of exercises; and indeed it goes so
heavily with my disposition that this goodly frame, the earth, seems
to me a sterile promontory; this most excellent canopy, the air,
look you, this brave, o'erhanging firmament, this majestical roof
fretted with golden fire,—why, it appears no other thing to me
than a foul and pestilent congregation of vapours. What a piece
of work is man! how noble in reason! how infinite in faculty! . . .
Man delights not me; no, nor woman neither, though by your
smiling you seem to say so.

Rosencrantz replies to this rhetorical arraignment of nature and
mankind by insinuating that then Hamlet will not like the strolling
players who are on their way to the court, but finds that the
melancholy Prince is pleased to hear of their coming. He recognizes them as old friends, reminds them of some of their former
performances and requests the first player to recite for him
Pyrrhus' slaughter of Priam and the grief of Hecuba, the victim's
wife. This the player does but breaks down in tears when he
comes to Hecuba's outburst of grief. Since the players have come
to Elsinore to amuse Hamlet, he arranges to have them give a
little play, *The Murder of Gonzago,* into which he introduces
some dozen or sixteen lines to fit the occasion in the court of
King Claudius. Hamlet is now left alone and begins to brood
over his own weakness and cowardice; his indifference toward
a real wrong done his father contrasts most strikingly with the
player's assumed sorrow for Hecuba—

HAMLET

Oh, what a rogue and peasant slave am I!
Is it not monstrous that this player here,
But in a fiction, in a dream of passion,
Could force his soul so to his own conceit
That from her workings all his visage wan'd,

Tears in his eyes, distraction in 's aspect,
A broken voice, and his whole function suiting
With forms to his conceit? and all for nothing?
For Hecuba!
What's Hecuba to him, or he to Hecuba,
That he should weep for her? What would he do,
Had he the motive and the cue for passion
That I have?

.　　　　　.　　　　　.

Fie upon 't! foh! About, my brain! I have heard
That guilty creatures sitting at a play
Have by the very cunning of the scene
Been struck so to the soul that presently
They have proclaim'd their malefactions;
For murther, though it have no tongue, will speak
With most miraculous organ.

.　　　　　.　　　　　.

The play's the thing
Wherein I'll catch the conscience of the king.

The King can gather nothing from the observations Rosencrantz and Guildenstern have made as to the cause of Hamlet's
lunacy, hence he is willing to adopt Polonius's suggestion that,
if the Prince's trouble is love-madness this fact will be manifest
when he is confronted by Ophelia. The King and Polonius plant
the maiden on a prie-dieu with a prayer-book in her hands and
themselves withdraw to a hiding-place. Hamlet now appears,
meditating suicide.

HAMLET

To be or not to be,—that is the question:
Whether 'tis nobler in the mind to suffer
The slings and arrows of outrageous fortune,
Or to take up arms against a sea of troubles
And by opposing end them? To die,—to sleep,—
No more; and by a sleep to say we end
The heart-ache and the thousand natural shocks
That flesh is heir to,—'tis a consummation

Devoutly to be wished. To die,—to sleep—
To sleep! perchance to dream! ay, there's the rub;
For in that sleep of death what dreams may come
When we have shuffled off this mortal coil
Must give us pause. There's the respect
That makes calamity of so long life;
For who would bear the whips and scorns of time,
The oppressor's wrong, the proud man's contumely,
The pangs of dispriz'd love, the law's delay,
The insolence of office, and the spurns
That patient merit of the unworthy takes,
When he himself might his quietus make
With a bare bodkin? who would fardels bear,
To grunt and sweat under a weary life,
But that the dread of something after death,
The undiscover'd country from whose bourne
No traveller returns, puzzles the will
And makes us rather bear those ills we have
Than fly to others that we know not of?
Thus conscience does make cowards of us all;
And thus the native hue of resolution
Is sicklied o'er with the pale cast of thought,
And enterprises of great pith and moment
With this regard their currents turn awry
And lose the name of action.—Soft you now!
The fair Ophelia!—Nymph, in thy orisons
Be all my sins remember'd.

OPHELIA
      Good my lord,
How does your honour for this many a day?

HAMLET
I humbly thank you; well, well, well.

OPHELIA
My lord, I have remembrances of yours
That I have longed long to deliver:
I pray you, now receive them.

HAMLET

No, not I;

I never gave you aught.

OPHELIA

My honour'd lord, I know right well you did,
And with them words of so sweet breath composed
As made the things more rich; their perfume lost,
Take these again, for to the noble mind
Rich gifts wax poor when givers prove unkind.

Instead of expressing love-madness, Hamlet manifests a mania
of a different sort. He questions the beauty and virtue of the
fair Ophelia, condemns marriage as the breeding ground of sinners, breaks out into a tirade against all women and bids the maiden
get her to a nunnery. Ophelia feels that a noble mind is quite
overthrown while the King and Polonius realize that the cause of
Hamlet's madness is not love.

Night has come and it is time for the strolling players to present
their little play, *The Murder of Gonzago*. The play deals with
second marriage and the Player Queen protests that, were her husband to die, she would never marry again. Queen Gertrude thinks
the lady "doth protest too much;" King Claudius suspects some
offense in the play. The climax comes when a certain Lucianus
pours poison into the ear of the Player King as he lies asleep on
the stage.

HAMLET

He poisons him i' the garden for 's estate. . . You shall see anon
how the murtherer gets the love of Gonzago's wife.

OPHELIA

The king rises!

HAMLET

What, frighted with false fire!

QUEEN

How fares my lord?

[581]

POLONIUS

Give o'er the play!

KING

Give me some light!—away!

It is evident to Hamlet, as also to Horatio whom Hamlet has
requested to watch the King, that Claudius is guilty of the elder
Hamlet's murder. Rosencrantz and Guildenstern now return to the
stage to tell Hamlet that his astonished mother wishes to speak
with him privately. On his way to his mother's bed-chamber, Hamlet comes upon King Claudius who, having laid his sword aside, is
kneeling in pentitential prayer. Seizing the King's sword Hamlet
was about to kill him but refrains on the ground that to slay him
at such a sanctified moment would be to insure the safe passage of
his soul to Heaven. Hamlet now makes his way to his mother's
chamber where Polonius for the purpose of eavesdropping has concealed himself behind the arras. Hamlet chides his mother for her
hasty second marriage especially with a man who is so inferior in
appearance to her first husband, his own father. He becomes so
violent that, in fear, she sends a call for help, which is echoed by the
hidden Polonius. Thinking it is the King who is concealed there,
Hamlet drives his sword through the arras and, crying out, "How
now! a rat? Dead, for a ducat, dead," and kills the miserable
chamberlain.

While Hamlet continues to chide his mother for her hasty second marriage, the Ghost appears again, this time being seen by
Hamlet alone—

HAMLET

How is it with you, lady?

QUEEN

Alas, how is 't with you,
That you do bend your eye on vacancy
And with the incorporeal air do hold discourse?

.   .   .

Upon the heat and flame of thy distemper
Sprinkle cool patience. Whereon do you look?

[582]

HAMLET

On him, on him! Look you, how pale he glares!
His form and cause conjoin'd, preaching to stones,
Would make them capable.—Do not look upon me;
Lest with his piteous action you convert
My stern effects: then what I have to do
Will want true color; tears perchance for blood.

It is now quite evident that Hamlet is insane and must be sent away to England. The king, well guarded and flanked by Guildenstern and Rosencrantz, accosts Hamlet, demands that he tell them what he has done with the body of Polonius and informs him that he is to be dispatched to England with Guildenstern and Rosencrantz as his guards. Hamlet gives them some idea of where they may find the corpse and assents to the plan to send him to England. On his way to the ship he encounters the Norwegian captain who is leading the expedition of young Fortinbras through Denmark to Poland, and contrasts his habitual hesitation with the thoughtless resolution of this delicate and tender prince from the north who knows nothing of Hamlet's scruple

Of thinking too precisely on the event,—
A thought which, quarter'd, hath but one part wisdom
And ever three parts coward.

The way Hamlet has spurned Ophelia and now her father's death has so upset the maiden's mind that she behaves strangely, kicking at straws, gathering wild flowers and singing bawdy songs. Her brother, Laertes, having learned of his father's death, returns to Denmark, gathers a little band of followers and attempts to wrest the throne from King Claudius, whom he suspects of the murder. While the king in majestic manner is appeasing the young man, Ophelia enters; she seems to be seeking the "beauteous majesty of Denmark" and distributes an apron-full of flowers to those present. Later on her body is found beneath the over-hanging branches of a willow at the bottom of a brook.

The King now lets Laertes know that it was Hamlet who killed his father, and together they plot the prince's death should he return to Denmark, and they have a suspicion that he is already

[583]

there. It so happened that Hamlet's ship was intercepted by a pirate craft and in the fracas he managed to board the other vessel which set him naked on the shores of Denmark. According to the plot, the King will inveigle Hamlet into a fencing duel with Laertes and will see to it that his sword will have no protecting button on its sharp point and, in addition to this, Laertes will dip the naked point into a strange poison bought of a mountebank in Paris. The King will complete the nefarious part by putting poison into the wine Hamlet will be likely to drink during the encounter.

Hamlet does make his return to Elsinore at the very hour they are burying Ophelia but, ignorant of whose grave yawns before him, he jests with the dissolute grave-digger who, in digging the young maid's grave, has exhumed the skull of a former court-fool, poor Yorick. The funeral procession approaches and Hamlet, with Horatio, retires to a deep shadow. The last rites, such as they were, have been said when Laertes, proclaiming deep love for his dead sister, leaps into her grave and bids them bury both the quick and the dead together. At this point, Hamlet emerges from the shadow and, protesting that his love for Ophelia was greater than that of "forty thousand brothers," exclaims—

> What is he whose grief
> Bears such an emphasis? Whose phrase of sorrow
> Conjures the wandering stars, and makes them stand
> Like wonder-wounded hearers? This is I,
> Hamlet the Dane!

Hamlet now leaps into Ophelia's grave and begins to wrestle with Laertes. They are parted and later their quarrel will be settled by the apparently friendly duel which King Claudius has arranged. When at last the duel comes off, Hamlet whips the murderous sword from Laertes's hand and politely proffers him his own. The deadly weapon has already pricked him but now he stabs Laertes with it. In the excitement, Queen Gertrude drinks from the bowl of poisoned wine and begins to swoon. Laertes falls and knowing he is fatally wounded repents and reveals the plot. While both Laertes and the Queen are dying, the King tries to skulk away but is pursued by Hamlet who, with what strength he has left, thrusts him through thus accomplishing at long last his revenge for the murder of his father.

The dying Hamlet falls into the arms of Horatio who, in his devotion to the Prince, would drink from the fatal bowl of wine but is prevented by Hamlet who, in dying says,

> If thou didst ever hold me in thy heart,
> Absent thee from felicity awhile,
> And in this harsh world draw thy breath in pain
> To tell my story.

> The rest is silence.

Afar off soldiers are marching and a shot is heard. Young Fortinbras has returned from the conquest of Poland. He surveys the tragic scene and bids four captains bear the body of Hamlet away.

> "Take up the bodies.—Such a sight as this
> Becomes the field, but here shows much amiss."

TARTUFFE

By

Molière

JEAN BAPTISTE POQUELIN MOLIÈRE (*1622–1673*) was probably
the greatest dramatist France ever produced. When he was 21
he embarked in theatrical affairs in Paris for three years and
then failed. His company proceeded to the provinces and
had enough success to carry on for twelve years and to enable
Molière to return triumphantly to Paris. His next farce, produced in Paris in 1659, took the capital by storm. For the ensuing fourteen years until his death, Molière produced one or
more plays every year which is one of the greatest dramatic
achievements in the history of the theatre. In 1665 the king
adopted Molière's troupe as a part of his court. There were
frequent attacks upon his plays as being vulgar, obscene or
impious but he answered his critics in a series of brilliant
satires. He died of a protracted lung disease and was buried in
the churchyard of St. Joseph. Many modern critics rank him
with Shakespeare and Aristophanes.

ORGON'S HOUSEHOLD should have been a very happy one. He had no
financial worries; his remarriage, after the death of his first wife,
to Elmire had been felicitous; his son Damis had grown up to be a
capable young man; and his daughter Mariane was betrothed to a
fine youth named Valère. Things would have progressed very
smoothly but for two people. The first of these was Mme Pernelle,
Orgon's mother, who criticized everything that Elmire did and
who was thoroughly in sympathy with the second trouble maker,
Tartuffe, a religious hypocrite whom the kind-hearted but all too
gullible Orgon, in a moment of misguided charity, had taken into
the bosom of his family. His stupid infatuation for Tartuffe may
be clearly seen in his conversation with his level-headed brother-

in-law Cléante and the servant Dorine, immediately upon Orgon's return home after a brief absence:

ORGON

Ah! good-morning, brother.

CLÉANTE

I am glad to see you back.

ORGON

Dorine . . . Just a moment, brother. You will let me find out how things have been going during my absence of two days. How is everybody?

DORINE

Day before yesterday Madame was feverish all day long and had a splitting headache.

ORGON

And Tartuffe?

DORINE

Tartuffe? Oh! he's fine, stout and fat, with a rosy complexion and ruddy lips.

ORGON

The poor fellow!

DORINE

When evening came she felt sickish, and her head ached so that she couldn't eat a mouthful.

ORGON

And Tartuffe?

DORINE

He ate his supper in her presence and very devoutly ate two partridges and half a leg of hashed mutton.

ORGON

The poor fellow!

DORINE

Her fever kept her awake all night. She didn't sleep a wink and we sat up with her until morning.

ORGON

And Tartuffe?

DORINE

Lulled by a pleasant drowsiness, he went straight from the table to his bed where he slept soundly and undisturbed until morning.

ORGON

The poor fellow!

DORINE

Finally, we induced her to allow herself to be bled and then she felt relieved.

ORGON

And Tartuffe?

DORINE

He regained courage, and fortifying his soul against all ills, and to make up for the blood that Madame had lost, he drank four big glasses of wine at breakfast.

ORGON

The poor fellow!

DORINE

Both are well again now and I shall go tell Madame how delighted you are over her recovery.

CLÉANTE

She is making fun of you, brother, and rightly so. How can you be so infatuated with a man as to forget all else?

ORGON

Stop there, my brother-in-law; you do not know the man of whom you are speaking. If you did, your astonishment would be boundless. I am quite another man since I have known him. He teaches me not to set my affections upon anything; he detaches my heart from all ties and I could see my brother, my children, my mother and my wife all die without worrying a bit about it.

CLÉANTE

Those are certainly humane feelings, my brother!

ORGON

You would have the same affection for him if you had seen him as I first saw him. Every day he used to come to church and with a pious air kneel down before me. The fervor of his prayers attracted the attention of the entire congregation. He would sigh deeply with saintly raptures and humbly kiss the ground. Having learned that he was poor I took him into my home and since then everything has seemed to prosper here. He reproves everything and, with a view to my honor, he shows extreme solicitude for my wife. He accuses himself of sin over the merest trifle. He was even heart-broken the other day for having killed a flea too angrily which he caught while he was saying his prayers.

Cléante used every argument possible to show Orgon the extent of his folly, but Orgon was unwilling to be convinced. Indeed, he seemed more than ever determined to heap bounties upon Tartuffe to the detriment of the members of his own family. His first act was to summon Mariane and tell her that he was making arrangements for her to marry Tartuffe. Mariane protested that Orgon had already given his promise that she might marry the man of her choice, Valère, but Orgon refused to listen to her entreaties. Valère, upon hearing the news, was so shocked that he almost had a serious quarrel with Mariane. Finally Dorine came to the rescue, prevailed upon Valère to enlist the aid of some of his friends to attempt to turn Orgon aside from his purpose, and promised to try to win over Madame Pernelle and secure the services of Cléante. Damis, thoroughly incensed upon hearing of Tartuffe's latest machinations, decided to lay a trap for him. Hiding in an alcove, he overheard the following conversation between the hypocrite and Elmire:

ELMIRE

I am very glad no one is watching us, for I want to speak to you privately on a certain matter.

TARTUFFE

I am equally delighted to find myself alone with you. I have often implored heaven to grant me this opportunity but it has always been denied me. I wish to lay bare my soul to you. (*He presses her fingers.*) Yes, Madame, such is my devotion . . .

ELMIRE

Oh! you are squeezing too hard!

TARTUFFE

It is from excess of zeal. I certainly had no intention of doing you any other harm. I would sooner . . . (*He places his hand on her knee.*)

ELMIRE

What is your hand doing there?

TARTUFFE

I am feeling your dress; the material is very soft.

ELMIRE

Oh! stop! I'm very ticklish. (*She pushes back her chair and Tartuffe draws his nearer.*)

TARTUFFE

Gracious! how marvelous the workmanship of this lace is; I couldn't imagine anything more beautifully made.

ELMIRE

True. But let us talk about our business. I hear that my husband means to break his word and give you his daughter. Is that true?

TARTUFFE

He did mention it, but really that is not the happiness for which I sigh. I see elsewhere the perfect attractions of that bliss that constitutes my desires.

TARTUFFE

ELMIRE

I am sure that your sighs tend heavenward and that nothing here on earth satisfies your desires.

TARTUFFE

And yet one's love of eternal beauty does not stifle one's love for temporal things. Our senses can easily be charmed by the perfect works that heaven has created. Its reflected loveliness shines forth in people like you. Your face has a beauty that dazzles one's eyes, and in gazing upon you I cannot fail to adore in you the author of nature. My heart is seized with a passionate love for the most beautiful of portraits in which He has depicted Himself. Such a passion cannot be guilty. It can easily be reconciled with modesty, and that is why I abandon my heart to you.

ELMIRE

This is a most gallant declaration, but rather surprising in a pious man like you.

TARTUFFE

Ah! perhaps I am pious, but I am none the less a man. When I gaze upon your celestial charms, my heart is captured and ceases to reason. After all, I am not an angel, and if you condemn me, you must lay the blame upon your beauty. If you would only take compassion upon me I should have for you a devotion beyond compare. Other people talk of their love affairs and dishonor the altar on which their love is sacrificed. But people like ourselves burn with a discreet passion and we know how to keep a secret. The care that we take of our reputation is an adequate guarantee to the woman we love, who, in accepting our devotion, enjoys love without scandal and pleasure without fear.

ELMIRE

But aren't you afraid that I might tell my husband about this?

TARTUFFE

Oh, I know that you are too gracious and that you will excuse my temerity. You realize that a man is not blind and that, after all, he is of the flesh.

[591]

ELMIRE

Others might act differently, but I shall say nothing to my husband provided that you will honestly do all you can to favor the marriage of Valère and Mariane.

At this juncture, Damis came from his hiding place and was just in the act of upbraiding Tartuffe for his conduct when Orgon came upon the scene. Assuming a bold front, Tartuffe admitted all of Damis's accusations. But Orgon believed that Tartuffe's admissions were made in order to prevent Orgon from being angry with his son. In a fit of rage he announced to Damis that he would disinherit him, and drove him from the house, telling him never to set foot in it again. Then, turning to Tartuffe, he told him to see Elmire frequently, in spite of everyone. He declared his intention of making Tartuffe his sole heir, and went in quest of his lawyer in order to deed over to the hypocrite all of his property.

When Orgon actually carried out his purpose, Cléante saw that there was nothing left to do but make a direct appeal to Tartuffe:

CLÉANTE

Granted that Damis may have acted unwisely and even may have made a false accusation against you, shouldn't you, as a Christian, forgive him? Should you allow yourself to be the cause of a father driving his own son away from home?

TARTUFFE

I do not bear Damis any ill-will, but the interests of heaven do not permit my interfering. If he returns, I must depart. After such behavior, any relations between us would give rise to scandal.

CLÉANTE

You are putting me off with slim excuses. Why do you take upon yourself the interests of heaven? Should fear of what people might think prevent you from doing a good deed?

TARTUFFE

I have already told you that I forgive him as heaven orders me to; but heaven does not command me to live with him.

TARTUFFE

CLÉANTE

And does heaven command you to take advantage of the whim of his father and accept as a gift property to which you haven't the slightest claim?

TARTUFFE

Those who know me will realize that I am not acting from selfish motives. If I accept this gift, it is because I fear that it might fall into wicked hands which might not use it, as I intend to do, for the glory of God and for the good of my fellowmen.

Thus, Cléante's efforts proved fruitless. When, however, Orgon persisted in his determination to make Mariane marry Tartuffe, Elmire could bear it no longer. After lengthy arguments, she prevailed upon Orgon to hide beneath a table, promising him that she would make Tartuffe disclose his true character and assuring her husband that he would see with his own eyes exactly how matters stood:

TARTUFFE

I hear that you wish to speak to me here.

ELMIRE

Yes, I have some secrets to reveal to you. But shut the door and look around for fear that we may be caught. We don't want to have another scene like the other one. Damis put me in a terrible fright on account of you. My husband having told us to be together all we liked gives me the opportunity of being shut up here alone with you without fear of blame. This justifies me in opening my heart to you, perhaps a bit too readily, in response to your love.

TARTUFFE

Such language is a little difficult to understand. A little while ago you assumed a different tone.

ELMIRE

Ah! if you are angry over such a refusal, how little do you understand about a woman's heart. In such moments our modesty always puts up a barrier against our tender feelings. Whatever reason we may find for the love which dominates us, we always feel a little ashamed in confessing it. We resist at first, but it is quite apparent that our heart surrenders. Can't you see that the reason I opposed your marriage with Mariane was that I took an interest in you and if the marriage took place I would find divided a love that I hoped would all be mine?

TARTUFFE

The happiness of pleasing you is my heart's fondest desire. But it may be that you are saying this merely in order to compel me to break off the promised marriage. To be very frank with you,, I shall not trust this tender speech of yours until it is verified by certain favors for which I sigh and which will convince me of the kindly feelings you bear me.

ELMIRE

(*Coughing to warn her husband.*) What, do you want to proceed so fast as to exhaust the tenderness of my heart at the outset? Will you not be satisfied unless we push things to the furthest extremity?

TARTUFFE

One's love can hardly be satisfied with mere words. I know I don't deserve your favors, but I shall not be convinced until you have satisfied my passion by real proofs.

ELMIRE

But how can I give in to your desires without offending the heaven about which you are constantly speaking?

TARTUFFE

· If heaven is the only thing that stands in the way, I can easily remove such an obstacle.

ELMIRE

But the decrees of heaven are terrifying.

TARTUFFE

Madame, I know the art of removing scruples. There is such a thing as rectifying the evil of an action by the purity of one's intention. I can instruct you on this point if you will permit yourself to be led by me. Satisfy my desire and have no fear. I shall answer for everything and take the sin upon my own shoulders. But you seem to be coughing a great deal, Madame.

ELMIRE

Yes, it is a most annoying cold. Well, I suppose that I must yield and grant you everything, for with less than that I can see that you will not be convinced. But go outside a moment to be sure nobody is looking.

ORGON

(*Coming out from under the table while Tartuffe is outside*): Well, I must confess he is an abominable man. I am simply stunned by this.

ELMIRE

What? You come out so soon? Get back again and wait until the end until everything is absolutely sure. Don't be in a hurry lest you be mistaken.

But Orgon had had enough and was fully convinced. When Tartuffe returned, Orgon told him to leave the house immediately, and was astounded when Tartuffe replied:

TARTUFFE

It is for you to leave, you who speak as if you were the master of it. I'll have you know that the house belongs to me. I'll show you how useless it is for you to resort to cowardly subterfuges in order to pick a quarrel with me. I'll punish this imposture of yours and I'll make you repent.

Tartuffe actually did own the house, for Orgon had deeded it over to him. But Orgon was even more worried about something else which he had kept secret from everyone. Orgon's friend Argas, in leaving the country, had entrusted a box of papers to Orgon for safekeeping, telling Orgon that his very life and fortune depended upon those papers. Orgon had foolishly given the box to Tartuffe, so that, in case of inquiry, he might deny having possession of it.

Orgon was in a bad predicament. As he fully expected, a bailiff came with orders for him to evacuate the house. But Tartuffe had overstepped himself in going to the king with accusations against Orgon, delivering to the court the box of papers. The king happened to have kindly recollections of Orgon who had once fought gallantly in his monarch's army. He therefore undertook to look into Tartuffe's past and discovered that he had a bad record. Thus a police-officer appeared just at the moment that Orgon was about to give up his home, and announced that Orgon's possessions were to be restored to him and that Tartuffe was to be packed off to jail. Delighted, Orgon exclaimed:

"Let us throw ourselves joyfully at the feet of our king and praise his kindness. And then, having accomplished this first duty, let us devote our attention to another matter and, by a happy wedding, crown in Valère the ardor of a generous and sincere lover."

THE RIVALS

By

Richard Brinsley Sheridan

RICHARD BRINSLEY BUTLER SHERIDAN (*1751–1816*), the third son of Thomas and Frances Sheridan, was born in Dublin. His mother says that he was a "dunce" at school; however, at Harrow, which he attended, he was very popular. He left Harrow School at seventeen and with the aid of a tutor continued his education. He soon distinguished the family name by his famous dramas. Through a romantic series of events he married Miss Linley secretly in 1772, and in 1773 they were openly married. He entered Parliament for Stafford in 1780 as a friend and ally of Charles James Fox. He was buried in Westminster Abbey on July 7, 1816, in great pomp.

DRAMATIS PERSONAE

Men	*Women*
SIR ANTHONY ABSOLUTE	MRS. MALAPROP
CAPTAIN ABSOLUTE	LYDIA LANGUISH
FAULKLAND	JULIA
ACRES	LUCY
SIR LUCIUS O'TRIGGER	*Maid, Boy, Servants, etc.*
FAG	
DAVID	
COACHMAN	

SCENE—Bath

TIME OF ACTION, within One Day

FAG, servant to Captain Absolute, meets the coachman of the captain's father in a street in Bath. Sir Anthony, the father, has just arrived in order to avoid an impending attack of gout and is ignorant of his son's presence in the city. Fag explains to the coachman that his young master is masquerading under the name of Ensign Beverley, since he has fallen in love with Lydia Languish, a wealthy belle of the town, who likes him better as a poor ensign than she would as son and heir of a rich baronet. They see Captain Absolute talking to Lucy, Lydia's maid, and giving her money. Fag rushes off to tell him of his father's arrival.

In a dressing-room in Mrs. Malaprop's lodging house Lydia is reclining on a sofa, a book in her hand. Lucy has been trying unsuccessfully to procure a certain volume from the circulating library and has brought a number of others instead. Lydia's cousin, Julia, comes to see her. Lydia has written her of her love for Beverley. Now she tells her that difficulties have arisen. Her aunt, Mrs. Malaprop, who has herself fallen in love with a tall Irish baronet, discovered the correspondence between Lydia and Beverley and has stopped it. Worse still, just prior to that, the lovers had quarreled. That is, desirous of a lover's quarrel, Lydia had written herself a letter which she signed "your friend unknown" in which she had accused Beverley of paying attentions to another woman. She had intended merely to tease him with this for a few days but, since their correspondence was stopped, had not had an opportunity of telling him that the letter was a hoax. She tells Julia farther that, if she marries without her aunt's consent, she will lose most of her fortune. This could be averted by waiting till she is of age but she could not love a man who desired to postpone marriage for such a reason.

Julia, who is Sir Anthony Absolute's ward, in her turn tells Lydia of her own difficulties. Her fiancé, Faulkland, is of a perplexing temperament.

JULIA

. . . if he is captious, 'tis without dissembling; if fretful, without rudeness. Unused to the fopperies of love, he is negligent of the little duties expected from a lover—but being unhackneyed in the passion, his affection is ardent and sincere; and as it engrosses his whole soul, he expects every thought and emotion of his mistress to move in unison with his. Yet though his pride calls for this full return, his humility makes him undervalue those qualities in him,

THE RIVALS

which would entitle him to it; and not feeling why he should be loved to the degree he wishes, he still suspects that he is not loved enough. This temper, I must own, has cost me many unhappy hours; but I have learned to think myself his debtor, for those imperfections which arise from the ardor of his attachment.

Lydia asks Julia if she would love Faulkland if he had not once saved her from drowning. The answer is that she loved him before that, though that alone might have been sufficient. To which Lydia replies that she would not love a man merely because he could swim.

Sir Anthony Absolute arrives with Mrs. Malaprop and Julia leaves hurriedly because Sir Anthony does not know she is in Bath and would insist on her spending a great deal of time with him, if he did.

The two new arrivals are scarce in the room when Mrs. Malaprop, who rarely mispronounces words but constantly misapplies them, commences to berate Lydia for throwing herself away on a man who hasn't a farthing in the world and whom, if she had an ounce of sense, she would "illiterate" from her mind. Lydia refuses to give up Beverley and hastens from the room.

Such behavior, says Sir Anthony, is what comes of teaching women to read. It is the libraries that are really at fault in the matter. Mrs. Malaprop thinks he is going a bit too far, so he asks her what she thinks a woman should know.

MRS. MALAPROP

Observe me, Sir Anthony. I would by no means wish a daughter of mine to be a progeny of learning; I don't think so much learning becomes a young woman; for instance—I would never let her meddle with Greek, or Hebrew, or Algebra, or Simony, or Fluxions, or Paradoxes, or such inflammatory branches of learning— neither would it be necessary for her to handle any of your mathematical, astronomical, diabolical instruments:—But, Sir Anthony, I would send her, at nine years old, to a boarding-school, in order to learn a little ingenuity and artifice. Then, sir, she should have a supercilious knowledge in accounts;—and as she grew up, I would have her instructed in geometry, that she might know something

[599]

of the contagious countries;—but above all, Sir Anthony, she should
be mistress of orthodoxy, that she might not misspell, and mispro-
nounce words so shamefully as girls usually do; and likewise that
she might reprehend the true meaning of what she is saying. This,
Sir Anthony, is what I would have a woman know;—and I don't
think there is a superstitious article in it.

Mrs. Malaprop and Sir Anthony decide that, since Lydia is so
unalterably opposed to her aunt's choice for her, a Mr. Acres, they
shall send for Captain Jack Absolute, whom his father fondly
imagines to be with his regiment, and arrange a match between the
two. Sir Anthony leaves, and Mrs. Malaprop immediately calls
Lucy to inquire whether she has seen the Irish baronet, Sir Lucius
O'Trigger. Lucy says she has not and Mrs. Malaprop goes off, after
enjoining Lucy to tell no one of the correspondence with Sir
Lucius. As soon as she is alone Lucy reveals that she is not the
simpleton that she appears to be; she has been taking money from
Lydia, from Beverley, from Acres, from Sir Lucius. And, most
astonishing of all, Sir Lucius is under the impression that his letters
are being delivered to Lydia, not to Mrs. Malaprop.

Sir Anthony has learned of his son's presence in Bath and, on
inquiring the reason for it is told by Fag that his master is recruit-
ing. Jack Absolute tells Faulkland that he loves Lydia and could
persuade her to go off with him but that she would then lose two-
thirds of her fortune; if, on the other hand, he makes his name
known, he would gain the aunt's consent but might lose Lydia's
interest. Faulkland talks of his own constant fears for the welfare
and constancy of his beloved Julia. At this moment Bob Acres
arrives. Acres, in love with Lydia, does not know that Absolute
has ever seen the girl, and constantly complains to him of a sneak-
ing rival for Miss Languish's hand, one Ensign Beverley. Faulkland
has been fearful lest Julia was unwell or unhappy in his absence.
Now, since Acres has just seen her, he is eager for information.
On learning that Julia is well and in good spirits, he is made unhappy at the thought that that means she has not missed him.

Sir Anthony arrives shortly after Faulkland's departure, to talk
with his son. He tells him that he has decided on a wife for Jack.
The son answers that his heart is already given. Sir Anthony is so

angered that he storms he will disinherit his son, strip him of his commission and, in short, ruin him.

Lucy bears Sir Lucius a message from Mrs. Malaprop, letting him think it is from Lydia. Then, meeting Fag, whom she knows as Ensign Beverley's man, she tells him that his master has a new rival, Captain Absolute. Fag hurries off to tell his master that the woman his father wants him to marry is none other than the one he loves.

Jack Absolute, fortified by the knowledge Fag has borne, hastens to his father to assure him that he repents the attitude he just expressed and will marry any one Sir Anthony names. On being informed that the beautiful Lydia Languish is the girl in question, he pretends never to have heard the name.

Faulkland goes to see Julia and charges her with being merry in his absence. She protests that it was but pretence; that she is only happy in his presence.

FAULKLAND

You were ever all goodness to me. Oh, I am a brute when I but admit a doubt of your true constancy!

JULIA

If ever without such cause from you, as I will not suppose possible, you find my affections veering but a point, may I become a proverbial scoff for levity and base ingratitude.

FAULKLAND

Ah! Julia, that last word is grating to me. I would I had no title to your gratitude! Search your heart, Julia; perhaps what you have mistaken for love is but the warm effusion of a too thankful heart!

JULIA

For what quality must I love you?

FAULKLAND

For no quality! To regard me for any quality of mind or understanding, were only to esteem me. And for my person—I have often wished myself deformed, to be convinced that I owed no obligation there for any part of your affection.

And so Faulkland plagues her until she leaves in tears and he is frightened at the thought that if she leaves him now it may be for ever.

Captain Absolute calls on Mrs. Malaprop, who forces Lydia to see him. She is startled at seeing the man she knows as Beverley, but Absolute explains that he has passed himself off on her aunt as his new rival.

Bob Acres complains to Sir Lucius O'Trigger that his rival, Ensign Beverley, has stolen the love of his lady. Sir Lucius persuades Acres that the only thing for a gentleman to do in such a situation is to fight a duel. Under this influence, Acres writes a challenge to Beverley. Since he does not know where to find his enemy he asks his friend, Captain Absolute, who purports to know Beverley, to deliver the challenge. Absolute, however, says he would find it difficult to be Acres' second, so the latter says he will ask O'Trigger.

Sir Anthony and Captain Absolute call on Mrs. Malaprop and Lydia and the young lover is forced to disclose the dual role he was playing. Lydia, who has fed her appetite for romantic novels, is so disappointed that she no longer has to elope with her lover that she is angry with him and chides him with treating her like a child. Sir Anthony interprets her behavior as a sign that his son had been her lover in reality and thinks that she is upset; nothing Jack says can make him think anything else. Lydia finally refuses to talk to Jack.

Sir Lucius, thinking that Captain Absolute had succeeded him in the affections of Miss Languish, seeks him out to challenge him to a duel. Absolute is in a bad humor because his romance has gone so badly, and so accepts at once.

In the meantime, though Julia tries to patch up their difficulties, Faulkland makes things worse and takes his leave of her unhappily.

Captain Absolute departs for his duels, a sword under his coat. His father learns of the impending bloodshed and hastens off to prevent it. Sir Lucius and Acres are already at the field, with pistols, preparing for Acres' duel, Sir Lucius giving instructions in the use of fire-arms on the field of valor. Absolute arrives with his friend, Faulkland, as his second. When Acres learns that Ensign Beverley is none other than his old friend, he refuses to fight a duel which had frightened him half to death in mere anticipation. Sir Lucius and Captain Absolute then take their swords in hand, determined to fight their battle at once.

Sir Anthony Absolute arrives on the scene accompanied by Mrs. Malaprop, Julia, Lucy, and Lydia. Lydia is so terrified at the thought that Jack might have been injured that she indulges in no more romantic whims but tells him forthright that she loves him and wants to marry him. It is disclosed to Sir Lucius that his notes have never reached Lydia and that the loving notes signed "Delia" which he received in response were the work of Mrs. Malaprop. He says that since he must give up Lydia he will show true generosity by giving up Mrs. Malaprop as well. Faulkland asks Julia if she can ever forgive him his boorish behavior and is delighted when she tells him that she finds nothing to forgive. Both pairs of lovers are advised by Sir Anthony to marry directly and thus prevent any further mishaps.

CAMILLE

By

Alexandre Dumas fils

ALEXANDRE DUMAS the Elder (*1802–1870*) was a French
novelist, the grandson of a French Marquis and a negress both
of Haiti. His father had been a General under Napoleon.
Dumas began his literary career with a volume of novels in
1826 but it was thirteen years before his first romantic play
was presented which at once established his fame. He engaged
in the revolution of 1830 and later produced the first of his
historical novels. This gave him the idea of turning the history of France into stories, which formed a series of nearly one
hundred volumes. He was frequently accused of plagiarism
and having a "novel factory" but he was always ready to buy
ideas or to have novels rewritten. His 298 works brought him
handsome rewards which he dissipated, and then wandered
from country to country for 19 years. His last four years of
poverty were relieved by his son whose boyhood he had
neglected. The son later achieved fame in his own right.

CAMILLE was one of the most envied women in Paris. Once a poor
dressmaker's apprentice, she had, in the course of years, risen to a
life of luxury. Her beauty had attracted many men who had been
only too happy to lavish gifts upon her in return for the privilege
of living with her. But she had paid the price. Consumptive, she
might have been cured by living a different life; now the rapid pace
of her existence had aggravated her illness. Nor had she ever been
able to find true happiness. Two of her closest friends, Gustave
and Nichette, adored each other. They lived together, it is true,
but their love was sincere, and they were anxious to marry as soon
as they could save enough money so that Nichette might give up
her position and settle down to family life. The happiness of these
two young people made more evident than ever before to Camille

the fact that, in spite of all her lovers, she had never known true love.

At the present time Camille's life was much more chaste than it had been. She was being maintained in luxury by an elderly gentleman, the Count de Giray, who had lost his beloved daughter and who saw in Camille a young woman who bore her a strong resemblance. All that he asked in return was that she lead a respectable existence. This she had endeavored to do, even turning away Arthur de Varville, who gladly would have made her his mistress.

One evening, a friend of Camille brought a guest, Armand Duval, to a dinner party at Camille's house. Curiously attracted by him, Camille learned that he had been in love with her for two years, never daring to meet her directly because he felt how impossible it would be for him, a penniless bourgeois, to compete with her wealthy lovers. During her recent illness he had come to the house daily to make inquiries concerning her health, never leaving his name.

During the frivolities of the evening party, Camille was suddenly seized with an attack of coughing and dizziness, and she hastily asked her guests to leave her. Armand, however, returned.

ARMAND

How do you feel now, Madame?

CAMILLE

Oh, it is you, Armand. Thank you, I am better. Besides, I am used to this.

ARMAND

You are killing yourself. I should like to be your friend, to prevent you from harming yourself thus.

CAMILLE

You are very kind. Look at the others. They don't bother about me.

ARMAND

The others don't love you the way I do.

CAMILLE

That's right. I forgot about that great love.

[605]

ARMAND

You are making fun of it.

CAMILLE

God forbid! I hear the same thing every day, so I have stopped making fun of it.

ARMAND

All I ask is that you take care of yourself.

CAMILLE

That's impossible. If I took care of myself I should die. It is the feverish life that I lead that sustains me. It is all right for society women, who have family and friends, to take care of themselves, but as for women like myself, as soon as we can no longer serve the pleasure or the vanity of people, they abandon us. Don't worry about me. You say you love me, but it is better that you forget me. A woman who spends a hundred thousand francs a year is all right for a rich old man like the Duke, but not for a young man like you. Love me as a friend; come and see me from time to time. But love some other woman or get married. Don't worry too much about my health. No matter how eternal your love for me may be, and no matter how short a time I shall live, I shall still live longer than you will love me.

Although she did not realize it at the moment, Camille had fallen deeply in love with Armand, and she at last had visions of the true love that had so long eluded her. In a second interview with Armand she could no longer hide her love and told him that she was making plans whereby she might leave Paris and go and live with him in the country. Hardly had Armand left Camille's house, when the Count de Giray appeared. Camille succeeded in getting from him a draught for 15,000 francs, pretending that it was to be used to pay some debts. At this point Nanine, Camille's maid, brought in a letter:

"I have no desire to play a ridiculous rôle, even in the presence of the woman I love. At the moment I left your house I saw the Count de Giray enter. Kindly pardon my only fault, that of not being a millionaire. Let us forget that we ever knew each other and that for a moment we believed that we loved each other. When you receive this letter, I shall have already left Paris.

ARMAND"

Amand's love, however, proved stronger than his jealousy. He returned to Camille and she found it in her heart to forgive him. She lost no time in selling many of her possessions, unknown to Armand, and hired a country house in Auteuil. To this charming retreat went the two lovers, accompanied by the maid Nanine. There they spent a month of perfect bliss. They both, however, realized that without money, this situation could not endure, and each made secret plans. Camille had been gradually selling her valuables through the intermediary of her friend Prudence. Armand was planning to go to Paris to visit his notary to convert into cash some bonds which he had inherited from his mother. Pretending that he had to go to visit his father, to whom he had not written for a month, he slipped off to Paris to obtain the money. He realized that the matter could no longer be delayed, for, suspecting that Camille was depriving herself of her possessions in order to meet expenses, he had questioned Prudence who finally admitted the truth.

During Armand's absence, his father, M. Duval, came to Auteuil. He accused Camille of allowing Armand to compromise himself and ruin himself on her account. When, however, he learned the true situation, he asked her pardon, but frankly explained to her the danger of their position:

M. DUVAL

I come to you as a father seeking the happiness of his two children.

CAMILLE

His two children?

M. DUVAL

Yes. I have a daughter, young, pure, and beautiful. She loves a young man and she, too, has made of this love the hope of her life. She has a right to this love, but the world makes certain demands.

No matter how purified you may seem in the eyes of Armand and in my own eyes, the world will always remember your past, and society will close its doors pitilessly in your face. The family of the man who expects to be my son-in-law has heard of your life with Armand and will take back its promise if this life continues. Thus, the future of a young girl who has done you no harm will be broken because of you. And so I must ask you to leave Armand.

CAMILLE

Never! You don't know how much we love each other. You don't know that I have no family, no real friends. In pardoning me he swore to be all that to me, and my whole life is wrapped up in his. You don't know that I am afflicted with a mortal illness and have only a few years to live. To leave Armand would kill me.

M. DUVAL

Are you sure of the eternity of this love? You are ready to sacrifice everything for him, but what can he give you in exchange? He will take the finest years of your life; then satiety will come, and what will happen? If he is like most men he will throw your past in your face and leave you. Or he will marry you or at best, keep you with him. Such an arrangement would have as its basis neither chastity nor religion. And what career will be open to him? What will you have when you have both grown old?

CAMILLE

Then, whatever she may do, a fallen woman can never rise again! God will pardon her, perhaps, but society will not. What man would make me his wife? What child would want to call me its mother?

In the long discussion with M. Duval, Camille felt compelled to bow before his inexorable logic and sacrifice her love. She promised him that she would act so that Armand would hate her. "In a few hours," she remarked, "Armand will have one of the greatest shocks that he has ever experienced and will need someone who loves him to be with him. You must stay here, for he may return any minute and everything would be lost if he found us together."

[608]

Thus, Camille left Auteuil, sending a letter to Armand in which she stated that she could no longer tolerate the dull life at Auteuil and had gone to Paris to be the mistress of Varville. Overcome, Armand fell sobbing into his father's arms.

For some time Armand and Camille saw nothing of each other, but their paths were destined to cross again. One evening both happened to be guests at the home of a mutual acquaintance, Olympe. During the course of the evening Armand did his utmost to provoke Varville, who succeeded in keeping his temper because Camille had begged him to do so. Varville could not, however, refuse to accept Armand's offer to gamble with him at cards. Unlucky in love, Armand was very lucky at cards, and won a considerable sum of money from Varville. At length Camille succeeded in getting Armand alone and begged him to leave:

CAMILLE

Don't censure me, Armand. Listen to me without hatred, without anger, without scorn. Come, give me your hand.

ARMAND

Never! If that is all you have to say to me . . .

CAMILLE

Who would ever have believed that you would turn away the hand that I held out to you. But never mind that. I beg you to leave and return to your father. Varville is about to provoke you to a duel. I prefer to be the only one to suffer.

ARMAND

And so you ask me to run away from a challenge, or, in other words, to be a coward. What other advice, indeed, could a woman like you give me?

CAMILLE

Armand, I swear to you that for the past month I have suffered so much that I hardly have the strength left to mention it. In the name of our past love, in the name of what I still shall have to suffer, in the name of your mother and sister, flee from me, return to your family, and even forget my name if you can.

ARMAND

I understand. You are afraid for your lover who represents a fortune to you. With one pistol shot I might ruin you. That certainly would be a great misfortune!

CAMILLE

The real misfortune is that you might be killed.

ARMAND

What do you care whether I live or die? When you wrote me that you were another man's mistress did you have any concern for my life? Even though it might cause your death, I swear that I shall kill him.

CAMILLE

Varville is innocent of everything that has happened.

ARMAND

Your loving him is sufficient reason for me to hate him.

CAMILLE

You know I don't love him, that I could not love that man.

ARMAND

Then why did you give yourself to him?

CAMILLE

Don't ask me, Armand, I can't tell you.

ARMAND

Then I'll tell you. You gave yourself to him because you are a heartless woman with no sense of loyalty, because your love belongs to any man who can pay for it.

CAMILLE

Yes, I did that. I admit that I am a miserable wretch and that I deceived you. And my vileness is the best reason for your forgetting me and for you to refuse to expose your life and the life of those who love you on my account. I beg you to go away.

[610]

ARMAND

I will, but on the condition that you come away with me.

CAMILLE

Never!

ARMAND

Listen, Camille. Utter just one word of repentance and I shall forget everything. Merely say that you still love me and I shall pardon everything. We shall leave Paris and go to the end of the world, if necessary, in order to be alone with our love.

CAMILLE

I would give my life for the happiness you suggest, but that happiness is impossible. An abyss separates us. We would be unhappy together. Go away and forget me. I have sworn it.

ARMAND

To whom?

CAMILLE

To the person who had the right to ask such an oath of me.

ARMAND

To Varville?

CAMILLE

Yes.

ARMAND

To Varville, whom you love. Tell me that you love him and I shall leave.

CAMILLE

Very well, then, I love Varville.

ARMAND

(*Going to the door and calling in all the guests from the other room.*) Do you see this woman, Camille? Do you know what she did? She sold all her possessions to live with me, so great was her love for me. That was a fine action, wasn't it. And do you know what I did? I acted like a wretch; I accepted her sacrifice without giving anything in return. But it isn't too late, and I am going to make up for it now. I call you all to witness that I no longer owe this woman anything. (*He throws the bank notes which he won from Varville in Camille's face.*)

VARVILLE

(*Scornfully slapping Armand's face with his gloves*): You certainly are a miserable coward!

Naturally, a duel was now inevitable. Armand wounded Varville, but the latter soon recovered. Armand went off and travelled alone, trying to forget Camille. Worn out by her emotions, she rapidly declined in health, and her old malady, consumption, soon undermined her frail constitution. On New Year's Day, confined to her bed, abandoned by most of her friends, and almost penniless, she lay reading a letter from M. Duval. Appreciating the nobility of Camille's sacrifice, he finally felt impelled to write to Armand and tell him the entire truth. Camille's one hope was that he might return to her before she died. This sad New Year's Day had been made somewhat more cheerful by the wedding of her old friends Gustave and Nichette. If Armand would only return her happiness would be complete.

Camille's prayers were answered. Armand did return, broken-hearted and humbled:

ARMAND

Yes, it is I, Camille, so repentant and so guilty of conscience that I hardly dared to cross your threshold. If I hadn't found you here I should have died, for I should have known that I had been the cause of your death. I haven't seen my father yet. Tell me that you pardon both of us. Ah, but it is good to see you again!

CAMILLE

Pardon you, my darling? I alone am guilty. I sought your happiness even at the expense of my own. But now your father will no longer separate us. Today we shall begin to live.

[612]

ARMAND

I shall never leave you. We shall leave this house. We shall never come back to Paris. My father knows how noble you are, and he will love you. My sister is already married. The future is before us!

But Camille was weaker than she imagined. Trying to rise from her bed she was seized with a spell and fell back gasping:

CAMILLE

I want to live! I must live! If your return can't save me, nothing will save me. Sooner or later every human being must die from that which has made him live. I lived on love and it will cause my death.

ARMAND

Don't say such things, Camille. You will live!

CAMILLE

Sit here next to me, Armand, as close as possible. I know that I am going to die, and I welcome death, for it waited until your return before it struck me. If my death had not been certain, your father wouldn't have written to you to return. If I were a good woman, if I had led a chaste life, perhaps I would weep at leaving the world in which you are going to remain, because the future would be full of promise and my past life would give me a right to happiness. With me dead, everything that you keep of me will be pure; if I were to live, there would always be stains upon my love. Believe me, everything that God does is well done.

ARMAND

I can't bear this!

CAMILLE

Must I give you courage? Listen to me, Armand! Open that drawer and you will find my portrait. It is a picture of me when I was beautiful. I had it made especially for you. Keep it. It may be of help to you. But if, some day, a beautiful young girl loves you and you marry her, as that is bound to happen and I hope it does happen, and if she finds this picture, tell her that it is the portrait

[613]

of a friend who is praying every day both for you and for her. If she is jealous of the past, as we all very frequently are, we women, and if she asks you to destroy this picture, do so without compunction. It will be right for her to ask you to do so and I pardon her now. A woman who loves suffers terribly when she feels that she is not loved!

At this moment Gustave and Nichette arrived, direct from their wedding, for they wished Camille to be the first to witness their happiness:

CAMILLE

I am dying, but I shall die happy, and my happiness will hide my death. So you two are married! What a strange thing this first life is; I wonder what the second will be like. And now, Armand, give me your hand. I am not suffering. I can almost feel life returning to me. I feel a strange sensation of comfort that I have never felt before. Ah! how good I feel! (*She seems to doze off.*)

GUSTAVE

She has fallen asleep!

ARMAND

(*Disturbed, and then terrified*): Camille! Camille! She is dead! Good God! what will become of me?

GUSTAVE

The poor girl! She loved you with all her heart, Armand.

NICHETTE

Sleep in peace, Camille! You will be pardoned for many things because you loved so deeply.

THE CHERRY ORCHARD

By

Anton Chekhov

ANTON PAVLOVITCH CHEKHOV (*1860–1904*) was a Russian writer of the school which included Gorky and Andriev. He was born of humble parents in southern Russia but obtained a good education, including a medical course at Moscow University. Soon after his graduation he decided to follow a literary career. His early writings were chiefly humorous and appeared in periodicals under a pseudonym. He commenced writing at the age of 19 and died of tuberculosis at 44. During his brief life he wrote over 150 short stories, numerous plays and one novel. He was sensationally popular in Russia and the printing presses would be urged to ten or more editions of his works when they appeared. Most of his works have been translated into the major languages.

ACT I

A ROOM in the Ranevsky household which has always been called the nursery. It is dawn in May and the sun rises during the scene. The cherry trees are seen to be in flower outside but it is cold in the garden with the frost of early morning. The windows are closed. Dunyasha, a young maid who has grown up in the service of the family, and has acquired the soft white hands and the affected mannerisms of a "lady" enters the dark room with a candle. She is followed shortly by Lopahin, a merchant who has come to await the arrival of Lyubov Andreyevna, Madame Ranevsky, the owner of the Cherry Orchard who is returning home after five years abroad with her young daughter, Anya, aged seventeen.

[615]

LOPAHIN

Yes, I'm a rich man, but for all my money, come to think, a peasant I was, and a peasant I am (*turns over the pages of a book*). I've been reading this book and I can't make head or tails of it. I fell asleep over it.

Soon Semyon Pantaleyevitch Epihodov, a clerk on the estate, who is known to the others as the "man of two and twenty misfortunes" because of his unending clumsiness enters with a nosegay for the maid to put in the dining-room. He wears a pea-jacket and highly polished topboots which creak loudly.

EPIHODOV

Permit me to call your attention to the fact that I purchased myself a pair of boots yesterday, and they creak, I venture to assure you, so that there's no tolerating them. What ought I to grease them with?

LOPAHIN

O, shut up! Don't bother me.

EPIHODOV

Every day some misfortune befalls me. I don't complain, I'm used to it, and I wear a smiling face.

Dunyasha comes in with the kvass she has gone to fetch for Lopahin and Epihodov who is in love with her turns to go and in doing so stumbles over a chair. He turns to the others triumphantly and exclaims "There you see now, excuse the expression, an accident like that among others. . . . It's positively remarkable" and departs.

Dunyasha and Lopahin gossip about Epihodov's proposal to the former when suddenly there is the sound of carriages driving up to the house and Lopahin and Dunyasha go out quickly to welcome the home-comers. A noise is heard in the adjoining rooms and Firs, the ancient retainer of Mme. Ranevsky, crosses the stage hurriedly leaning on a stick and muttering to himself. The noise outside increases and a voice urges "Come, let's go in here." Then Mme. Ranevsky, Anya and the middle-aged governess, Charlotta

Ivanovna, with a pet dog on a chain, enter. The three women are
clad in travelling dresses. Varya, a plain girl of twenty-four who is
Mme. Ranevsky's adopted daughter and who has taken charge of
the estate during her absence follows. She is in an outdoor coat
and with a kerchief over her head. Leonid Andreyevitch Gaev,
Mme. Ranevsky's brother, Semyonov-Pishtchik, a land-owner,
Lopahin, Dunyasha with bag and parasol and servants with other
articles follow.

ANYA

Let's come in here. Do you remember what room this is,
Mamma?

VARYA

How cold it is, my hands are numb. (*To Lyubov*) Your rooms,
the white room and the lavender one, are just the same as ever,
Mamma.

LYUBOV

My nursery, dear delightful room . . . I used to sleep here
when I was little . . . (*cries*). And here I am, like a little child
. . . (*kisses her brother and Varya and then her brother again*).
Varya's just the same as ever, like a nun. And I knew Dunyasha
(*kisses Dunyasha*).

CHARLOTTA

(*To Pishtchik*). My dog eats nuts, too. Pishtchik (*wonderingly*)
Fancy that!

They all go out except Anya and Dunyasha.

Dunyasha immediately begins to tell Anya about Epihodov's
proposal and also informs her that Pyotr Sergeyevitch Trofimov,
her dead brother's former tutor, is back. Varya then returns, a
bunch of keys dangling at her waist and Dunyasha leaves to prepare coffee for Mme. Ranevsky. Varya rejoices that her "Little
Darling" has come back and pets her. Anya complains about the
trip abroad with Charlotta and the arrival in Paris where she found
her mother completely without funds and surrounded by a shabby
entourage of French people. She says that her mother's extravagance seems to be incurable and that even Charlotta, the
governess, has adopted her mother's ways. Varya interrupts her

to state that the Cherry Orchard will have to be sold in August
as the arrears on the mortgage have not been paid. At this point,
Lopahin peeps in at the door, moos like a cow and disappears.
Varya weeps and shakes her fist after him.

ANYA

(*Embracing Varya, softly*). Varya, has he made you an offer?
(*Varya shakes her head.*) Why, but he loves you. Why is it you
don't come to an understanding? What are you waiting for?

VARYA

I believe there never will be anything between us. He has a
lot to do, he has no time for me . . . and takes no notice of me.
. . . Everyone's talking of our being married, everyone's con-
gratulating me, and all the while there's really nothing in it. It's
all a dream. (*In another tone*) You have a new brooch like a bee.

Dunyasha returns with the coffee pot and is making coffee while
Varya goes out with Anya to see that she gets to sleep as it is
now past three. Very shortly, Yasha, a peasant lad who has been
Mme. Ranevsky's valet abroad, enters with a rug and a travelling
bag and crosses mincingly to Dunyasha, asking her who she is. She
tells him that she is little Dunyasha and Yasha cockily announces
"You're a peach," and after glancing around to make certain there
are no on-lookers embraces her. Dunyasha shrieks and drops a
saucer and Yasha departs hastily. Varya and Anya enter discussing
the manner in which they will inform their mother of Trofimov's
arrival as they feel that his presence will serve to remind her of
the drowning of their little brother, Grisha, who had been
Trofimov's charge six years before. It was the drowning which
had precipitated Mme. Ranevsky's flight abroad.
Firs then enters in a pea-jacket, white waistcoat and white gloves
to see that everything is in order for his mistress. He fusses around
the coffee pot and mutters to himself. Varya asks him what he is
saying and Firs replies gleefully that his lady has come home and
now that he has lived to see her again, he can die. He begins
weeping from sheer joy as Lyubov Andreyevna, Gaev and
Semyonov-Pishtchik enter. Gaev, as he comes in, makes a gesture

with his arms and his whole body as though he were playing billiards which is his favorite occupation. Anya bids them all good night and Lyubov begins to drink her coffee. Firs puts a cushion under her feet and she says "Thanks, dear old man," and kisses him. Varya goes out to attend to the unpacking.

LYUBOV

Can it really be me sitting here (*laughs*). I want to dance about and clap my hands. (*Covers her face with her hands.*) And I could drop asleep in a moment! God knows I love my country, I love it tenderly; I couldn't look out of the window in the train, I kept crying so. (*Through her tears*) But I must drink my coffee, though. Thank you, Firs, thanks dear old man, I'm so glad to find you still alive.

FIRS

The day before yesterday.

GAEV

He's rather deaf.

LOPAHIN

I have to set off for Harkov directly, at five o'clock. . . . It's annoying! I wanted to have a look at you and a little talk. . . . You are just as splendid as ever.

PISHTCHIK

(*Breathing heavily*). Handsomer, indeed. . . . Dressed in Parisian style . . . completely bowled me over.

LYUBOV

I can't sit still, I simply can't. . . . (*Jumps up and walks about in violent agitation.*) This happiness is too much for me. . . . You may laugh at me, I know I'm silly. . . . My own bookcase (*kisses the bookcase*). My little table.

Gaev, who is rather childish in spite of his fifty-one years sucks on some caramels and tell her of various deaths that have occurred during her absence. Lopahin interrupts to talk practicalities. He tells Lyubov that although the sale of her estate is set for August

THE 101 WORLD'S CLASSICS

there is still a way of saving it, that is, by cutting it up into little three-acre plots and leasing them for summer villas. Of course, he adds, all the buildings will have to be torn down including the house they are in and the cherry orchard will have to be chopped down, too. When Lyubov hears this she protests agitatedly recalling the fame of the cherry orchard throughout the whole province and how it was even listed in the encyclopaedia. But Lopahin pushes his point stating that while there used to be only gentlefolk and peasants in the country now there are "these summer visitors." He says that perhaps eventually, the summer visitor will take to working his bit of land and then the cherry orchard would become rich, happy and prosperous.

Soon, Varya enters and opens the old-fashioned bookcase to get some telegrams which she has been keeping for her mother. Lyubov tears them up, unopened, saying she is through with Paris. Gaev tells Lyubov that he has discovered that the bookcase is exactly one hundred years old. He addresses a speech to the bookcase:

"Hail to thee who for more than a hundred years hast served the ideals of good and justice; thy silent call to fruitful labor has never flagged . . . maintaining in the generations of man (*in tears*) courage and faith in a brighter future and fostering in us ideals of good and social consciousness."

LOPAHIN

Yes. . . .

LYUBOV

You are just the same as ever, Leonid.

GAEV

(*A little embarrassed*). Cannon off the right into the pocket!

Charlotta Ivanovna, a very thin lanky woman in a white dress with a lorgnette comes in and Lopahin asks her to show them some tricks as Charlotta is famous for her assortment of parlor tricks. She declines saying she is too sleepy and goes out. Lopahin prepares to leave reminding Lyubov of his plan and offering to lend her fifty thousand roubles to get the project under way.

VARYA

(*Angrily*). Well, do go, for goodness sake.

GAEV

Low-born knave! I beg pardon, though. . . . Varya is going to marry him, he's Varya's fiancé.

VARYA

Don't talk nonsense, uncle.

LYUBOV

Well, Varya, I shall be delighted. He's a good man.

As Pishtchik wakes up from a snooze he asks Lyubov for a loan of some money in order to pay off his mortgage. When Lyubov tells him she is broke he laughs and says something will be sure to turn up. The others all look out of the window at the cherry orchard in bloom and Lyubov associates it with her carefree youth and innocence. She fancies that she sees her mother walking, walking all in white, down the avenue. Just then Trofimov, wearing a shabby student's uniform and spectacles enters to greet his former mistress. Lyubov breaks into tears when she recognizes him, remembering the drowned Grisha. She asks Trofimov if he is really a student still and he replies that he is likely to be a perpetual student. Then Lyubov, Trofimov, Pishtchik and Firs leave in order to retire but not before Lyubov orders her brother to give Pishtchik the money he needs to pay off his mortgage.

When Varya tells the valet, Yasha, that his old mother awaits him in the servant quarters, he replies insolently "Oh, bother her!" Varya reproves him and he, too, departs.

Varya and her uncle discuss Lyubov's extravagance and Gaev proposes some fantastic schemes for redeeming their fortunes. Just as Gaev says that although his sister is good, and kind and nice, "there's no denying she's an immoral woman," Anya sleepily enters announcing that she cannot fall asleep and asks him what he has just said about her mother. Gaev apologizes and forthwith outlines his schemes for saving the estate. He swears that he will not let it come to an auction and Anya rejoices. Old Firs enters and reproaches his master for remaining up so late and Gaev

leaves still chattering and making imaginary billiard shots. Varya
begins to recount a trivial household anecdote to Anya and suddenly notices the young girl is asleep. She leads her out still half-
asleep and far away beyond the orchard a shepherd plays on a pipe.
Trofimov crosses the stage and seeing Anya and Varya, stands still.

VARYA

Come, my own, come along. (*They go into Anya's room.*)

TROFIMOV

(*Tenderly*). My sunshine! My spring!

ACT II

The open country. There is an old abandoned shrine and near
it a well with large stones that once were tombstones and an old
garden seat. The road to Gaev's house is seen. On one side rise
dark poplars; and there the cherry orchard begins. In the distance
a row of telegraph poles and far away on the horizon there is
faintly outlined a great town. It is near sunset. Charlotta, Yasha,
and Dunyasha are sitting on the seat. Epihodov is standing near,
playing something mournful on the guitar. All are thoughtful and
Charlotta who has taken a gun from her shoulder and is tighten-
ing the buckle on the strap muses aloud about her childhood and
her loneliness.

CHARLOTTA

Who my parents were, very likely they weren't married. . . . I
don't know (*takes a cucumber out of her pocket and eats*). One
wants to talk and has no one to talk to. . . . I have nobody. . . .
And who I am, and why I am on earth, I don't know (*walks away
slowly*).

As usual, Epihodov talks ceaselessly of his learning and "cultivation"; but it is evident that all this is to impress the pert Dunyasha
to whom he is about to propose, again. He even hints that if he
doesn't find out what he is "precisely inclined for" he may shoot

himself and to Dunyasha's horror exhibits a revolver. However, while he goes back to fetch a mantle for her she assures Yasha, the valet, that she is passionately in love with him. Yasha puffs on a cigar and accepts her adoration patronizingly.

YASHA

(*Yawns.*) . . . My opinion is this: If a girl loves anyone, that means she has no principles (*a pause*). It's pleasant smoking a cigar in the open air. (*Listens.*) Someone's coming this way . . . the gentlefolk (*Dunyasha embraces him impulsively*). Go home, as though you had been to the river to bathe; go by that path, or else they'll suppose I have made an appointment with you here. That I can't endure.

Dunyasha departs as instructed and Lyubov, Gaev and the merchant, Lopahin enter.

Lyubov is still refusing Lopahin a definite answer to the proposition regarding the summer villas. She changes the subject and reproaches Gaev for talking to the waiters in the restaurant about the Decadents of the seventies. Yasha begins to laugh insolently which annoys Gaev so much that Lyubov is forced to order him away. Again Lopahin reminds them of the necessity of a decision if they wish to save the estate to which Gaev replies with his gesture of playing billiards and continues to eat caramels.

GAEV

They say I've eaten up my property in caramels (*laughs*).

LYUBOV

Oh, my sins! I've always thrown my money away recklessly like a lunatic. I married a man who made nothing but debts. My husband died of champagne. . . . To my misery, I loved another man, and immediately, it was my first punishment, . . . here, in the river . . . my boy was drowned . . . I shut my eyes and fled distracted and *he* after me . . . pitilessly, brutally. I bought a villa at Mentone, for *he* fell ill there, and for three years I had no rest day or night . . . and last year when my villa was sold to pay my debts, I went to Paris and there he robbed me of everything and abandoned me for another woman; and I tried to poison myself

. . . And suddenly I felt a longing for Russia, for my country, for my little girl (*dries her tears*) . . . I got this to-day from Paris. He implores forgiveness, entreats me to return (*tears up telegram*). I fancy there is music somewhere (*listens*).

GAEV

That's our famous Jewish orchestra.

LYUBOV

That still in existence? We ought to send for them one evening and give a dance.

LOPAHIN

(*Listens.*) I can't hear. . . . (*Hums softly.*) "For money the Germans will turn a Russian into a Frenchman." (*Laughs.*) I did hear such a piece at the theatre yesterday. It was funny.

LYUBOV

And most likely there was nothing funny in it. You shouldn't look at plays, you should look at yourselves a little oftener. How grey your lives are! How much nonsense you talk.

LOPAHIN

That's true. . . . In reality I am just such another blockhead and idiot as my father. I've learnt nothing properly. . . . I write so that I felt ashamed before folks like a pig.

LYUBOV

You ought to get married, my dear fellow.

LOPAHIN

Yes . . . that's true.

LYUBOV

You should marry our Varya, she's a good girl.

LOPAHIN

Yes. . . . Well? I'm not against it. She's a good girl (*pause*).

At this point old Firs enters with an overcoat for Gaev. He is followed shortly by Trofimov, Anya and Varya and Lopahin immediately proceeds to tease Trofimov about his perpetual studying. Trofimov takes it ill-naturedly, however, and finally bursts out that as far as he is concerned Lopahin has the same use in society as a wild beast in the economy of nature who devours everything that comes its way. Then he avows his belief in the perfectibility of humanity and the need for constant work.

TROFIMOV

Here among us in Russia the workers are few in number as yet. The vast majority of intellectual people I know, seek nothing, do nothing, are not fit as yet for work of any kind. They call themselves intellectual, but they treat their servants like inferiors, behave to the peasants as though they were animals, learn little, read nothing seriously, do practically nothing, only talk about science and know very little about art . . . the vast majority of us, ninety-nine percent, live like savages . . . eat piggishly, sleep in filth and stuffiness, bugs everywhere, stench and damp and moral filth. . . . I fear and dislike very serious faces. I'm afraid of serious conversations. We should do better to be silent.

Lopahin agrees and soon they see Epihodov advancing in the background playing his guitar.

The sun is setting and Gaev delivers a short peroration to divine nature which is terminated at the request of Varya and Anya. Presently, the company all sit submerged in thought and there is perfect stillness except for the subdued muttering of Firs. Suddenly, there is a sound in the distance, as it were from the sky the sound of a breaking harp string, mournfully dying away. They are all saddened by the sound and prepare to leave but not before Lyubov gives some gold pieces to a drunken beggar who accosts them. Somehow Anya and Trofimov are left alone. Trofimov who is very much in love with Anya, although "above it" as he says, urges her to take a definite attitude toward the future, to expiate the sins of her slave-holding ancestors, the owners of the cherry orchard, whose every leaf is tortured by visions of the past. They hear Epihodov's mournful guitar while the moon rises and just as the student utters a prophecy for the future, Varya is heard calling for Anya. The two young idealists decide to escape down to the river and Varya continues, vainly, crying "Anya, Anya!"

ACT III

It is evening in the Ranevsky drawing-room and a dance is in progress. The Jewish orchestra can be heard playing polkas in the ante-room. There is the sound of billiards being played in an adjoining room. The music ceases and amid general banter, Charlotta the mischievous governess, entertains the guests with various parlor tricks. Pishtchik the comical land-owner is quite taken by her talent and follows her when she goes out. Trofimov begins to tease Varya about Lopahin to retaliate for her continual meddling between him and Anya until Varya leaves the room in tears. Lyubov kindly tells him that she would gladly let him marry Anya if only he would take his degree instead of being tossed by fate from place to place. Then she tells Trofimov that her former lover is imploring her to return to him and that, while realizing he is a mill-stone about her neck, she loves the stone and can't live without it. But when Trofimov protests that the man is a wretch and that everyone is aware of it except Lyubov grows angry and tells the student that he is a "freak" not to have a mistress at the age of twenty-seven. He runs out in horror and is heard falling down the stairs which makes Lyubov instantly repentant.

When Trofimov returns Lyubov calls to him to dance in order to make it up to him. Dunyasha enters still giddy from a dance and taunts Yasha who is growing bored with provincial life that the post-office clerk has just told her she is like a flower. Yasha yawningly departs and immediately Epihodov enters to press his suit with Dunyasha. She rebuffs him and just then Varya enters and reproaches him for mingling with the visitors. She grows so angry that she follows Yasha to the door swinging a stick at him just as Lopahin enters. The entire household rushes in to greet Lopahin and Gaev who have been to the sale of the cherry orchard. Lopahin informs them that he has bought it and they are all overcome. Varya throws away her keys to indicate she is mistress no longer and Lyubov breaks down completely while Anya tries to console her mother.

ANYA

Let us go, darling, away from here! We will make a new garden, more splendid than this one. . . . And joy, quiet deep joy, will sink into your soul like the sun at evening! And you will smile. Mamma! Come, darling, let us go!

ACT IV

The nursery, bare now, except for piled up furniture, travelling bags, and trunks. Outside there is the hum of peasants who have come to say good-bye. Lyubov, pale and nervous, crosses the room. Trofimov and Lopahin begin to banter but finally Trofimov who is returning to the university at Moscow confesses that after all he is very fond of Lopahin: ". . . you have fine delicate fingers like an artist, you've a fine delicate soul." Lopahin is touched and offers him some money for the journey.

In the distance can be heard the stroke of an axe on a tree, when Anya appears in the door-way and says that Lyubov asks that they do not chop down the cherry orchard until she is gone. Lopahin immediately goes to attend the matter. Dunyasha enters to bid a tender farewell to Yasha who is busy consuming champagne meant for the others who soon enter to bid a last farewell to the old house. They all talk feverishly of the new life in order to hide their sadness even from themselves. Lyubov says that only two matters still worry her and they are old Firs' illness and Varya's unwedded state. Lopahin, who has returned, says that he, too, wonders why he and Varya always seem to avoid each other when they are obviously so well-suited to one another. Lyubov goes to fetch Varya in order to settle the matter then and there. Varya enters anticipating a proposal at last but somehow the affair is muffed, as usual, and Lopahin finally leaves without proposing. The others all go until brother and sister are left alone in the old room. They embrace each other and weep for their childhood, their home, and then they, too, depart. There is the sound of the carriages driving away and then a long silence.

In the stillness, the dull stroke of an axe on a tree clangs mournfully. Footsteps are heard and suddenly the ancient Firs whom the others had sent off to a hospital in the morning enters. He is ill.

FIRS

(*Goes up to the doors and tries the handles.*) Locked! They have gone. . . . (*sits down on sofa*) They have forgotten me. . . . Never mind. . . . I'll sit here a bit. . . . I'll be bound Leonid Andreyevitch hasn't put his fur coat on and has gone off in his thin overcoat (*sighs anxiously*). . . . These young people . . . (*mutters something indistinguishable*). Life has slipped by as though I hadn't lived (*lies down*). I'll lie down a bit. . . . There's no strength in you, nothing left you—all gone! Ech! I'm good for nothing (*lies motionless*).

A sound is heard that seems to come from the sky, like a breaking harp string, dying away mournfully. All is still again and there is heard nothing but the strokes of the axe far away in the cherry orchard.

VI

BELLES LETTRES

ON READING OLD BOOKS

By

William Hazlitt

WILLIAM HAZLITT (*1778–1830*) was a critic and essayist, who was born at Maidstone, England. When he was about twenty he became a friend of Coleridge who encouraged him to write, which resulted in Hazlitt's *Essay on the Principles of Human Action* which was published in 1805. He continued to write a book a year for several years when he commenced contributing his essays to the *London Magazine*. *On Reading Old Books* is generally considered the finest essay in the complete edition of his works of twelve volumes.

I HATE to read new books. There are twenty or thirty volumes that I have read over and over again, and these are the only ones that I have any desire ever to read at all. I do not think altogether the worse of a book for having survived the author a generation or two. I have more confidence in the dead than in the living. Contemporary writers may generally be divided into two classes— one's friends or one's foes. Of the first we are compelled to think too well, and of the last we are disposed to think too ill, to receive much genuine pleasure from the perusal, or to judge fairly of the merits of either. One candidate for literary fame, who happens to be of our acquaintance, writes finely, and like a man of genius; but unfortunately has a foolish face, which spoils a delicate passage; another inspires us with the highest respect for his personal talents and character, but does not quite come up to our expectations in print. All these contradictions and petty details interrupt the calm current of our reflections. If you want to know what any of the authors were who lived before our time, and are still objects of anxious inquiry, you have only to look into their works. But the dust and smoke and noise of modern literature have nothing in common with the pure, silent air of immortality.

When I take up a book that I have read before (the oftener the better), I know what I have to expect. The satisfaction is not lessened by being anticipated. When the entertainment is altogether new, I sit down to it as I would to a strange dish—turn and pick out a bit here and there, and am in doubt what to think of the composition. There is a want of confidence and security to second appetite. New-fangled books are also like made dishes in this respect, that they are generally little else than hashes and *rifaccimenti* of what has been served up entire and in a more natural state at other times. Besides, in thus turning to a well-known author, there is not only an assurance that my time will not be thrown away, or my palate nauseated with the most insipid or vilest trash, but I shake hands with, and look an old, tried and valued friend in the face, compare notes and chat the hours away. It is true, we form dear friendships with such ideal guests— dearer, alas! and more lasting, than those with our most intimate acquaintance. In reading a book which is an old favorite with me (say the first novel I ever read) I not only have the pleasure of imagination and of a critical relish of the work, but the pleasures of memory added to it. It recalls the same feelings and associations which I had in first reading it, and which I can never have again in any other way. Standard productions of this kind are links in the chain of our conscious being. They bind together the different scattered divisions of our personal identity. They are landmarks and guides in our journey through life. They are pegs and loops on which we can hang up, or from which we can take down, at pleasure, the wardrobe of a moral imagination, the relics of our best affections, the tokens and records of our happiest hours. They are "for thoughts and for remembrance!" They are Fortunatus's Wishing Cap—they give us the best wishes—those of Fancy; and transport us, not over half the globe but (which is much better) over half our lives, at a world's notice.

Nay, sometimes the sight of an odd volume of these good old English authors on a stall, or the name lettered on the back among others on the shelves of a library, answers the purpose, revives the whole train of ideas, and "sets the puppets dallying." Twenty years are struck off the list, and I am a child again. A sage philosopher, who was not a very wise man, said, that he would like very well to be young again, if he could take his experience along with him. This ingenious person did not seem to be aware, by the gravity of his remark, that the great advantage of being young is to be without this weight of experience, which he would fain place upon the shoulders of youth, and which never comes too late with years. Oh! what a privilege to be able to let this hump, like Christian's burthen, drop from off one's back, and transport onself, by the help of a little musty duodecimo, to the time when "ignorance was bliss," and when we first got a peep at the rarce-show of the world, through the glass of fiction—gazing at mankind, as we do at wild beasts in a menagerie, through the bars of their cages—or at the curiosities in a museum, that we must not touch!

For myself, not only are the old ideas of the contents of the work brought back to my mind in all their vividness, but the old associations of the faces and persons I then knew, as they were in their lifetime return, and all my early impressions with them. This is better to me—those places, those times, those persons and those feelings, and all those feelings that come across me as I retrace the story and devour the page, are to me better far than the wet sheets of the latest novel. It is like visiting the scenes of early youth. I think of the time "when I was in my father's house and my path ran down with butter and honey"—when I was a little thoughtless child, and had no other wish or care but to con my daily task and be happy! *Tom Jones,* I remember, was the first work that broke the spell. It came down in numbers once a fortnight in Cooke's pocket edition, embellished with cuts. I had hitherto read only in school-books and a tiresome ecclesiastical history (with the exception of Mrs. Radcliffe's *Romance of the Forest*): but this had a different relish with it—"sweet in the mouth," though not "bitter in the belly." It smacked of the world I lived in, and in which I was to live—and showed me groups, "gay creatures" not "of the element," but of the earth; not "living in the clouds," but travelling the same road that I did;—some that had passed on before me, and others that might soon overtake me.

Many a dainty repast have I made of the *New Eloise;*—the de-

[633]

scription of the kiss; the excursion on the water; the letter of St. Preux, recalling the time of their first loves; and the account of Julia's death; these I read over and over again with unspeakable delight and wonder. Some years after, when I met this work again, I found I had lost nearly my whole relish for it (except some parts), and was, I remember, very much mortified with the change in my taste, which I sought to attribute to the smallness and gilt edges of the edition I had bought, and its being perfumed with rose-leaves. Nothing could exceed the gravity, the solemnity with which I carried home and read the Dedication to the *Social Contract*, with some other pieces of the same author, which I had picked up at a stall in a coarse leathern cover.

I remember, as long ago as the year 1798, going to a neighboring town and bringing home with me, "at one proud swoop," a copy of Milton's *Paradise Lost*, and another of Burke's *Reflections on the French Revolution*—both of which I have still; and I still recollect, when I see the covers, the pleasure with which I dipped into them as I returned with my double prize. I was set up for one while. The time is past "with all its giddy raptures:" but I am still anxious to preserve its memory, "embalmed with odours."

To have lived in the cultivation of an intimacy with such works, and to have familiarly relished such names, is not to have lived quite in vain.

THE LONDON FIRE
From the Diary
of
Samuel Pepys

SAMUEL PEPYS (*1632–1703*) is most famous for his *Diary* which was first published in 1825 under the editorship of Lord Braybrooke. The *Diary* is an invaluable mine of information as a record of the court and times of Charles II. It commenced January 1st 1660 and was continued for about nine years when defective eyesight caused Pepys to abandon the work. His only other important publication was his *Memoires Relating to the State of the Royal Navy* published in 1690.

SEPTEMBER 2d. (Lord's Day). Some of our maids sitting up late last night to get things ready for our feast to-day. Jane called us up about three in the morning, to tell us of a great fire they saw in the City. So I rose, and slipped on my night-gown, and went to the window; and thought it might be on the back-side of Marke-lane at the farthest; but, being unused to such fires as followed, I thought it far enough off; and so went to bed again, and to sleep. About seven rose again to dress myself, and there looked out at the window, and saw the fire not so much as it was, and further off. So to my closet to set things to rights, after yesterday's cleaning. By and by Jane comes and tells me that she hears that above 300 houses have been burned down to-night by the fire we saw, and that it is now burning down all Fish Street, by London Bridge. So I made myself ready presently, and walked to the Tower; and there got up upon one of those high places, Sir J. Robinson's little son going with me; and there I did see the houses at that end of the bridge all on fire, and an infinite great fire on this and the other side the end of the bridge; which, among other people, did trouble me for poor little Michell and our Sarah on the bridge. So down, with my heart full of trouble, to the Lieutenant of the Tower, who tells me that it begun this morning in the King's baker's house in Pudding-lane, and that it hath burned down St. Magnus's Church and most part of Fish Street already. So I down to the water-side, and there got a boat, and through bridge, and there saw a lamentable fire. Poor Michell's house, as far as the Old Swan, already burned that way, and the fire running further, that, in a very little time, it got as far as the Steele-yard, while I was there. Every body endeavouring to remove their goods, and flinging into the river, or bringing them into lighters that lay off; poor people staying in their houses as long as till the very fire touched them, and then running into boats, or clambering from one pair of stairs, by the waterside, to another. And, among the other things, the poor, poor pigeons, I perceive, were loth to leave their houses, but hovered about the windows and balconys, till they burned their wings, and fell down. Having staid, and in an hour's time seen it get as far as the Steele-yard, and the wind mighty high, and driving it into the City; and everything, after so long a drought, proving combustible, even the very stones of churches; and, among other things, the poor steeple by which pretty Mrs. —— lives, and whereof my old schoolfellow Elborough is parson, taken fire in the very top, and there burned till it fell down; I to White Hall, with a gentleman with me, who desired to go off from the Tower, to see the fire, in my boat; and there up to the King's closet in the Chapel, where people come about me, and I did give them an account dismayed them all, and word was carried in to the King. So I was called for, and did tell the King and Duke of York what I saw; and that, unless his Majesty did command houses to be pulled down, nothing could stop the fire. They seemed much troubled, and the King commanded me to go to my Lord Mayor from him, and command him to spare no houses, but to pull them down before the fire every way. The Duke of York bid me tell him, that if he would have nay more soldiers, he shall; and so did my Lord Arlington afterwards, as a great secret. Here meeting with Captain Cocke, I in his coach, which he lent me, and Creed with me to Paul's; and there walked along Watling Street, as well as I could, every creature coming away loaden with goods to save, and, here and there, sick people carried away in beds. Extraordinary good goods carried in carts and on backs. At last met my Lord Mayor in Canning Street, like a man spent, with a handkercher about his neck. To the King's message, he cried, like a fainting woman, "Lord, what can I do? I am spent: people will not obey me. I have been pulling down houses; but the fire overtakes us faster than we can do it." That he needed more soldiers; and that, for himself, he must go and refresh himself, having been up all night. So he left me, and I him, and walked home; seeing people all almost distracted, and no manner of means used to quench the fire. The houses, too, so very thick thereabouts, and full of matter for burning, as pitch and tar, in Thames Street; and warehouses of oyle, and wine, and brandy, and other things. Here I saw Mr. Isaac Houblon, the handsome man, prettily dressed and dirty at his door at Dowgate, receiving some of his brother's things, whose houses were on fire; and, as he says, having been removed twice already; and he doubts, as it soon proved, that they must be, in a little time, removed from his house also, which was a sad consideration. And to see the churches all filling with goods by the people who should have been quietly there at this time. By this time, it was about twelve o'clock; and so home, and there find my guests, who were Mr. Wood and his wife Barbary Shelden, and also Mr. Moone: she mighty fine, and her husband, for aught I see, a likely man. But Mr. Moone's design and mine, which was to look over my closet, and please him with the sight thereof, which he hath long desired, was wholly disappointed; for we were in great trouble and disturbance at this fire, not knowing what to think of it. However, we had an extraordinary good dinner, and as merry as at this time we could be. While at dinner, Mrs. Batelier come to inquire after Mr. Woolfe and Stanes, who, it seems, are related to them, whose houses in Fish Street are all burned, and they in a sad condition. She would not stay in the fright. Soon as I dined, I and Moone away, and walked through the City, the streets full of nothing but people; and horses and carts loaden with goods, ready to run over one another, and removing goods from one burned house to another. They now removing out of Canning Street, which received goods in the morning, into Lombard Street, and further: and, among others, I now saw my little goldsmith Stokes receiving some friend's goods, whose house itself

[637]

was burned the day after. We parted at Paul's; he home and I to
Paul's Wharf, where I had appointed a boat to attend me, and
took in Mr. Carcasse and his brother, whom I met in the street,
and carried them below and above bridge too. And again to see
the fire, which was now got further, both below and above, and
no likelihood of stopping it. Met with the King and Duke of
York in their barge, and with them to Queenhithe, and there called
Sir Richard Browne to them. Their order was only to pull down
houses apace, and so below bridge at the water-side; but little was
or could be done, the fire coming upon them so fast. Good hopes
there was of stopping it at the Three Cranes above, and at But-
tulph's Wharf below bridge, if care be used; but the wind carries it
into the City, so as we know not, by the water-side, what it do
there. River full of lighters and boats taking in goods, and goods
swimming in the water; and only I observed that only one lighter
or boat in three that had the goods of a house in, but there was a
pair of Virginalls in it. Having seen as much as I could now, I
away to White Hall by appointment, and there walked to St.
James's Park; and there met my wife, and Creed, and Wood, and
his wife, and walked to my boat; and there upon the water again,
and to the fire up and down, it still encreasing, and the wind
great. So near the fire as we could for smoke; and all over the
Thames, with one's faces in the wind, you were almost burned
with a shower of fire-drops. This is very true: so as houses were
burned by these drops and flakes of fire, three or four, nay, five or
six houses, one from another. When we could endure no more upon
the water, we to a little ale-house on the Bankside, over against
the Three Cranes, and there stayed until it was dark almost, and
saw the fire grow; and, as it grew darker, appeared more and
more; and in corners and upon steeples, and between churches and
houses, so far as we could see up the hill of the City, in a most
horrid, malicious, bloody flame, not like the fine flame of an
ordinary fire. Barbary and her husband away before us. We staid
till, it being darkish, we saw the fire as only one entire arch of
fire from this to the other side of the bridge, and in a bow up the
hill for an arch of above a mile long: it made me weep to see it.
The churches, houses, and all one fire, and flaming at once; and a
horrid noise the flames made, and the cracking of houses at their

ruine. So home with a sad heart; and there find every body discoursing and lamenting the fire; and poor Tom Hater come with some few of his goods saved out of his house, which was burned upon Fish Street Hill. I invited him to lie at my house, and did receive his goods; but was deceived in his lying there, the news coming every moment of the growth of the fire; so as we were forced to begin to pack up our own goods, and prepare for their removal; and did by moonshine, it being brave, dry and moonshine and warm weather, carry much of my goods into the garden; and Mr. Hater and I did remove my money and iron chests into my cellar, as thinking that the safest place. And got my bags of gold into my office, and my chief papers of accounts also there, and my tallies into a box by themselves. So great was our fear, as Sir W. Batten hath carts come out of the country to fetch away his goods this night. We did put Mr. Hater, poor man! to bed a little; but he got but very little rest, so much noise being in my house, taking down of goods.

3d. About four o'clock in the morning, my Lady Batten sent me a cart to carry away all my money, and plate, and best things, to Sir W. Rider's, at Bednall Greene, which I did, riding myself in my night-gown, in the cart; and, Lord! to see how the streets and the highways are crowded with people running and riding, and getting out of carts at any rate to fetch away things. I find Sir W. Rider tired with being called up all night, and receiving things from several friends. His house full of goods, and much of Sir W. Batten's and Sir W. Pen's. I am eased at my heart to have my treasure so well secured. Then home, and with much ado to find away, nor any sleep all this night to me nor my poor wife. But then all this day she and I and all my people labouring to get away the rest of our things, and did get Mr. Tooker to get me a lighter to take them in, and we did carry them, myself some, over Tower Hill, which was by this time full of people's goods, bringing their goods thither; and down to the lighter, which lay at the next quay, above the Tower Dock. And here was my neighbor's wife, Mrs. ——, with her pretty child, and some few of her things, which I did willingly give way to be saved with mine: but there was no passing with anything through the postern, the crowd was so great. The Duke of York came this way by the office, and spoke to us, and did ride with his guard up and down the City to keep all quiet, he being now General, and having the care of all. This day, Mercer being not at home, but against her mistress's order gone to her mother's, and my wife going thither to speak with W. Hewer, beat her there, and was angry; and her mother saying that she was not a 'prentice girl, to ask leave every time she goes abroad, my wife with good reason was angry; and, when she come home, did bid her be gone again. And so she went away, which troubled me, but yet less than it would, because of the condition we are in, in fear of coming in a little time to being less able to keep one in her quality. At night, lay down a little upon a quilt of W. Hewer's in the office, all my own things being packed up and gone; and, after me, my poor wife did the like, we having fed upon the remains of yesterday's dinner, having no fire nor dishes, nor any opportunity of dressing anything.

THE HAPPINESS OF A LIFE
Led According to Nature

By

Samuel Johnson

SAMUEL JOHNSON (*1709–1784*) was an English essayist, critic and lexicographer. When he was 23 he left Oxford without a degree and attempted school mastering and translating. Broke, he married a widow who had a small competence, when he was 26. At 27 with only a few pennies in his pocket he went with Garrick, his pupil, to London where he had a long hard struggle to make a living writing. Ten years later he published his proposal of a new Dictionary of the English language which he eventually produced in 1755. During this period he lived mainly in a house near Fleet Street, London, which is still standing. When he had to meet the expenses of his mother's death he wrote *Rasselas* in the evenings of a single week. The Crown bestowed a pension of $1500 a year upon him during the last 22 years of his life. Boswell met him in 1763 and became his devoted follower which contact resulted in the famous biography. About 1765 he made the acquaintance of Thrale and his wife with whom he traveled and was happy during the latter years of his life. He was a brilliant talker but wrote little and much of his best wit is supposed to have found outlets in his conversations. Johnson is buried in Westminster Abbey near Garrick and Dryden, and many editions of his works have been published since his death.

RASSELAS went often to an assembly of learned men, who met at stated times to unbend their minds, and compare their opinions. Their manners were somewhat coarse, but their conversation was instructive, and their disputations acute, though sometimes too violent, and often continued until neither controversialist recalled upon what question they began. Some faults were almost general among them: every one was desirous to dictate to the rest, and

[641]

every one was pleased to hear the genius or knowledge of another depreciated.

In this assembly Rasselas was relating his interview with the hermit, and the wonder with which he heard him censure a course of life which he had so deliberately chosen, and so laudably followed. The sentiments of the hearers were various. Some were of the opinion, that the folly of his choice had been justly punished by condemnation to perpetual perseverance. One of the youngest among them, with great vehemence, pronounced him a hypocrite. Some talked of the right of society to the labor of individuals, and considered retirement as a desertion of duty. Others readily allowed that there was a time when the claims of the public were satisfied, and when a man might properly sequester himself, to review his life, and purify his heart.

One, who appeared more affective with the narrative than the rest, thought it likely that the hermit would, in a few years, go back to his retreat, and perhaps, if shame did not restrain or death intercept him, return once more from his retreat into the world: "For the hope of happiness," said he, "is so strongly impressed, that the longest experience is not able to efface it. Of the present state, whatever it be, we feel, and are forced to confess, the misery: yet, when the same state is again at a distance, imagination paints it as desirable. But the time will surely come, when desire will be no longer our torment, and no man shall be wretched but by his own fault."

"This," said a philosopher, who had heard him with tokens of great impatience, "is the present condition of a wise man. The time is already come, when none are wretched but by their own fault. Nothing is more idle than to inquire after happiness, which nature has kindly placed within our reach. The way to be happy is to live according to nature, in accordance with that universal and unalterable law with which every heart is originally impressed; which is not written on it by precept, but engraven by destiny, not instilled by education, but infused at our nativity. He that lives according to nature will suffer nothing from the delusions of hope, or importunities of desire; he will receive and reject with equability of temperament, and act or suffer as the reason of things shall alternately prescribe. Other men may amuse themselves with subtle definitions, or intricate ratiocinations. Let them learn to be wiser by easier means: let them observe the hind of the forest, and the linnet of the grove; let them consider the life animals, whose motions are regulated by instinct: they obey their guide and are happy. Let us therefore, at length, cease to dispute, and learn to live, throw away the encumbrance of precepts, which they who utter them with so much pride and pomp do not understand, and carry with us this simple and intelligible maxim—that deviation from nature is deviation from happiness."

When he had spoken, he looked round him with a placid air, and enjoyed the consciousness of his own beneficence. "Sir," said the prince with great modesty, "as I, like all the rest of mankind, am desirous of felicity, my closest attention has been fixed upon your discourse; I doubt not the position which a man so learned has so confidently advanced:—let me know only what it is to live according to nature."

"When I find young men so humble and so docile," said the philosopher, "I can deny them no information which my studies have enabled me to afford. To live according to nature, is to act always with due regard to the fitness arising from the relations and qualities of causes and effects; to concur with the great and unchangeable scheme of universal felicity; to coöperate with the general disposition and tendency of the present scheme of things."

The prince soon found that this was one of the sages whom he should understand less as he heard him longer. He therefore bowed and was silent; and the philosopher, supposing him satisfied, and the rest vanquished, rose up, and departed with the air of a man that had co-operated with the present system.

DREAM–CHILDREN
A Reverie

By

Charles Lamb

CHARLES LAMB (*1775–1834*) was an English essayist, critic and humorist. When he was 17 he became a clerk in India House where he stayed for over thirty years. When he was 21 his sister murdered his mother and he sacrificed his life for thirty-eight years to devote to his sister. But this tragedy did not dim his literary output. His individuality was expressed in the verses on *Old Familiar Faces,* published when he was only 23. Continued poverty and the care of his sister were forces constantly urging him to write. When he was 42 a publisher urged him to collect his scattered verses in two volumes which resulted in an invitation to an editorship. Failing in health he resigned from India House in 1825 and retired to a small village where he and his sister spent the last days of their lives.

CHILDREN LOVE TO LISTEN to stories about their elders when *they* were children, to stretch their imagination to the conception of a traditionary great-uncle or grandame whom they never saw. It was in this spirit that my little ones crept about me the other evening to hear about their great-grandmother Field, who lived in a great house in Norfolk, which had been the scene of the tragic incidents which they had lately become familiar with from the ballad of the Children in the Wood. Certain it is that the whole story of the children and their cruel uncle was to be seen fairly carved out in wood upon the chimney piece of the great hall, the whole story down to the Robin Redbreasts, till a foolish person pulled it down to set up a marble one of modern invention in its stead with no story upon it.

Here Alice put out one of her dear mother's looks too tender
to be called upbraiding. Then I went on to say how religious and
how good their great-grandmother Field was, how beloved and
respected by everybody, though she was not indeed the mistress
of this great house, but had only the charge of it committed to
her by the owner. But still she lived in it in a manner as if it
had been her own, and kept up the dignity of the great house in
a sort while she lived, which afterwards came to decay and was
nearly pulled down, and all its old ornaments stripped and carried away to the owner's other house, where they were set up and
looked as awkward as if some one were to carry away the old
tombs they had seen lately at the Abbey, and stick them up in
Lady C.'s tawdry gilt drawing-room. Here John smiled as much
as to say, 'that would be foolish indeed.'

And then I told how, when she came to die, her funeral was attended by a concourse of all the poor, and some of the gentry
too, of the neighborhood for many miles around, because she had
been such a good and religious woman; so indeed that she knew
all the Psaltery by heart, aye, and a great part of the Testament
besides. Here little Alice spread her hands. Then I told what a
tall, upright graceful person their great-grandmother Field was, and
how in her youth she was esteemed the best dancer—here little
Alice's right foot played an involuntary movement till, upon my
looking grave, it desisted. Then I told how she used to sleep
by herself in a lone chamber of the great lone house, and she believed that an apparition of two infants was to be seen at midnight gliding up and down the great staircase near where she slept,
but she said 'those innocents would do her no harm;' and how
frightened I used to be, though in those days I had my maid to
sleep with me, because I was never half so good or religious as she
—and yet I never saw the infants. Here John expanded all his
eye-brows and tried to look courageous.

Then I told how good she was to all her grand-children, having
us to the great house in the holydays, where I in particular used
to spend many hours by myself, in gazing upon the old busts of
the Twelve Caesars, that had been Emperors of Rome, till the old
marble heads would seem to live again, or I to be turned into
marble with them; how I could never be tired with roaming

about that huge mansion, with its vast empty rooms, with their
worn-out hangings, fluttering tapestry and carved oaken panels
with the gilding almost rubbed out—sometimes in the spacious,
old-fashioned gardens, which I had almost to myself, unless when
now and then a solitary gardening man would cross me—and how
the nectarines and peaches hung upon the walls without my ever
offering to pluck them, because they were forbidden fruit—and
because I had more pleasure in strolling about among the old
melancholy-looking yew trees or the firs, and picking up the red
berries and the fir-apples which were good for nothing but to look
at—or in lying about upon the fresh grass with all the fine garden
smells around me—or basking in the orangery, till I could almost
fancy myself ripening too along with the oranges and the limes
in that grateful warmth—or in watching the dace that darted to
and fro in the fish-pond at the bottom of the garden, with here
and there a great sulky pike hanging midway down the water
in silent state, as if it mocked at their impertinent friskings. I had
more pleasure in these busy-idle diversions than in all the sweet
flavors of peaches, nectarines, oranges and such like common baits
of children. Here John slyly deposited back upon the plate a bunch
of grapes which, not unobserved by Alice, he had meditated
dividing with her, and both seemed willing to relinquish them
for the present as irrelevant.

Then in somewhat a more heightened tone, I told how, though
their great-grandmother Field loved all her grand-children, yet
in an especial manner she might be said to love their uncle,
John, because he was so handsome and spirited a youth, and a
king to the rest of us; and instead of moping about in solitary
corners like some of us, he would mount the most mettlesome
horse he could get, when but an imp no bigger than themselves,
and make it carry him half over the county in a morning, and
join the hunters when there were any out—and yet he loved the
old great house and gardens too, but had too much spirit to be
always pent up within their boundaries—and how their uncle grew
up to man's estate as brave as he was handsome to the admiration
of everybody, but of their great-grandmother Field most especially;
and how he used to carry me upon his back when I was a lame-
footed boy many a mile when I could not walk for pain—and how

in after life he became lame-footed too, and I did not always make allowances enough for him when he was impatient and in pain nor remember sufficiently how considerate he had been to me when I was lame-footed; and how when he died, though he had not been dead an hour, it seemed as if he had died a great while ago, such a distance is there betwixt life and death; and how I bore his death as I thought pretty well at first, but afterwards it haunted and haunted me; and though I did not cry and take it to heart as some do, and as I think he would have done if I had died, yet I missed him all day long and knew not till then how much I loved him. I missed his kindness, I missed his crossness and wished him to be alive again to be quarreling with him rather than not have him again, and was as uneasy without him as he their poor uncle must have been when the doctor took off his limb.

Here the children fell a-crying and asked if their little mourning which they had on was not for their uncle John, and they looked up and prayed me not to go on about their uncle but to tell them some stories about their pretty dead mother. Then I told how for seven long years, in hope sometimes, sometimes in despair, yet persisting ever, I courted the fair Alice W——n; and as much as children could understand what coyness and difficulty and denial meant in maidens—when suddenly, turning to Alice, the soul of the first Alice looked out at her eyes with such a reality of representment that I became in doubt which of them stood there before me, or whose that bright hair was; and while I stood gazing, both the children gradually grew fainter to my view, receding and receding until nothing at last but two mournful features were seen in the uttermost distance which, without speech, strangely impressed upon me the effects of speech: 'We are not Alice nor of thee nor are we children at all. The children of Alice call Bartrum father. We are nothing, less than nothing and dreams. We are only what might have been and must wait upon the tedious shores of Lethe millions of ages before we have existence and a name'— and immediately awaking, I found myself seated in my bachelor arm-chair where I had fallen asleep with the faithful Bridget unchanged by my side—but John L. (or James Elia) was gone for ever.

SESAME AND LILIES

By

John Ruskin

JOHN RUSKIN (*1819–1900*) was an English author, art critic
and reformer. He published his first volume of *Modern
Painters* when he was 24 and wrote technical essays for many
years following. For ten years after 1869 Ruskin was Slade
professor of art at Oxford and in 1871 he gave $25,000 for
the endowment of a Master of drawing there. He was re-
elected professor in 1883 but resigned in the following year
to retire to the country on Coniston Lake. Ruskin was
primarily a critic of art but to him it was closely and in-
separably bound up with truth, morals and religion.

SESAME. OF KINGS' TREASURIES

I AM NOT going to talk to you of kings regnant nor of treasuries
of wealth, but of the royal treasures hidden in books. When we
consider education we observe that it is commonly supposed to
be carried on for the sake of a position in life, advancement in
life or in response to our thirst for applause and love of praise.
We wish we could associate with sensible and well-informed persons, but we cannot choose our friends as we will or know whom
we would. For all the higher circles of human intelligence are only
momentarily and partially open, so that we are fortunate to obtain a glimpse of a great poet or put a question to a man of science
or have ten minutes talk with a cabinet-minister. Meanwhile there
is open to us a society of people who will talk to us as long as we
like in the best words they can choose about the things nearest
their hearts. This we find in the books of all time, not in the books
of the hour which are little more than letters or newspapers in
good print. But in what is really a "book" is something in which

the great reader, the great statesman, the great thinker sets down forever his scripture as if to say, "This is the best of me."

Will you go and gossip with your house-maid or stable-boy when you may talk with kings and queens? Will you jostle with the crowd for an *entrée* into the society of lords or an audience with philosophers when there is ever open to you an eternal court with its society wide as the world and multitudinous as its days, with the chosen and mighty of every place and time? But you must love these people if you are to be among them and show that you desire to enter into their thoughts and be taught by them; and you must realize that their thought is like gold which, instead of being heaped upon the mountain-tops, is hidden away in little fissures of the earth so that one must toil like an Australian miner to find it. So do not hope to get at the meaning of any good author without sharp tools and a fusing fire which you must use before you can gather one grain of his metal.

You must get into the habit of looking at words and assure yourself of their meaning in their every syllable and even letter. A well-educated gentleman may not know many languages and may not be able to speak any but his own, but whatever language he knows he knows precisely so that the accent or turn of expression in a single sentence will at once mark the scholar. In a language so mongrel in breed as the English there is a fatal power of equivocation put into the hands of men in their being able to use Greek and Latin words for an idea when they want it to be awful, and Saxon or common words when they want it to be vulgar. This does not imply knowing or trying to know Greek or Latin or French, which might take a life-time; yet you can easily ascertain the meanings through which the English word has passed and those which in a good writer's work it must still bear.

Having then faithfully listened to the great teachers so that you may enter into their thoughts, you have yet to enter into their hearts. As you go to them first for clear sight, you must stay with them that you may share at last their just and mighty passion. We come to the great concourse of the dead not merely to learn from them what is true but to feel with them what is just, and to feel with them we must be like them. In nothing is a gentleman to be distinguished from a vulgar person or a gentle nation from a mob more than that their feelings are constant and just as the result of due thought and consideration.

But why should we talk about reading books when we stand in need of sharper discipline in an age when the insanity of avarice has rendered us incapable of thought? We despise literature for we do not spend as much on our books as on our horses. How little would the contents of the book-shelves in the United Kingdom bring in comparison with the contents of its wine-cellars! We despise science and while we may be foremost in discovery and invention such scientific work is carried on in spite of the nation by the zeal and money of private people. We despise art and while we have our art-galleries and art-exhibits it is all for the sake of the shop, for we would sell canvas as well as coal and crockery as well as iron. You have despised nature, or all the deep and sacred sensations of natural scenery and as the French revolutionists made stables of the cathedrals of France, we have made race-courses of the cathedrals of the earth. You have despised compassion. To do a piece of common Christian righteousness in a plain English word or deed or to make Christian law any rule of life—we know too well what our faith comes to for that. You might sooner get lightning out of incense-smoke than true action or passion out of your modern English religion.

I have no words for the wonder with which I hear Kinghood still spoken of even among thoughtful men. Yet the visible king may be a true one also, if he will come to measure his kingdom by the force of it and not by geographical boundaries. Suppose an order of kings should arise who would so believe in Wisdom as to bring forth treasures of it for their people. Then we should bring up our peasants to a book-exercise instead of a bayonet-exercise, drill armies of thinkers in place of armies of stabbers, find national amusements in reading-rooms as well as in rifle-grounds and give prizes for a fair shot at a fact as well as for a leaden splash on a target. You have got your corn laws repealed, try if you cannot get corn laws established for dealing in better bread, bread made of that old enchanted Arabian grain, the Sesame, which opens doors, doors not of robbers' but of Kings' Treasuries.

LILIES. OF QUEENS' GARDENS

There is only one pure kind of kingship; it consists in a stronger moral state, in a truer thoughtful state than that of others. But what special portion or kind of this royal authority may rightly be possessed by women and how far they are called to a truly queenly power, not over their households only but over all within their sphere? We cannot determine what the queenly power of women should be until we are agreed what their ordinary power should be, or consider how education may fit them for any widely extending duty until we are agreed what is their true constant duty. Now the first use of education was, as we have seen, to enable us to consult with the wisest and greatest men on all points of earnest difficulty. Let us hear the testimony they have left respecting the true dignity of woman and her mode of help to men.

First let us take Shakespeare and note that he has no heroes but only heroines. Except for the slight sketch of Henry the Fifth and Valentine in *Two Gentlemen of Verona* there is not one heroic figure on his stage. Othello would have been one if his simplicity had not made him a prey to baseness around him. Coriolanus, Caesar and Antony stand in flawed strength and fall by their vanities. Hamlet is indolent and drowsily speculative, Romeo an impatient boy, the Merchant of Venice languidly submissive to adverse fortune, Orlando the despairing toy of chance. Yet there is hardly a play which has not in it a perfect woman, steadfast in grave hope and errorless purpose. Cordelia, Desdemona, Isabella, Hermione, Imogen, Queen Katherine, Perdita, Sylvia, Viola, Rosalind, Helena and Virgilia are all faultless, conceived in the highest heroic type of humanity. The catastrophe of every play is caused by the folly or fault of a man, the redemption if there be any is brought about by the wisdom and virtue of a woman.

Next, take the testimony of the great Italians and the Greeks. In the plan of Dante's great poem, Beatrice stoops to pity, never to love and yet saves him from Hell. He is going eternally astray in despair but she comes down from Heaven to his help leading him with rebuke upon rebuke from star to star. You may think that a Greek knight would have a lower estimate of women than this Christian lover, but consider the simple mother's and wife's heart of Andromache, the divine yet rejected wisdom of Cassandra, the playful kindness and simple princess-life of happy Nausiciaas, the wifely calm of Penelope, the fearless yet hopeless piety of Antigone, the submission of Iphegenia and the sublimity of Alcestis who to save her husband had passed calmly through the bitterness of death.

Are these great men mistaken or are we? Are Shakespeare and Dante, Homer and Aeschylus merely dressing dolls for us, or unnatural visions the realization of which would bring anarchy into all households and ruin into all affections? We are foolish in speaking of the "superiority" of one sex to the other as if they could be compared in similar things, for each has what the other has not. The man's power is active, progressive, defensive; woman's for sweet ordering, arrangement and decision. Her great function is praise; she enters into no conquest but infallibly judges the crown of conquest. She must be enduringly and incorruptibly good, instinctively and infallibly wise, but not with the narrowness of insolent and loveless pride but with the passionate gentleness of an infinitely variable modesty. In that sense is found the true changefulness of woman—*la donna è mobile,* but only in the sense that light is variable that it may take the color of all that it falls upon and exalt it.

Such is the place, such the power of woman; what kind of education is to fit her for these? I believe that with the exception of theology, of which woman must beware, a girl's education in its course and material of study should be the same as a boy's, but quite differently directed. A woman in any rank of life ought to know whatever her husband is likely to know but in a different way, for his command of knowledge should be foundational and progressive, hers general and accomplished for daily and helpful use. But what is woman's office with respect to the State? The man's duty as a member of the commonwealth is to assist in the maintenance, advance and defense of the State. The woman's duty is to assist in the ordering, comforting and beautiful adornment of the State. What the man is at his own gate defending it against insult and spoil, that is the woman to be within her gates as the centre of order, the mirror of beauty and balm of distress.

This whole country of England is but a little garden not more than enough for your children to run on its lawns if you will let them run there, and yet this little garden you will turn into a furnace-ground and fill it with heaps of cinders and those children of yours will suffer for it. For the fairies will not be all banished, since there are fairies of the furnace as there are fairies of the woods and their first gifts seem to be "sharp as the arrows of the mighty," but their last gifts are "coals of juniper." You have heard it said that flowers flourish only in the garden of some one who loves and you would think it pleasant magic if you could flush your flowers into bright bloom by your kind look upon them; nay, more if your look had the power not only to cheer but to guard them.

Far among the moorlands and the rocks, far in the darkness of the terrible streets feeble flowerets are lying with all their fresh leaves torn and their stems broken. Will you not go down among them and set them in order in their little fragrant beds, nor fence them in their trembling from the fierce wind? Shall morning follow morning for you but not for them and the dawn rise to watch far away those frantic dances of death, but no dawn rise to breathe upon these living banks of wild violet and woodbine and rose, nor call to you through your casement saying—

> *"Come into the garden, Maud,*
> *For the black bat, night, has flown,*
> *And the woodbine spices are wafted abroad*
> *And the musk of the roses blown?"*

Who is it, think you, who stands at the gate of this sweeter garden alone waiting for you? Did you ever hear, not of a Maud but a Madeleine who went down to her garden at the dawn and found one waiting at the gate, whom she supposed to be the gardener? At the gate of this garden He is waiting always, waiting to take your hand, ready to go down to see the fruits of the valley, to see whether the vine has flourished and the pomegranate budded. There you shall see with Him the little tendrils of the vines that His hand is guiding and the pomegranate springing where His hand cast the sanguine seed. Oh, you queens, you queens! Among the hills and happy greenwood of this land of yours, shall the foxes have holes and the birds of the air have nests while in your cities the stones cry out against you that they are the only pillows where the Son of Man can lay his head?

LONDON

By

Heinrich Heine

HEINRICH HEINE (*1797–1856*), the German poet, was born at
Düsseldorf of Jewish parents. His father was a businessman
and his mother, the daughter of a physician, was a woman of
great character and energy. Heine was the eldest of four children. He was educated first in private schools, then in the
Lyceum of Düsseldorf. Though not specially diligent, he acquired a knowledge of French and English as well as some
tincture of the classics and Hebrew. He admired Napoleon
who had freed the Jews from many of the political disabilities
under which they suffered. Heine began writing poetic essays
in Berlin and was deeply influenced by Hegel. When he went
to Paris he met and married Eugenie Mirat, a saleswoman in
a Paris boot shop. She was vain and extravagant but he loved
her dearly. Having an ineradicable sense of justice, in 1830
when news of the July Revolution in Paris came to him, he
went there feeling that a new era of freedom was beginning.
Above all things, Heine was great as a wit and a satirist.

I HAVE SEEN the greatest wonder which the world can show to the
astonished spirit; I have seen it, and am more astonished than
ever—and there still remains fixed in my memory that stone forest
of houses, and amid them the rushing stream of faces, of living human beings, with all their motley passions, all their terrible impulses of love, of hunger and of hate—I am speaking of
London.

Send a philosopher to London, but no poet. Send a philosopher
there, and let him stand at the corner of Cheapside, he will learn
more there than from all the books of the last Leipzig fair; and as
the human waves roar round him, and the Eternal Spirit which

moves upon the face of the waters will breathe upon him; the most hidden secrets of social harmony will be suddenly revealed to him, he will hear the pulse of the world beat audibly, and see it visibly—for, if London is the right hand of the world, its active, mighty right hand, then we may regard that which leads from the Exchange to Downing Street as the world's radial artery.

But send no poet to London. This downright earnestness of all things, this colossal uniformity, this machine-like movement, this moroseness even in pleasure, this exaggerated London, smothers the imagination and rends the heart. And should you ever send a German poet thither—a dreamer, who stands staring at every single phenomenon, even a ragged beggar-woman or a shining jeweler's shop—why, then he will find things going badly with him, and he will be hustled about on every side, or even be knocked over with a mild imprecation—the damned pushing! I soon saw that these people have much to do. They live on a large scale, and though food and clothes are dearer with them than with us, they must still be better fed and clothed than we are—as gentility requires. Moreover, they have enormous debts, yet occasionally in a vain-glorious mood they make ducks and drakes of their guineas, pay other nations to fight for their pleasures, give their respective kings a handsome *douceur* into the bargain—and, therefore, John Bull must work day and night to get the money for such expenses; by day and by night he must tax his brain to discover new machines, and he sits and reckons in the sweat of his brow, and runs and rushes without looking about much from the Docks to the Exchange, and from the Exchange to the Strand, and, therefore, it is quite pardonable if, when a poor German poet, gazing into a print-shop window, stands in his way at the corner of Cheapside, he should knock him aside with a rather rough oath.

How much more pleasant and homelike is our dear Germany! How dreamily comfortable, how Sabbatically quiet all things glide along here! Calmly the sentinels are changed, uniforms and houses shine in the quiet sunshine, swallows flit over the flagstones, fat court-councillors smile from their windows, while along the echoing streets there is room enough for the dogs to sniff at each other, and for men to stand at ease and chat about the theatre, and bow low—oh, how low—when some small aristocratic scamp or vice-scamp, with colored ribbons on his shabby coat, or some powdered and gilded court-marshal struts by, graciously returning salutations!

I had made up my mind not to be astonished at the immensity of London of which I had heard so much. But it happened to me as to the poor school-boy, who had made up his mind not to feel the whipping he was to receive. The facts of the case were, that he expected to get the usual blows with the usual stick in the usual way on the back, whereas he received a most unusually severe thrashing on an unusual place with a slender switch. I anticipated great palaces, but saw nothing but mere small houses. But their very uniformity and their limitless extent are wonderfully impressive.

These houses of brick, owing to the damp atmosphere and coal smoke, become uniform in color, that is to say, of a brown olive green; they are all of the same style of building, generally two or three windows wide, three stories high, and adorned above with small red tiles, which remind one of newly-extracted bleeding teeth; so that the broad and accurately-squared streets seem to be bordered by endlessly long barracks. This has its reason in the fact that every English family, though it consists of only two persons, must still have a house to itself for its own castle, and rich speculators, to meet the demand, build wholesale entire streets of these dwellings, which they rent singly.

At the opposite side of the town, which they call the West End, where the more aristocratic and less-occupied world lives, this uniformity is still more dominant; yet here there are very long and very broad streets, where all the houses are large as palaces, though outwardly anything but distinguished, unless we accept the fact that in these, as in all the better class houses in London, the windows of the first story are adorned with iron-barred balconies, and also on the ground floor there is a black railing protecting the entrance to certain cellar apartments buried in the earth. In this part of the city there are also great squares, where rows of houses like those already described form a quadrangle, in whose centre there is a garden enclosed by a black iron railing, and containing some statue or other. In all of these squares and streets the eye is never shocked by the dilapidated huts of misery. Everywhere we are stared down on by wealth and respectability, while crammed away in retired lanes and dark, damp alleys poverty dwells with her rags and her tears.

The stranger who wanders through the great streets of London, and does not chance right into the regular quarters of the people, sees little or nothing of the misery there. Only here and there, at the mouth of some dark alley, stands a ragged woman with a suckling babe at her wasted breast, and begs with her eyes. Perhaps if those eyes are still beautiful, one glances into them and shrinks back at the world of wretchedness within them. The common beggars are old people, generally blacks, who stand at the corners of the streets cleaning pathways—a very necessary thing in muddy London—and ask for "coppers" in reward. It is in the dusky twilight that Poverty with her mates, Vice and Crime, glide forth from their lairs. They shun daylight the more anxiously, the more cruelly their wretchedness contrasts with the pride of wealth which glitters everywhere; only Hunger drives them at noonday from their dens, and then they stand with silent, speaking eyes, staring beseechingly at the rich merchant who hurries along, bustling and jingling gold; or at the lazy lord who, like a surfeited god, rides by on his high horse, casting now and then an aristocratically indifferent glance at the mob below, as though they were swarming ants, or, at all events a mass of baser things, whose joys and sorrows have nothing in common with his feelings. Yes, over the vulgar multitude which sticks fast to the soil, soar, like beings of a higher nature, England's nobility, who regard their little island as only a temporary resting place, Italy as their summer garden, Paris as their social salon, and the whole world as their inheritance. They sweep along knowing nothing of sorrow or suffering, and their gold is a talisman which conjures into fulfillment their wildest wish.

Poor Poverty! How agonizing must thy hunger be where others dwell in scornful superfluity! And when some one casts with indifferent hand a crust into thy lap, how bitter must the tears be wherewith thou moistenest it! Thou poisonest thyself with thine own tears. Well art thou in the right when thou alliest thyself to Vice and Crime. Outlawed criminals often bear more humanity in their hearts than those cold, blameless citizens of virtue, in whose white hearts the power of evil is quenched, but also the power of good. I have seen women on whose cheeks red vice was painted, and in whose hearts dwelt heavenly purity. I have seen women—I would I saw them again!

JOAN OF ARC

By

Thomas De Quincey

THOMAS DE QUINCEY (*1785–1859*) was an English author, born in Manchester. His parents retrieved him from a runaway expedition early in his life and sent him to Oxford where he remained five years. It was here that he first resorted to opium to allay pain and the use of the drug became a lifelong habit. In his early twenties he became acquainted with Coleridge, Wordsworth, Southey, Lamb and Hazlitt and he espoused a career of literature. He became an editor when he was thirty and a year later published his *Confessions of an English Opium-Eater* which gave him immediate fame. He moved to Scotland in 1828 where he lived until his death. De Quincey's writings include *Style and Rhetoric, Joan of Arc* and *The Flight of a Tartar Tribe*.

WHAT is to be thought of her? What is to be thought of the poor shepherd girl from the hills and forests of Lorraine, that—like the Hebrew shepherd boy from the hills and forests of Judea—rose suddenly out of the quiet, out of the safety, out of the religious inspiration, rooted in deep pastoral solitudes, to a station in the deep van of armies, and to the more perilous station at the right hand of kings?

The Hebrew boy inaugurated his patriotic mission by an act, by a victorious act such as no man could deny. But so did the girl of Lorraine, if we read her story as it was read by those who saw her nearest. Adverse armies bore witness to the boy as no pretender, but so they did to the gentle girl. Judged by the voices of all who saw them from a station of good will, both were found true and loyal to any promises involved in their acts. Enemies it was that made the difference between their subsequent fortunes.

The boy rose to a splendor and noon-day prosperity, both personal and public, that rang through the records of his people, and became a by-word amongst his posterity for a thousand years, until the sceptre was departing from Judah. The poor, forsaken girl, on the contrary, drank not for herself from that cup of rest which she had secured for France. She never sang together with the songs that rose in her native Domrémy, as echoes to the departing steps of invaders. She mingled not in the festal dances of Vaucouleurs which celebrated rapture the redemption of France. No! for her voice was then silent. No! for her feet were dust.

Pure, innocent, noble-hearted girl! This was amongst the strongest pledges for thy side—that never once, no, not for a moment of weakness, didst thou revel in the vision of coronets and honor from man. Coronets for thee! Oh, no! Honors, if they come when all is over, are for those that share thy blood. Daughter of Domrémy, when the gratitude of thy king shall awaken, thou will be sleeping the sleep of the dead. Call her, King of France, she will not hear thee! Cite her by thy apparitors to come and receive a robe of honor, but she will be found *en contumace*. When the thunders of universal France, as even yet may happen, shall proclaim the grandeur of the poor shepherd girl that gave up all for her country, thy ear, young shepherd girl, will have been deaf for five centuries.

To suffer and to do, that was thy portion in this life. To do—never for thyself, always for others; to suffer—never in the person of generous champions, always in thy own—that was thy destiny, and not for a moment was it hidden from thyself. Life, thou saidest, is short, and the sleep which is in the grave is long! Let me use that life so transitory for the glory of those heavenly dreams destined to comfort the sleep which is so long.

Never once did this holy child, as regarded herself, relax from her belief in the darkness that was travelling to meet her. She might not prefigure the very manner of her death; she saw not in vision, perhaps, the aerial altitude of the fiery scaffold, the spectators without end on every road pouring into Rouen as to a coronation, the surging smoke, the volleying flames, the hostile faces all around, the pitying eye that lurked but here and there until nature and imperishable truth broke loose from artificial restraints; these might not be apparent through the mists of this hurrying death. But the voice that called her to death, that she heard forever.

Great was the throne of France even in those days, and great was he who sat upon it; but well Joanna knew that not the throne nor he that sat upon it was for her, but on the contrary that she was for them. Not she by them but they by her should rise from the dust. Gorgeous were the lilies, and for centuries they had the privilege to spread their beauty over land and sea, until in another century the wrath of God and man combined to wither them. But well Joanna knew, early in Domrémy she had read that bitter truth, that the lilies of France would decorate no garland for her. Flower nor bud, bell nor blossom would ever bloom for her.

The education of this poor girl was mean according to the present standard, was ineffably grand according to a purer philosophic standard, and only not good for our age because for us it would be unattainable. She read nothing, for she could not read; but she had heard others read parts of the Roman martyrology. She wept in sympathy with the sad *Misereres* of the Romish chaunting, she rose to heaven with the glad triumphant *Gloria in Excelsis,* she drew her comfort and her vital strength from the rites of her church. But, next after these spiritual advantages, she owed most to the advantage of her situation. The fountain of Domrémy was on the brink of a boundless forest, and it was haunted to that degree by fairies that the parish priest was obliged to read mass there once a year, in order to keep them in decent bounds. But the forests of Domrémy—these were the glories of the land, for in them abode mysterious powers and ancient secrets that towered into tragic strength.

.   .   .

The shepherd girl that has delivered France, she from her dungeon, she from her baiting at the stake, she from her duel with fire, as she entered her last dream, saw Domrémy, saw the fountain of Domrémy, saw the pomp of forests in which her childhood had wandered. That Easter festival which men had denied her languishing heart, the resurrection of the spring-time which the darkness of dungeons had intercepted from her, hungering after the glorious liberty of forests, were by God given back into her hands as jewels that had been stolen from her by robbers. With those, perhaps, was given back to her by God the bliss of childhood. By special privilege for her might be created in this farewell dream a second childhood innocent as the first, but not like that sad with the gloom of a fearful mission in the rear.

This mission had now been fulfilled. The storm was weathered, the skirts even of that mighty storm were drawing off. The blood that she was to reckon for had been exacted; the tears that she was to shed in secret had been paid to the last. The hatred to herself in all eyes had been faced steadily, had been suffered, had been survived, and in her last fight upon the scaffold she had triumphed gloriously; victoriously had she tasted the stings of death. For all, except this comfort from her farewell dream, she had died— died amidst the tears of ten thousand enemies, died amidst the drums and trumpets of armies, died amidst peals redoubling upon peals, volleys upon volleys from the saluting clarions of martyrs.

Bishop of Beauvais, I know that you also entering your final dream saw Domrémy. That fountain showed itself to your eyes in pure morning dews, but neither dews nor the holy dawn could cleanse away the bright spots of innocent blood upon its surface. By the fountain, Bishop, you saw a woman seated that hid her face, but as you drew near the woman raises her wasted features. Would Domrémy know them again for the features of her child? Ah, but you know them, Bishop, well. Oh, mercy! what a groan was that which the servants waiting outside the Bishop's dream at his bedside heard from his laboring heart, as at this moment he turned away from the fountain and the woman, seeking rest in the forests afar off. In the forests in which he prays for pity will he find a respite?

What a tumult, what a gathering of feet is there! In glades where only wild deer should run armies and nations are assembling, towering in the fluctuating crowd are phantoms that belong to departed hours. There is the great English Prince, Regent of France. There is my Lord of Winchester, the princely Cardinal that died and made no sign. There is the Bishop of Beauvais, clinging to the shelter of thickets. What building is that which hands so rapid are raising? Is it a martyr's scaffold? Will they

[663]

burn the child of Domrémy a second time? No, it is a tribunal that rises to the clouds and two nations stand round it waiting for the trial. Shall my Lord of Beauvais sit again upon the judgment seat and again number the hours for the innocent? Ah, no; he is the prisoner at the bar.

Already all is waiting, the mighty audience is gathered, the court is hurrying to their seats, the witnesses are arrayed, the trumpets are sounding, the judge is going to take his place. Oh, but this is sudden. My lord, have you no counsel? "Counsel I have none, in heaven above or on earth beneath, counsellor there is none now that would take a brief from me; all are silent." Is it indeed come to this. Alas! the time is short, the tumult is wondrous, the crowd stretches away into infinity, but yet I will search in it for somebody to take your brief, I know of somebody that will be your counsel.

Who is this that cometh from Domrémy? Who is she that cometh in bloody coronation robes from Rheims? Who is she that cometh with blackened flesh from walking the furnaces of Rouen? This is she, the shepherd girl, counsellor that had none for herself, whom I choose, Bishop, for yours. She it is, I engage, that shall take my Lord's brief. She it is, Bishop, that would plead for you; yes, Bishop, SHE—when heaven and earth are silent.

LA GIOCONDA

By

Walter Pater

WALTER HORATIO PATER (*1839–1894*) was an English essayist who was born in the east of London. He was educated at both Canterbury and Oxford and was elected fellow of Brasenose College. From then on he passed his entire life at Oxford except for short trips abroad and a brief residence in London. He entered college with the intention of becoming a clergyman but by his twenty-sixth year he had lost all belief in Christian doctrines and changed his mission to interpreting the spirit of the Renaissance in art and literature. He used the essay mainly but also the historical novel and story to advance his ideas.

LA GIOCONDA is in the truest sense Leonardo's masterpiece, the revealing instance of his thought and work. In suggestiveness only the *Melancholia* of Dürer is comparable to it, and no crude symbolism disturbs the effect of its subdued and graceful mystery. We all know the face and hands of the figure set in its marble chair, in that cirque of fantastic rocks, as in some faint light under the sea. Perhaps of all ancient pictures time has chilled it least. As often happens with works in which invention seems to reach its limit, there is an element in it given to, not invented by, the master. In that inestimable folio of drawings, once in the possession of Vasari, were certain designs by Verrochio, faces of such impressive beauty that Leonardo in his boyhood copied them many times. It is hard not to connect these designs of the elder, by-past master, as with its germinal principle, the unfathomable smile, always with a touch of something sinister in it, which plays

[665]

over all Leonardo's work. Besides, the picture is a portrait. From childhood we see this image defining itself on the fabric of his dreams, and but for express historical testimony, we might fancy that this was but his ideal lady embodied and beheld at last. What was the relationship of a living Florentine to this creature of his thought? By means of what strange affinities had the person and the dream grown up thus apart, and yet so closely together? Present from the first incorporeally in Leonardo's thought, dimly traced in the designs of Verrochio, she is found present at last in Il Giocondo's house. That there is much of mere portraiture in the picture is attested by the legend that by artificial means, the presence of mimes and flute-players, that subtle expression was protracted on the face. Again, was it in four years and by renewed labor never really completed, or in four months and as by stroke of magic that the image was projected?

The presence that thus rose so strangely beside the waters is expressive of what in the ways of a thousand years men had come to desire. Hers is the head upon which all "the ends of the world are come," and the eyelids are a little weary. It is beauty wrought out from within upon the flesh, the deposit, little cell by cell, of strange thoughts and fantastic reveries and exquisite passions. Set it for a moment beside one of those white Greek goddesses or beautiful women of antiquity, and how would they be troubled by this beauty into which the soul with all its maladies has passed! All the thoughts and experience of the world have etched and moulded there, in that which they have of power to refine and make expressive the outward form, the animalism of Greece, the lust of Rome, the reverie of the middle age with its spiritual ambition and imaginative loves, the return of the Pagan world, the sins of the Borgias. She is older than the rocks among which she sits; like the vampire she has been dead many times and learned the secrets of the grave; and has been a diver in deep seas and keeps their fallen day about her; she trafficked for strange webs with Eastern merchants; and, as Leda, was the mother of Helen of Troy and, as Saint Anne, the mother of Mary; and all this has been to her but as the sound of lyres and flutes, and lives only in the delicacy with which it has moulded the changing lineaments, and tinged the eyelids and the hands. The fancy of a perpetual life, sweeping together ten thousand experiences, is an old one; and modern thought has conceived the idea of humanity as wrought upon by and summing up in itself all modes of thought and life. Certainly Lady Lisa might stand as the embodiment of the old fancy, the symbol of the modern idea.

THE POETIC PRINCIPLE

By

Edgar Allan Poe

EDGAR ALLAN POE (*1809–1849*) one of the greatest American poets and prose writers was born in Boston. He was adopted by a wealthy merchant when he was orphaned in his third year. He became a student in 1826 at the University of Virginia but his gambling debts caused his patron to remove him to business. He continued writing and when he was 21 was admitted to West Point from where he was discharged in two years. Meanwhile he had been composing poetry constantly and two years later won a prize offered by a Baltimore periodical. In 1835 he became an editor in Richmond and a year later married his cousin Virginia. Thence he moved to New York and then to Philadelphia. In 1842 his wife became seriously ill and his own weakness for liquor commenced injuring him although he won another prize with *The Gold Bug* the next year. Returning to New York he became a critic, wrote *The Raven* and won immediate success. He moved to a small cottage in Fordham where in the deepest poverty his wife died. This caused his own prostration and breakdown. Recovering, he printed occasional papers. In his fortieth year he was found unconscious in a drinking place in Baltimore, was taken to a hospital, and died four days later.

———

HERE IN THE BEGINNING, permit me to say a few words in regard to a somewhat peculiar principle which, whether wrongfully or rightfully, has always had its influence in my own critical estimate of the poem. I hold that a long poem does not exist. I maintain that the phrase, "a long poem," is simply a flat contradiction in terms. I need scarcely observe that a poem deserves its title only inasmuch as it excites by elevating the soul. The value of the poem is in ratio of this elevating excitement. That degree of excitement which would entitle a poem to be so called at all cannot be sustained throughout a composition of any great length; after the lapse of half an hour at the very utmost, it flags, fails, a revulsion comes, and then the poem is in effect and fact no longer such.

There are no doubt many who have found difficulty in reconciling the critical dictum that the *Paradise Lost* is to be devoutly admired throughout with the absolute impossibility of maintaining for it during perusal the amount of enthusiasm which that critical dictum would demand. This great work in fact is to be regarded as poetical only when, losing sight of that vital requisite in all works of art—Unity, we view it merely as a series of minor poems. In regard to the *Iliad* we have, if not positive proof, very good reason for believing it intended as a series of lyrics; but, granting the epic intention, I can say only that the work is based on an imperfect sense of art. The modern epic is but an inconsiderate and blind-fold imitation. But the day of these artistic anomalies is over. If at any time any very long poem were popular in reality, which I doubt, it is at least clear that no very long poem will ever be popular again.

On the other hand, it is clear that a poem may be improperly brief. Undue brevity degenerates into mere epigrammatism. A very short poem, while now and then producing a brilliant effect, never produces a profound or enduring one. Every poem, it is said, should inculcate a moral, and by this moral is the poetical merit of the work to be adjudged. We Americans especially have patronized this happy idea; we have simply taken it into our heads that to write a poem simply for the poem's sake, and to acknowledge such to have been our design, would be to confess ourselves radically wanting in the true poetic dignity and force. But the simple fact is that, would we but permit ourselves to look into our own souls, we should immediately discover there that under the sun there neither exists nor can exist any work more thoroughly dignified, more supremely noble than this very poem, this poem *per se,* this poem which is a poem and nothing else, this poem written solely for the poem's sake.

With as deep a reverence for the True as ever inspired the bosom of man, I would nevertheless limit, in some measure, its modes of inculcation. I would limit to enforce them; I would not enfeeble them by dissipation. The demands of Truth are severe; she has no sympathy with myrtles. All that which is so indispensable in song is precisely all that with which she has nothing whatever to do. It is but making her a haunting paradox to wreathe her in gems and flowers. In enforcing a truth we need severity rather than effloresence of language. We must be simple, precise, terse; we must be cool, calm, unimpassioned. In a word, we must be in that mood which as nearly as possible is the exact converse of the poetical. He must be blind indeed who does not perceive the radical and chasmal difference between the truthful and poetical methods of inculcation. He must be theory-mad beyond redemption who, in spite of these differences, shall still persist in attempting to reconcile the obstinate oils and waters of Poetry and Truth.

Dividing the world of mind into its three most immediately obvious distinctions, we have the Pure Intellect, Taste and the Moral Sense. I place Taste in the middle because it is just this position which it occupies in the mind. It holds intimate relations with either extreme, but from the Moral Sense is separated by so faint a difference that Aristotle did not hesitate to place some of its operations among the virtues themselves. Nevertheless, we find the offices of the trio marked with a sufficient distinction. Just as the Intellect concerns itself with Truth, so Taste informs us of the Beautiful, while the Moral Sense is regardful of Duty. Of this latter, while Conscience teaches the obligation and Reason the expediency, Taste contents herself with displaying the charms, waging war upon vice solely on the ground of her deformity, her disproportion, her animosity to the fitting, to the appropriate, to the harmonious; in a word, to Beauty.

The struggle to apprehend the supernal Loveliness—this struggle on the part of souls fittingly constituted has given to the world all that which the world has ever been enabled at once to understand and to feel as poetic. The poetic sentiment of course, may develop itself in various modes—in painting, in sculpture, in architecture, in the dance, very especially in music, and very peculiarly and with a wide field in the composition of the landscape garden. Our present theme, however, has regard only to its manifestation in words. I would in brief define the poetry of words as the Rhythmical Creation of Beauty. Its sole arbiter is Taste. With the Intellect or with Conscience it has only collateral relations. Unless incidentally, it has no concern whatever with Duty or with Truth.

A few words, however, in explanation. That pleasure which is at once the most pure, the most elevating and the most intense is derived, I maintain, from the contemplation of the Beautiful. In the contemplation of Beauty alone we find it possible to attain that pleasurable elevation or excitement of the soul which we recognize as the Poetic Sentiment, and which is so easily distinguished from Truth, which is the satisfaction of the Reason, or from Passion which is the excitement of the heart. Therefore, I make Beauty, using the word as inclusive of the sublime, the province of the poem, simply because it is an obvious rule of Art that effects should be made to spring as directly as possible from their causes; no one as yet having been weak enough to deny that the peculiar elevation in question is at least most readily attainable in the poem.

It by no means follows, however, that the incitements of Passion, or the precepts of Duty, or even the lessons of Truth may not be introduced into a poem, and with advantage. For they may serve incidentally the general purposes of the work, but the true artist will always contrive to tone them down in proper subjection to that Beauty which is the atmosphere and the real essence of the poem.

VII

PHILOSOPHY AND RELIGION

THE ALLEGORY OF THE CAVE

A Dialogue Between Socrates and Glaucon
In the Republic

By

Plato

PLATO (*427-347* B.C.) was a Greek philosopher. Few real facts about his life are known except that his actual name was Aristocles. He received the usual education of an Athenian youth which was somewhat limited by the siege during the Peloponnesian War period. Aristotle stated that Plato was familiar with the earlier philosophers from his youth on. The keynote of the Platonic philosophy is that reality belongs not to the individual thing such as, this book, but to the general idea, as a book. Plato's writings exercised tremendous influences on Aristotle, Cicero, Plutarch, the Christian Fathers and the philosophers and poets of the Renaissance.

BEHOLD! said Socrates, human beings living in a sort of underground den, which has a mouth open towards the light and reaching all across the den. They have been here from their childhood, and have their necks and legs chained so that they cannot move and can see only before them. For the chains are arranged in such manner as to prevent them from turning their heads around. At a distance above and behind them the light of a fire is blazing, and between the fire and the prisoners there is a raised way. If you look you will see a low wall built along the way, like the screen which marionette players have before them and over which they show the puppets.

I see, said Glaucon.

And do you see, said I, men passing along the wall carrying vessels which appear over the wall, also figures of men and animals made of stone and wood and various other materials?

[675]

That is a strange idea, said he, and they are strange prisoners.

Like ourselves, I replied; they see only their own shadows or the shadows of one another which the fire throws on the opposite wall of the cave.

True, said he, for how could they see anything but the shadows, if they were never allowed to move their heads?

And of the objects which are being carried they would see only the shadows, would they not?

Yes, said he.

And if they were able to talk with one another, would they not suppose that they were naming what was actually before them?

Very true.

And suppose further that the prison had an echo which came from the other side, would they not be sure to fancy that the voice which they heard was that of a passing shadow?

No question, he replied.

There can be no question, said I, that the truth would be to them just nothing but the shadows of the images.

That is certain.

And now look again and see how they are released and cured of their folly. At first, when any one of them is liberated and compelled suddenly to go up and turn his neck around and walk and look at the light, he will suffer sharp pains. The glare will distress him and he will be unable to see the realities of which in his former state he had seen the shadows. Then imagine some one saying to him that what he saw before was an illusion, but that now he is approaching real being and has a truer sight and vision of more real things. Will he not fancy that the shadows which he formerly saw are truer than the objects which are now shown to him?

Far truer.

And if he is compelled to look at the light, will he not have a pain in his eyes which will make him turn away to take refuge in the object of vision which he can see, and which he will conceive to be clearer than the things which are now being shown to him?

True, said he.

And suppose once more he is reluctantly dragged up a steep

and rugged ascent and held fast and forced into the presence of
the sun himself, do you not think that he will be pained and
irritated, and when he approaches the light he will have his eyes
dazzled and will not be able to see any of the realities which
are now affirmed to be the truth?

Not all in a moment, said he.

He will require to get accustomed to the sight of the upper
world. At first he will see the shadows best, next the reflection of
men and other objects in the water, and then the objects themselves. Next he will gaze upon the light of the moon and the
stars, and he will see the sky and the stars by night better than
the sun or the light of the sun by day, will he not?

Certainly.

At last he will be able to see the sun and not mere reflections of
him in the water, but he will see him as he is in his proper place
and not in another, and he will contemplate his nature.

Certainly.

And after this he will reason that the sun is he who gives the
seasons and the years and is the guardian of all that is in the
visible world, and in a certain way the cause of all things which
he and his fellows have been accustomed to behold.

Certainly he would come to the other first and to this afterwards, said he.

Imagine, I said, that such an one suddenly coming out of the
sun were to be replaced in his old situation, is he not certain to
have his eyes full of darkness?

Very true, said he.

And if there were a contest and he had to compete in measuring
the shadows with the prisoners who have never moved out of
the den, would he not be ridiculous? Men would say of him that
up he went and down he comes without his eyes and that there
was no use in even thinking of ascending; and if any one tried
to loose another and lead him up to the light, let them only
catch the offender in the act and they would put him to death.

No question, said he.

Now, according to this allegory the prison is the world of sight,
the light of the fire is the sun, the ascent and vision of the things
above you may truly regard as the upward progress of the soul

into the intellectual world. That is my poor belief to which I have given expression. Whether I am right or not God only knows, but whether true or false my opinion is that in the world of knowledge the idea of the Good appears last of all and is seen only with an effort. When seen it is inferred to be the author of all things beautiful and right, parent of light and the lord of light in this world, the source of truth and reason in the other. This is the first great cause which he who would act rationally in public or private life must behold.

I agree, said he, as far as I am able to understand you.

I would like to have your agreement in another matter, for I would not have you marvel that those who attain to this beatific vision are unwilling to descend to human affairs, but their souls are ever hastening into the upper world in which they desire to dwell, for this is very natural if our allegory may be trusted.

Certainly, that is quite natural.

And is there anything surprising in one who passes from divine contemplation to human things misbehaving himself in a ridiculous manner? If, while his eyes are blinking and before he has accustomed himself to the darkness visible, he is compelled to fight in courts of law, or in other places, about the images or shadows of images of justice, and is endeavoring to meet the conceptions of those who have never yet seen the absolute justice?

There is nothing surprising in that, said he.

Then, said I, the business of us who are the founders of the State will be to compel the best minds to attain that knowledge which has been already declared by us to be the greatest of all. To that eminence they must ascend and arrive at the Good, and when they have ascended and seen enough we must not allow them to do as they do now.

What do you mean?

I mean that they must not remain in the upper world but must be made to descend again among the prisoners in the den and partake of their labors and honors whether they are worth having or not. Thus the order of our State will be a waking reality and not a dream, as is commonly the manner of States, for in most of them men are fighting with one another about shadows and are distracted in the struggle for power which in their eyes is a great good.

.   .   .

You say, Socrates, that cities will not cease from evil until philosophers rule in them and that until philosophers bear rule in States the evils in States and individuals will never cease? I understand you to speak of that city of which we are the founders and which exists in idea only, for I do not think there is such an one anywhere on earth.

In heaven, replied Socrates, there is laid up a pattern of such a city and he who desires may behold this and govern himself accordingly. But whether there really is or ever really will be such an one is of no importance to him, for he will act according to the laws of that city.

THE NICOMACHEAN ETHICS

By

Aristotle

ARISTOTLE (*384–322* B.C.) was one of the great philosophers and a famous pupil of Plato. Born in a Greek colony in Macedonia, his father was royal physician to the grandfather of Alexander the Great. When he was seventeen years old he was sent to the school of Plato in Athens where he remained until the death of Plato twenty years later. He became a tutor for Alexander the Great and when Alexander set out upon his Asiatic conquests Aristotle returned to Athens, in his fiftieth year, and opened a school of philosophy in the Lyceum which he continued for twelve years when a charge of impiety was brought against him. To avoid the fate of Socrates he fled to Chalcis where he died. Aristotle and Plato are considered the most famous of ancient philosophers. In his studies he accumulated a vast number of facts and observations which were to a great extent the beginings of physical science. He was the founder of the science of logic and Kant has stated that since the time of the Greek sage logic has made neither progress nor retrogression. The principles and methods of Aristotle have inspired some of the greatest systems of philosophy and are still considered the forces of religion and metaphysics. He was a prolific author and some of his better known books include *Ethics, Metaphysics, First Philosophy, Rhetoric, Poetics, Politics* and *De Anima,* the first systematic treatise on the human mind ever written.

EVERY ART AND SYSTEM, every action and choice aims at some good, hence the Chief Good is that which all things aim at. There is a difference in the ends or things aimed at, for in one case it may involve only the acts of exercise, in another works, or tangible results. Now the accomplished works are better than the mere acts of exercise. The ends sought in actions are various; in healing art, it is health; in shipbuilding it is a vessel; in military art victory; and in economic management wealth. Since of all the things that may be done there is one End which we desire for its own sake without any further end in view, this must be the Chief Good. But what is the nature of this Chief Good, the highest of all goods? As far as the name of it goes, this is Happiness, which consists both in being well and doing well.

The way in which happiness is formulated as the chief good seems to depend upon the ways in which men live. Those who live the private life of pleasure are inclined to seek happiness in sensual enjoyment. Those who favor public life seek happiness in the form of honor, but this is superficial since it depends upon those who bestow rather than upon those who receive it, while we feel instinctively that the Chief Good must be something individual and inseparable from us. In like manner this happiness must be thought of as something final and self-sufficient, being the end of all things which are done and may be done.

In order to determine more clearly the nature of happiness we must relate it to the very nature of man. Are we to suppose that, while the carpenter and cobbler have certain works of their own, man as man has none? Shall we assume that the eye or hand or foot each has some special work but that the whole man distinct from these has none? The good of man cannot be mere life, for he shares that with the vegetables and we are seeking what is peculiar to man. Nor can this good be sensation, for this is found in animals like horse and ox. That which is peculiar to man is his rational nature so that the work of man is the exercise of the soul in accordance with reason. But to this idea of exercise we must add that of excellence. The work of a harp-player is to play the harp, and that of a good harp-player to play it well. So the good exercise of the soul must be in accordance with excellence. Such is our rough sketch of the Chief Good. Happiness has been seen to be an exercise of the soul according to virtue.

When this conception of happiness is compared with the opinions commonly held on the subject, it appears that, in addition to the immediate and intrinsic goods of the soul, there are goods of the body and external goods also. While agreeing with those lovers of the fine and noble who assert that happiness needs no sort of appendage to it, we must admit that it does require the addition of external goods. Without such appliances it is not easy and may be impossible to do noble things, since friends, money and political influence are in a way instruments whereby many things are done. Good birth, fine off-spring and even personal beauty may be necessary to happiness, for one who is ill-born, childless and ugly is not altogether capable of happiness. Hence the addition of prosperity does seem necessary to make the idea of happiness complete. But even with misfortune the happy man can never become wretched even if he cannot become blessedly happy.

For the man who is truly good and sensible bears all kinds of fortunes becomingly and always does what is noblest under the circumstances. He is like a good general who employs to the best advantage the force he has with him, or is like the good shoe-maker who makes the handsomest shoe he can out of the leather which has been given him. Such a happy man will not be easily shaken by ordinary misfortune and when, this overtaking him, he loses his happiness for the time being, he should be able to regain it after a long period in which he has made himself master of great and noble faculties. While such happiness does not belong to the class of things praise-worthy, as justice does, it does belong to the class of things precious and perfect.

In addition to the excellence which is found in happiness there is also a moral excellence. These *more* excellences, or virtues, come from custom, as the very term indicates, and not from nature. It is by nature that a stone falls and fire rises and no change of custom could make the stone ascend and the fire descend. While the virtues come neither by nature nor despite nature we are furnished by nature with a capacity for receiving them and are by custom perfected in them. We get the faculties of virtue first and perform the exercises afterwards in the way that men come to be builders by building, and harp-players by playing the harp. Thus we become just by performing just acts and attain to self-mastery by performing acts of self-mastery. Both virtue and art are produced or destroyed by actions whereby both good and bad harp-players, good and bad builders, just or unjust men are formed.

What is virtue? We have said that it is a state wherein man comes to be good and performs his proper work well, but the more characteristic nature of virtue is found in a quantitative way by observing that, as a point may be equidistant from certain termini, so virtue is a mean between extremes. Or if it be a more real matter of food, the proper diet is found by taking a mean between eating too much and eating too little. Those who are possessed of skill or virtue, as the case may be, avoid both excess and defect and choose the mean between them. Virtue is the middle state between two faulty ones and in reference to what is best and right is the highest state possible.

Now that virtue has been determined as the mean between extreme or faulty states of either emotion or action it must be shown how it applies in particular cases. He who would make virtue his aim must avoid the extremes of both Scylla and Charybdis especially that extreme which is more contrary to the mean than the other, or Charybdis as it was in the case of Odysseus. We ought to feel as did the old counsellors toward Helen who were impressed by the beauty of the woman but not affected by them, in contrast with Paris who went to the extreme of warmth and Hector whose attitude was too severe. The proper choice is within our voluntary power to make. In the matter of courage, it may be said that this virtue is the mean between having too little or too much of the quality in question; the mean between fear and boldness. The courage of citizenship appears when the members of a community brave dangers for the sake of the State. Experience and skill is thought to be a species of courage, whence Socrates thought that courage was knowledge. There is a third kind of courage in mere animal spirit or when that which is noble co-operates with it. A spurious form of courage appears in the hearts of the sanguine and hopeful whose boldness in danger arises from their frequent victories. Finally those who act under ignorance have a show of courage something like that of the hopeful but they tend to fly from combat as soon as they become aware of danger.

The virtue of Liberality is a mean state between prodigality and stinginess; between those who lack self-control in matters of wealth and those who are over-careful about it. Since liberality is a mean state in respect to giving and receiving wealth, the liberal man will give and spend on proper objects in things both great and small, and all this with pleasure to himself. Likewise he will receive from right sources and in due proportion. As to the extremes of this virtue, it may be said that prodigality exceeds in giving and forbearing to receive, while stinginess is deficient in giving and exceeds in receiving. The virtue of Magnificence is the mean between meanness and vulgar profusion. These extremes are due to want of taste. The magnificent man is like a man of skill because he can see what is fitting and can spend largely in good taste. The magnificent man must be a liberal man also because he will spend what he ought to and in the proper manner; it is the large scale in giving which is distinctive of the magnificent man and even without spending more money than another man he will make the work more magnificent. It is characteristic of the magnificent man to do magnificently whatever he is about, for whatever is of this kind cannot be easily surpassed and bears a proportion to the expenditure. Such, then, is the magnificent man.

The very name of Great Mindedness implies that great things are its object-matter. He is thought to be great-minded who values himself highly and at the same time justly; the man who estimates himself in a lowly manner and at the same time justly is not great-minded but modest, since this quality implies greatness, just as beauty implies a large bodily conformation, while small people may be neat and well-made but not beautiful. Now he who values himself highly without just grounds is a vain man, while he who values himself below his real worth is small-minded. The small-minded man is deficient but with respect to himself and to his estimate of the great-minded, while the vain man is in excess with respect to himself, although he does not get beyond the great-minded man. The virtue of great-mindedness seems to be a kind of ornament to all the other virtues in that it makes them better and cannot be without them; and for this reason it is a difficult matter to be really and truly great-minded.

Gentleness has anger for its object-matter, but the mean of this virtue is difficult to name, as are also the extremes of it. Yet we may speak of gentleness as the mean between anger itself and what might be called angerlessness. In one extreme we find the cross-grained or choleric person, at the other the phlegmatic one. In determining the virtue of Friendliness, we find the extremes of the over-complaisant person and the contentious one. One is over-complaisant when he acts solely with the view of giving pleasure, agreeing with everything and offering no opposition, while the contentious person follows the very opposite line of action. These extremes are to be blamed and the mean between them praised, although there is no special name for it, except it be called friendship, a virtue in the field of social intercourse.

In the same field of social intercourse, and likewise without appropriate name we find a virtue of Truthfulness, the mean between exaggeration and dissembling. The exaggerator appears to lay claim to things reflecting credit on himself both when these things do and do not belong to him, and thus becomes a braggart. The dissembler, or what might be called the ironical man, denies those things which really belong to him, or else depreciates them. The mean character is found in the plain, matter-of-fact person, who, by admitting existence of what really does belong to him, no more and no less, is truthful in life and word. Further, as the life of social intercourse has its pauses and admits of pastimes, it provides for a kind of fitting intercourse in the form of jocularity. Those who exceed in the direction of the ridiculous are the buffoons, while those who avoid all forms of wit are the morose. The mean between these extremes is found the equality of Tact, or easy pleasantry. We cannot speak of Shame, which causes a person to turn red, as a virtue and better than we can consider fear, which makes one turn pale, a moral state. However, shame may be a kind of virtue in a young man in whom this feeling acts as a check upon the passions; but it is not a virtue in an old man since he ought not to do the things that cause shame.

Now we must inquire concerning Justice, its object-matter and between what two extremes it lies as a mean. This virtue involves a moral disposition toward and a capacity for justice, as also the performance of just acts from moral choice. Now both the terms "just" and "unjust" are used in more ways than one. He who violates the law is grasping and unequal is called the unjust man while he who acts according to law and is equal is styled just. Hence the "just" will be the lawful and equal, the "unjust" the unlawful and unequal. But when we say generally that the just man is he who keeps the law, we mean by just those things which are calculated to produce and preserve happiness and its ingredients for the social community. In this sense, justice is not a mere part of virtue but is co-extensive with it, just as injustice is co-extensive with vice. When an act implies a moral state it is simply virtue, but when it has respect to one's neighbor it is justice. There is a kind of injustice distinguishable from that which is co-extensive with vice and related to it only as a part to the whole. Suppose one man seduces another man's wife with a view to gaining some advantage from his act while another man does the same thing merely from the impulse of lust and to his own disadvantage. In the latter case, the man is deemed lacking in self-mastery but is not thought of as grasping, while in the former case is to be blamed not for his lack of self-control but for his lack of justice.

There are two kinds of justice—the Distributive and the Commutative. One has to do with the proportionate equality of merit, the other with the absolute equality of legal rights. Since justice is a proportionable thing, the just man is said to be equal, the unjust man unequal. In this manner we may speak of a greater and a less, which is often the case in actual transactions, and he who acts unjustly gets the greater share while he who is treated unjustly gets the less of that which is good. In commutative justice also is there this idea of proportion in gain or loss with justice as the proper mean between them. It is for this reason that, a dispute arising, men go to a judge as the personification of the just. Judges are thus called "middle men" under the supposition that if they can hit upon the mean they can hit upon the just, for it is the office of a judge to make things equal. Justice itself is a mean between loss and gain arising in voluntary transactions. Finally it appears that it is wrong to deal unjustly and to be unjustly dealt by, a mean between doing wrong and suffering wrong.

Now that we have spoken of the virtues it remains to describe Happiness, since we assume this to be the one end of all human beings. This happiness cannot be identified with pleasure for there are many things about which we should be diligent even though they brought no pleasure. Pleasure is something which exists at a given moment in which its whole nature is complete while that which guides life is a kind of movement with a definite duration and a certain end in view. Pleasure itself does not come into being without activity, although it perfects activity. Then, again, as far as bodily pleasures are concerned, any ordinary person or even a slave may enjoy such just as well as the best man living, but no one imagines a slave to share human happiness any more than he shares the social life of citizens.

Happiness is a kind of activity in the way of the highest virtue or the best principle in man. Since the intellect is the highest principle in man, it follows that the exercise of intellect, or contemplation, will afford the highest happiness. The energy of the intellect aims at no end beyond itself for it is the highest principle in man, hence the highest happiness comes from the exercise of this principle. Happiness is a kind of contemplative energy or such as we commonly attribute to the gods, who cannot be thought of as engaging in the common activities of men even such moral actions as those of justice. Now if from a living being you take away action, what remains but contemplation? So then the energy of the gods, eminent in blessedness, will be one apt for contemplative speculation; and of all human energies that one will have the greatest capacity for happiness which is nearest akin to this. Happiness, then, is co-extensive with contemplative speculation, and in proportion as people have the act of contemplation, so far also they have the ability to be happy, not incidentally but in the manner of contemplative speculation, because it is in itself precious.

NOVUM ORGANUM

By

Francis Bacon

FRANCIS BACON, BARON VERULAM AND VISCOUNT ST. ALBANS (*1561–1626*) was an English philosopher and statesman. He entered Trinity College, Cambridge, when he was twelve and he was an attendant to the English Ambassador to France when he was sixteen. Bacon sat in Parliament several times and engaged in several brushes with Queen Elizabeth's councilors. In the last days of Elizabeth's reign Bacon tried to act the part of mediator between the crown and commons and recommended a tolerant policy in Ireland. He was knighted by James the Ist in 1603 and was made a commissioner for the union of Scotland and England. During his leisure he had been writing and in 1605 published his *Advancement of Learning*. In 1612 Bacon informed the king that he was willing to devote himself exclusively to politics and offered to manage Parliament. In the following years came a succession of political honors until 1618 when he was raised to the peerage. In 1621 the Commons investigated his activities and he was found guilty, in one instance at least, of polluting justice. He was ordered to be fined $200,000, be imprisoned during the king's pleasure and be banished from Parliament and the court. On his release from the Tower the king pardoned him but refused to allow him to return to Parliament or the court and he retired to his family residence where he engaged in literary work. In March 1626 he caught cold while stuffing a fowl with snow in order to observe the effect of cold on the preservation of flesh. Among the better known of his scores of published works are *Novum Organum, Essays, Maxims of the Law* and *Historia Ventorum*.

MAN, as the minister and interpreter of nature, does and understands as much as his observations of the order of nature permit. The unassisted hand and mind possess but little power, since effects can be produced only by means of instruments and helps which promote and regulate the movements of hand or mind. Knowledge and power are the same, yet nature is to be subdued only by submission to its rules. The cause and root of almost every defect in the sciences is that we falsely admire the powers of the human mind but do not search for its real helps. Now, the sciences of the present are useless for the discovery of effects just as the present system of logic is useless, for the discovery of the sciences. The syllogism, being unequal to the subtlety of nature and dealing with words rather than with things, is so useless that our only hope lies in induction.

There are only two ways of discovering truth. One hurries on from the senses to the most general axioms; the other constructs its axioms from the senses by ascending gradually until it finally arrives at them. In the first instance, we find anticipations of nature based on a few familiar occurrences on which are based deductions which satisfy the imagination and appeal to the understanding. Interpretations, on the contrary, are deduced from various widely spread subjects which cannot strike the understanding but seem as difficult and discordant as the mysteries of faith. It is in vain to expect any great progress in the sciences as long as we are content to engraft new matters upon old, and no correct judgment can be formed by the anticipations of knowledge now in use. Hence men must renounce their classic notions and begin to form an acquaintance with things in particular in their regular series and order.

Four species of Idols beset the human mind—the Idols of the Tribe, inherent in the human nature and the very tribe or race of man; Idols of the Den, peculiar to the nature of singular disposition of the individual; Idols of the Market formed by the reciprocal intercourse of man with man; Idols of the Theatre, or various dogmas of peculiar systems of philosophy which are like plays brought out and performed to create fictitious or theatrical worlds of their own. The only fitting remedy for these artificial anticipations of nature is the formation of axioms and notions based on true induction. Now, the doctrine of idols bears the same relation to the interpretation as that of the confutation of sophisms does to common logic.

The Idols of the Tribe arise from the peculiar nature of the human understanding, whereby it is wont to presume a greater degree of order in things than it actually finds; hence the fiction that all celestial bodies are in perfect circles and various other dreams of a like nature. Although many things in nature are irregular, the human understanding tends to agree with the uniformity of the mind. So violent are the prejudices of the understanding that it inclines to accept anything which tends to support the propositions it has already laid down, from the belief it involves or the pleasure it affords, but to reject and despise instances which may exist to the contrary. So limited are the faculties of the understanding that it supposes everything in nature to be similar to the few objects which have taken possession of the mind and is reluctant to accept remote and heterogeneous things. While it seems to aim at progress in its knowledge, the understanding refrains from seeking immediate causes in the subordinate objects in nature and falls back upon the idea of final causes. Instead of being a dry light, the human understanding is so imbued with feeling and tinctured with the will and its passions that it is inclined to believe what it prefers. The greatest impediment and aberration of the understanding proceeds from the dullness and errors of the senses so that what is seen is accepted and no regard is paid to invisible objects. Hence all the more delicate parts and changes in coarser substances like the very nature of common air is unknown. Now, it is better to dissect than to abstract nature to discover the laws of action rather than the forms of being.

The Idols of the Den derive their origin from the particular nature of each individual's mind and body. Some men have such predominant pursuits that they become attached to the particular sciences which they have studied. If such men apply themselves to philosophy they, like Aristotle before them, wrest and corrupt universal nature so that it may agree with their preconceived fancies. Men's dispositions differ so markedly that some are acute in discerning differences while others observe resemblances so that they fall into the excess of catching nice distinctions or shadows of resemblance. Then there are dispositions which incline men to indulge unbounded admiration for antiquity while others eagerly embrace novelty. Thus instead of correct judgments we have factions of the ancients and moderns. In general, he who contemplates nature should suspect whatever particularly takes and fixes his understanding, and should use so much the more caution to preserve it equable and unprejudiced.

The Idols of the Market, which have twined themselves round the understanding from the association of words and names, are the most troublesome of them all. Men may imagine that reason governs words, but words so react upon the understanding that philosophy and the sciences have been rendered sophistical and inactive. Hence we have the great and solemn disputes of learned men which often terminate in controversies about words and names when it would be better for them, imitating the caution of the mathematicians, to bring such disputes to a regular issue by definitions. Such idols are of two kinds; they are either about the names of things which have no existence, as fortune, the first mover, the planetary orbits and the like; or they are confused names of actual objects whose meanings are thus distorted, as in the case of words like moist, heavy, light, rare, dense or to generate, to change, to corrupt. In all these terms there must be some notions better than others in proportion as a greater or less number of things come before the senses.

The Idols of the Theatre are not innate but are instilled and cherished by the fictions of theories and depraved rules of demonstrations. Our doctrine relates only to the path to be pursued not in the ease and speed with which it is pursued, for the lame in the right path outstrip the swift who wander from it. There are three aberrations from the path of knowledge, three sources of error, the sophistic, empiric and superstitious. Of sophistical error Aristotle is the most eminent instance, since he corrupted natural philosophy by logic and formed the world upon the categories of the mind, being more anxious about the wording of his propositions than the truth of things. The empiric school has produced dogmas of a more deformed and monstrous nature not founded on common notions but based on the obscurity of a few experiments. We have a strong instance of this in the alchemists and their dogmas against which men must be warned, since in the resort to experiment, in itself commendable, there is the danger of jumping or flying to generalities and the principles of things. The corruption of philosophy by the admixture of superstition and theology is of much wider extent. There is a clear example of this among the Greeks especially in Pythagoras where superstition is coarse and overcharged, in Plato where it is refined and more dangerous. Some of the moderns have indulged this folly when they have endeavored to build a system of natural philosophy on the first chapter of Genesis or the book of Job, when it were wiser to render unto faith the things that are faith's that heretical religion may be avoided.

We have now treated each kind of idols and their qualities, all of which must be abjured and renounced with firm and solemn resolution. The understanding must be completely freed and cleared of them so that the access to the kingdom of man, which is founded on the sciences, may resemble that of the kingdom of heaven where no admission is conceded except to children.

Having spoken of the bad species of philosophy in the received systems of the day, we must observe certain signs of weakness in them as these appear in their origin, their fruits, their progress, the confessions of their authors and the unanimity with which they cling to an antiquated system. Vicious demonstrations are the support of idols and those which we possess in logic merely subject and enslave the world to human thoughts and thoughts to words. Before we can lay down the true way of interpreting nature, we must go through an expiatory process and the purification of the mind.

The sciences we possess have been derived principally from the Greeks, and the name of sophists which the philosophers transferred to such rhetoricians as Gorgias and Protagoras might well suit Plato and Aristotle, also. The more ancient Greeks like Empedocles, Democritus and the like betook themselves to the investigation of truth and thus acted more wisely, but time like a river bore down to us that which was light and inflated, and sank the more solid and heavy. To consider the fruits produced by the systems of the Greeks in so long a period as that of their existence is to observe that scarcely one single experiment can be culled out that has a tendency to elevate or assist mankind. As we are cautioned by religion to show our faith by our works, we may properly apply the principle to philosophy accounting what is unproductive to be futile, and even worse if instead of grapes and olives it yields but the thistle and thorns of dispute and contention.

If the ancient systems of philosophy and the sciences had been founded upon nature they would have grown like plants in the earth and we should note increase and progress in them. But the ancient sciences, torn up by their roots, having bloomed under the hands of their first author, faded away. But the mechanical arts which are founded on nature and the light of experience seem full of life and thrive and grow. The very authorities whom men now follow were wont to betake themselves to complaints about the subtlety of nature, the obscurity of things and the want of man's wit thus converting the defects of their own discoveries into a calumny on nature and a source of despair to every one else. Hence arose the new academy which openly professed skepticism and consigned mankind to eternal darkness and gave themselves up to dissensions and a variety of schools making it manifest that there was nothing sound in either the systems themselves or in the methods of demonstration. It cannot be claimed truly that among the ancients there was a general unanimity as to the philosophy of Aristotle or that there is unanimity now. For true unanimity is that which proceeds from a free judgment of those who arrive at the same conclusion after an investigation of the facts, but those who have assented to the philosophy of Aristotle have bound themselves from prejudice and the authority of others.

In seeking the causes of the errors in natural philosophy we must consider the narrow limits of the time devoted to the subject. For during the twenty-five centuries with which the learning and memory of man is conversant only six can be selected as fertile in science and favorable for its progress. There have been but three epochs, the Greek, the Roman and the modern in which scarcely two centuries each were rich in and productive of natural philosophy. And during even these fruitful times the sciences have seldom gained possession of an individual free from all other pursuits, unless it was a monk in his cell or a nobleman in his villa. In this manner natural science has had to act as handmaid for medicine or mathematics or be employed to wash immature youths and imbue them with a first dye that later they might receive and retain another. As a result of such neglect astronomy, optics, music, the mechanical arts, moral and political philosophy and the logical sciences have no depth but only glide over the surface of a variety of things.

Furthermore, the advancement of the sciences has meant little because its goal, which should be the endowment of human life with new inventions and riches, has not been fixed. If therefore no one has laid down the real end of science we cannot wonder that there should be error in points subordinate to that end. The path likewise has been ignored. It is astonishing to the reflective mind that nobody should have cared or wished to open and complete a way for the understanding, setting off from the senses and regular experiments, but rather have been abandoned to the mists of tradition, the whirl and confusion of argument, the waves and mazes of chance and desultory experiment. Let men cease to wonder why the whole course of science is not run when all have wandered from the path, deserting experience or involving themselves in its mazes while a regularly combined system would lead them in a sure track through its wilds to the open day of axioms.

Not only reverence for antiquity but admiration for his own works has forced man to rest satisfied with his present discoveries, so that we are more inclined to admire our wealth than to perceive our poverty. The discoveries on which we pride ourselves, like the manufacture of the clock, the discovery of heavenly motions in astronomy, harmony in music, in the alphabet and grammar, the production of wine, beer and bread and luxuries of the table are either of ancient origin or might have been discovered by mere chance or contemplation. It is no wonder that great prejudice has been excited against new discoveries when impostors have taken them to load mankind with promises of retarding old age, prolonging life, alleviating pain, the transmutation of substances, the control of celestial influences, the divination of the future and the like. Want of energy and the littleness of the tasks human industry has taken have done additional injury to the sciences and while men are satisfied with scanty and puerile tasks no magnificent discoveries have been brought to light. Immoderate zeal for religion attempts to combine divinity with philosophy but in such a way as to include doctrine only so that any novelty of science scarcely escapes banishment and extermination. In the schools and universities everything is found to be opposed to the progress of the sciences, for the lectures and exercises are so ordered that anything out of the common track can scarcely enter the thoughts and contemplations of the mind. But in the arts and sciences, as in the mines, everything should resound with new works and advances.

Those who have treated of the sciences have been either empirics or dogmatical. The former like ants only heap up and use their store, the latter like spiders spin out their own webs. The bee, a mean between both, extracts matter from the flowers of the garden and the field but works and fashions it by its own efforts. The true labor of philosophy resembles hers, for it neither relies on the powers of the mind nor yet lays up in the memory the matter afforded by the experiments of natural history or mechanics in its raw state, but changes and works it in the understanding. Natural philosophy is not yet to be found unadulterated but is impure and corrupted by ancient philosophy, yet we may hope for better results from pure and unmixed natural philosophy. We have hope of bidding farewell to the errors of past ages, let us examine whether there be other grounds for hope.

Now, if many useful discoveries have occurred to mankind by chance or opportunity, much more may be brought to light by attention and investigation if it be regular and orderly, not hasty and interrupted. We may derive some hope, also, from the circumstance that several actual inventions like those of gun-powder, silk, the compass, printing, paper and the like, have been of such a nature that scarcely any one could have formed a conjecture about them previous to their discovery. Let men consider their expenditure of time, talent and fortune to matters of inferior value and they will realize that small portion of these will be sufficient to overcome every difficulty. Then let those who distrust their own powers consider my example as that of one engaged in public business and not strong in health who is the first explorer of this course of study following the guidance of none nor even communicating my thoughts to a single individual and yet have somewhat advanced the matter I now speak of.

When we ourselves come to the interpretation of nature, we would not found any philosophic sect like that of the ancient Greeks or those of certain moderns. Neither would we promise any particular effects, but in our capacity as legitimate interpreters of nature we would deduce causes and axioms from effects and

experiments and new effects from those causes and axioms. We
are compelled to admit into our interpretation the most common
objects even when they involve the meanness and filthiness of
particulars, for whatever is deserving of existence is deserving of
knowledge. Let it not be objected that the contemplation of truth
is more dignified than any extent of effects and their utility, for
in nature truth and utility are perfectly identical. But when we
talk of perfecting natural philosophy, it is our intention to include
logic, ethics and politics, also, for we do not desire to destroy the
philosophy, arts and sciences now in use but readily cherish their
practice, cultivation and honor.

The empire of man over things is founded on the arts and sciences
alone, and nature is to be commanded only by obeying her. Thus
the contemplation of things as they are is much more dignified
than all the advantages to be derived from discoveries. Only let
mankind regain their rights over nature assigned to them by the
gift of God and thus obtain that power whose exercise will be
governed by right reason and true religion.

MEDITATIONS
On the First Philosophy

By

René Descartes

RENÉ DESCARTES (*1596–1650*) was a French mathematician and
philosopher. An earnest student, he was sent to Paris to spend
two years in social life but he withdrew to a secluded house
in order to devote himself to reflection and mathematical
investigations. In 1617 he enlisted as volunteer in the Thirty
Years' War, later traveling through Europe and devoting himself to observations of nature and human life. His one purpose
was to free himself from all tradition and develop an independent thought-system of his own. He never married. He
maintained correspondence with the foremost thinkers in
Europe which kept his mind alert and fresh and extended his
reputation. In 1649, Queen Christina of Sweden persuaded
him to move to her country where he died from the rigors of
the northern climate. Though Descartes was primarily a mathematician, his philosophical achievements have gained ascendancy. He invented analytic geometry and expanded algebra.
He was the first to show clearly the difference between mind
and matter. *Metaphysical Meditations* was his favorite work.
Principles of Philosophy and *Discourse upon Method* are
among his masterpieces.

SEVERAL YEARS have now elapsed since I first became aware that I
had accepted many false opinions for true, and from that time I
was convinced of the necessity of undertaking once in my life to rid
myself of all the opinions I had adopted, and commencing anew
the work of building from the foundation, if I desired to establish
a firm and abiding superstructure in the sciences. All that I have
up to the moment accepted as possessed of the highest truth and
certainty I received either from or through the senses, but these

sometimes mislead me. Nor can I forget that at times I have been deceived in sleep by illusions and I perceive clearly that there exist no certain marks by which the state of waking can ever be distinguished from sleep, hence I could almost persuade myself that I am now dreaming.

Nevertheless the belief that there is a God, who is all-powerful and who created me such as I am, has for a long time obtained steady possession of my mind. How then do I know that he has not arranged that there should be neither earth nor sky nor any extended thing, but has provided for the persuasion that such do not exist otherwise than as I perceive them? Or I will suppose that not the Deity, who is sovereignly good and the fountain of truth, but some malignant demon has employed all his artifice to deceive me. Then I will suppose that the sky, the earth, the air and all external things are nothing better than the illusions of dreams by whose means this being has laid snares for my credulity. And I will consider myself as without hands, eyes, flesh, blood or any of the senses but as believing falsely that I am possessed of these.

I will continue in this path of doubt until I find something that is certain. Archimedes demanded only one firm and immovable point on which he could move the whole earth, and so I shall be entitled to entertain the highest expectations if I am fortunate enough to discover just one thing that is certain and indubitable. What is there then that can be esteemed true? I had the persuasion that there was absolutely nothing in the world, neither earth nor sky, neither minds nor bodies, but was not I there persuaded that I did not exist? Doubtless then I exist since I am deceived, and let the Deity or some malignant spirit deceive me as he may, he can never bring it about that I am nothing as long as I am conscious that I am something. So that it must be maintained that this proposition, I am, I exist is necessarily true each time it is expressed by me or conceived in my mind.

But what can I now say that I am? Can I affirm that I possess the attributes which belong to the nature of the body, as walking, being nourished and perceiving through my senses? Thinking is another attribute of my soul, and herein I discover what properly belongs to myself, what is inseparable from me. I am, I exist—this is certain but how often? As often as I think, for it might happen that if I should wholly cease to think I should altogether cease to be. I am, however, a real thing and really existent, but what thing? I am not an assemblage of members called the human body nor a thin and penetrating wind diffused through all its members, for I have supposed that all these did not exist and without changing that supposition I find that I still feel assured of my existence. I am thus a thinking thing that doubts and understands, affirms or denies, imagines or perceives. What I imagine may not be true, still the power of imagination does not cease to exist in me and form part of my thought. I may be dreaming, but it is certain that although I may seem to see light, hear a noise or feel heat, or what is called perceiving, is nothing else than thinking. I have now reverted to the point I desired for I have discovered that nothing is more easily or clearly apprehended than my own mind. I think, therefore I am.

I will now close my eyes, stop my ears and turn all my senses away from their objects and will efface all images of corporeal things and will hold converse with myself alone. I am a thinking thing; that is, a being who doubts, affirms, denies, knows a few objects and is ignorant of many; one who loves and hates, wills and refuses, perceives or imagines. I am assured that all these modes of consciousness exist in me. Yet before I was assured of the existence of myself I received as wholly certain things which afterwards I found to be doubtful—the earth and sky, the stars and other objects. I do not deny that the ideas of those objects are found in my mind, but can I affirm the existence of objects external to me from which those ideas proceed? For it has occurred to me that a God might have given me such a nature as that I should be deceived in matters which appear to me most evidently true.

In truth I have no grounds for believing the Deity deceitful and indeed I have not even considered the reasons by which the existence of a Deity can be established. Now I must inquire whether there is a God, and must consider likewise whether he can be a deceiver, for without the knowledge of these two truths I do not see that I can ever be certain of anything. Among my ideas some appear to be innate, others adventitious and still others factitious, and I may come to the opinion that all of my ideas are of one of these classes or of the others, for I have not yet discovered their origin. What I have to do now is to consider whether the ideas that appear to come from certain objects outside my mind are like those objects. If the objective reality of any one of my ideas be such as to convince me that this reality does not exist in me, nor am I the cause of it, then it follows that I am not alone in the world but that there is some other being who exists as the cause of that idea. On the contrary, if no such idea is found in my mind I shall have no sufficient ground of assurance of the existence of any other being besides myself.

Among my ideas, besides that which represents myself, there is one that represents a God, others that represent corporeal and in-animate things, others angels and others men like myself. As to animals, men and angels, I can easily suppose that the ideas of these were formed in my mind by the mingling and composition of other ideas there. With regard to corporeal objects, I have never discovered in them anything so great or excellent which I myself did not appear capable of originating. Some of my ideas of corporeal things seem as though they might have been taken from the idea I have of myself, as those of duration, substance, number and the like. For when I think that a stone is a substance, I consider how I also am a substance, although a thinking and non-extended thing. Yet both ideas seem to have in common the idea of substance and because I myself am a substance it seems possible that all the qualities which go to make up the idea of corporeal objects may be virtually contained in me.

There remains to be considered only the idea of God and I must consider whether that can be supposed to originate within myself. By the term God I understand that of a substance independent, all-knowing and all-powerful by which I myself and everything else that exists, if any such there be, were created. But these properties of the Deity are so great and excellent that the more I consider them the less I feel persuaded that the idea I have of them owes its origin to myself alone. Thus it is absolutely necessary to conclude that God exists. Since I am a substance I have the idea of substance in my mind, but I am a finite substance hence my idea of an infinite substance could not have been in my mind unless it was given me by some substance in reality infinite.

Now I must not imagine that I do not apprehend the infinite as a true idea but only by negation of the finite, as darkness by the absence of light. On the contrary I perceive that there is more reality in the infinite substance than in the finite, and in some way I possessed the notion of the infinite before I had that of the finite. Otherwise how could I know that I doubt and desire or that something is wanting in me and that I am not wholly perfect, if I did not possess the idea of a being more perfect than myself by comparison with which I observed the deficiencies of my nature? It cannot be said that this idea of God may be materially false and may have arisen from nothing, for on the contrary this idea is very clear and distinct and contains in itself more objective reality than any other. There can be no idea of itself more true or less open to suspicion of falsity than that of God.

But perhaps I am something more than I suppose myself to be, so that all those perfections which I attribute to God may in some way exist in me potentially, although they do not show themselves. I am conscious that my knowledge is being increased by degrees and I can see nothing to prevent it from thus gradually being increased to infinity, whereby I might be able to acquire all the other perfections of the Divine nature. Yet, upon looking more closely into the matter, I discover that this cannot be, since all these possible excellences make not the slightest approach I have of the Deity in whom perfection is not potential but actually existent, and it is an unmistakable token of imperfection that it is increased by degrees. But I conceive of God as actually infinite so that the being of an idea cannot be produced by a being that is merely potentially existent but by a being actually existent.

Thus it is absolutely necessary to conclude from all this that I am and that I possess the idea of a being absolutely perfect; that is, the idea of God. There remains only the inquiry concerning the way in which I received this idea from God. I have not drawn it from my senses, nor has it been presented to me unexpectedly, as is usual with the ideas of sensible objects when these are presented to the external organs of the senses. Nor is this idea a pure production or fiction of my mind, for it is not in my power to take from or add to it. Consequently there remains nothing else to say but that the idea of God is innate in the same way that the idea of myself is innate. It is not to be wondered at that at my creation God implanted this idea in me to serve as it were for the mark of the workman impressed on his work. And considering that God is my creator it is highly probable that in some way he fashioned me after his own image and likeness. I perceive this likeness in which is contained the idea of God through the same faculty by which I apprehend myself. I could not possibly be of such nature as I am and yet have in my mind the idea of a God, if God did not really exist.

In all this having detached my mind from my senses, I have come to observe that there is exceedingly little to be known respecting corporeal objects. For we know much more of the human mind and still more of the Deity than we know about them. I am conscious that I possess a certain faculty of judging, which doubtless I received from God, and it is certain that he has not given me a faculty that will ever lead me into error, provided I use it aright. Since God has not implanted in me any faculty that is deceitful, it seems as though I could never fall into error, and yet experience assures me that I am subject to innumerable errors. When I come to consider the cause of these, I discover that in my mind there is the positive idea of a God who is supremely perfect, but also a certain negative idea of nothing as though it were at an infinite distance from perfection. I myself appear to be a mean between God and nothing, so that I seem to participate in some degree of nothing or non-being, hence it is not surprising that I should fall into error. Further it seems as though error were not anything real depending for its existence upon God but is simply defect. Yet this idea is not wholly satisfactory since error is not pure negation but the privation or want of some knowledge which I ought to possess.

When I consider what my errors are I observe that they depend upon the concurrence of two causes—the understanding and the will. When I consider the faculty of understanding which I possess I find that it is of very small extent, so that I can form the idea of another faculty of the same nature but much more ample or even infinite. The faculty of will, however, appears to be so great that I am unable to conceive the idea of another will that should be more ample and extended, and it is chiefly my will, or freedom of choice, which leads me to discern that I bear a certain image and likeness of Deity. For although actually the faculty of will in the Deity is incomparably greater than it is in me, when considered formally and precisely in itself it does not appear to be greater. For its power consists only in our ability to do or not to do, to affirm or deny.

Whence, then, spring my errors? They arise from the fact that I do not restrain my will which is of so much wider range than the understanding and which extends it to things which I do not understand and, being indifferent to these, readily falls into error and sin by choosing the false instead of the true, and evil instead of good. If I abstain from judging of a thing when I do not conceive it with sufficient clearness, I act rightly and am not deceived; but if I resolve to deny or affirm I do not make a right use of my free will, and if I affirm what is false it is evident that I am deceived. It is in this wrong use of the freedom of the will in which is found the privation which constitutes the form of error.

When, for example, I imagine a triangle although there may not be any such place in the universe, it remains true that this figure possesses a certain determinate nature, form or essence which is immutable and eternal and not framed by me nor in any way dependent upon my thought. It is no less certain that I find the idea of God in my consciousness than that I find the idea of such a figure. It appears that the existence of God can no more be separated from the essence of God than the idea of a mountain from that of a valley, for it is not in my power to conceive a God without existence. For God is a being possessed of all possible perfections, and existence is one of them.

Now there remains only the inquiry as to whether material things exist. I will recall to my mind the things I have hitherto held as true, examine the reasons that constrained me to doubt them and consider, finally, what I ought to believe about them. I perceived that I had a body made up of head, hands and feet as well as various sensations which gave me the means of distinguishing sky, earth and sea and bodies generally. It was not without reason that I conceived certain objects wholly different from my thought, or bodies from which those ideas proceeded. But wide experience has sapped the faith I had reposed in my senses, and as I began to know myself better it seemed that I ought to doubt the teaching of the senses. But as God is no deceiver, I discover that it is impossible for him ever to deceive me, and it is plain that he does not of himself communicate the false idea of external objects to my mind. I do not see how he could be vindicated from the charge of deceit if the idea of these objects proceeded from any other source than that of corporeal things, hence I must conclude that such corporeal objects exist. Thus, on the ground that God is no deceiver, I think I may with safety conclude that I possess within myself the means of arriving at the truth of things in nature. And by nature I understand nothing more than God himself, or the order and disposition established by God in created things; and by my nature in particular I understand the assemblage of all that God has given me.

THE INTELLECTUAL LOVE OF GOD
From the Ethics Of

Spinoza

BENEDICT SPINOZA (*1632–1677*) was a Dutch-Jewish philosopher who was born in Amsterdam. When he was 24 he was excommunicated and banished from Amsterdam. Thereafter his life was quite uneventful and he earned his living as a lens grinder at the Hague, devoting his leisure time to the study of philosophy. Spinoza's system was built upon Descartes' and is mainly contained in his *Ethica* which is a complete philosophy rather than a treatise of ethics. He reduced his theories to a mathematical formula after the manner of Euclid. He published more than a dozen works from his thirtieth year on.

WE PERCEIVE and form our general notions from particular things represented to our intellect fragmentarily, confusedly and without order through our senses, as also from experience. I call this knowledge of the first kind. From the fact that we have notions common to all men, and adequate ideas of the properties of things, we have reason and this I call knowledge of the second kind. Besides these two kinds of knowledge there is a third kind which we call intuition. This kind of knowledge proceeds from an adequate idea of the absolute essence of certain attributes of God to the adequate knowledge of the essence of things. The highest endeavor of the mind and the highest virtue is to understand things by the third kind of knowledge. In proportion as the mind is more capable of understanding things by the third kind of knowledge, it desires to understand things by that kind.

From this third kind of knowledge arises the highest possible mental acquiescence, consequently he who knows things by this kind of knowledge passes to the summit of human perfection, and is therefore affected by the highest pleasure, such pleasure being accompanied by the idea of himself and his own virtue. Thus from this kind of knowledge arises the highest possible acquiescence. The endeavor or desire to know things by the third kind of knowledge cannot arise from the first, or sensuous kind of knowledge, but from the second or rational kind. Ideas which are clear and distinct in us cannot follow from ideas which are fragmentary and confused, but must follow from adequate ideas of the second or rational kind of knowledge.

Whatsoever the mind understands under the form of eternity, it does not understand by virtue of conceiving the present actual existence of the body, but by virtue of conceiving the essence of the body under the form of eternity. In so far as the mind conceives the present existence of the body, it to that extent conceives duration which can be determined by time, and to that extent only has it the power of conceiving things in relation to time. But eternity cannot be explained in terms of duration. Therefore, to this extent the mind has not the power of conceiving things under the form of eternity, but it possesses such power because it is of the nature of reason to conceive things under the form of eternity, and also because it is of the nature of the mind to conceive the essence of the body under the form of eternity, for besides these two there is nothing which belongs to the essence of mind.

This power of conceiving things under the form of eternity only belongs to the mind in virtue of the mind's conceiving the essence of the body under the form of eternity. Things are conceived by us as actual in two ways—either as existing in relation to a given time and place or as contained in God and following from the necessity of the divine nature. Whatsoever we conceive in this second way as true or real, we conceive under the form of eternity, and their ideas involve the eternal and infinite essence of God. Our mind, in so far as it knows itself and the body under the form of eternity has to that extent a necessary knowledge of God, and knows that it is in God and is conceived through God. Eternity is the very essence of God in so far as this involves necessary existence. Therefore, to conceive things under the form of eternity is to conceive things in so far as they are conceived through the essence of God as real entities, or in so far as they involve existence through the essence of God. Wherefore our mind, in so far as it conceives itself and the body under the form of eternity has to that extent necessarily a knowledge of God.

The third kind of knowledge depends upon the mind as its formal cause in so far as the mind itself is eternal. In proportion as a man is more potent in this kind of knowledge he will be more completely conscious of himself and of God. In other words, he will be more perfect and blessed. But we must observe here that although we are already certain that the mind is eternal, in so far as it conceives things under the form of eternity, yet in order that what we wish to show may be more readily explained and better understood, we will consider the mind itself as though it had just begun to exist and to understand things under the form of eternity, as indeed we have done hitherto. This we may do without any danger of error so long as we are careful not to draw any conclusion unless our premises are plain.

Whatsoever we understand by the third kind of knowledge we take delight in and our delight is accompanied by the idea of God as cause. From this kind of knowledge necessarily arises the intellectual love of God and the pleasure accompanied by the idea of God as cause; that is, the love of God, not in so far as we imagine him to be present, but in so far as we understand him to be eternal. This is what I call the intellectual love of God. The intellectual love of God, which arises from the third kind of knowledge, is eternal, and he who loves God cannot endeavor that God should love him in return. The love towards God cannot be stained by the emotion of envy or jealousy; contrariwise, it is the more fostered in proportion as we conceive a greater number of men to be joined to God by the same bond of love.

Although this love towards God has no beginning, it yet possesses all the perfections of love just as though it had arisen in relation to God as present. Nor is there here any difference, except as the mind possesses as eternal those same perfections which we feigned to accrue to it, and they are accompanied by the idea of God as eternal cause. If pleasure consists in the transition to a greater perfection, assuredly blessedness must consist in the mind being endowed with perfection itself. Only while the body endures is the mind subject to those emotions which are attributable to passions. Imagination is the idea wherewith the mind contemplates a thing as present, yet this idea indicates the present disposition of the human body rather than the nature of the external thing. Hence it follows that no love save intellectual love is eternal.

From what has been said we clearly understand wherein our salvation, or blessedness, or freedom consists: namely, in the constant and eternal love towards God, or in God's love towards men. This love or blessedness is in the Bible called Glory, and not undeservedly. For whether this love be referred to God or to the mind, it may rightly be called acquiescence of spirit, which is not distinguished from glory. In so far as it is referred to God, it is pleasure, if we may still use that term, accompanied by the idea of itself and, in so far as it is referred to the mind, it is the same.

Since the essence of our mind consists solely in knowledge, whereof the beginning and foundation are God, it becomes clear to us in what manner and way our mind, as to its essence and existence, follows from the divine nature and constantly depends on God. I have thought it worth while to call attention to this in order to show by this example how the knowledge of particular things which I have called intuitive, or of the third kind, is potent and more powerful than the universal knowledge which I have styled knowledge of the second kind, or of reason. Now the intellectual love of God which arises from the third kind of knowledge, or intuition, is eternal. There is nothing in nature which is contrary to this intellectual love, or which can take it away.

AN ESSAY CONCERNING HUMAN UNDERSTANDING

By

John Locke

JOHN LOCKE (*1632–1704*) was an English philosopher. Upon his graduation from Oxford he became a tutor and later a lecturer of the Greek, rhetoric and moral philosophy. Shortly after he was forty he became Secretary to the Council of Trade. He worked on his *An Essay Concerning Human Understanding* for 17 years and it was finally published in 1690. Three years later he published *Some Thoughts of Education* which volume has had a considerable influence on modern education. In 1696 he was appointed a member of the new Council of Trade at a salary of about $5000 a year. He wrote numerous tracts on government in which he expounded the philosophy that the will of the people is sovereign; that when they enforce their will against the government there is no rebellion; that they are acting within their rights. His philosophical treatise marks the beginning of English Empiricism.

To INQUIRE INTO "the original, certainty, and extent of human knowledge, together with the grounds and degrees of belief, opinion, and assent" is the object of this essay. Since the understanding distinguishes man from the brute, and yields man control over all nature, it is both interesting and valuable to conduct such an inquiry. To make of the understanding an *object* will perhaps beset us with difficulties; but it is certain to cast some light upon ourselves, and the value of our intellectual researches.

It is only through a knowledge of our own mental capacities that we can lay a proper foundation for a further study of the world. And there can be no better cure for the idleness born of despair about our ability to know anything, as well as for the scepticism which is suspicious of every effort to arrive at truth. Perhaps it is

because the usual method of metaphysics was to start with statements and speculations about the vast sea of *being,* that it never
arrived at any clear conclusions, or formulations. If we discover
what man is by nature fitted to know, what the limits of the human
understanding actually are, then we can readily confess to ignorance
in some fields, while busying ourselves in those studies where we
can obtain satisfactory conclusions, and gain the practical knowledge which is necessary to the conduct of our lives.

Since in the subsequent essay there will be continual employment
of the word "idea" it is essential that I point out its meaning and
use. "Idea" is that term which will be used for "whatsoever is the
object of the understanding when a man thinks." It stands for
whatever is meant by words like *phantasm, notion,* or *species.* Anything a man thinks on, or thinks about, is an idea.

It was the generally received opinion for some men that there
were in the understanding certain innate principles, or primary
notions: characters which were thought to be *imprinted* upon the
mind of man at birth, which then accounted for the knowledge
he could have about the world. Now this does not seem to be the
case; and if I can show that men, barely by the use of their natural
faculties, achieve all the knowledge they can have—it is plainly
superfluous to endow them with additional "innate" principles. But
a review of the chief arguments which have been adduced in support of innate ideas will reveal even more clearly why we can not
continue to believe in them.

In the first place, it was contended that *universal consent* about
certain speculative and practical principles, on the part of all mankind, proved that they were innate. Now, even if these principles
did in fact exist, it would not follow that they were innate: assuming that there could be found some other way that these ideas
reach the mind (which we shall try to demonstrate), the principles
could not be used as proof for the theory of innate ideas. But, as a
matter of fact, when we demand what are these incontrovertibly
received principles, about which the whole of mankind is in agreement, we soon see that there are none such. For example, the well-
known laws of logic "What is, is" and "It is impossible for the
same thing to be, and not to be"—which have been conceded to be
the most certain of all—are not known by idiots, children or sav-

ages. To avoid this inescapable accusation, it is usually answered that all men know and assent to them, *when they come to the use of reason*. But we can reply that if reason discovered them, that would not prove them innate. Moreover, how can men who define reason as nothing but the faculty of deducing unknown truths from principles, or propositions, that are already known, claim that reason is necessary to the discovery of innate truths? After all, it is well known that reasoning involves search, trying many different possibilities, and great patience and application. Then what sense is there in asserting that what was imprinted by nature, as the foundation and guide of our reason, nevertheless needs the use of reason to discover it?

If the defenders of this doctrine now shift their ground to this: that calling these principles innate is nothing more than saying that when the terms and propositions are understood, man must assent to them, the reply can be made that a thousand trivial propositions would be in the same boat. For example, that one and two are equal to three; or, that sweetness is not bitterness, and so on would all have to be accredited as innate principles if this criterion were to be employed. Usually, however, an attempt is made to exclude such principles by charging that they are not general enough; and thus, can not be the first elements in our knowledge. Yet generality can hardly be claimed as the earliest interest of men; observe any child, and see whether it will give readier assent to the proposition that "an apple is not fire" than to the more general "Innate" proposition "that it is impossible for the same thing to be and not to be!" The reason for this seems clear. Utter a proposition to a child in words which stand for ideas he has not yet in his mind; and neither assent nor dissent can be given by him to a matter of which he is ignorant. "For words being but empty sounds, any further than they are signs of our ideas, we cannot but assent to them, as they correspond to those *ideas* we have, but no further than that."

It is our first conclusion, then, that these first principles of knowledge and science which we have just examined are not universally assented to; that the assent they receive is no different from that accorded to countless other propositions; and that the assent given them is produced another way (which we will see later), but does not come from natural inscription. Since these principles have been found not to be innate, no other speculative maxims can with better right pretend to be so.

When we turn then to a consideration of practical principles, it is essential to bear in mind that no moral principle is so clear and so generally received as the speculative maxims we have just disposed of. Take, for illustration, *justice,* and *keeping of contracts,* as moral principles which most men seem to agree in. But it needs no examination to assert that these have been flagrantly violated; and that men who live by fraud and rapine can not·have innate principles of truth and justice, which they admit and without exception, assent to. If the objection be made that the silent assent of these men's minds agrees to what their practice contradicts, I would counter with the following objections. (1) I have always thought the actions of men the best interpreters of their thoughts. (2) Practical principles, unlike speculative principles, are there for operation, and must produce conformity of action; for if they only produce bare speculative assent, in virtue of what are they to be distinguished from speculative principles?

Besides it is even more apparent here than in the case of speculative principles, that any moral rule at all that we can mention, has at some time been broken by some people. Were we, moreover, to ask which moral principles are innate, different men of different sects would heatedly urge those principles which they, or their schools, or their churches had accepted as their doctrine. The *contrary* tenets of equally passionate and sincere contenders should be sufficient proof against their being innate. A more likely explanation seems to be that men remember but dimly the scenes of their early childhood; and thus invest with reverence the accidental moral notions which their nurse, their elders, or their tutors may have found it to their inclination to teach to them. Before leaving this subject, it should be remarked that the idea of God is no more innate than these other moral principles. Ideas of God vary in different men; and often, indeed, contradict each other. This should settle once and for all the candidacy of any other idea for innateness; since, it is sensible to concede that if God imprinted any innate ideas on the mind of the creature he made, an idea of his own likeness would be the first and foremost.

[712]

It is my contention, in opposition to the theory we have just examined, that our knowledge depends upon the right use of those powers nature bestowed upon us, and not upon innate principles. Men must think and know for themselves. We must seek for truth in the consideration of *things themselves;* and then the private prejudices and authoritarian dogmas of teachers and writers will be submitted to that impartial and independent examination in the light of reason that will disclose their pretences or reveal their real value. And in conclusion, those ideas which were formerly accounted innate, are those which were generally and easily received. In truth, ideas and notions are not born with us, although some of them do offer themselves to our faculties more readily than others; but this depends upon *how our faculties are employed.* To show how the understanding proceeds in the attainment of ideas and truths is the aim of the remaining section. And throughout this investigation, I shall appeal to men's own unprejudiced experience and observation for the confirmation of what I say.

Let us suppose the mind to be white paper, completely devoid of any characters. How then does it become furnished? "To this I answer, in one word, from *experience;* in that all our knowledge is founded, and from that it ultimately derives itself." All the knowledge we have comes from this source; either observation about external, sensible objects, or observation about the internal operations of our minds, as perceived and reflected on by us. First, our senses convey into the mind distinct perceptions of things, according to the ways in which those objects affect them. Thus do we arrive at "sensible qualities" like yellow, white, heat, soft, bitter, sweet, etc. This great source of the majority of our ideas, we will call *Sensation.* Another set of ideas, which could not be derived from external things, are such as perception, thinking, doubting, believing, reasoning, knowing, willing. This source of ideas we have wholly in ourselves; it is our internal sense; we will designate it by the word *Reflection.* Anything in our minds must come from one of these two sources of Sensation or Reflection. An observation of children will bear out this truth; their earliest ideas are formed from the surrounding bodies that perpetually and diversely affect them. Usually the ideas of reflection come later, because they need more attention.

The mind, then, at birth is a tabula rasa; and if it is asked *when* a man begins to have any ideas, the answer is, when he first has any sensation. No matter how elevated we may think our ideas to be, regardless of where the mind may wander, it can never go beyond those ideas which sense or reflection provide for its contemplation. But ideas are of different kinds; some are simple, and some complex. Simple ideas are united and blended in the things themselves; but, in entering the mind, they are unmixed and uncompounded; they contain but one uniform appearance, and are not distinguishable into different ideas. These simple ideas can neither be made nor destroyed by the mind; and the mind is passive in the reception of them. For this reason no one can frame or invent a simple idea by himself; try to imagine the taste of something never tasted, or a scent unlike any ever smelled, and the inability to do so should be a fresh proof of our description of simple ideas.

Complex ideas, on the other hand, are made by the mind out of simple ones. The activity of the mind over simple ideas are mainly three: 1. "Combining several simple ideas into one compound one, and thus all complex ideas are made. 2. The second is bringing two ideas, whether simple or complex, together, and setting them by one another, so as to take a view of them at once, without uniting them into one; by which way it gets all its ideas of relations. 3. The third is separating them from all other ideas that accompany them in their real existence; this is called *abstraction:* and thus all its general ideas are made." Thus, although man can not make the materials of knowledge, he can unite them, or contrast them, or wholly separate them. To recapitulate, complex ideas are ideas made up of several simple ones put together; for example, ideas like beauty, gratitude, a man, an army, the universe: while simple ideas enter separate and uncompounded into the mind, like solidity, motion, size, cold, heat, pain, sweetness, and the ideas also which are derived from reflection, like perception, retention, memory.

At this point it is necessary to make a fresh distinction, better to clarify the nature of ideas. Whatever the mind perceives in itself, or is the immediate object of perception, thought, or understanding is an *idea;* whatever has the power to produce ideas in the mind, is a *quality* in the subject. Qualities, however, are of different kinds: primary, secondary, and powers. Primary qualities are such as are utterly inseparable from the body, through all its changes, and which sense constantly finds in every particle of matter. No matter how often we divide any piece of matter, it will have the properties of solidity, extension, figure, number and mobility. These are the primary qualities. The secondary qualities, are nothing in the objects themselves, but powers to produce various sensations in us by their primary qualities. These are the sensible qualities which are produced by the operation of the insensible primary qualities on our senses. Thirdly, there are the powers in any body, due to the particular constitution of its primary qualities, to change the primary qualities in another body in such a way that it operates on our senses differently from what it did before. However, it is only the ideas or primary qualities which are resemblances of what exists outside; secondary qualities, like color, sound, taste, smell are not in the external world at all; they are only ideas in our minds. Exactly *how* the arrangements of the insensible primary qualities of bodies come to produce secondary qualities in us, is not known. Someday, if we learn enough, it may be known. But this should not be allowed to interfere with our confidence in what we do know, or impair the "certainty of the senses." Even though the secondary qualities are known only through effects in us, we can study those effects; and from an observation of them, win that degree of knowledge of things which concern us most closely and vitally.

But now that we have described the sources of knowledge, and seen that ideas can be both simple and complex—what is knowledge? How reliable is our knowledge? How does knowledge differ from opinion, and error? Knowledge may be defined as the perception of the agreement or disagreement of ideas. The only certainty we can have is of this type: it is the certainty that comes from the perception that white is not black, or that two and two are four, or that the three angles of a triangle are equal to two right ones. Wherever this perception of the agreement or disagreement of ideas exists, there is knowledge; and where it is not, one always falls just short of knowledge. When the perception of agreement or disagreement is *immediate,* our knowledge is *intuitive.* This kind of knowledge is the clearest and most certain of all. Certainty depends so completely on this intuition, that in the next most reliable degree of knowledge, namely the demonstrative, every intermediate idea must be an intuition of this kind. This knowledge by intervening proofs, though it is certain, is not so clearly perceived, or so immediately assented to. But it is only intuitive and demonstrative knowledge which is entitled to the name "knowledge"; all the rest, no matter how convincing it may be, is only faith, judgment, or opinion. Knowledge by sensation yields certain knowledge of the existence of particular external objects; and so it may be added to the list.

The *extent* of knowledge is then limited in the following ways. In the first place, it can not extend beyond our ideas, which in itself must always fall far short of actually existing real things. Secondly, it applies only to ideas which can be known intuitively, demonstratively, or sensitively. Of those ideas we know sensitively, we can not include the complex ideas of substance—which are so important in science, and in daily life. Since we never know the real constitution of the minute parts of which the qualities which go to make up a substance, we never can say what other qualities must necessarily co-exist with it. In regard to the sciences, it is mathematics and the abstract science of morals that we can, with certainty, claim as knowledge. As to the real, actual existence of things, we have an intuitive knowledge of our own existence; and a demonstrative knowledge of the existence of a God; but of the existence of any thing else, we have only that sensitive knowledge of the objects present to our senses. Thus the scantiness of our knowledge is apparent; and I assign it to these causes: (1) want of ideas (2) want of a discoverable connexion between the ideas we have (3) want of tracing and examining our ideas.

Suppose however we ask about the *reality* of our knowledge, so that we may know if it can be put to use or no. Then, we must reply that our knowledge is real so far as there is a conformity between our ideas and the reality of things. There are two sorts of ideas that agree with things themselves: they are, simple ideas and all our complex ideas, except substance. All complex ideas, except substance, being archetypes of the mind's making, need not be copies of any external thing.

[716]

However, since the understanding faculties are given to man to help him in the conduct of his life, as well as for speculation, if he had no other guide but the knowledge we have just designated as true or certain knowledge, he would remain at a standstill, in this world. Indeed he would have little else to do than to sit still, and perish. Therefore, in addition to knowledge, there is another faculty of the mind, known as *judgment*. Judgment is "the putting ideas together, or separating them from one another in the mind, when their certain agreement or disagreement is not perceived, but presumed to be so . . . And if it so unites, or separates them, as in reality things are, it is right judgment." Probability, which is the likeliness to be true, makes up for the scantiness of our certain knowledge. The assent it induces from our minds is known as belief, opinion, or faith. Although probable knowledge, or judgment, is like twilight compared to the clear daylight of certain knowledge it is sufficient to direct our steps in the practical concerns of life.

AN ESSAY ON MAN

By

Alexander Pope

ALEXANDER POPE (*1688–1744*) was one of the most eccentric of English poets. He had rather an informal education. In his tenth year he contracted an ailment, probably infantile paralysis, which deformed him. Yet in his 12th year he wrote his *Ode on Solitude* and at 14 he composed the mature poem *Silence*. He became a friend of Addison, Steele, Swift and other wits and literary men of the day. His *Essay on Criticism*, published when he was 23, placed him in the front rank of the men of letters of his time. Three years later he had published his translation of the *Iliad* which gave him money to buy a villa. He wrote almost constantly and in his later life he tilted pens with a number of critics. He is in the first rank of English poets in the realm of satire.

WHEN we consider Man in his relation to the world, we see that, while God is revealed in the myriad systems of the stellar universe, Man is to be known only in connection with the earth. To this terrestrial order is he well suited and he must not be judged imperfect because he is not similarly adapted to the whole universe of things—

> *Then say not Man's imperfect, Heaven in fault;*
> *Say rather, Man's as perfect as he ought.*

Man's knowledge is commensurable with the place he occupies in the world and for the span of his brief life. His happiness is due to his ignorance of the future, since he reads but the present page in the book of fate; due is it, also, to his hope of future bliss, for

AN ESSAY ON MAN

Hope springs eternal in the human breast:
Man never Is, but always To be blest.
The soul, uneasy and confined from home,
Rests and expatiates in a life to come.

It is presumptuous of man to pretend to more knowledge than he actually possesses; it is impious on his part to pass judgment upon the ways of God in the world. It is only human pride which assumes that Man is the final cause of Creation; it is human folly to expect that the natural world of things shall be as perfect as the moral order. How inconsistent it is of Man to desire both the spiritual perfection of angels and the physical qualities of beasts, like the strength of bulls and the fur of beasts. Instead of dreaming of such extremes, Man should observe that in nature there are gradations in the natural order wherein thin partitions separate different orders of life from the sensuous below to the rational above.

So vast and complicated is the chain of being that we know not how far above or deep below us it may extend. We know only that were one link in the chain of being broken, the whole system would be destroyed.

All are but parts of one stupendous whole,
Whose body Nature is, and God the soul;
That, changed through all, and yet in all the same;
Great in the earth as in the ethereal frame

. . . .

As full, as perfect, in vile man that mourns,
As the rapt seraph that adores and burns:
To him no high, no low, no great, no small;
He fills, he bounds, connects and equals all.

. . . .

And spite of pride, in erring reason's spite,
One truth is clear, Whatever is, is right.

[719]

II

It is the proper office of Man to know his own nature, not that of the Divine Being, hence it is said—

> *Know then thyself, presume not God to scan;*
> *The proper study of mankind is man.*

Man is in a kind of middle state having the nature of both a god and a beast; he is the lord of all things yet the prey of all; the sole judge of truth yet ever threatened with error; and both the glory and jest of all things he is the riddle of the world. In his knowledge he can be a Plato or a Newton but in himself he is often an ape or fool. Two principles rule in human nature—self-love and reason, of which self-love must be the stronger since it is by this that man is motivated and impelled to action. Yet both of these principles, the low and high, work toward the same end, which is that of happiness.

> *Self-love and reason to one end aspire,*
> *Pain their aversion, pleasure their desire.*

The different modes of self-love are known as the passions, which carry man along in life as the winds a ship. While these passions in particular may engender strife, their general working is in the direction of harmony—

> *These mixed with art, and to due bounds confined,*
> *Make and maintain the balance of the mind:*
> *The lights and shades whose well-accorded strife*
> *Gives all the strength and color of our life.*

In man's nature virtue and vice are mixed and in their operations they unite to serve man's interests—

> *The surest virtues thus from passions shoot,*
> *Wild nature's vigor working at the root.*
> *What crops of wit and honesty appear*
> *From spleen, from obstinacy, from hope or fear!*

[720]

See anger, zeal and fortitude supply;
Even avarice, prudence; sloth, philosophy;
Lust, through some certain strainers well refined,
Is gentle love, and charms all womankind;
Envy, to which the ignoble mind's a slave,
Is emulation in the learned or brave;
Nor virtue, male or female, can we name,
But what will grow on pride or grow on shame.

In itself vice is odious and just as deceptive since he who possesses it is not fully aware of its presence in his life—

Vice is a monster of so frightful mien,
As, to be hated, needs only to be seen;
Yet seen too oft, familiar with her face,
We first endure, then pity, then embrace.

All are both virtuous and vicious in certain degrees, but the imperfections of Man still serve the common interest of the race and Man's happy frailties work for the general good and accomplish the purpose of a Divine Providence.

III

To behold the nature of the world is to see that the principle of mutuality prevails, and all things seem to be but links in a single chain of love. Atom tends to atom, matter attracts matter, dying vegetables sustain life, beasts aid men and men aid beasts. All contribute to the general happiness. They may be guided by reason or by instinct but each particular thing is served by what suits it best. It is by means of instinct that animals, "the nations of the field and wood," act with the precision of rational human beings. In human society the interests of mankind are served by similar instincts which bring society up to a certain level and where instinct stops reflection or reason enters in to improve the ties which bind men together.

In their original condition, men were not moved by blind self-

love or moved to mutual strife, for men were likewise unselfish
and peaceful—

> *Nor think, in nature's state they blindly trod;*
> *The state of nature was the reign of God:*
> *Self-love and social at her birth began,*
> *Union the bond of all things, and of man.*

Following the pattern set by instinct, reason proceeds to invent
the arts and form civil states—

> *Great Nature spoke; observant man obeyed;*
> *Cities were built, societies were made:*
> *Here rose one little state; another near*
> *Grew by like means, and joined through love or fear.*

States were formed in this natural way with nature as law and
liberty as love, but at length they came to place the power in the
hands of one who became their king and formed a monarchy.

The origin of true government and true religion, of king and
priest, was thus in love. Tyranny and superstition on the contrary
rose from fear. When tyranny grew oppressive, the monarch
learned that it was to his self-interest to rule in behalf of the
public welfare—

> *Forced into virtue thus by self-defence,*
> *Even kings learned justice and benevolence:*
> *Self-love forsook the path it first pursued,*
> *And found the private in the public good.*

There are various forms of government but only fools will contend which in itself is the best one, which is true, also, of different forms of religion. That State, that Church is best which is
best administered and best ministers to the welfare of mankind—

> *For forms of government let fools contest;*
> *Whate'er is best administered is best:*
> *For modes of faith let graceless zealots fight;*
> *He can't be wrong whose life is in the right:*
> *In faith and hope the world will disagree,*
> *But all mankind's concern is Charity.*

IV

The end of human life is happiness but since there are so many conflicting sentiments on this subject, it is best to say, "happiness is happiness." Such human happiness is attainable by all and while some are richer, some wiser than others it does not follow that such are happier. This is due to the fact that

> 'the Universal Cause
> Acts not by partial, but by general laws.'

The necessary balance of benefits is kept up by hope and fear; hope in the hearts who still lack happiness, fear in the hearts of those who, possessing it, fear to lose it. True happiness consists of health, which necessitates temperance; peace, which depends upon virtue; and competence the satisfactions of which depend upon whether one has gained fortune by fair means or ill.

It is folly to imagine that God alters His laws for the sake of those he favors and while the good may merit His special consideration we are in no position to judge just who these may be. All that we can assume is that such people are the happiest. Nor can it be concluded that worldly possessions make for happiness, since these may be destructive of both happiness and virtue. The same holds true of honors, titles, greatness and fame—

> Worth makes the man, and want of it the fellow;
> The rest is all but leather and prunella.

A man may enjoy all the benefits that the world can confer and yet, as we observe in Bacon, Cromwell and others, be far from both happiness and goodness.

The happiness which is to be lasting must be universal and connected with virtue—

> Know then this truth (enough for man to know)
> 'Virtue alone is happiness below.'

The only bliss which God can bestow upon a man is that wherein both virtue and happiness conform to the divine plan revealed in

Nature. When the soul of man is united with this plan, he has a hope of bliss here on earth and faith in bliss hereafter.

Is not all this the true nature of man and a proper estimate of his happiness and shall not the poet's Muse be the guide of men when statesmen, heroes and kings lie in the dust?

> *When statesmen, heroes, kings in dust repose,*
> *Whose sons shall blush their fathers were thy foes,*
> *Shall then this verse to future age pretend*
> *Thou wert my guide, philosopher and friend?*

CRITIQUE OF PURE REASON

By

Immanuel Kant

IMMANUEL KANT (*1724–1804*) was a German metaphysician. He was born in Konigsberg and took his degree at the University there in 1755 when he began to deliver lectures. He was made professor in 1770 being appointed to the chair of logic and metaphysics which post he occupied until his death. His greatest work *Critique of Pure Reason* was published in 1781.

OUR REASON has the peculiar fate to be troubled by questions which spring from the very nature of reason and yet which transcend the powers of reason. Hence there must be set up a court of appeal in which the claims of reason may be heard and that court is none other than the *Critique of Pure Reason*. The question is what we can hope to achieve with reason when all the material assistance of experience is taken away. Experience is no doubt the first product of our understanding while it is employed in fashioning the raw material of our sensations, but it can tell us only what is, not what must be. But we would penetrate into a region beyond our experience to consider the inevitable problems of reason itself, or God, Freedom and Immortality.

Whatever the process by which our knowledge reaches its objects, there is one which reaches them directly—Intuition. The science which deals with intuition is called Transcendental Aesthetic; Its aim is to discover the transcendental or *a priori* element in sensation; that is, the universal and necessary. Such permanent forms of sensation are found in Space and Time, which are prior to all perception and the necessary conditions of it. Space is not a concept derived from external experience, for if I am to refer certain of my sensations to objects outside myself the idea of space must be there already. Space is thus a necessary form of the mind and the basis of all external perception. I can imagine a space without objects to fill it but I cannot imagine a condition in which there should be no space. All geometry with its pure and deductive forms of reasoning depends upon this transcendental or mental character of space. Thus it is only from the human standpoint that we can speak of space since it is nothing but the form of the phenomena which we perceive. Unlike such a thing as color, space is a universal and necessary condition of all external perception.

In addition to the intuition by means of which we receive impressions and obtain content for our knowledge, there is also thought with its fundamental ideas or concepts. Thoughts without contents are empty; intuitions without concepts are blind, for the understanding cannot see nor the senses think. Thus it is necessary to advance to a *Transcendental Logic* to serve as a canon of critical knowledge. When we set any faculty of knowledge in play we discover that it operates according to a fixed principle, which is that of judgment whereby one idea is necessarily connected with another in a necessary way as the idea of matter with that of extension. All knowledge is judgment, all judgment is the connection of concepts, or ideas, according to a rule. By means of the table of judgments supplied by logic we may determine all the possible forms of our knowledge. Aristotle endeavored to determine all the fundamental concepts of the mind by picking them up as they occurred to him but in a system of logic all these are already present in the form of compartments which need only to be filled to make of them the categories, or basic principles, of the human understanding.

These judgment-categories, or mental compartments, are fourfold in form—Quantity, Quality, Relation such as causality, and Modality, or possibility, reality and necessity. But these categories must be deduced logically and not merely discovered as matters of fact; we must determine more than their existence *quid facti* by deducing their right to exist *quid juris*. There are only two ways in which this the Transcendental Deduction of the Categories is possible. If we begin on the outside and affirm that the object makes the ideas of the subject, we have Transcendental Realism in which, however, we should find no necessary truths, no *a priori* certainty. But if we start from inside the circle of categories and thus make the subject determine the object of its knowledge we obtain that logical certainty which is peculiar to the human understanding.

However exaggerated and absurd it may sound, the human understanding is the law-giver of nature so that without the understanding nature in the sense of a unified system of phenomena would not exist. For if we were to take away the thinking subject the whole material world would vanish. This thinking subject is the human soul, the permanent and unchanging Ego, or Transcendental Apperception. It operates, first, as a mere synopsis in sense by means of space and time; then, as a synthesis of reproduction in imagination; and, finally, as a synthetical unity of recognition by means of which all perception, all experience, all knowledge is related inwardly to the pure and transcendental self.

The transcendental or *a priori* character of our knowledge is such that we possess Axioms of Intuition so that, apart from any experience with things, we are certain that $7 + 5 = 12$, and that the three interior angles of a triangle are equal to two right angles. In like manner the understanding is able to anticipate all its possible perceptions in the matter of the degrees through which a phenomenon will pass in diminishing from a certain given sum to zero. If we desire to discover the true ground of causal connection among phenomena we observe that this consists in nothing but the necessary connection between the ideas of cause and effect in our minds which are bound to think of these two separate phenomena according to an order dictated by reason and without which all experience would be impossible. What is called possibility is that which is in agreement with the formal conditions of our experience. The real is that which is connected with the material conditions of our experience. Necessity indicates agreement with the universal conditions of experience. It is not the existence of things which is necessary, for the idea of necessity applies only to what must follow from their existence by way of effect.

We see now that the understanding with its *a priori* principles borrows nothing from experience but draws everything from within itself, yet while its categories are not derived from they are devoted to experience and exist not for themselves as abstract forms of thought but for no other purpose than experience itself. The understanding must take its independent categories and apply them to the conditions of actual experience and render them perceptible. Thus there must be a sensuous quality in arithmetic, as in counting on the fingers or by means of the beads in an abacus, just as in geometry, when one is reasoning *a priori* about the nature of the triangle one must be able to construct the figure in space. Wherever an abstract concept cannot be represented in sense there is no sense to it. Hence all our categories must be susceptible to some sort of sensuous representation as for example that which we can find in the intuition of time, which idea we express by raising the question 'how many times,' or seven times five is thirty-five.

After we have traversed the whole domain of the human understanding we find that it is an island, a land of truth, surrounded by a wide and stormy ocean which tempts us to believe in new lands and thus involves us in adventures which we can never leave and yet never bring to an end. While we know that our categories which were deduced for the sake of experience can never transcend the limits of a possible experience, we are bound to venture out upon the unknown sea of the metaphysical. The illusion which besets the mind is no simple one which can readily be banished from our thought: it is an inevitable one like that which makes the sea appear higher than the land when surveyed at a distance from the shore. What we have in our mind is a system of transcendental ideas according to which there must be within the mind a thinking being, or soul; that the world must have had a beginning in time; and that there must be a Supreme Being. But, in reasoning upon these three propositions we cannot come to any rational conclusions. Instead of these we arrive at the Paralogisms or sophistical conclusions of Psychology, the Antinomies, or inevitable contradictions of Cosmology, and the mere Ideals of Theology.

The table of categories involved in its idea of a permanent and unchanging ego is the supreme test of rational psychology, which is the 'I think.' Yet this formal affair cannot be taken to mean a substantial soul related to another thing called the body. To soul and body as things in themselves the category of substance does not apply. The notion of a thinking self has no objective but only a subjective meaning. In place of a simple and indestructible being such as is found in rational psychology, we find only the logical unity of consciousness. For the doctrine of the ideality of space forbids that we should regard either souls or bodies as realities. In like manner the supposed personality of the ego as an entity amounts only to the idea of an identity in consciousness. Finally it is illogical to relate a supposed soul-substance to a supposed body-substance in the form of a coarse dualism; the real dualism is that between two forms of knowledge—sense and understanding. A rational psychology of the soul is impossible and transcends the powers of human reason. The human self is indeed a knower but it does not know itself through the categories; it knows the categories through itself. Rational psychology begins where it ends —in a formal 'I think.'

When we turn to ideas of Cosmology we come upon a natural antithetic and are confronted by four Antinomies. These are really enlarged categories and spring from the attempt on the part of the human understanding to pass out from the realm of ideas conditioned by experience to the sphere of the unconditioned. What is sought is absolute completeness in thought which thus far has been limited by experience in the phenomenal world. Proceeding with the category of quantity the understanding endeavors to grasp the world by showing that it had a beginning in time and is limited in space. But when the world is thus viewed as limited and bounded the resulting concept is too small for the understanding. On the other hand when it is assumed that the world had no beginning and has no limits in space, the ideas of infinite time and space are too large for the understanding to grasp.

In like manner, when it is asserted that every compound substance must consist of simple parts which compose it, the subdivision which stops at a certain point and has arrived at something indivisible is too small a concept for the understanding. Yet, when, in the antithesis, it is claimed that there are no such simple parts to things, or indivisible things existing in divisible space, the idea

[729]

which naturally follows from such an endless subdivision is too large for the understanding. The simple substance in question is something not material but spiritual, the indivisible, incorruptible soul.

A third conflict among the metaphysical ideas of the understanding arises when it is claimed that, in addition to natural causality, there is also the causality of freedom. This is asserted in order to provide for a primary beginning for a series of events in the world, but the regressus to such a beginning involves a series of limited events too small for the understanding. But when this spontaneous beginning of things is denied and the causal regressus is continued infinitely, the resulting concept is too large for the mind to grasp. It is thus impossible to decide for or against the idea of a first and free beginning made by the Prime Mover of the world.

When, finally, in the fourth antinomy, it is stated first that there exists a Necessary Being belonging to the world either as a part or the cause of it the idea involved becomes too large to be grasped in a continual regressus toward it. If it be included in the idea of the world it sets up a form of existence unapproachable by the mind which can calculate according to experience only. But if the Unconditioned is left out of the calculation the idea therein implied is too small for our concept of the world.

In spite of these antinomies with the arguments for the thesis and antithesis in a perfect balance, there is a subjective demand for a solution of problems in which reason has a deep interest. The questions are—whether the world was created in time and space; whether my thinking self is indivisible and indestructible: whether I am free or am led by the hand of fate; and whether there is a Supreme Cause of the world. These are the foundation stones on which morals and religion are built up. Moreover, we have a speculative interest in the thesis which attempts to limit things within boundaries for then we can grasp the whole chain of conditions involved. But, on the other hand, the negation of all these propositions as it is offered by the antithesis has the speculative advantage of permitting the field of knowledge and all possible experience to enlarge itself indefinitely.

There is also an objective demand for the solution of the

cosmological problem since the world is something given to us in our experience and the only question is whether we have an adequate idea of it. The key to the solution of the cosmological problem is found in transcendentalism according to which space and time whose limits we have been trying to determine are nothing but forms of our human perception. Thus we are not required to raise the question whether the world as a thing existing by itself is something finite or infinite. If somebody were to say that every material substance must have either a good smell or a bad smell, a third view that it has no smell at all is possible. In like manner, if it is claimed that the world must be a finite thing or an infinite thing it may be no thing at all. Both views are false.

When, however, it is a conflict between freedom and causality both ideas are true so that freedom and nature can exist together without any conflict and were we to yield to Materialism, or Transcendental Realism we should have neither nature nor freedom. In like manner we may entertain both of the contrary ideas that the world of sense is entirely contingent and yet we may entertain a view of it as involving an unconditionally Necessary Being. For, whereas all things in particular must be viewed as conditioned and purely contingent the series of these as a whole may be viewed as unconditioned. This unconditioned being, or God, may be viewed as the highest reality of which all things in particular are only different modes in the way that there is one endless space of which various geometrical figures are only limiting modes.

But the attempt to realize this general truth in the definite form of theistic proofs is not so satisfactory. These attempted proofs are three in number—the Physico-theological, the Cosmological and the Ontological. The first two depend for their validity upon the last. The ontological argument attempts to prove the existence of God from the idea of God, the argument insisting that the idea of the most perfect being includes the notion of his existence. If one accepts the subject 'God' he must accept, also, the predicate 'existence,' otherwise he is guilty of a logical contradiction, but if one rejects the subject as well as the predicate the contradiction vanishes. 'Being' is not a predicate and cannot add any quality to the concept of a thing, for there is no difference between thinking of a thing and thinking of a thing as existing. The real contains no more than the possible and a hundred real dollars contain not a penny more than a hundred possible dollars, for the hundred dollars thought of are not increased through their actual existence. The idea of a Supreme Being is a valuable one but in itself is incapable of increasing our knowledge of what exists.

The ideal of a Supreme Being is a regulative principle of reason which obliges us to consider everything in the world as if it arose from an all-sufficient and necessary cause, an original, creative reason. If then with reference to theology we are asked whether there is a Being different from the world and yet as ground of the world, we answer 'certainly there is.' And if people proceed to ask whether we may admit the existence of a wise and omnipotent Author of the world, 'certainly, we answer, and not only may we but we must.' However, we admit only the idea of that Being as a maxim for our thought, not the existence and knowledge of that Being as such. Since we possess only the idea of God and the future life as thoughts it is vain to suppose that the future will produce proofs of these two cardinal propositions for whence would reason find grounds for its attempted demonstrations? Or how could such matters be argued pro and con?

When it is said that there is a Supreme Being and that everything which thinks is immortal and it is said on the other side that there is no Supreme Being nor any imperishable soul, the conflict is one which cannot be decided, hence the controversy is one which should be avoided. For how can two persons dispute on subjects whose reality they can neither affirm nor deny? Both parties beat the air and fight with their own shadows because they have gone beyond the limits of nature so that there is nothing real they can lay hold of. They may fight to their hearts' content, the shadows which they are cleaving grow together again like the heroes in Valhalla in order to disport themselves once more in these bloodless contests. When I hear that some uncommon genius has demonstrated away the freedom of the human will, the hope of a future life or the existence of God, I am certain without having seen his book that he has not disproved any single one of these doctrines. For the transcendental critique has convinced me that, as reason cannot establish affirmative propositions in this sphere of thought, it is even more powerless to establish negative ones.

The ultimate aim of pure reason is directed toward the comprehension of these three objects—God, Freedom and Immortality, but the ultimate purpose in considering these questions is to determine what ought to be done if the will is free, if there is a God and a future world. Without a God and without a world not visible to us now, the glorious ideas of morality would not be springs of action and purpose because they would fail to fulfill their aims which are natural to every rational being. The highest aim of pure reason is the ideal of the supreme good, a kingdom of grace in which morality and happiness are united in the form of the *summum bonum*. Happiness, therefore, in exact proportion with the morality of rational beings who are made worthy of happiness by it constitutes alone the supreme good of a world in which we must necessarily place ourselves according to the commands of pure but practical reason. We shall believe ourselves to be serving Him only by promoting everything that is best in the world both in ourselves and others.

THE WORLD AS WILL AND IDEA

By

Arthur Schopenhauer

ARTHUR SCHOPENHAUER (*1788–1860*) was a German philosopher who was born in Danzig, the son of a rich banker and merchant. His pessimistic philosophy probably arose from his moody, irritable temperament and violence in passions. The evil of the world and the tragedy of life were always foremost in his thought, somewhat in the manner of the ancient Hindu philosophies with which he felt himself in close harmony. His conception of the supreme wisdom of life is one of resignation.

"THE WORLD IS MY IDEA." This is a truth which holds good for everything that lives and knows, though man alone can bring it into reflective and abstract consciousness. It becomes clear to him that what he knows is not a sun but an eye that sees the sun, not an earth but a hand that feels the earth. This truth is by no means new; it was the fundamental text of the Vedanta philosophy, was involved implicitly in the skeptical reflections of Descartes, was rendered distinct first by Berkeley but was neglected by Kant. But the view of the world as idea is one-sided so that its defectiveness must be corrected by another one, which is the impressive and awful truth—"the world is my will."

That which knows all things and yet is known by none is the subject of knowledge, the supporter of the world and the condition of all phenomena. The world as idea, the only aspect in which we consider it at present, has two necessary halves—the subject and object. Hence any one percipient subject with the object constitutes the whole world as idea, and if this one were to disappear then the whole world would cease to exist. The universal forms of all objects, as Kant has shown, are space, time and causality, which may be discovered and known apart from the objects in which they appear, all of these being expressions of the principle of sufficient reason. May not our whole life be a dream? Or how may we distinguish between dream and reality? Kant attempted to answer this question by stating that the connection of ideas according to the law of causality constitutes the difference between them. But the long life-dream, in distinction from our short dreams, has throughout complete connection according to the principle of sufficient reason—

> *We are such stuff*
> *As dreams are made on, and our little life*
> *Is rounded with a sleep.*

Life and dreams are leaves of the same book, the book we read through, and the one whose leaves we turn idly to read a page here and there.

The system of philosophy starting with the object has always the whole world of perception as its problem; the most consistent form of these is simple materialism. It regards time and space and with them matter as existing absolutely, ignoring the relation to the subject of knowledge in which alone these exist. Then it lays hold of the law of causality as its guiding principle, when it is by the understanding alone that causality holds. Materialism seeks most simple states of matter and then tries to develop all others from it ascending from mere mechanism to chemism, to vegetable and animal life, to sensibility and thought. But such thought or knowledge which materialism reaches so laboriously was presupposed as its starting-point in the subject that perceives matter, or the eye that sees it, the hand that feels it, the understanding that knows it.

Opposed to this system is that of idealism which starts with the subject and tries to derive the object from it but it overlooks the fact that there can be no subject without an object. Like materialism, this idealism begins by assuming what it is supposed to deduce. The method of our system is different from both of these for we start from neither the object nor the subject but from the idea as the first form of consciousness. Its essential form is the antithesis of subject and object. Our own body is for each one of us the starting-point in our perception of the world and we consider it like all other real objects simply as an idea. The understanding which develops ideas could never come into operation if there were no simple bodily sensations from which to start.

If the thinker were no more than a pure knowing subject, a winged cherub without a body, the nature of the world would not be known to him, for he would be like a man going round a castle merely sketching its façades and seeking in vain an entrance to it. All reality would be a riddle were it not for the fact that the subject of knowledge is also an individual with his bodily nature and to this is the world revealed in the will. Every true act of the will is a movement of the body for the action of the body is nothing but the will objectified; or, in a certain sense, the will is knowledge *a priori* of the body, the body knowledge *a posteriori* of the will. My body and my will are one.

The double knowledge which each one has of his own body, as both outer idea and inner will, may be used as a key to the nature of every phenomenon in the world. Phenomenal existence is an idea and nothing more, real existence or the thing-in-itself, is will. That which in us pursues its ends by the light of knowledge and in nature strives blindly and dumbly in a one-sided and unchangeable manner come upon the common name of will; just as the first dim light of dawn must share the name of sunlight with the rays of the full mid-day. If we consider the impulse with which the waters hurry to the ocean, the way in which the magnet turns to the north pole, the eagerness with which electric poles seek to be united, the way the crystal takes form we recognize our own nature. For the name *will* denotes that which is the inner nature of everything in the world.

The world as will is one and knows nothing of the multiplicity of things in the perceptual world of space and time, hence the quantitative notion of more and less can have no application to it. For this reason it cannot be said that there is a small part of the will in a stone and a large part in man, since the relations between part and whole belong to the idea of space which is not applicable to the will. As reality, or thing-in-itself, the will is present entire and undivided in every object of nature, in every living thing. Yet in the objectification of the will in inorganic matter, in vegetation, animal life and the conscious will of man we find different grades of this objectification. The lowest of these appear in the most universal forces of nature in the form of gravity, rigidity, elasticity, electricity and the like, which are in themselves immediate manifestations of the will just as much as are human actions, both being wholly groundless. The higher grades of objectivity are seen in the case of man, wherein the will assumes the form of individuality and consciousness. It is here that the will shows its second side, for with the objectification of itself in the human brain it has created an organ capable of comprehending it so that, as if kindled by a spark, it brings the whole world as idea into existence as if at one stroke.

In this manner, knowledge of either the sensuous or rational sort proceeds from the will and is destined for the service of the will in the accomplishment of its aim of full objectivity. In all brutes and in most men knowledge remains in subjugation to the will. Yet in certain individual men knowledge can deliver itself from this bondage and throw off the yoke and make the subject of knowledge exist for itself as a pure mirror of the world. As a rule, knowledge remains subordinate to the service of the will and grew, so to speak, on the will as the head on the body. In the case of the brutes, both body and head are deformed while the head is directed toward the earth where lie the objects of its will. But in the case of man the head is elevated and set freely upon the body as in the Apollo Belvedere, where the head of the god stands so freely on his shoulders, so that it seems wholly delivered from the body and no longer subject to its cares.

That which the pure subject of knowledge beholds is the grades of the objectification of the will in the form of Platonic Ideas in which things attain to adequate objectivity. The transition from the individual's knowledge of the particular things to the knowledge of the Idea takes place suddenly; it comes about when the knowledge of the will in the individual changes him into the pure will-less subject of knowledge contemplating things as they are in themselves. If, raised by the power of the mind, a man relinquishes the common way of looking at things, gives himself up to quiet contemplation, forgets both his individuality and his will, he becomes the pure, will-less, timeless, painless subject of knowledge. This appears in the genius, for it is as if when genius appears in an individual a far larger measure of the power of knowledge falls to his lot than is necessary for the service of an individual will, and this superfluity of knowledge being free now becomes subject purified from will, a clear mirror of the inner nature of the world.

There are two parts to this aesthetical mode of contemplation—the pure, will-less subject of knowledge and its object not as individual thing but as Platonic Idea. All willing arises from want; the satisfaction of a desire ends it, but for one wish which is satisfied there remain ten which are denied. No attained object of desire can give lasting satisfaction, for it is like the alms thrown to a beggar that keeps him alive today that his misery may be prolonged till tomorrow. The care for the constant demands of the will continually occupies and sways our consciousness so that the subject of willing is constantly stretched on the revolving wheel of Ixion, pours water into the sieve of the Danaids and is the ever-longing Tantalus.

But when we are lifted out of this endless stream of willing so that we can comprehend things free from their relation to the will without any subjectivity or personal interest, then the peace we have been seeking comes of its own accord. For we are for the moment set free from the miserable striving of the will; the wheel of Ixion stands still and we keep the Sabbath of the penal servitude of willing.

It is the function of the fine arts to provide adequate objectivity for the Platonic Ideas and express directly to perception the grades of the will which is striving to objectify itself. Matter as such cannot be an expression of the Idea, but when it is expressed by an art like architecture its characteristics of gravity, cohesion and hardness, universal qualities of stone, appear as a direct although low grade of the objectified will. In the building, nature reveals itself as a conflict between the gravity of the building as load and the rigidity of the structure as support, as in the simplest form of the column. The problem of architecture, apart from its practical utility, is to make this conflict appear distinctly so that the building material involved instead of being a mere heap of matter bound to the earth is raised above it so that the roof, for example, is realized only by means of the columns or arches which support it. The aesthetic pleasure which comes from beholding a beautiful building consists pre-eminently in the fact that the beholder is set free from the knowledge which serves the will and is raised to the kind of knowledge which comes from will-less contemplation.

The objectification of the will at the highest grade is found in the expression of human beauty which reveals the Idea of man. No object transports us so quickly into pure aesthetic contemplation as the most beautiful human countenance and form. We know human beauty when we see it, but with true artists this is revealed with such clearness that it surpasses what we have seen in nature. With the genius of the sculptor we find an anticipation of that which nature sought to express, for here in the figure her half-uttered speech is made articulate, so that it is as if we were to present his statue to nature saying, 'this is what you wanted to say.'

Historical painting as an art has character as well as beauty and grace for its object, for it attempts the representation of the will at the highest grade of its objectification in the Idea of humanity. This however must not be in the abstract form of the concept or must the picture attempt, as it does at times in allegorical painting, to represent other than what is perceived. In poetry the relation is reversed, for here what is given directly in words is the concept from which the reader must be led away to the object of perception. This is done by means of trope, metaphor, simile, parable, allegory and the like. The aim of all poetry is the representation of man; when it is a representation of the poet himself we have the lyric. The lyric poet reveals himself in joy or more often grief as the subject of his own will but along with this, as the sight of nature impresses him, there is the consciousness of himself as the subject of pure, will-less knowing whose blissfulness now appears in contrast to the stress of desire imposed upon him by the will. Epic poetry reveals man more historically in connection with significant situations in human life.

Drama in the form of tragedy is not only the summit of poetic art but most significant of our whole system, since it is the strife of the will with itself unfolded at the highest grade of its objectivity. It becomes visible in human suffering brought about by fate or error or wickedness in which one and the same will lives and appears while its phenomena fight against and destroy one another. The tragic effect in poetry may be produced by means of a character of extraordinary wickedness, as Iago in *Othello* or Creon in the *Antigone;* by blind fate, as in the *Oedipus Rex* of Sophocles; by circumstance and the position in which the character finds itself, as Hamlet and the *Cid* of Corneille. In the tragic character we observe how the noblest of men, after a long personal conflict and inward suffering, come at last to renounce the pleasures of life and the particular ends once so keenly sought for a joyful surrender to life itself. It is in this sense that Hamlet renounces life for himself but bids Horatio remain a while and in this harsh world draw his breath in pain to tell Hamlet's story and clear his name.

Beginning with architecture in which gravity and rigidity reveal the lowest grade of the conflict of the will with itself and ending with tragedy wherein this conflict reaches its highest grade, we have considered the arts in their representative form. Music stands quite alone cut off from all the other arts, since it is not a mere copy of any Idea of existence in the world. Where the other arts objectify the will indirectly by means of the Ideas, music is as direct an objectification of the whole will as is the world itself. Accordingly we may regard nature and music as two different expressions of the same thing, and may thus understand how music speaks a universal language. In the deepest tones of harmony in the bass we recognize the lowest grades of the objectification of the will, for bass is in harmony with the crudest matter on which all things rest and from which they originate. Moving slowly the deep bass is representative of the crudest mass while the higher complemental parts, which are parallel with animal life, move more rapidly although without melodious connection or significant progress. In the melody of the high voice singing, the principal part, leading all the music and progressing with unrestrained freedom, we recognize the highest grade of the objectification of the will in the effort and intellectual life of man.

The pleasure we receive from beauty, the consolation we derive from art and the enthusiasm of the artist rest on the fact that, whereas existence in the world is something sorrowful and terrible, the aesthetic contemplation of the world as Idea is both significant and soothing. But in the case of the artist the contemplation of beauty does not become a quieter of the will or provide a pathway out of life as with the saint who has attained to resignation. The deliverance from the will occurs in moments of occasional consolation; complete deliverance comes only when one, tired of the play, renounces life and lays hold on the real.

When the will, a blind and incessant impulse in nature, attains to self-consciousness in man, it is recognized as the "will-to-live." Man may affirm or deny it. Man affirms the will-to-live when, having become conscious of it as that which has produced nature and his own life, he adds his own volitions to it. The denial of the will-to-live occurs when the attainment of consciousness and self-knowledge means the end of volition. The phenomena of the world no longer act as motives for willing for the comprehension of the world as Idea frees the will and allows it to quiet and suppress itself.

It is the essential nature of the will, nowhere free but everywhere omnipotent, to strive endlessly incapable of any final satisfaction. Gravitation is ceaseless striving toward a mathematical centre which would not cease if the whole universe were rolled into a single ball. The solid will become a fluid, the fluid a gas and the existence of the plant is a restless, unsatisfied striving through ascending forms until it goes to seed where it finds a new starting-point. All animate nature is a struggle in which internecine war is waged; the striving is in vain yet cannot be abandoned. All this is identical with what appears in us in whom the blind striving of nature becomes the self-conscious will-to-live. The fate of the will is in keeping with its striving nature in the face of constant hindrance, and any one who will consider the character and destiny of the will-to-live will be convinced that suffering is essential to all life. From whence, then, than from the actual world did Dante take the materials for his Hell? When it came to describing the delights of Heaven he had an insurmountable task since the world could offer him no proper materials.

The fatal assertion of the will-to-live has produced man's body and the desire to preserve and perpetuate it so that the assertion of the will is really the assertion of the body. In such personal self-assertion we find the source of all egoism, as also the meaning of all wrong-doing. But such selfhood is an illusion due to the false philosophy whereby the individual, himself only a manifestation of the one will-to-live, imagines that he lives to himself alone. Just as a sailor sitting in a boat trusts to his frail barque in a stormy sea, so in the world of sorrows the individual man sits quietly trusting to the principle of individuation whereby he knows things only superficially or as they appear in phenomena. But when he comes to understand that the one will-to-live exists in all men alike, he realizes that the difference between him who inflicts the suffering and him who bears it is only apparent, so that in seeking happiness at the expense of another the wicked man is like a wild beast which under pressure of excitement buries its teeth in its own flesh injuring itself as it attempts to injure another. No matter how completely the veil of illusion may envelop the bad man the sting of conscience within him creates the secret presentiment that the gulf which seems to separate him from another is only phenomenal and illusory.

As all hatred and wickedness rest upon egoism as this rests upon the assertion of the will-to-live, so all goodness and virtue spring from the denial of the will-to-live. The will turns round and no longer asserts its own nature but denies it. Man then denies his own nature as expressed in his body and no longer desires sensual gratification under any condition. Voluntary and complete chastity is the first step in the denial of the will-to-live. Doubtless then the human race would die out and with it the mind in which the world is reflected as that without a subject of knowledge there would be no object. To those in whom the will-to-live has turned and denied itself, this world of ours with all its suns and milky ways is—nothing.

UTILITARIANISM

By

John Stuart Mill

JOHN STUART MILL (*1806–1873*) was a British philosopher, the elder son of James Mill, the economist. When he was 17 he secured an appointment under his father in India House from which he retired as head of his department when he was 42. Before he was 20 Mill was accredited as the future leader of the Utilitarian School in philosophy and politics. One of the most original and important of his works, his *System of Logic*, was published when he was 37. But it was not until he was 55 that his great work, *Utilitarianism*, which defends the greatest happiness theory, appeared. Also he argued heartily for individual liberty of thought and action. He wrote somewhat voluminously on politics and was for a time a member of Parliament where he voted with the advanced Radical party. He was one of the earliest advocates of women's suffrage, in 1867.

FROM THE DAWN OF PHILOSOPHY the question concerning the *summum bonum* or the foundation of morality has been accounted the main problem in speculative thought, has occupied the most gifted intellects and divided them into sects and schools. After more than two thousand years the same discussions continue, philosophers are still ranged under the same contending banners. The controversy over morals is not to be settled by having recourse to a natural faculty, a sense or an instinct informing us what is right, what is wrong. For this very moral instinct is itself one of the matters of dispute, so that those who have any pretensions to philosophy have been obliged to abandon the idea that it discerns what is right in the way that our senses discern their objects. Our moral faculty supplies us with only the general principles of moral judgments in the abstract, not with particular perceptions of it in the concrete. The general principle which here is presented as a contribution to moral philosophy is that of Utility or Happiness. What is the meaning of such Utilitarianism?

Utilitarianism is a creed which accepts Utility or the Greatest Happiness principle as the standard of all morality. It holds that actions are right in proportion as they tend to promote happiness, wrong as they tend to produce the reverse of happiness. By happiness is meant pleasure and the absence of pain; by unhappiness, pain and the privation of pleasure. In dealing with pleasure it is quite compatible with the principle of utility to recognize the fact that some kinds of pleasure are more desirable and valuable than others. The more desirable, more valuable pleasure is the one to which irrespective of any moral obligation we give a decided preference. One superior pleasure in a small amount is preferable to an inferior pleasure in a large amount. "It is better to be a human being dissatisfied than a pig satisfied; better to be a Socrates dissatisfied than a fool satisfied." According to the Greatest Happiness Principle, the ultimate end of life is an existence exempt as far as possible from pain and as rich as possible in enjoyments both in point of quantity and quality. It is in short the greatest happiness of the greatest number.

It is a misapprehension of such utilitarian ethics to regard it as a "godless doctrine," for if we believe that God desires the happiness of His creatures and that this was His purpose in creating them, Utilitarianism is more profoundly a religious doctrine than any other. Nor is Utilitarianism a doctrine of mere "expediency" in the sense that an act may be expedient for the particular interest of him who performs it, for such supposed expediency would prove harmful and thus anti-utilitarian. The true principle of Utilitarianism is concerned with that general public utility of the highest sort. It is in vain that the opponents of this doctrine argue that to determine the good would require an extended calculation of the useful effects of action for which at the moment of action there would be no time. But this would be like contending that under similar circumstances to guide our conduct by Christianity we should have to read all of the Old Testament and the New. The time required for the utilitarian calculation has been amply supplied by the experience of the race in the whole duration of the human species. Finally it is vain to object to Utilitarianism by saying that such is the infirmity of human nature that each one would be inclined to make his own case an exception to moral rules, but this tendency to cheat conscience is something observable in all moral creeds, not the utilitarian one only.

The question concerning the sanction, or authority, of the principle of Utility involves no peculiar difficulty. Customary morality based on education and public opinion has such a halo about it that we are disposed to regard it as being in itself obligatory. But every system which endeavors to analyze morality and reduce it to general principles is bound to encounter the question of sanction which seems to embarrass the utilitarian. Utilitarianism has all the sanctions which belong to any other system of morality. These sanctions are external when they involve the hope of favor or the fear of displeasure from our fellow-creatures or from the Ruler of the Universe. The internal sanction appears in the conscientious feelings of mankind in the form of remorse upon the violation of the moral law. Such moral feelings may be cultivated in connection with Utilitarianism as well as with any other system of morals. It may be seen that when morality is thought of as a transcendental principle innate in the human mind it is more binding than when it is regarded as a subjective sense gradually acquired. But this scruple may be overcome when we observe that utilitarian morality has a firm foundation in the social feelings of mankind. When one thus understands Utilitarianism he will have no misgivings about the sufficiency of the ultimate sanction for happiness morality. But how can Utilitarianism be proved?

"The only proof capable of being given that an object is visible is that people actually see it. The only proof that a sound is audible is that people hear it. In like manner the sole evidence it is possible to produce that anything is desirable is that people do actually desire it. No reason can be given why the general happiness is desirable except that each person, so far as he believes it to be attainable, desires his own happiness. This, however, being a fact we have not only all the proof which the case admits of, but all that it is possible to require, that happiness is a good: that each person's happiness is a good to that person and the general happiness, therefore, a good to the aggregate of all persons." It is evident that happiness is one of the ends of conduct and one of the criteria of morality, but not the only end, not the sole criterion. People may desire more than happiness; they may desire virtue and the absence of vice just as they desire pleasure and the absence of pain.

"The desire for virtue is not as universal but is as authentic a fact as the desire for happiness." The utilitarian does not deny that virtue is to be desired for its own sake as a good in itself but accepts virtue as one of the ingredients of happiness, or a part of it. Virtue was originally a means to an end but has become an end in itself. By long association with what was useful to man it has come to be esteemed for its own sake and cherished for as something more than a means of utility. A parallel is found in the case of money which at first was prized for what it would buy but is now valued as something in itself desirable, and what at first was no more desirable than a heap of glittering pebbles is now regarded as though it possessed intrinsic value. The result is that the love of money is one of the strongest moving forces in human life and the desire to possess it is often stronger than the desire to use it. Much the same may be said of other objects in human life such as power and fame except that these include a certain amount of immediate pleasure, which cannot be said of money.

According to a wise provision of nature, various things directly related to our primitive desires become by association to be more valuable than the primitive pleasures to which at first they conduced. Virtue is a derivative good of this sort. Originally there was no desire for it save as something conducive to pleasure but the association with pleasure thus formed has changed virtue into an acquired desire. The love of virtue is distinct from the love of money, power and fame, for these often render the individual obnoxious to society whereas the love of virtue makes one a blessing to his fellow-men. Hence Utilitarianism enjoins and requires the love of virtue as being above all things an important factor in the general happiness.

In reality nothing is desired except happiness; whatever else is desired is but a part of that happiness. Since happiness is the sole end of human action, it follows that it must be the criterion of morality, which is but a part of it. What else than happiness does man desire? Desiring a thing and finding it pleasant, feeling aversion for it and finding it painful are inseparable phenomena. They are but two different ways of stating the same psychological fact, and to desire anything which is not pleasant is a physical and metaphysical impossibility. It might seem as though a person of confirmed virtue may carry out his purposes without any thought of the pleasure in them being guided by will rather than desire. The will was originally a part of desire, an offshoot which detached itself and took root elsewhere. It is now rooted in habit so that many things which once were done for the sake of pleasure are now done indifferently as a matter of habit. Where these habits are virtuous they require no discussion. Where they are vicious it becomes necessary to inculcate a desire for virtue, which is to be done showing the person of vicious will that virtue leads to pleasure, vice to pain. This is the very essence of Utilitarianism.

There is a necessary connection between Justice and Utility. It cannot justly be claimed that we have an immediate feeling of justice as though it were like the sensation of color or taste; it is a derivative feeling formed by combination with other feelings. In general people are willing to admit that justice coincides with general expediency yet the subjective feeling for justice is so impressive, so imperative that people are not so ready to think of justice as merely a particular kind or branch of expediency. Hence it is necessary to consider some of the distinguishing characteristics of justice, or its opposite—injustice.

It is considered unjust to deprive any one of his personal liberty or property or any other thing which belongs to him by law; that is, to deprive him of his legal rights. But these legal rights may be rights which ought not to have belonged to the person in question since they may have been conferred on him by a bad law. It is evident from this that justice must be taken to mean something more than mere legality. Accordingly injustice must be understood as the act of taking or witholding from a person his moral rights. Justice is expected to apportion to each person that which he deserves whether good or evil, and the idea of desert is the clearest and most emphatic one in the general mind. Further it is unjust to disappoint expectations raised by our own conduct and thus break faith with another. Justice is supposed to avoid partiality toward certain individuals by showing preference for one over another, for by its very nature it involves the idea of equality, although this principle is subject to certain variations. Now what is the mental link which binds all these conceptions of justice together?

The etymology of the term "just" points to an origin in either positive law or accepted custom and the idea of conformity to law continued to set the standard of justice even after the justice of the law itself ceased to be accepted. But at first there was nothing to distinguish particular legal obligation from moral obligation in general; but now it is recognized that in the conceptions of both injustice and any kind of wrong there is the common idea of penal sanction. The wrong-doer of either the legal or moral sort deserves some kind of punishment. This punishment may be by the law itself, by the unfavorable opinion of one's fellow-men or by the reproaches of one's own conscience. This yields the idea that what is wrong is something deserving of punishment.

In the idea of justice there is, also, the notion of obligation or something which is due as though it were a debt to be paid. This is considered a "perfect obligation" when duty in one person implies a correlative right in another, "imperfect obligation" when no such extra right is involved. In the first sense, justice implies a claim on the part of one or more individuals; injustice arises when this claim is not met. Thus understood, justice includes two factors—one who does wrong and one to whom the wrong is done. Did the sentiment of justice spring up by some special dispensation of nature or has it grown up in connection with general expediency? In this sentiment there is both the desire to punish the one who has done the harm and to take the side of the one upon whom the harm has been done. It is a combination of self-defense, or the animal desire to repel or retaliate an injury, and sympathy for one who has been injured. But how shall punishment be meted out? By way of example for the purpose of deterring others from wrong-doing? Shall it be for the benefit of the wrong-doer himself? Or shall society assume that it is itself to blame and thus let the wrong-doer go unpunished? Social utility alone can decide, for it is on this that the idea of justice is based.

Thus understood, justice is the name for certain classes of moral rules and moral requirements which stand highest in the scale of social utility. There is no necessity to assume any peculiar origin for justice, since it is simply the natural feeling of resentment moralized by being made coextensive with the demands of social good. The sentiment of justice differs from the milder feeling that one ought to promote human pleasure; its commands are more definite as its sanctions are sterner and more exacting.

SARTOR RESARTUS

By

Thomas Carlyle

THOMAS CARLYLE (*1795–1881*) was a Scottish writer who was
educated at Edinburgh University with a view to entering the
Scottish church. He was an excellent student and the stories
about his immense reading are almost fabulous. Declining to
become a preacher he taught for a short period and then chose
literature as a profession, first becoming an encyclopedist. He
soon became a regular critical contributor to British magazines
and in 1825 his *Life of Schiller* was accorded high literary
praise. After his marriage in 1826 he retired to the "loneliest
nook in Britain" where he devoted most of his time to German literature and it has been said that through Carlyle's
writings England discovered Germany. His masterpiece *Sartor
Resartus* was written on his moorland farm and is a mixture
of opinions, speculations, inward agonies and trials of Carlyle
himself. He was offered royal decorations by England and
Germany but refused them all. Upon his wife's death in 1866
he was overwhelmed with grief and in his last years was sad
and gloomy. He is regarded as one of the most inspiring forces
in English literature.

I

WITH ALL THE ADVANCEMENT man has made in his culture and
science he has not developed a theory of clothes. He has a theory of
gravitation which insures the future of the solar system, a geological theory which makes the creation of the world seem as
simple as cooking a dumpling, and various theories of the political
and economic sort. But he has yet to explain how it came about
that man the naked animal became a clothed animal. This question, neglected by the English, has of late been taken up by the
speculative German mind represented by Professor Teufelsdröckh

of Weissnichtwo in his work entitled, *Clothes, Their Origin and Effect*. It is this volume which the Editor will now review.

But how could such a work be presented before the English public whose party journals would hardly welcome it article after article, for this might endanger its circulation? But since the Editor has received a letter from the Professor's friend, Herr Hofrath Heuschrecke, offering to supply him with materials concerning the Professor's life, the editor will attempt a *Biography of Teufels-dröckh,* which, however will aim to expound truth, not merely to glorify a man. It is impossible to say much about the actual life of the man, who like Melchidezek seems to have been without father or mother, but it can be said that in the university at Weissnichtwo he was "Professor of Things in General." The town saw little of him except as he appeared in the coffee house known as the Green Goose; he himself was wont to retire to the attic of the highest house in the town upon which he gazed as though upon a wasp's nest or bee-hive. His philosophy of clothes was couched in the form of Transcendentalism according to which all things are so much Spirit; his learning was boundless, his style although vigorous and inspiring was more crude than cultured yet gave the impression that the Professor reeling of ethereal love could embrace the universe.

The Professor wrote on his work *The Spirit of Clothes* much as Montesquieu wrote on the *Spirit of Laws,* except that he did not follow the common principle of casuality. He infers from what history relates of Adam and his two wives that clothes were not adopted for comfort but for decoration, yet as man advanced in his industries he became a tool-using animal and found it expedient to adopt aprons such as a blacksmith wears for protection. Now as the Editor observes there are aprons of all sorts even to that of the Bishop's cassock, but what interests the Professor is the later history of clothes in the true era of extravagance in costume from the Middle Ages down to the end of the Seventeenth Century, although he himself favors a natural costume unhampered by the superfluous.

Having thus discoursed on the origin of clothes, Professor Teufelsdröckh has something more important to say about the effects they produce. In considering the moral, political and religious influences of clothes, the Professor lays down the grand proposition that man's earthly interests are all hooked and buttoned together so that it is as though society were founded upon cloth. The world itself is clothed with all sorts of tissues peculiar to commerce, politics and historical events but which after all are much like dreams or shadows which envelope us making the world seem to be what the Earth Spirit in *Faust* called the Garment of God. All things are but appearances to the true philosopher who has learned what it means to say, "I am," and "I think." But, alas! how men thatch themselves over with the dead fleeces of sheep, the bark of vegetables, hides of beasts, entrails of worms and the like.

What we seem to have in Professor Teufelsdröckh, as the Editor observes, is much more than a Sanscullotist, for he seems to be a new Adamite in the Nineteenth Century. He should consider the practical benefits derived from clothes from the blankets and bibs of babes to breeches, the garb of dandies and the like. Would the Professor have us go about again like the aboriginal savage in a thick natural fell? But the Professor, who is really no Adamite, appreciates the value of clothes but would have them understood in a mystical sense whereby clothes shall become emblematic of man as a spirit who garbs himself significantly as on the bench, within the drawing-room, in the church, in army, navy and the like. Strip them and they would appear ridiculous.

From the standpoint of pure reason, a naked world may exist beneath the clothed one just as there may be a real man under the garments of flesh he wears. To the eyes of pure reason, man is not "an omnivorous biped that wears breeches but a soul of divine apparition." The beginning of all wisdom is to look upon clothes till they become transparent and it is the philosopher who is able to look through the clothes of a man until he sees the man himself. In addition to this note on wisdom, the Professor has a word on the subject of wonder, which itself is not to be destroyed by either science or logic. As understood by the Professor, the world is not an aggregate but a whole of which all things are as emblematic garments. In like manner the philosophy of clothes informs us that man may be clothed with authority, that language is the garment of thought and man, the Me, clothed with a body. But now arrive the biographical material about Professor Teufelsdröckh but so chaotic is it that the Editor is bound to be bothered by it.

II

From a psychological point of view it is a question whether birth and genealogy afford much insight, yet the genesis of the Clothes Philosopher demands some attention. From the biographical material furnished the Editor, he gathered that the genesis of the Professor was on this wise: that he was brought to the household of a certain Andreas Futteral and his wife, being conveyed thence in a basket overhung with green Persian silk. The bearer of this mysterious burden was a reverend-looking stranger, who promised the astonished couple a reward if they took great care of this that he called a "loan," promising them punishment if they did not. Upon removing the Persian veil they discovered a sleeping infant beside which lay a roll of gold banknotes and a baptismal certificate, from which latter they deciphered the name of the infant, which grew up to be Herr Diogenes Teufelsdröckh, who in his years of maturity suffered much from the longing to know who his father was.

His boyhood was idyllic and before his formal education began he had learned much from what his eyes beheld in the charming landscape and from the events that transpired in the little village about him. Such natural education taught him lessons of necessity and duty, what one can and cannot, should and should not do. In the school with its books and teachers, he learned some facts of history and gathered ideas about Time and Eternity, in the light of which true education is to be distinguished from false. In this period of his life, Andreas Futteral died and he learned from mother Gretchen that he was only a foster-child. At the university he formed the acquaintance of Herr Towgood, or Herr Toughgut, an Englishman, with whom he experiences the now obsolete sentiment of friendship. After quitting college, young Teufelsdröckh had difficulty in getting under way, for while he rejoiced in certain capabilities he required Hunger to make a craftsman of him, or to cultivate the Bread Studies of a practical profession. Thus by necessity he learned the flux of time whereby he must enact the stern monodrama of "No Object and no Rest." Saturn or Chronos or what we call Time has a way of devouring its children, hence it is only by incessant running or working that one can escape, but in young Teufelsdröckh's case the running was not good nor was work to be had.

Teufelsdröckh has given up his profession of law and now falls in love with a maiden named Blumine. They have many happy meetings but at length the lovely maiden dissolves the blissful bonds between them that she may marry a richer man. In his sorrow, Teufelsdröckh becomes a pilgrim, takes leave of his native town and makes for the mountains where he gives himself up to sorrowful thoughts showing that he has yet to learn that the end of man is an Action, not a Thought. This pilgrimage, which is really within his own soul, brings the wandering Teufelsdröckh to the region of the Everlasting No, where he doubts the reality of truth and duty. "Is there no God?" he asks; "at best an absentee God sitting idle ever since the first Sabbath at the outside of the universe seeing it go." He would believe in himself as in one who has a work to do, and is thus led to change the maxim, "Know thyself" to "Know what thou canst work at." Yet the Everlasting No kept ringing through all the recesses of his being, of his Me.

The philosophic pilgrim now turns to the Not-me for more wholesome for his spiritual hunger, considers the history of great events and great men and thus passes through the Centre of Indifference which lies between negative and positive poles of his inner being. "Temptations in the wilderness" confront him as he moves onward toward his Everlasting Yea, but he overcomes temptation by the act of inward self-annihilation. Now he is able to see, as he says, "that man's unhappiness comes of his greatness; it is because there is an Infinite within him." Thus the humblest creature, as a shoe-black, cannot be made happy by all the satisfactions of the universe; for, given a whole ocean of fine wine and he will desire a better vintage. To be truly happy one should decrease the denominator in the fraction of his life rather than try to increase the numerator. Satisfaction is so relative that if a man is to be hanged he will feel happy at the prospect of being shot. The problem of evil is solved and the secret of life found in work. "Produce, produce! Up, up! Work while it is called today!" The study of Teufelsdröckh's life now comes to a pause since the Editor is beginning to suspect that there is something fictitious in the biographical records and while they have afforded much insight into the Professor's soul they are not wanting in mystification. Hence we had better turn again to his Philosophy of Clothes.

III

According to Teufelsdröckh's philosophy of clothes, one of the most remarkable events in history occurred when George Fox, a shoemaker, made himself a suit of leather. The Editor, however, thinks it doubtful whether in an age of refinement, vanity and wealth any considerable class in the community will be satisfied with such plain and perennial suits. Church clothes, he continues, are the most important of vestures, since they were first spun and woven by society for its own preservation. Government may be the skin of the body politic but religion is the pericardium which encases the circulatory system. Clothes are likewise symbols by which one in silence speaks, so that the printing press with its newspaper is nothing compared with clothes and the tailor's goose. Man can find symbols all about him and should recognize them as revelations of the Infinite in the finite. Symbols have an extrinsic value in coats-of-arms and military banners; an intrinsic value in true works of art, noble lives and deaths and religions. Like garments which wax old, symbols become antiquated whence the wise legislator should gently remove them.

From his notes on Heuschrecke's tract on population, it is plain that Teufelsdröckh is not impressed with the Malthusian doctrine of the increase of population and no such increase of food. He is concerned with the individual laborer who toils for his bread and the spiritual laborer who toils for the bread of life. Only such workmen will he honor. The real pity is not so much that the poor lack food but that they lack knowledge in a world where science is so plentiful. The world too crowded! exclaims the Professor; only a small portion of the globe has been tilled and vast fields still remain in Asia, Africa and America. Society in the sense of the soul of religion is now dead and exists only by virtue of the gregarious instinct, and instead of being a home is only a kind of lodging-house. The soul politic having departed from the body politic, the economists and utilitarians responsible for its destruction are now carrying the corpse to the funeral pile where it will be burnt. But, Phoenix-like, a fairer society will rise from the ashes, for as Saint-Simon said, "the golden age which blind tradition has placed behind us in the past is before us."

While decidedly radical, the Professor of Clothes is not wanting in reverence but believes that this should be expressed toward man as a living being whether he carry the sceptre or sledge-hammer. Often he turns into the Old Clothes Market to worship as in a Sanhedrim of stainless ghosts and silent witnesses of the past with all its deeds and passions. It would seem to the Editor that it will take about two centuries for the World Phoenix to be reduced to ashes, but according to the Professor destruction and creation go on together, for as the ashes of the Old are blown about in the air organic filaments of the New are being spun to take their place. In this manner men are united, whether by the soft binding of Love or the iron chain of Necessity, just as generation is bound to generation in a world where nothing is completed but is ever completing. Yet in all the changes going on, the Professor believes that kings will remain. The Editor dissents from this, feels that political freedom cannot be promoted by mechanical devices like the ballot-box and would find the corner-stone and living rock of future politics in Hero Worship. But he agrees with the Professor that man stands in need of religion.

The Philosophy of Clothes takes a leap into Transcendentalism when the Professor, who has long struggled with cloth-webs and cob-webs, grapples with the embracing phantasms of Space and Time. Human science which deals with these, cannot appreciate the meaning of the miracles occurring everywhere. Even to the wisest of men, as a scientist with his "System of the World," nature remains hidden from the vision of him who computes its limits in square miles and centuries. When we appreciate the fact that Space and Time are only forms of the mind, continues the Professor, we can understand the myth of Fortunatus who by means of his wishing-cap could be transferred from where he was to anywhere in space. Suppose a hatter were to manufacture such space-annihilating hats whereby one could go from his "Here" to "Anywhere:" suppose another hatter were to manufacture time-annihilating hats whereby one could move from his "Now" to "Any-then;" what a world that would be. Yet in the idea of Immortality we have just such means of overcoming space and time, the tomb and mortality.

But, the Editor inquires, have many British readers arrived with him and the Professor of Clothes after their journey from the woollen hulls of man, his flesh-garments, social garniture and the space-time garments of his soul? Doubtless the British reader is puzzled by the Professor's idea of the new birth of society, but he should be able to understand that there are miracles in common things, and that all life is so much weaving and that all customs and forms are only clothes. Naturally we should conclude by considering the millions of spinners, weavers, washers and wringers who puddle and muddle to make us clothes, but we will look at two kinds of cloth-animals who live and move and have their being in cloth—the Dandies and Tailors.

A Dandy is a man whose office in life it is to wear clothes; the divine idea of cloth is born with him. He belongs to a secular sect which has perpetuated the primeval superstition of Self Worship and would keep itself unspotted from the world. Their sacred books are fashionable novels; their articles of faith involve coats, collars, waistcoats, trousers and the like. They stand out in strange contrast with the Drudge Sect whose members worship the earth and from birth, or even before, take the vow of poverty. Their costumes are made up of such bits of clothing as they can gather together, their diet that of potatoes, although a few of them indulge in salted herrings. It is possible that, as the Professor surmises, the sects of Dandiacal Self Worship and Drudgical Earth Worship may spread and divide England between them. They are like an electrical machine with its positive pole of money and negative pole of hunger and when the whole nation is in an electric state the touch of even a child's finger may bring them together to shatter the very earth.

The tailor, as Teufelsdröckh says in conclusion, is still to be recognized as the true creator of noblemen and other dignitaries whom he clothes in royal mantles and pontifical robes. Poets and moral teachers are only tailors who clothe men with their beliefs.

But we must take leave of Professor Teufelsdröckh of Weissnich-two: he himself, as a letter from Hofrath Heuschrecke announces, has disappeared from that place. The Editor is not really per-plexed by this strange disappearance, for he conjectures that Teufelsdröckh is in London.

NATURE

By

Ralph Waldo Emerson

RALPH WALDO EMERSON (*1803–1882*) was the first distinctively New England author to become eminent in American literature. Descended from five generations of ministers, he entered Harvard Divinity School and became pastor of the Old North Church in Boston, 1829–32. He resigned because he ceased to regard the Lord's Supper as a necessary rite. He sailed for England to meet the literary men of the day and there formed a life-long friendship with Carlyle. From 1835 to 1837 he delivered a number of lectures on literature and philosophy in Boston and published one anonymous book. His first *Essays* appeared in 1841. He became editor of the organ of Transcendentalism, the *Dial,* until the collapse of the enterprise in 1844. During the following years he published numerous essays and several books of poems. He was a friend of most of the great literary lights of his day.

TO GO INTO SOLITUDE a man needs to retire as much from his chamber as from society, for although nobody is with him he is not alone while he reads or writes. If a man would be alone, let him look at the stars and consider how men would believe and adore and preserve for many generations the remembrance of the city of God, if those stars appeared only one night in a thousand years. Always present yet ever inaccessible, the stars awaken a certain reverence while all natural objects make a kindred impression to the mind open to their influence. Few adult persons can see nature and as few can see the sun, which illuminates only the eye of man but shines into both the eye and the heart of the child. Within the woods, a man casts off his years and becomes a child, returns to reason and faith and feels that no calamity can befall him which nature cannot repair. There, my head bathed by the blithe air and uplifted into infinite space, I am nothing but become a transparent eye-ball which sees all while the currents of the Universal Being so circulate through me that I become part and parcel of God.

Whoever considers the final cause of the world will discern a multitude of uses that enter as parts of that result, and which can be classified as commodity, beauty, language and discipline.

Under the general name of Commodity I rank those mediate and temporary benefits and advantages which our senses owe to nature. What angel invented these splendid ornaments and con-veniences like the ocean of air above, the ocean of water beneath and between them this firmament of earth with its zodiac of lights, its tent of dripping clouds, striped coat of climates and the four-fold year? The wind sows the seed, the sun evaporates the sea, the rain feeds the plant, the plant feeds the animal and thus the endless circulations of the divine charity nourish man. The use-ful arts formed by man are but reproductions of the same natural benefactors. By means of steam man realizes the fable of Aeolus' bag and carries two and thirty winds in the boiler of his boat. He paves the road with iron bars and mounting a coach with a ship-load of men, animals and merchandise darts from town to town. By the aggregate of such aids how has the face of the world changed from Noah to Napoleon! But all this mercenary benefit has respect to a further good, for a man is fed in order that he may work.

In the form of Beauty a nobler want of man is served by nature; its aspects appear in a threefold manner. The simple perception of natural forms is a delight in itself for nature seems to deify us with a few cheap elements. The dawn is my Assyria, the sun-set my Paphos, broad noon is the England of my senses and understanding, and the night my Germany of mystic philosophy and dreams. But the presence of the spiritual element in beauty is necessary for its perfection, since beauty is the mark God sets upon virtue. When a noble deed is done in a scene of great natural beauty, as when Leonidas and his three hundred martyrs die in Thermopylæ and the sun and moon come to look at them in the deep defile, or when Arnold Winkelried in the high Alps gathers in his side a sheaf of Austrian spears, are not these heroes entitled to add the beauty of the scene to the beauty of the deed? Yet the beauty of the world may be viewed as an object of the intellect, also, which searches out the absolute order of things as they stand in the mind of God. Thus does the beauty which comes unsought remain in the mind for the apprehension and pursuit of the intellect, which re-forms it and makes of it a new creation. Beauty, however, is not ultimate and must stand as a part rather than as the whole or highest expression of the final cause of nature.

The third use which nature subserves to man is Language. Words are signs of natural facts which are the symbols of spiritual facts while all nature is the symbol of spirit. Every word used to express a moral or intellectual fact, if traced to its root, is found to have been borrowed from some material appearance; as right means straight, wrong crooked, spirit wind and transgression the crossing of a line. But this is our least debt to nature, for it is not words only that are emblematic but things, which are symbols of spiritual facts. There is a radical correspondence between visible things and human thoughts so that, as we go back in history, we find language more and more picturesque until its infancy when it is all poetry. The corruption of man is followed by the corruption of language so that, when the simplicity of character and sovereignty of ideas is broken up by the desire for riches, for pleasure, power and praise, new imagery ceases to be created, and old words are perverted to stand for things which are not, as paper currency is employed when there is no bullion in the vaults. But wise men pierce this rotten diction and fasten words to visible things again. But how great is our language to convey such pepper-corn information as we possess! Did it need such a profusion of forms, such a host of orbs in heaven, to furnish man with the dictionary and grammar of his municipal speech? When we use the grand medium of language to express the affairs of pot and kettle, we have not put it to its authentic use, but are much like travellers using the cinders of a volcano to roast their eggs. The relation between mind and nature is not a poet's fancy but stands in the will of God and is open to the minds of all men.

When in our fortunate hours we ponder over this miracle, we wonder whether we are not blind and deaf, for—

> Can these things be,
> And overcome us like a summer's cloud
> Without our special wonder?

Nature is likewise a Discipline for the understanding, which may learn from her lessons of likeness and difference, being and seeming, of progressive arrangement and the combination of manifold forces in one end. What tedious training day after day, year after year to form common sense and so train the hand of the mind that it feels how good thoughts are no better than good dreams unless they are executed. The same good office of discipline is performed by property with its system of debit and credit, so that debt is a preceptor whose lessons cannot be forgone and is needed most by those who suffer from it most. Yet the great principle of discipline is the lesson in power by the exercise of will whereby the world as a realized will becomes the double of the man.

The sensible objects of nature so conform to the premonitions of reason that all things are reflected by conscience and become moral. Therefore is nature glorious with form, color and motion while every globe in the remotest heaven, every chemical change, the form of vegetation and the function of the animal hints or thunders to man the laws of right and wrong and echoes the Ten Commandments. What is a farm but a mute gospel, or what the experience of the sailor, the shepherd, the miner and merchant but that of the moral sentiment which scents the air, grows in the grain, and impregnates the waters of the world? Herein is especially apprehended the unity in nature where one art and one law hold true, pervading all thought and made conspicuous by words and actions. These are like fountain-pipes on the unfathomed sea of thought and virtue where unto they alone are the entrances.

But now the noble doubt of Idealism suggests itself to raise the question whether nature outwardly exists or whether what we call sun and moon, man and woman, house and trade are only a certain number of congruent sensations. In my utter impotence to test the authenticity of the report of my senses, what difference does it make whether Orion is up there in the heavens or some god paints the image in the firmament of the soul? What is the difference whether land and sea interact and worlds revolve without number or whether, without the relations of time and space, the same appearances are inscribed in the constant faith of man? Be it what it may the world is ideal to me so long as I cannot try the accuracy of my senses.

To the senses there clings an instinctive belief in the absolute existence of nature, but she herself gives a hint of the Ideal philosophy and conspires with spirit to emancipate us. We are strangely affected by seeing the shore from a moving ship or a balloon and a man who seldom rides needs only to get into a coach and traverse his own town to turn the street into a puppet-show. What new thoughts are suggested by viewing the face of the country in the rapid movement of the railroad car whence the most wonted objects please us most. Thus by means of motion does nature apprize us that, while the world is a spectacle, something in man is stable. In a higher manner the poet communicates the same pleasure in the Ideal, for he unfixes the land and sea and makes them revolve about the axis of his thought. This transfiguration which all material objects undergo through the passion of the poet might be illustrated by a thousand examples from the plays of Shakespeare wherein the poet makes free with the most imposing phenomena of the world and asserts the predominance of the soul.

Where the poet animating nature with his thoughts proposes beauty as his main end, the philosopher sets up truth and postpones the apparent order and relations of things to the empire of thought. Even in physics the seemingly solid block of matter is pervaded and dissolved by thought and the feeble human being penetrates the vast masses of matter with an informing soul, whereby it carries centuries of observations in a single formula. Intellectual science, also, begets a doubt about the existence of matter by fastening attention upon immortal and uncreated natures, or Ideas, in whose presence all outward things seem but a shade. Religion and ethics, or the practice of Ideas, put nature under foot and urge the devotee to flout nature, despise the vanities of the world and seek the realities of religion.

Yet I have no hostility to nature but rather a child's love of it, so that I do not wish to fling stones at my gentle mother nor soil my gentle nest. I wish only to indicate the true position of nature in regard to man by means of a culture which inverts the vulgar view of the world and brings man to call apparent what he used to call real, and to call real what he used to call visionary. The advantage of the Ideal theory over the popular faith is that it presents the world in precisely that view which is most desirable to the mind.

Now all the uses of nature admit of being summed up in one, which is Spirit, for the views already presented do not include the whole circumference of man. Idealism, which says that matter is not substance, but phenomenon, is a hypothesis to account for nature by other principles than those of carpentry and chemistry, yet if it only denies the existence of matter and leaves God out of me it does not satisfy the demands of the spirit. Many truths arise to us out of the recesses of consciousness. We learn that the highest is present to the soul of man, that the dread universal essence is not wisdom or love, beauty or power alone but all in one, and that behind and throughout nature spirit is present. Spirit, or the Supreme Being, does not build up nature around us but puts it forth through us as the tree puts forth new branches, and as a plant upon the earth so a man resting upon the bosom of God is nourished by unfailing fountains and at his need draws inexhaustible power. The world proceeds from the same spirit as the body of man and is a more remote and inferior incarnation of God, but since it is not subjected to the human will its serene order is inviolable by us and is therefore the present expositor of the divine mind.

The Prospects of the advancing spirit are conditioned by the action of man upon nature with his entire force. The highest reason for things is always the truest, the deepest is among the eternal verities. Empirical science is apt to cloud the mind with particulars and deprive the student of the contemplation of the whole order of things. But his relation to the world is not to be learned by mere addition and subtraction or other comparison of known quantities, but by untaught sallies of the spirit in which a guess may be more fruitful than an indisputable affirmation, a dream more significant than a hundred experiments.

At present, man applies to nature but half his force, since he works on the world with his understanding alone and produces only a penny-wisdom. It is as if a banished king should attempt to resume his power by buying his territory inch by inch instead of vaulting at once into his throne. History has examples of an in-streaming power with reason's momentary grasp of the sceptre, but these reveal the difference between the actual and temporal application of power and the ideal force which man might exert. The problem of restoring the world its original and eternal beauty is solved by that redemption of the soul whereby it will regain its lost unity. Every spirit builds itself a house and beyond its house a world and beyond its world a heaven. Build therefore your own world, and as fast as you conform your life to the pure idea in your mind, that world will unfold its great proportions.

SYNTHETIC PHILOSOPHY
First Principles

By

Herbert Spencer

HERBERT SPENCER (*1820–1903*) was an English philosopher. When he was 17 he became a railroad civil engineer which profession he continued for about eight years. Soon after he became a financial editor at which time he began to develop his ethical and political ideas in print. Before Darwin published his famous book, Spencer had incorporated an indefinite form of the doctrine of evolution in one of his volumes. In 1862 he published his *First Principles,* tracing the functions of evolution as realized in life, mind, society and morality. He gave several lectures in the United States in 1882 and, returning to England, continued a further output of books mainly on ethics, which was the copestone of his philosophy.

OF ALL ANTAGONISMS OF BELIEF, the oldest, the widest, the most profound and most important is that between Religion and Science. It may seem absurd to set forth any justification of Religion and equally absurd to defend Science, yet one of these attempts is as needful as the other. Some have a repugnance for Religion, others are prejudiced against Science, but they are not prepared to give reasons for their respective dislikes. Now there must be right on both sides of this controversy. Religion, everywhere present as a warp running through the weft of human history, expresses some eternal fact, while Science is an organized body of truths ever growing and ever being purified of its errors. Both of these must be in harmony, for it is impossible that there should be two orders of truth in absolute and everlasting opposition.

It is only in some highly abstract proposition that Religion and

Science can find a common ground. This is not to be found in either such dogmas as those of the trinitarian or unitarian on the one side or the special doctrines of science found in mathematics or chemistry on the other. But the most abstract truth contained in Religion and the most abstract truth contained in Science must be the one in which the two coalesce. The most ultimate religious idea is that God cannot be understood, for religions are in agreement with one another in the idea that the power which the universe manifests to us is inscrutable. In like manner ultimate scientific ideas, as space and time, matter and motion, are representations of realities which cannot be comprehended. If Religion and Science are to be reconciled, the basis of reconciliation must be this deepest, widest and most certain of facts—that the Power which the universe manifests to us is incomprehensible. It is the Unknowable.

After concluding that we cannot know the ultimate nature of that which is manifested to us, there arise the questions—what is it that we know, in what sense do we know it, and in what consists our highest knowledge of it? Given the sphere to which human intelligence is restricted, the Knowable, it is necessary to define that product of human intelligence which may be called philosophy. How is philosophy constituted? It is constituted by carrying knowledge to the highest degree of generality. Science means merely the family of sciences, or a sum of knowledge formed from their special contributions; but when these are reduced to some mechanical axiom, a principle of molecular physics or a law of social control, they are contemplated as corollaries of some ultimate truth the knowledge of which constitutes philosophy. Knowledge of the lowest kind is un-unified knowledge, Science is partially unified knowledge, philosophy is completely-unified knowledge.

As a primordial datum of philosophy we find consciousness, which must be accepted as a competent judge between the likeness and unlikeness of its states, whereby it is enabled to distinguish between the congruity and incongruity running throughout all our cognitions. But in addition to this fundamental process of thought, we must recognize a fundamental product of thought so that, along with the validity of the act of knowing, there must be a piece of knowledge, also. If consciousness is trustworthy so also are its deliverances. What is the meaning of this? The meaning of it is that with the consciousness of likeness and unlikeness and the idea of congruity and incongruity we have two manifestations of the Unknowable. The division between them corresponds to the distinction between subject and object, or that between ego and non-ego. In the subject or ego we find a faint manifestation of some power that is manifesting itself while in the object or non-ego that power manifests itself in vivid forms. Further we are made conscious of a region of power or being indefinitely extended beyond both these faint and vivid manifestations of both the phenomenal ego and non-ego. This is reality and by reality we mean persistence in consciousness.

We think in relations like those of difference and likeness for which reason we can have no cognition of the Absolute since it is wanting in such relations. The relations that we think are of two orders; when they are relations of co-existence we have Space, when they are of sequence we have Time. Our Space-consciousness, relative to our own minds, is produced by some mode of the Unknowable and the unchangeableness in our conception of it implies a complete uniformity in the effects wrought by this mode of the Unknowable upon us. The same principles of reasoning apply to Time also.

Our conception of Matter, reduced to its simplest shape, is that of co-existent positions which offer resistance, as contrasted with the co-existent positions of Space which offer no resistance. Thus we think of Body as something bounded by surfaces and made up of parts which offer resistance. In our conception of matter we find two inseparable elements—extension and resistance of which resistance is primary, extension secondary. The conception of Motion involves Space, Time and Matter. The constituents of the idea of Motion are—something perceived, a series of positions occupied by it in succession and a group of co-existent positions united in thought with the successive ones. To this must be added the idea that a moving body is under the necessity to go on changing its position. Although Space and Time, Matter and Motion seem to be necessary data of intelligence, they are not ultimate; for Space and Time are but the forms of various mental relations of which Matter and Motion are the contents. Deeper down than these are the primordial experiences of Force, which is the ultimate of ultimates. The necessary data of consciousness, or the principles we are obliged to postulate, are The Indestructibility of Matter, The Continuity of Motion and The Persistence of Force. By means of this Force, Matter demonstrates itself as existing while Motion demonstrates itself as acting.

These truths, holding of existence at large, are of the kind required to constitute philosophy, but as they stand they do not form a philosophy, which cannot be constituted of any number of truths known separately. That which alone can unify knowledge must be a law of co-operation of the factors. The changes which are going on everywhere in the universe slowly altering the structure of our galaxy or constituting chemical decomposition imply that, along with a new arrangement of Matter, there arises a new arrangement of Motion. Hence it follows that there must be a law of the concomitant re-distribution of Matter and Motion which holds of every change and which, by unifying all changes, must be the basis of philosophy. In searching for this law of re-distribution, we observe that Philosophy must formulate the whole series of changes passed through by existences separately and as a whole, from the imperceptible to perceptible, from the perceptible to the imperceptible. It must state the truth that the concentration of Matter implies the dissipation of Motion and, conversely, that the absorption of Motion implies the diffusion of Matter.

The processes everywhere in antagonism, everywhere gaining now a temporary and now an enduring predominance the one over the other we call Evolution and Dissolution. In its most general form, Evolution is the integration of matter and concomitant dissipation of motion, while Dissolution is the absorption of motion and concomitant disintegration of matter. The final formula of Evolution stands thus—Evolution is an integration of matter and concomitant dissipation of motion, during which the matter passes from an indefinite, incoherent homogeneity to a definite, coherent heterogeneity, and during which the retained motion undergoes a parallel transformation. We need not dwell long on Dissolution, which has none of the various and interesting aspects which Evolution presents, yet something must be said of it.

When Evolution has run its course—when an aggregate has reached that equilibrium in which its changes end, it thereafter remains subject to all actions in its environment which may increase the quantity of motion it contains and which in course of time are sure to give its parts such excess of motion as will cause disintegration. According as its size, its nature and its conditions determine, its dissolution may come quickly or may be indefinitely delayed, may occur in a few days or may be postponed for billions of years. But exposed as it is to the contingencies, not simply of its immediate neighborhood, but of a Universe everywhere in motion, the time must come at last when, either alone or in the company of surrounding aggregates, it has its parts dispersed.

If Evolution of every kind is an increase in complexity of structure and function that is incidental to the universal process of equilibration, and if the equilibration must end in complete rest, what is the fate towards which all things tend? If the Solar System is slowly dissipating its energies, if the Sun is losing its heat at a rate which will tell in millions of years, if with the decrease of the Sun's radiations there must go on a decrease in the activity of geologic and meteorologic processes as well as in the quantity of vegetable and animal, if man and society are similarly dependent upon this supply of energy which is gradually coming to an end, are we not manifestly coming to an end, are we not manifestly progressing towards omnipresent death? Is that motionless state called death, which ends all Evolution in organic bodies, typical of the universal death in which Evolution at large must end? Have we thus to contemplate as the outcome of things a boundless space holding here and there extinct suns fated to remain forever without further change?

To so speculative an inquiry none but a speculative answer is to be expected. If, pushing to its extreme the argument that Evolution must come to a close in complete equilibrium or rest, the reader suggests that for aught which appears to the contrary there must be a universal death which will continue indefinitely, two replies may be made. First, the evidence presented in the heavens at large implies that, while of the multitudinous aggregates of matter it presents, most are passing through those stages which must end in local rest, there are others which, having barely commenced the series of changes constituting Evolution, are on their way to become theatres of life. The second reply is that when we contemplate our Sidereal System as a whole, certain of the great facts which science has established imply potential renewals of life, now in one region now in another, followed possibly at a period unimaginably remote by a more general renewal.

Quickly following the arrest of Evolution in aggregates of matter which are unstable and following it at periods often long delayed, Dissolution must eventually come. We see grounds for the belief that local assemblages of those far vaster masses we know as stars will eventually be dissipated, but the question whether our Sidereal System as a whole may not at a time beyond the reach of finite imagination share the same fate. While inferring that in many parts of the visible universe dissolution is following evolution, and that throughout these regions evolution will presently recommence, the question whether there is an alteration of evolution and dissolution in the totality of things is one which must be left unanswered as beyond the reach of human intelligence. We have no right to infer from the general progress toward equilibrium in the Universe that a state of universal quiescence or death will be reached, for if one process of reasoning ends in that conclusion, another points to renewals of life and activity.

If we lean to the belief that what happens to the parts will eventually happen to the whole, we are led to entertain the conception of Evolutions that have filled an immeasurable past and Evolutions that will fill an immeasurable future. We can no longer contemplate the visible creation as having a definite beginning or end, or as being isolated. It becomes unified with all existence before and after, and the Force which the Universe presents falls into the same category with its Space and Time as admitting of no limitation in thought.

This conception is congruous with the conclusion reached at the beginning where we dealt with the relation between the Knowable and Unknowable. It was there shown by analysis of both religious and scientific ideas that, while knowledge of the Cause which produces effects on consciousness is impossible, the existence of a Cause for these effects is a datum of consciousness. Belief in a Power which transcends knowledge is that fundamental element in Religion which survives all its changes of form. This inexpugnable belief proved to be likewise that on which all exact science is based. This is also the implication to which we are now led back by our completed synthesis. The recognition of a persistent Force, ever changing its manifestations but unchanged in quantity throughout all past time and all future time, is that which we find alone makes possible each concrete interpretation and at last unified all concrete interpretations.

Hence the reasonings contained in this work afford to either of the antagonist hypotheses respecting the ultimate nature of things. Their implications are no more materialistic than they are spiritualistic, no more spiritualistic than they are materialistic. The establishment of correlation and equivalence between the forces of the outer and the inner worlds serves to assimilate either to the other according as we set out with one or the other term. But he who rightly interprets the doctrine contained in this work will see that neither of these terms can be taken as ultimate. He will see that though the relation of subject and object renders necessary to us these antithetical conceptions of Spirit and Matter, the one is no less than the other to be regarded as but a sign of the Unknown Reality which underlies both.

A GENEALOGY OF MORALS

By

Friedrich Nietzsche

FRIEDRICH WILHELM NIETZSCHE (*1844–1900*) was a great German philosopher. He studied the classics at the universities of Bonn and Leipzig. In 1869 while still an undergraduate he was appointed to an extraordinary professorship of classical philology in the University of Basel and was rapidly promoted to an ordinary professorship. Here he began his brilliant literary career which became more and more philosophic. In 1876 eye (and brain) trouble caused him to take a leave, and in 1879 he was pensioned. During the next ten years he lived in various health resorts. His violent revolt against the civilization in which he lived molded his philosophy, which is famous for its epigrammatic brilliance, vigor, and uncompromising revolt against all conventions. In 1888 he was declared hopelessly insane.

WE PERCEIVERS are strangers to ourselves for the reason that we have never sought ourselves, hence we are unaware of the origin of our moral prejudices. Thus arises a demand for a criticism of our moral values; the very value of these values must be questioned. What was the origin, what is now the value of "good" and "evil"? How did the ideas of "guilt" and "bad conscience" arise? What do "ascetic ideals" mean?

I

Under what circumstances did man invent those valuations we call "good" and "evil"; what value have they now? We are indebted to the English psychologists for their attempt to unearth the origin of morality, but do not thank them for finding this in something purely mechanical and accordingly stupid. The English trace the "good" back to customs which originally were useful to the race but whose utility has been forgotten. But they seek the "good" in the wrong place, since the judgment of what was "good" was not invented by the race, or by those to whom goodness was shown, nor would the race, or herd, ever be able to forget the utility of what they had begun to call the "good." Now it has been only democratic prejudice which has prevented us from discovering the real genealogy of morals.

The idea of the "good" was invented by noble and powerful men who, high-minded and socially elevated, and at a pathos of distance from the mass of men took upon themselves the right to create values and coin names for them. The term "good" has no necessary connection with useful and unselfish actions, for these are but expressions peculiar to the herding instinct among men while the essential idea of goodness has something aristocratic about it. The very etymology of our terms, "good" and "bad" reveals this. Whereas the "good" man is the superior and noble person, the "bad" man is he who is simple mean, as indicated by the German word *schlect* (bad) which is identical with *schlicht* (simple). In the matter of race and color of the skin, the Latin *malus* (bad) may be placed side by side with the Greek *melas* (black) thereby indicating the flaxen-haired man in distinction from the black-haired aborigine. The Latin *bonus* (good) might be traced back to *duonos* (warrior), the ancient man of quarrel and battle. Such a type man was esteemed originally as the "good" man in whose noble attributes the true values of life were found. They were the values of Paganism.

But a trans-valuation of values set in when the Jews in their vindictiveness turned against the "good" ones as the noble, powerful, beautiful and happy and set up a standard of value according to which the wretched, poor, impotent, and lowly are the good ones. This Jewish valuation, *sub hoc signo* Israel, achieved its vengeance on the morality of the *noblesse* in a roundabout manner by crucifying the seeming adversary and destroyer of Israel so that he with his humane ideals might make appeal to all the world, or to the enemies of Israel. This was the other origin of the good, or the origin of the other "good," or that of slave-morality in distinction from master-morality. By such means the blond beast was changed into a tame, civilized, domestic animal as though such were the proper course of civilization, but from time to time the noble animal appears again in the form of Homeric heroes and Scandinavian Vikings, in Roman and Arabian, Germanic and Japanese nobility.

Thus two antithetical values, "good and bad," "good and evil," have fought a terrible battle lasting thousands of years; the symbol of this struggle appears most clearly in Rome against Judea, Judea against Rome. The Romans were the strong and noble men of their time; the Jews, a priestly people, filled with resentment and possessed of great ingenuity in morals. By such means was the morality of the masters vanquished for Rome did indeed succumb, although the Renaissance did witness a dazzling re-awakening of the classic ideal of life and the one-time noble manner of valuation. But thanks to the German and English Reformation Judea triumphed anew, restored the church and reduced the Roman ideal to sepulchral silence. Judea triumphed anew in the French Revolution, but then the most unexpected thing happened, for the antique ideal of master morality thrust itself out in the person of Napoleon, that synthesis of monster and superman.

II

The long story of human responsibility has its origin in the task of rearing an animal which can promise. This is the free man whose free will endows him with that superiority which comes from his ability to pledge himself and give his promise. This dominating instinct of man is called his conscience; it has experienced a long history and transmutation of forms until it became the tendency to pledge and say yes to one's self. The primeval problem of human responsibility was not solved in any delicate but in a frightful way so that it might be burned into the memory. By means of blood, torture, the sacrifice of the first-born, self-mutilations and other barbarous ritual observances the memory of obligation was forever fixed in the mind as that of something which never ceases to hurt. A glance at the German penal code should convey the idea of the effort expended to rear a "nation of thinkers." Here we find punishment by stoning, the rack, piercing the criminal with pales, boiling in oil and wine, cutting flesh out of the breast and the like. The memory of such things was supposed to make people "reasonable" and fix within them the dreary affair called reflection, or conscience.

But how did the other dreary affair known as guilt and bad conscience come to make its appearance in earth? In the genealogy of morals, the fundamental notion of moral "guilt" has its origin in the material idea of "debt." The very secret of it appears in the agreement between creditor and debtor, as old as the existence of law with its legal parties to an agreement and pointing back to the fundamental forms of commerce and intercourse, of buying and selling. Here promises are made so that the problem was to make a memory for him who promised and provide him with a storehouse of all that is stern, cruel and painful. In order to guarantee the promised payment it was necessary for man to impress upon his consciousness such a sacred conception of debt that he will pledge his very body, his wife, his freedom or even the salvation of his soul. On the other hand, the creditor by punishing the debtor shares the privilege of masters and is thus inspired by the lofty feeling of being able to despise and maltreat some one lower than himself, or of seeing the debtor properly despised and maltreated by the authorities.

In such a cradle of moral concepts is to be found "guilt," "conscience" and "duty," whose origins were thoroughly saturated with blood. The act of making another suffer by way of compensation for a debt unpaid seems to have produced the highest kind of pleasure, as it were a kind of festival, and to have ended in a kind of disinterested malignity. And yet because we had not come to feel ashamed of its cruelty, life on earth was more pleasant than it is now. In connection with the feeling of "guilt," thus understood as debtor-creditor relationship, person stood face to face with person, and person weighed itself with person whence the idea of value arose. Man named himself as the being which weighs values and thus became the valuing animal as such. Then came man's great generalization—that all things have their price and that everything can be paid off. Thus arose a naïve canon of justice and equity.

In primeval times, it was the community which stood in the relation to its member-debtors and to it were all the members bound, to it all were naturally pledged. Now if these members do not pay their obligations, what will happen? As the disappointed creditor, the community will have to be indemnified for the breach of contract on the part of him who is now a criminal. For he is a debtor toward the whole community whose common weal he shared, and in his failure to meet his obligations he is repudiated by the community, which is now in open hostility to him. As its power increases, the community attaches less and less weight to the transgressions of the individual as such and tends to think more of the wrong done than of the wrong-doer. Thus the community makes an effort to localize the case and, compromising with the anger of those immediately suffering from the misdeed, it seeks to guard against further crimes.

It is a mistake on the part of false genealogists of morals to attribute to punishment the desire for revenge for while such a desire does exist in man it cannot be taken as the origin of law and justice. In fact the idea of punishment is not to be traced back to any one principle but to a variety of these. Punishment may be regarded as a means of rendering the criminal harmless so that the equilibrium of the community may not be disturbed. Or punishment is used as a means of inspiring others with the fear of it, or may be taken as a kind of equivalent for the advantages the criminal enjoyed but did not pay for, as when he is used as a slave in the quarries. Or it is perhaps a festival celebrated when victory over the violator of the law has been achieved. Among still other things, punishment may be used to make a memory for one who suffers it, as also for the spectator who witnesses an execution. Punishment is really brimful of utilities of every sort.

Yet in the long list of utilities peculiar to punishment, we fail to find that feeling of guilt which is known as bad conscience. In fact, punishment itself may retard the development of that very feeling. Since in both the long pre-historic as well as in that of civilization remorse among criminals is such a rare thing, it must appear that punishment was not the instrument by which bad conscience was produced, for punishment tends to harden the heart, strengthens the power of resistance and increases the feeling of estrangement from the community. Bad conscience, this most dismal and yet most interesting plant in our subterranean vegetation, could not have sprung up from such a soil. How then did the remorse of conscience arise?

Man himself became the inventor of bad conscience when, having shifted from instinct to reflection, from nature to the community, he found himself locked within the ban of society and peace. It was as though a water-animal to avoid perishing became a land-animal which was expected to go on its own feet instead of simply being carried by the water, the abrupt change having the effect of unharnessing their instincts and rendering them worthless. Those instincts, however, were still there but, no longer rejoicing in the power to discharge themselves outwardly, they received an inward direction whereby they produced the internalization of man. With political bulwarks like those of punishment all about the instincts of freedom, these turned inward against man himself, so that enmity, cruelty, persecution and destruction were thus directed at man's own nature. After man had broken violently with his past animal history with all its terribleness and cruelty, he began to make war upon himself in the form of self-antagonism and a cruelty directed toward himself. Hence the original instinct of free-dom, suppressed and imprisoned within consciousness, vents and discharges itself inwardly upon itself. Now this is the origin of bad conscience.

To return to the original relation of debtor to creditor, it may be pointed out that man's terrible feeling of obligation will direct itself towards all who are living at a given time, but not to them only but also to those who have lived in the past, or to one's ancestors to whom hardly enough can be given in the way of food, festivals, temples, obedience and the like. This sense of a debt to the past continues until at last it is directed toward God, the Great Progenitor; and it is this sense of obligation toward Godhead which has grown greater the more elevated the idea of Godhead has become. The sublimest stroke in all this feeling of obligation came about in Christianity in which God Himself pays the age-old debt by sacrificing Himself for the guilt of mankind.

III

What do ascetic ideals mean to artists, philosophers, priests and saints? The ascetic ideal means much to man and is a necessity for his will which so abhors a vacuum and so needs a goal that it would rather will nothingness than not will at all. This negation assumes the form of the hypnotic subduing of all sensibility; of machinal activity against depression; and the degradation of man by modern science, which itself is the latest and noblest form of the ascetic ideal on earth.

Take the case of Richard Wagner and ask yourself what it means when, in the eve of his life, he gives an ovation to chastity. In the best and strongest, most joyful and most courageous period of his life, Wagner contemplated an opera on "Marriage of Luther," which would combine chastity and sensuality, as happens in every marriage, every true love-affair. But instead of such a work, Wagner wrote "The Master Singers." In consummating his career as artist, Wagner should have turned to something gay or at least satiric, which would have been in keeping with the career of a great tragedian, but with Wagner it was *Parsival*. Was this final work meant to be an anathema on the senses and intellect and a return to sickly, obscurantist ideals? All his life he had striven after the highest spiritualizing and highest sensualizing of his art, and here was the self-negation, the self-annulment of the artist. Evidently the older Wagner unlearned his former creed. From being modern indeed he had to revert to mediaeval antitheses and fall into a kind of intellectual perversity. It is greatly to be wished that the artist had taken farewell from us in a different manner, in a manner more victorious, more self-confident, more Wagnerian; less misleading, less double-dealing, less nihilistic. What do ascetic ideals mean to an artist? Nothing!

Now it was from the philosopher Schopenhauer that the artist Wagner got his idea of music as an art which speaks the universal language of the will and reality, as though it were a telephone from another world. Schopenhauer, following Immanuel Kant, looked upon the beauty of art as that which pleases us without our having any interest in it, and it was the "disinterested" that both these philosophers exalted as the very essence of beauty. Compare this ideal with the contrary one of Stendhal, who styles beauty "a promise of pleasure," and appreciate the enormous difference between them. The ascetic ideal of beauty finds rapt expression in the philosophy of this German youth, who referred to the sense of beauty as "the painless state which Epicurus praised as the

highest good and as the state of the gods, for we are for that moment set free from the vile striving of the will." Vile striving of
the will, indeed! What vehemence of language! What pictures of
torture! With Stendhal, it is the function of beauty to stimulate
the will by the promise of pleasure, or by means of the very
"interest" which Schopenhauer disowned. Now what does it mean
when a philosopher renders homage to the ascetic ideal? He gives
us a hint; he wishes to get rid of a torture. All ascetic philosophers
in their aerial asceticism are willing to practice a certain amount of
renunciation for the sake of their pure and unruffled contemplation, but they are not unbiased witnesses since they think only of
themselves. This is not the case with the ascetic priest, the saint.

In his case we find an earnest representation of the ascetic ideal.
His valuation of life is such that he is forced to turn against life
itself, and so influential is he that viewed from afar our earth must
look like an essentially ascetic star. For some reason, the life-
inimical species of priestly ascetics continues to flourish, suggesting that, although asceticism is against life, it is pursued with an
interest in life. The ascetic ideal is prompted by what is self-
protective and self-preservative, for by means of this ideal, life is
struggling against death so that it is really an artifice for the
preservation of life. Since the ascetic priest wishes for a state of
being different from and higher than that which now is, hence it is
his wish for life which makes of him a tool for bringing about
more favorable conditions. Thus the Nay which he pronounces
upon life brings to light the Yea of a better and more abundant
life.

Now the sick are the greatest danger for the sound; the sick, not
the evil nor the beasts of prey. Then come the priestly ascetics,
who consider themselves alone the good and just, the men of
good-will; they come and take care of the sick. This is his vast,
historic mission—to be the saviour and herdsman of the sick herd.
As a physician he has his salves and balms, but his poison also
to pour into the wound, but in this appears his greatest value.
He changes the direction of resentment. The sick and afflicted
naturally desire to blame some one for their plight and reek vengeance upon him. Here the ascetic priest does admit that some
one is to blame for the sufferer's sad plight but points out that

it is the sufferer himself who is to blame. The resentment which otherwise might have gone out into the world and done harm is thus turned inward upon the sick man.

In addition to such hypnotic subduing of sensibility we find machinal activity as a remedy for states of depression. This may be called "the blessings of labor," with such appurtenances as absolute regularity, punctuality, obedience with the natural effect of filling up one's time, making one impersonal and generating the ideal of self-contempt. To these man's machinal activity adds herd-organization, interest in the community and even love of neighbor. Asceticism can be found in science as well as in society.

Science, which seems to believe in itself but really does not, is the latest form of the ascetic ideal. The particular laborers in this field are worthy enough but that does not prove that science itself has a goal, a will or an ideal. It is really a subterfuge for every kind of discontent, unbelief, self-contempt and bad conscience. Thus it stands in need of a vindication; it is the best ally of the ascetic ideal, since it is the most secret, most subterranean. The poor in spirit and the scientific adversaries of that ideal have acted in concert, hence let people guard themselves against the idea that the scientists are really different, or that they are the rich in spirit. They have so worked for the self-diminution of man that ever since Copernicus man has been sliding down an inclined plane into the Nothing. The result is self-contempt in place of man's one-time self-esteem.

In the last analysis, all such asceticism is centered in the ethics of Christianity but this, as a moral code, must perish. We stand on the threshold of that event, that grand drama of one hundred acts reserved for the next two centuries of Europe; the most questionable and perhaps also the most hopeful of all dramas. In his growing horror of life, man wills the will to the Nothing, but he would rather will the Nothing than not will at all.

HOW WE THINK

By

John Dewey

JOHN DEWEY (*1859–*   ) is an American philosopher, psychologist and educator, born in Burlington, Vt., and graduated at the age of 20 from the State University in Vermont. He first served as professor of philosophy in Columbia University in 1904. His first original work was in the field of ethics and then he turned to logic where he developed the theory that reality is experience and that everything is what it is experienced as being. With the death of William James, Professor Dewey became the leader of the pragmatic school in the United States. He has been on educational visits to China, Japan, Turkey, Russia and Great Britain. *The Quest for Certainty, Individualism New and Old, The Public and Its Problems* are some of his later books.

THERE ARE SEVERAL WAYS in which people "think" but only one way, which we call reflective thinking, is a superior and productive mental process. This is the kind of thinking that consists in turning a subject over in the mind and giving it serious and consecutive consideration. On the other hand, the reveries, chance, recollections, momentary attentions, uncriticized beliefs, and unguided streams of thought which ordinarily occupy our minds may be pleasant and even recreational, but they are not capable of giving us truth. Only that thinking which gives, or tries to give, objective truth is strictly worthy of the name "thoughtful."

Such an intellectual mental process takes place whenever some event in our experience arouses an idea and suggests that this idea may possibly be true; and it involves, in addition, taking steps to determine whether the idea really is true, or not. Thus, when it occurs to an overworked housewife that an unexpected gift of money would be a blessing, there is certainly a "thought" present but it does not include any assumption of truth, and the woman does nothing to verify her idea. There is, in fact, nothing to be verified. On the other hand, if it occurs to her that going to market through a different street may save her time, she is beginning a process of real reflection; if she tests her idea by trying the new route, and thus turns her belief into definite knowledge she completes the process and has, as we say, "been using her head." She has been to a degree intellectual.

This is a simple case of what takes place even in the most advanced scientific or philosophic inquiry. Three main acts are involved: coming upon a suggestion, considering it, verifying it. Of course the question must be one to which the individual really wants an answer, otherwise it is not genuine, and will not spur him on to the act of searching.

In any process of reflection, it will be found that a felt demand for the solution of a perplexity is the steadying and guiding factor. The person looks for evidence which will solve the problem and thus end the necessity for further thinking about this particular situation. If the problem is sufficiently involved, it may take years or a lifetime to solve it. Thus, for some people, the evidence indicating what is most truly valuable in life is never quite complete, no conclusion proves entirely satisfactory, and there is constant re-evaluation. To be truly reflective, one must be willing to endure suspense and undergo the trouble of searching for the facts. Only a small quantity of reflective thought is involved when a person, even though he has a genuine problem, jumps to a conclusion, and, in an over-positive and dogmatic fashion, holds to it without reasonable evidence.

DESCRIPTION OF THE REFLECTIVE PROCESS

The two limits of every unit of thinking are a perplexed, troubled or confused situation at the beginning and a cleared-up, unified, resolved situation at the end. The first may be called pre-reflective —out of it thinking grows. The second situation is post-reflective —it involves a direct experience of mastery, satisfaction, enjoyment.

In between, as states of thinking, are (1) suggestions, in which the mind leaps forward to a possible solution (2) intellectual clarification of the situation, so that the nature of the problem becomes definite (3) the collection of data, this process being guided by whatever suggestions (hypotheses) are found most likely to be useful and true (4) the mental elaboration of each idea or hypothesis, reasoning about it in view of all the evidence (5) testing the hypothesis by overt or imaginative action.

These steps do not necessarily come in this order. At times, they may overlap, at times come together; one phase may be greatly expanded; or, the intellectual movement may be backward and forward, involving now one, now the other. Also, when step five is taken, new events will happen in consequence and these may lead to further suggestions, hypotheses, fact-finding, and testing. In fact, worth-while reflective thought invariably does lead beyond the original situation to new problems. One scientific discovery leads to another; appreciation by the ten year old that arithmetic helps in all measuring may encourage him to combine his drawing and arithmetic to figure out a new way to cover certain territory on a hike.

It is important to realize that when the problem is a moral or serious practical one, the fifth step, the overt testing, is irretrievable. One must now stand the consequences of his act. He can, however, and this is what he should do, keep his experimental attitude and give alert attention to what these consequences teach him about his own conduct. Children taught to do this in early life grow into more responsible and clearer-minded adults than those taught to follow rules without attention to actual consequences.

The scientist hunting knowledge for its own sake does not usually have to stand the consequences in the same way. His overt act, his step five, does not affect other people, or his own character, in an irretrievable fashion. If he is dissatisfied with the outcome, he can go back and begin his experiment over, none the worse off unless his materials and time are very valuable, and with a real fund of new knowledge, for his failures as well as his successes teach him much about his materials and his methods.

Likewise, in moral and other practical situations, a failure is *not mere failure.* It can enlighten, instruct, make future acts more meaningful.

Though "leading on to further activity" in the sense of discovering new interests is a desirable outcome of each reflective act, it is not the only one. People who are really skilled in reflective thinking invariably consider the new conclusion in the light of other tested conclusions, and try to find relationships among them. What does one thing mean in the light of another? Ability thus to relate and interpret ideas is ability to *organize* knowledge. It involves the use of ideas discovered in the personal and racial past, and it generates scientific forecasts of probable future events. Thus, a conclusion showing that Einstein's theory does not hold water would mean to its author not only that definite fact, but also that the future of physical science would be different from what it would be if Einstein's theory were verified as true.

All students need to have the facts in the above paragraph emphasized, lest they form the habit of not persistently applying new conclusions *in this wider sense* by organizing their knowledge. Schools are notably weak in this phase of the educational program.

The person who thinks reflectively exhibits the characteristics we call *logical*. His thought is orderly, reasonable; there is consecutiveness in what he says and does, and the means he uses are well calculated to reach the end he has in mind. The illogical person wanders aimlessly; shifts his topic without being aware of it; skips about at random; he not only jumps to conclusions (all of us have to do that now and then), but he fails to retrace his steps to see whether the conclusion to which he has jumped is supported by evidence; he makes contradictory, inconsistent statements without being sensitive to what he is doing. His thinking, we say, is full of fallacies.

To be logical in our actual thinking, we need to use the method we have called reflective. It is equivalent to being thoughtful, or having habits of heeding facts, pondering, deliberating, weighing evidence and suggestions. It is the opposite of taking words, ideas, and the evidence of the senses at face value.

The word *reason* is etymologically connected with the word *ratio*. The underlying idea here is *exactness of relationship*. All reflective thinking is a process of detecting relations, and the best thinking is not satisfied with "any old kind" of relation but searches for the most accurate that conditions permit.

Psychologically then, we can say that an actual process of thought has the quality of logicalness when it is alert, careful, thorough, definite, and accurate in achieving its products.

But when we examine these products—these ideas which we have at the end of a careful thought process—we find we can now organize them in what is called logical arrangement, thus using the word "logical" in another sense. When we say certain books, or maps, or speeches are logical, what do we mean? We mean that the product of thought has been ordered in clear form for someone else's use.

It is here that the system of "Formal Logic" contributed by Aristotle and found in every text book on logic has its uses. It is a method of organizing material so that all the relationships are clear. Which ideas are the premises and which the conclusions is definitely shown, and thus fallacies are avoided. Obviously, this process of arranging the elements of the thought product in their proper relationships may come during the "five steps" as well as after the conclusion is reached, thus being a ready means of checking possible errors, and of making new implications clearer.

A knowledge of Formal Logic will not of itself do much to produce better thought products, but taken in conjunction with an awareness of the main steps in reflective thinking it is an aid to clarity and a help in arranging the material for future use. Also, it helps in criticizing the work of others, as when one analyzes an editorial, a political speech, or a scientific treatise. In studying the product, a stranger is not particularly interested in the psychological process whereby it was reached, but in the objective claims to validity of the conclusions and of the evidence offered in support.

SUBORDINATE UNITIES WITHIN THE REFLECTIVE PROCESS

We have been dealing so far with the act of reflection as an entirety. Now we are to analyze certain subordinate unities upon the character of which depends the *efficiency* of the whole undertaking. We can group them under two headings—Judgment and Understanding.

1. *Judgment*

From one point of view the whole process of thinking consists of making a series of judgments that are so related as to support one another in leading to a final judgment—the conclusion. Judging is the act of selecting and weighing the facts and suggestions which present themselves, of deciding whether the alleged facts really are facts, the ideas sound or merely fanciful. Judgment occurs only when there is doubt or controversy, when rival interpretations are possible. It then becomes a process of defining and elaborating the rival claims, making the issue itself clearer than it was, and making certain which principles that are involved are really appropriate and which facts are really evidential. The last step of the judgment is a final decision closing the particular matter in dispute, and also serving as a rule or principle for deciding future cases.

To be a good judge involves a knack, or a power of insight and discernment, which is partly instinctive or inborn, and partly the funded outcome of long-familiarity with like operations in the past. Teachers who realize this will make it their business to give children much definite practice in the making of many varieties of judgments.

Technically speaking, judgment has two functions: analysis and synthesis. Analysis is clearing up of confused data, making emphatic what is relevant and important. Synthesis is bringing together, unifying, placing facts and ideas in their proper context.

2. *Understanding*

a. Ideas and Meanings
b. Conception and Definition.

a. We may compare a complete reflection to a paragraph; then the judgment is like a sentence in the structure of the paragraph, and an idea is like a word in the sentence. Ideas are elements in judgments, tools of interpretation.

We can define ideas in terms of meaning: while a meaning is being only conditionally accepted for use and trial, it is an *idea,* a supposal; when the meaning is positively accepted, some object or event is understood.

A thing understood, i. e., a thing with a meaning, is different from both an idea (which is a doubtful and still unattached meaning) and from a mere brute, physical thing. I can stumble against something in the dark and get hurt without understanding what the thing is; I can form a guess (an idea) of what it is; I can get a light and investigate. *Then* it is a known object, a thing understood, a thing with a meaning—all three being synonymous expressions.

There are two modes of understanding, which constantly interact in all genuine intellectual progress. The first is direct grasp or taking in of meaning: to apprehend; noscere; kennen; connaître. The second is indirect, circuitous understanding: to know *about,* to comprehend; scire; wissen; savoir.

The way things gain meaning is by being used as *means to bring about consequences,* or, as *standing for consequences for which we have to discover means.* Nothing is really known unless it is understood, and nothing is understood unless it has been *used* in some appropriate context.

b. When ideas become established or definitely accepted meanings we call them *conceptions.* They are now *standards of reference,* so familiar in their meaning that their significance is settled. They thus enable us to generalize; to standardize our knowledge by introducing permanence into what would otherwise be endlessly shifting. They help us identify the unknown by providing a store of meanings to fall back upon; they supplement the meaning of the *sensibly present* by helping us read into it characteristics we can not directly perceive; and they enable us to understand the new object or event in terms of the whole system of meanings to which it is now seen to belong.

In forming conceptions, nothing is so dangerous as vagueness. It is a constant source of misunderstanding and mistake, it is the aboriginal logical sin, above all things to be guarded against.

Definition and classification are tools for such guarding. Definition is the process of making a meaning clear, self-contained, single, detached. It makes certain the meaning which exclusively and characteristically attaches to a term, thus (technically) indicating its *intension.* Classification of meanings makes certain their *extension,* it shows this particular group as distinguished from other relevant groups and yet in relation to them.

The Three Types of Definition

a. Denotative: a type required for all sense qualities, and all emotion and moral qualities. It indicates something which must have been experienced in order for the definition to be adequately comprehended.

b. Expository: socially and educationally useful as a connection between types *a* and *b.* Combinations and variations built on the already experienced are involved here. Illustrations belong to this class.

c. Scientific. These definitions select *conditions* of *causation, production,* and *generation* as their characteristic material. The basic way in which things are related is what scientific definition points out.

Systematic Method

a. Control of data and evidence.
b. Control of reasoning and concepts.

a. An untrained person trying to be reflective is likely to "grab" at the first facts that offer themselves; jump to the first solution occurring to him, generalize an idea far beyond all supporting evidence.

The person trained in the scientific method (and this *method* is *essentially* the same with the housewife endeavoring to save time and energy and the astrophysicist studying a new star) will (1) distinguish what is really observed from what is merely inferred, (2) collect sufficient instances to distinguish what is important and significant from what is non-evidential and irrelevant, and use both positive and negative cases for whatever light they may throw, (3) vary the conditions experimentally (in imagination or practically), regulate them so as to secure a *typical, crucial case* with express reference to the difficulty in question.

Experiment is an absolute necessity in science, a useful tool in practical life. We have it whenever we form observations by variation of conditions *on the basis of* some idea or theory, as contrasted to forming observations on the merely empirical basis of happening to notice that two events usually go together.

Its three main advantages are found in the overcoming of defects due to (a) the rarity, (b) the subtlety and minuteness (or the violence), and (c) the rigid fixity of facts as we ordinarily meet them.

b. The formation of conceptions needs to be carefully controlled as much as does the collection of data. The most important thing here is to secure methods of relating our concepts in a serial or systematic fashion. Popular concepts built without definite method do not take us very far—they do not lead to such generalizations as are basic and in our day almost commonplace in science: electron, atom, molecule, mass, energy, evolution, gene, etc. Also, popular concepts lead us astray: people call a bat a "bird" and a whale a "fish."

Scientists have systematized their concepts in various ways. Using the tools of mathematics, they have organized according to quantity, they have *measured*. Thus today color phenomena are definitely related to other events of an (apparently) totally different nature: to infra-red and ultra-violet, radio-active phenomena, sound, electro-magnetism.

Also, they have aimed at establishing special sets of concepts for each particular science—geology, chemistry, zoology, arithmetic, algebra. These concepts are the intellectual keys to the phenomena classified in each field.

Lastly, to the specialist conceptual meanings become a subject matter of their own. It is an intellectual satisfaction to develop them in their logical relations of interdependence, of implication, without any reference at all to their immediate or even ulterior application of actual existence. This gives an admirable kind of aesthetic pleasure. It is something many children are capable of and should be encouraged in.

A warning comes in here: such artistic "playing" with ideas may make a suggested idea very rich and plausible but—it will not settle the validity of the idea. This can be done only in the domain of concrete observation, and those who would have *truth* must everlastingly remember this fact.

Empirical and Scientific Thought

Empirical inferences are those gained by noticing that two things are associated (go together) but without knowing why. All early knowledge was gained in this way, and much of it was very useful. Modern science could hardly have developed without the mass of observations thus acquired. Yet science was also hindered by them.

The disadvantages of purely empirical thinking are obvious. The main ones are: (1) its tendency to lead to false beliefs (such as, because a thing happens *after* another, it comes *because* of the other); (2) its inability to cope with the novel (since it rests on uniformities, it has no reasonable explanation of the unwonted and new); (3) its tendency to engender mental inertia and dogmatism (old explanations become traditional, and worst of all, certain classes of men come to be the guardians of established doctrines, and persecute all who dare offer new ideas. Loyalty to these powers, passivity and acquiescence instead of mental activity and open-minded inquiry, become the accepted ideals).

In contrast, the scientific method replaces emphasis on the repeated coincidence of certain events with search for a single comprehensive explanatory fact. It breaks up the coarse or gross facts of observation into a number of minuter processes not directly accessible to perception, and studies the causal connections in each of them. The scientist gathers his data by varying the conditions one by one and noting just what happens when each is eliminated. He may do this (a) by extending the empirical method, noticing the results of a great number of observations that have occurred accidentally under *different* conditions, (b) by *intentionally* varying conditions and noting what happens. The second is the far more useful.

Analysis and synthesis (discrimination and identification) of materials are equally present in experimental thinking, careful disentangling of details, followed by their careful integration into meaningful wholes is thus the clue to truly scientific effort. Analysis gives added certainty, and synthesis means ability to cope with the new and variable.

I. In this process, abstraction is a constantly valuable tool. It means detaching a quality or relation from the vague blur in which it is commonly obscured and making it stand out.

It is the act of digging beneath the familiar and inertia-producing surface of events to some unfamiliar property or relation that is scientifically or philosophically significant. It is chiefly valuable when it seizes upon some quality not previously grasped at all. For example, seeing the wing of the bird to be identical, morphologically, with the forearm or foreleg of other animals; seeing the pod of peas and beans to be a modified form of leaf and stem.

II. Faith in human progress through the intelligent regulation of existing conditions is, of course, the natural result of the scientific method of regulation. In the social as well as the physical world we are coming to be willing to use experiment, not waiting for nature to accidentally happen to offer us material, but going ahead ourselves and producing cases for study.

CREATIVE EVOLUTION

By

Henri Bergson

HENRI LOUIS BERGSON (*1859–*) is a French philosopher of Jewish descent. He was born in Paris, educated at the Ecole Normale and in 1900 was appointed to the Chair of Philosophy at the College de France. In his philosophy he gives scant attention to metaphysics, striving rather to exhaust the problem of life itself as a perpetual development or a creative evolution. His philosophy is founded on the belief that Life is the true Being or essence of things. His most important works are *l'Evolution creatrice* and *l'Energie spirituelle.*

THE EXISTENCE of which we are most assured and know best is our own; but what does it mean when we say we "exist"? I find that I pass from state to state, am warm or cold, idle or at work and that there is nothing within me that is not undergoing change. My mental condition on the road of time is like that of a snowball which rolls up its past within it and gnaws its way into the future. This continuous, forward movement is duration; it is an irreversible process, its course is unforeseeable. Hence, for a conscious being to exist is to change, to change is to mature, to mature is to go on creating oneself endlessly. Can this be said of existence in general?

A material object, however, appears to remain as it is, or to change only under the influence of some external force which brings about only a dislocation and relocation of parts. It is just what it is, time does not bite into it, so that it seems possible for a superhuman intellect to calculate at any moment of time its particular position in space. All existence seems to resemble a fan already patterned and needing only to be spread out in the fixed course of time. And yet real succession is an undeniable fact even in the material world, which seems to be made up of systems which can be treated in a fixed geometrical way. For the whole endures and its real duration means invention, the creation of new forms and the continual elaboration of the absolutely new. What we call things are only actions, as states of things, their qualities, are but tendencies.

As in the individual so in nature also is there the ceaseless process of maturing, of ageing, for wherever anything lives a register is open for time to be inscribed. If it is our desire merely to think objects and act upon them, we may use purely abstract time and move either forward or backward over the temporal series, but if we wish to gather the meaning of all things as they surge onward we must deal with real time as it is lived by our own minds. Is it not true that life, like conscious activity, is invention, is unceasing creation? This we see in evolution, a system of transformism in which life is like a current passing from germ to germ through the medium of the developed organism. This natural process involves the ideas of novelty in things and unforseeability in minds and against these our intellects tend to revolt, for they are inclined to believe that the life-process is explicable mechanically on the basis of physical and chemical ingredients. But, in reality, life is no more made up of these than a circle is composed of straight lines.

When we attempt a mechanistic interpretation of life, we are balked by the factor of time, for duration makes a definite impression upon an organism but glides over a mechanism without penetrating it. Since time is real we cannot assume that all is given in such a way that an extraordinary mind, reasoning upon the basis of what exists now, could calculate every detail of what is to be in the future. Such a prospect is dazzling but we cannot sacrifice experience to the dreams of a universal mathematic. The course of things, not to be calculated mechanistically from the past, is just as independent of a final plan set up for it in the future; for, like Mechanism, such Finalism makes time useless again. The attraction of the future is just as invalid an idea as the impulsion of the past. Mechanism and Finalism, which consider all things in the light of a pre-conceived plan, are of value to us when we wish to act on fixed things and think about them in a definite way, but they are only external views of our whole conduct which is more extensive and vital. Much of our native mentality has shrunk to a tight form of geometry and logic and ignores the fringe of vague intuition which surrounds it so that we tend to take the intellectualized part of the mind for the whole of mental life as such.

How can we transcend both Mechanism and Finalism which have rejected the important factor of time? How shall we understand evolution? We cannot do this by viewing the course of life in a unilinear series, since the divergent paths of evolution present a multilinear one. What we find is that life, working on divergent lines of evolution, manufactures like apparatus by unlike means, as sexuality in both plants and animals, the eye of the mollusc and the vertebrate. These typical phenomena, that of the eye in particular, challenge those mechanistic systems of evolution which seek to explain life on the basis of purely accidental variations influenced by external conditions. In the case of the eye, we find a highly complicated organ equipped with a delicate structure like the retina, as also the visual centre in the brain. To assume that the evolution of the eye has been brought about gradually by means of accidental variations calls upon us to explain how all the separate variations involved in different parts of the eye could take place at the same time, since one variation here would have to wait for a complementary variation there. Some good genius would have to be appealed to in order to preserve and accumulate these variations differently placed and timed in the whole optical apparatus. This unsurmountable difficulty is overcome, however, when we revert to an original impetus of life forcing its way through matter and proceeding not by association and addition, but by dissociation and division. Vision as an act of the organism has managed to canalize its course so that what we find in the whole visual process is not so much a sum of means employed as a sum of obstacles avoided. The whole method of evolution seems to be in accordance with a vital thrust from within rather than after the manner of mechanistic or finalistic forces operating from without.

The course of evolution would be a simple one to trace if life had followed a single line, but life has taken divergent directions whose different results are mutually complementary rather than analogous. Life has spread out like a sheaf in the general directions of plant and animal, the cause of the division being due to something life bore in its bosom, so that it is life itself which must explain what mechanism and finalism cannot account for. Now, our interest in evolution lies in the path that leads to man, but we must examine the process in plant and animal. The plant differs from the animal in the mode of alimentation, the plant being able by means of its chlorophyllian function to derive from air, water, soil such elements, especially nitrogen and carbon, as it needs to sustain life, taking them in mineral form. The animal, being unable to fix the nitrogen and carbon which are to be found everywhere, must seek its particular nourishment from the vegetables that have already taken these elements. For the purpose of feeding, the animal must be able to move about and must thus be in possession of a locomotor apparatus directed by some sort or degree of consciousness or feeling.

The common source of all food-energy is to be found in the sun. The problem of the animal consists in obtaining this solar energy but, more than that, it must be able to store it up to expend it later in the form of an explosive released, as it were, by a trigger. Among the higher animals the part played by food is highly complex in the way it makes use of the albuminoids, carbohydrates and fats which, in the form of glucose are conveyed by the arterial blood into the tissue to be deposited as glycogen in the various cells. This glycogen is for the sake of the muscular and nervous systems, the former being well stocked and the latter readily served with it. The animal is the nervous system, or a nervous system installed upon a system of digestion. When deprived of adequate food the organism sacrifices everything for this sensori-motor apparatus so that in instances of animals which have died of hunger the brain, unlike the other organs which have lost weight and been impaired, is found almost unimpaired.

The development of animal life has depended upon movement, upon mobility. In the animal kingdom life has been successful along the lines of the arthropods, especially the insects, and vertebrates, especially man; and as men are the lords of the soil the ants are the lords of the sub-soil. One group excels in instinct, the other in intelligence both of which are equally fitting solutions of one and the same life-problem. Human intelligence dates from and has been dependent upon the ability of man, *homo faber,* to make and use tools; the history of it extends from the stone implements of the Cro-Magnon man to the steam-engine of civilized man in modern times. Now, how do instinct and intelligence differ?

They differ generally in their respective relations to consciousness which is a kind of light playing about the zone of possible action. In instinct this consciousness is immediately stopped up by action as the creature proceeds at once to its object. With intelligence there is an interval between conscious representation and action, between potential and real activity. Instinct is an innate knowledge which bears on things, intelligence an indirect knowledge bearing on relations; one implies a matter, the other a form. Expressed logically, instinctive knowledge is categorical and extensive, intelligence hypothetical and intensive. There are things that intelligence alone is able to seek but which by itself will never find; these things instinct alone could find but will never seek.

The mechanism of intelligence aims to establish relations between mind and its object for the sake of acting upon it, for the faculty of understanding is an appendage to the faculty of action. Our intelligence as it leaves the hand of nature has for its chief object the unorganized solid, and it is never quite at ease when confronted by real duration, or the time-flow in nature. Of the discontinuous and immobile, of the inert and dead does the intellect form a clear idea. It is characterized by a natural inability to comprehend life. It acts upon nature as though it were a picture-puzzle to be taken apart and put together again, for it has unlimited power to decompose according to any law and recompose according to any system.

Instinct, on the contrary, has been moulded upon the very form of life so that it proceeds organically, not mechanically. Life itself is something instinctive resembling a hive in which each cell is a bee united to the other cells by invisible bonds in a whole sympathetic toward itself. Instinct cannot be understood by resolving it into so many intelligent actions or into mechanisms built up piece by piece such as our intelligence combines. Its mental existence is something lived, not something represented. It is a kind of sympathy turned toward life as intelligence is an interest directed toward matter.

Intuition is self-conscious instinct capable of reflecting upon its object and enlarging it indefinitely. Instead of going around life to obtain as many external views as possible, intuition follows instinct by entering into life. It is a vague nebulosity surrounding the luminous nucleus of intellect. At the base of all life is a consciousness which in order to free itself from matter was forced to divide itself into plant and animal and then separate into instinct and intelligence. It is as if a vague and formless being whom we may call man or Super-man had sought to realize itself and had succeeded only by abandoning a part of himself on the way. Life has made a sudden leap from the animal to man so that it is as though from the vast spring-board from which life has taken its leap, while all the other species have stepped down finding the cord stretched too high, man alone has cleared the obstacle.

In the case of human intelligence, whose systems of logic, geometry and physics show it to be at home in the world of matter, it remains to be seen how the intellect has been formed and how its genesis is parallel with the genesis of materiality. This is an attempt more daring than the boldest speculations of the metaphysicians. The secret of this problem is to be found in the idea of space, which is not as alien to the mind or as native to matter as we imagine. Intellect and materiality, while moving in opposite directions, have progressively adapted themselves to each other in order to attain at last to a common spatial form. The more consciousness is intellectualized, the more is matter spatialized. But how has this common form of spatiality come about?

It has come about on the part of the intellect through its tendency to relax its firm grasp on things and let its faculties expand. Thus instead of acting we dream. Then the free and vital intuition of things begins to degrade itself into extended forms, just as the reading of a poem may decline from a full appreciation of its theme into separate stanzas, sentences, words or even syllables of which indeed it is composed but in which in their extended form the meaning is lost. This spatializing tendency on the part of the mind draws us away from the original vital order of things into a geometrical order, for even in such logical processes as those of deduction and induction we find a latent geometry. The movement at the end of which is spatiality lays down along its course the faculty of induction as well as that of deduction, in fact, intellectuality entire. With the ideas, or genera, of ancient philosophy and the natural laws of modern science we find that the geometrical order has been developed at the expense of the vital order resulting in the dogmatism of the ancients and the relativism of the moderns. All our intellection has come about by descending from the vital to the geometrical order, by slipping from tension to extension, from freedom to mechanism. There is an admirable order indicated by the astronomer but no less admirable is the free and vital order created by the composer, as in a symphony by Beethoven.

The counterpart of this process of relaxing and expanding into space appears in the complementary realm of materiality. Here it is more definite, being found in the principle of the degradation of energy. This is expressed definitely in the second law of thermodynamics according to which all physical changes have a tendency to be degraded into heat which is then distributed along bodies in a uniform manner to end in elementary vibrations perpetually repeated, a condition of entropy. The condition of the universe will be like that of a man who keeps his strength as he grows old but spends it less and less in actions and comes, at length, to employ it in making his lungs breathe and his heart beat.

But in the special phenomenon of life we observe an effort to remount the incline that matter descends, although in life this inverse direction of energy succeeds only in retarding the down course of things it cannot stop. It is as if from an immense reservoir of life jets of steam were gushing forth and falling back in drops each of which is a world only to be retarded in their fall by a small jet of steam which for the time remains uncondensed. Reality, life, supra-consciousness, God is a process of continually shooting out as in an enormous fire-works display. As the blackened cinders of the spent rockets fall back dead, life, the last of the rockets to be discharged, tears a fiery path through the whole charred mass to vivify and lighten it up in the form of organisms.

The truth is that life is possible wherever energy descends the incline indicated by thermo-dynamic law, and where a force of inverse direction can detard the descent; that is to say, from all the worlds suspended from all the stars. On flows the current of life running through human generations and subdividing itself into individuals. All the living hold together, all yield to the same tremendous push. The animal stakes its stand upon the plant, man bestrides animality, and the whole of humanity in space and time is one immense army galloping beside and before and behind each one of us in an overwhelming charge able to clear the most formidable obstacles and beat down every resistance, perhaps even death itself.

THE BOOK OF JOB

THERE WAS A MAN in the land of Uz named Job, who was perfect and upright, feared God and despised evil. Moreover he had much property and was the greatest of all the men of the East. Now upon a day when the sons of God presented themselves unto the Lord Satan also appeared and declared that Job loved not God for nought but for the blessings he had received, so that if the Lord were to remove these from him Job would curse God to his face. In order to test the heart of Job, the Lord puts Job and all he has in the power of Satan.

Now while all were feasting in Job's household there came a messenger telling him that the Sabeans had taken his oxen and asses and slain his servants. Another messenger comes to tell him that a fire from heaven has consumed his sheep and their shepherds, while a third one appears to announce that the Chaldeans have carried his camels away and slain those that tended them. Even while he was yet speaking a fourth messenger comes to announce that a wind from the wilderness had come upon the house of his eldest son so that it fell and destroyed all his children who were feasting there. Then Job arose, rent his mantle, shaved his head, fell down upon the ground and worshipped, saying, "the Lord gave, the Lord hath taken away; blessed be the name of the Lord."

When the sons of God again presented themselves to the Lord, Satan appeared again and obtains permission to try Job further, this time by touching his very bone and flesh. Satan now afflicts Job with boils from the sole of his foot to his crown so that he must scrape himself with a potsherd and sit down among the ashes. His wife bids him curse God and die but Job rebukes her for her folly. Now three of his friends, Eliphaz the Temanite, Bildad the Shuhite and Zophar the Naamanite come to mourn with and comfort him and, rending their mantles and sprinkling dust upon their heads, they sat on the ground with him seven days and seven nights but spake not a word. Now Job curses the day wherein he was born and longs for death, and is rebuked by Eliphaz the Temanite, who declares that the judgments of the Lord are not directed against the righteous but the wicked. Further he recounts a dream in which there came to him a vision in which a voice said, "shall mortal man be more just than God, a man more pure than his Maker," Job is further admonished that man is born unto trouble as naturally as the sparks fly upward and that he himself should not despise the chastening of the Lord.

Job replies to this rebuke by trying to estimate the immensity of his affliction and the weakness of his soul, for his strength is not that of stones or his flesh of brass. Thus the argument of his friend is as wind to one who is so desperate as he. Since man lives for but an appointed time he has, he thinks, a right to desire the death of his body which is now so stricken. He complains that the Lord seems to have set a watch over him and put a mark upon him and wishes that the Lord would leave him to his misery and speaks as though he would hide in the dust from him.

Bildad the Shuhite now takes up the rebuke and insists that Job must have sinned or God would not have visited him with all this affliction, and insinuates that Job has been a hypocrite. In reply Job admits that man cannot contend with God because of God's power by which He moves mountains, shakes the earth, who made Arcturus, Orion and the Pleiades and could command them to rise not. It seems that in His power God deals alike with the perfect and the wicked and laughs at the trial of the innocent and allows the earth to pass into the hands of the wicked. If God were a man even as is Job he would answer Him as now he fears to do. Indeed he does complain to God for the way He has afflicted him and asks that for the remainder of his days God may cease troubling him so that in peace he may pass into the land of darkness where even the light is as darkness.

The way in which Job seems to challenge God, justifying himself in the face of Him who had brought him into the world, arouses Zophar the Naamanite, who proceeds to rebuke Job's presumption. Whatever affliction Job has been called upon to endure it is less than his iniquity really deserves, and besides he does not know the secrets of God's wisdom. "Canst thou by searching find out

God?" he asks him, and then indicates the range of God's wisdom, which is as high as Heaven, deeper than Hell, longer than the earth and broader than the sea. "Vain man would be wise though man be born like a wild ass's colt." Instead of expostulating against God's ways Job should repent, prepare his heart and stretch out his hands toward Him. Let Job remove iniquity from his hand so that he may lift up his face without spot to God. Then his present misery shall be remembered but as waters that pass away.

The rebukes of his three friends, who had condemned Job without letting him know why he was thus afflicted, arouses Job to irony. They have presumed to speak for all mankind, and it is as though wisdom would die with them when as a matter of fact he is not inferior to them but has understanding as well as they. They should ask the beasts and the fowls of the air to teach them, or let the earth and the sea with the fishes in it tell them what wisdom is. He himself understands the wisdom and power whereby God destroys things, controls the waters so that either they dry up or come forth like a deluge, spoils counsellors, makes judges fools, overthrows princes, destroys nations and brings deep things out of the darkness. He knows these things as well as they, who are such forgers of lies and physicians of no value that he would have them hold their peace so that he may speak, come what may. Now, having declared his confidence in God by saying, "though He slay me yet will I trust Him," he then entreats God to withdraw from him the hand of His affliction and let him know for what iniquities he is being punished. Life, as Job observes, is brief and full of trouble, yet when a man dies he may live again, for there is hope for a tree which, having been cut down, may sprout again.

The reproaches of the three friends begin a second time when Eliphaz the Temanite rebukes Job for his vain words which seem to fill his belly with the east wind. He challenges Job's claim to wisdom saying, "art thou the first man that was born or wast thou made before the hills?" By an appeal to the age-old tradition of wise men Eliphaz asserts that punishment ever comes upon the unrighteous man who, his prosperity destroyed, begs bread, dwells in desolate cities and is beset by trouble and anguish. Job lets his friends know that he is familiar with all such things, calls them "miserable comforters" and tells them further that were they in his place he could say just such things to them. His own condition is terrible, for God has delivered him to the ungodly who have vented their wrath upon him, and God Himself has taken him by the neck to shake him and set him up as a mark for cruel persecution. He would be justified in the sight of God and exclaim, "Oh that one might plead for a man with God as a man pleadeth for his neighbor!" But men are so unjust and unmerciful that Job's hope cannot be in life but in death.

Bildad the Shuhite now rebukes Job a second time demanding to know why Job considers them as vile beasts, and then returns to the theme that punishment always follows in the paths of wicked men whose very dwellings on earth terrified their contemporaries and then became the subject of amazement to posterity. Job can respond only as he has done before by protesting that his friends are cruel to him and that his cry for compassion is not heard. Even his kinsmen, children and servants treat him with contempt. Cannot these his friends have pity upon him? When the third friend in the group, Zophar the Naamanite, seeks to administer rebuke a second time he can do no more than repeat the general theme the common fate of the wicked man and the horrible heritage appointed unto him by God. In his reply Job takes exception to the rule his friends have laid down by stating that the wicked often live on and become mighty in power and, as he goes on to say, death often treats the righteous and iniquitous in the same way, for one dies the sweet death of ease and quiet, another in the bitterness of his soul. It may be, as he surmises, that the judgment of the wicked will come in another world.

Eliphaz now speaks for the third time varying the theme of iniquity and punishment by putting this question to Job—"Can a man be profitable unto God, as he that is wise is profitable unto himself. Is it pleasure to the Almighty that thou art righteous or gain to Him that thou makest thy ways perfect?" Then he accuses Job of various sins—he gave no water to the weary or bread to the hungry, sent the widows away empty and broke the arms of the fatherless so that the only way open to him is that of repentance, hence he should seek God. Job's reply to this is the exclamation, "Oh that I knew where I might find Him that I might come even to his seat!" but go as he will, forward or backward, to left or right, he cannot see Him; moreover the mind of God is not to be changed by man. The wicked, as he had said, often go unpunished and yet they are exalted for the time only and will come at last to the day of destruction.

Bildad the Shuhite now appears for the third and last time concluding his criticism of Job by saying that, since the dominion of the Deity is so vast and His nature so exalted that even the moon is not bright or the stars pure in His sight, there can be no justification for man, who is but a worm. Job now complains that Bildad has not helped him and goes on to declare the greatness of God which Bildad had so plentifully expounded. God forbid that Job should justify such a hypocrite as Bildad whom God will not hear when he in his trouble calls upon Him. He will teach all of these friends who have spoken in vain, and thus he tells them of the various calamities which befall the wicked.

Zophar the Naamanite fails to appear but Job discourses at some length beginning by observing the limitations of man's knowledge. Man has found precious and valuable things in the earth but not the sources of wisdom. He has discovered the vein where silver and the place where gold are found, has taken iron from the earth and melted brass from the stone and has discovered paths unknown to the fowl or the vulture's eye, to the fierce lion and its whelps. But the place where wisdom and understanding are found is unknown to him who is ignorant of their price. Both the deep earth and the sea confess, "it is not in me, not in me." The value of wisdom is such that it cannot be obtained for gold or silver, its worth is not equalled by the gold of Ophir, the precious onyx or the sapphire to say nothing of coral or pearls, by rubies or the topaz of Ethiopia. But God who understands has said, "Behold the fear of the Lord is wisdom and to depart from evil is understanding."

In sad retrospect Job now recalls his former prosperity and prestige when in the days of his youth the Almighty was with him. So great was his good fortune that he washed his steps with butter and the rock poured him out rivers of oil, while his repute was such that in his presence old men stood up in reverence while young men fled in fear; noblemen were silent, the princes laying their hands on their mouths and the tongue of the nobles cleaving to the roof of their mouths. He delivered the poor and fatherless and caused the widow's heart to sing for joy; eyes was he to the blind and feet to the lame. Thus he was as a chief or king among them. But now he is held in contempt and has become a derisive song or by-word with them, and with the great calamity which has come upon him he is no more than a brother to dragons or a companion for owls.

But to the very end Job insists upon his integrity and wonders why God has not observed how carefully he took his ways. He had made a covenant with his eyes so that he should not think upon a maid. He had walked not with vanity or was his heart deceived by a woman or had he been guilty of infidelity to his wife. He was just with his servants, generous with the poor and did not rejoice in his great wealth. He rejoiced not at the destruction of his enemies and did not curse them and unlike Adam he sought not to cover his transgressions. If his adversary has written a book, or kept a record of Job's life, and it can be shown that he has done such evil things then let thistles grow instead of wheat, cockle instead of barley. Thus ended the words of Job.

Job's three friends are now thoroughly silenced, but now Elihu, son of Barachel the Buzite, appears upon the scene and attacks Job because he had justified himself rather than God, and rebukes his three friends because they had condemned Job without answering his defence of himself. Elihu was a young man and for the time had hesitated to speak in the presence of those whose years should have given them wisdom which, however, has not been forthcoming from their mouths. Elihu is so bursting with the desire to speak that his belly is as wine without vent and ready to burst like new bottles. Job had desired that the Almighty answer him and now young Elihu, although formed out of clay, has the spirit of God within him and will speak in God's stead. In Elihu's hearing, Job had vaunted his righteousness and had set himself against God. According to Elihu, God calleth man to account by means of visions in the night, by painful chastenings of his flesh and by His messengers. It will be well for Job to heed the words of Elihu.

Job has been at grievous fault in questioning the justice of God and has spoken without knowledge of the fact that with the Almighty there can be no injustice. Better is it for a man to repent and humble himself before God and as for Job it is best that he be tried to the very end. Man sins when he attempts to apply his ideas of righteousness to the Almighty and should realize that God's righteousness is higher than man's even as the clouds of heaven are above his head. In their affliction men cry unto God for help but do not seek him out in their hearts, and it was in this way, continues Elihu, that Job had multiplied words without knowledge. If Job will but listen, Elihu will show him how just and merciful is God, who would graciously have helped the afflicted man had it not been for his sins. Job should magnify the works of God as these are manifested in the skies and on the earth, and should see how limited is his knowledge compared with the wisdom of God manifested in all His works.

At last God Himself speaks and answers Job out of the whirlwind, bidding him gird himself like man and answer the questions He will put to him. "Where wast thou when I laid the foundations of the earth when the morning stars sang together?" Who is it, He asks further, who causes the dayspring to know its place? Does Job know the depth of the sea or the width of the earth, the place where light dwells and darkness hides, by what way the light is parted and the rain caused to fall? Has Job power to bind the sweet influences of the Pleiades, to loose the bands of Orion, bring forth Mazzaroth in its season or guide Arcturus with his sons? Among the things of earth, does Job know the habits of such creatures as the wild goat and wild ass, the unicorn and peacock, the ostrich, eagle and hawk?

Now Job, feeling that he is vile, cannot answer but lays his hand upon his mouth whereupon God speaks again from the whirlwind bidding him gird himself and make answer. Let Job display his righteousness, his power and majesty if he can and God will admit that Job's right hand has power to save him. Has Job such power that he can draw out the Leviathan with a hook, play with him as with a bird and with his companions make a feast of his great body? Because of God's great power the Leviathan is made invulnerable to all of man's weapons as spears, darts and arrows, while in his power he is able to make the sea boil and become a king over the children of pride. Job then submits to God and repents in dust and ashes. God then accepts Job and requires his three friends to offer up burnt offerings for themselves because they had not spoken truly and justly of God. Job then prayed for his friends and God gave him twice as much as he had before so that he had fourteen thousand sheep, six thousand camels, a thousand yoke of oxen and a thousand she asses. After living a hundred and forty years Job died, being old and full of days.

THE BHAGAVADGITA

A VAST ARMY of the sons of Pandu are drawn up in battle array with their large bows and great cars, and a civil war is imminent. The hero of the *Gita,* Arjuna, is in command of the host but is averse to engage in battle with his kinsmen; he feels weak, his mouth is dry, his hair stands on end and his bow drops from his hand. Rather than kill his kinsmen he would have them kill him, and having thus spoken he casts aside his bow and arrows and sits down in his chariot.

Krishna, an incarnation of the Deity, now appears in the disguise of a charioteer, chides him for his weakness and bids him cast off fear. For himself Arjuna protests that he would rather be a miserable beggar than a successful warrior and yet in his ignorance he would have Krishna tell him whether it is better to vanquish enemies or be vanquished by them. Krishna, speaking from the depths of wisdom, would obliterate the distinction between the vanquishing and the vanquished, for such beings do not really exist. That which really does exist is something indestructible and inexhaustible, so that "he who thinks it to be the killer and he who thinks it to be killed, both know nothing. It kills not, is not killed; it was not ever born nor does it ever die." Now that Arjuna knows what is real within him he should cast aside all thoughts of pleasure and pain, life and death and do his duty as a member of the warrior-caste, Kshatriya.

The knowledge which Krishna has revealed to the young Arjuna is that of the Sankhya, or speculative philosophy, and Yoga, or philosophy of action. Krishna, in evaluating these, appears to assume the higher standpoint of the Vedanta philosophy according to which contemplation is superior to conquest and devotion of the mind preferable to the action of the will. When Arjuna has risen to such a height his mind will be free from delusion and he will rejoice in that steadiness of mind which comes from the attainment of the Self. As the tortoise draws its members back into its shell so the man of steady Self withdraws his senses from the world to which he no longer feels attachment. But, asks Arjuna, if contemplation is so superior to action, how can Krishna bid him take up such fearful action as that of war? Krishna replies to this question by admitting that action of some sort is incessant in human life, but that action in the ordinary sense of the term can be surmounted when he who practices Yoga acts without attachment to particular objects and without regard to selfish motives. It is desire which produces sin, hence it is the duty of the young prince to deliver himself from it by restraining his senses and releasing his understanding.

Krishna now reveals himself as an incarnation of the Divine Being, as one who has passed through many births and who is born for the protection of good people and the destruction of evildoers. He would have Arjuna know the secret of action, or the heart of the Yoga philosophy, and see both action in inaction and inaction in action. This difficult standpoint is attained by those who in approaching Krishna are ready to forsake attachment to their deeds and expect no fruits from them. Such a true disciple of the doctrine is satisfied with what comes to him, is free from all animosity and has his mind fixed on knowledge as its goal.

Arjuna is puzzled by the paradox of renouncing actions and pursuing them at the same time, hence it is for him to learn, as Krishna warns him, that both renunciation and pursuit are ways to happiness, although pursuit is superior. Children may talk of the Sankhya of thought and the Yoga of action as though they were distinct, but he who pursues either one well obtains the fruit of both. Truly seen Sankhya and Yoga are one. Unless desire is renounced, no action can be right and yet without action there can be no detachment from the world. It is as though by working one attained to a kind of worklessness. The Sankhya is right in emphasizing the intellect, the Yoga right in stressing the will, but to see these doctrines as one and the same, as by means of the Vedanta Krishna seems to do, is the highest wisdom. Action while secondary to thought and devotion can cease only after the disciple is detached from the world; when he has thus purified himself he is prepared for contemplation. "As a light standing in a windless place flickers not, that is declared to be the parallel for the devotee whose mind is restrained and who devotes his self to abstraction." But Arjuna feels that the mind is so fickle, boisterous and strong that to restrain it is as difficult as to restrain the wind, which Krishna admits and thereupon proceeds to the true secret of knowledge.

True knowledge, says Krishna as he reveals himself more fully, is knowledge of the Supreme Self, who is taste in the water, light in the sky, sound in space, fragrance in the earth, refulgence in the fire and manliness in human beings. The world, deluded by its confused qualities of goodness, passion and darkness, is unable to comprehend this Absolute Self, but those who do good and have knowledge worship him truly but do not know his nature as pure being. When Arjuna asks the Deity who this supreme being, this Brahman is, the Deity informs him that he is an imperceptible, indestructible being who can be known by the mind of the devotee, since he who is possessed of reverence and gives himself up to continuous meditation attains to that transcendant and divine Being whose brilliance is like that of the sun and who is beyond darkness. Even though the nature of Deity is so hopelessly transcendant it is yet possible for all beings to come to him, even such as are of sinful birth, women, slaves and the like and to this Deity is Arjuna invited to come.

Arjuna has drunk in this divine "nectar," as he calls it, and yet feels no satiety, hence he would have the Deity tell him how he can be known, or by means of what emanations of his divine being he can be recognized. Of such emanations there is no end but the Deity is willing to mention his chief one as these appear in sun and moon, in mountain and forest, in consciousness and love, in the gods and the Vedas. Arjuna is impressed by this description of the Deity and his various manifestations but would have a vision of him so that he may behold the Deity's inexhaustible form. In response to this request the Deity while not revealing just who he is gives the young warrior a vision of himself as a being of violence and destruction, as death and the destroyer of worlds and bids Arjuna follow his terrific example and slay the warriors about him. Before this manifestation of the

Deity in such a fierce form Arjuna bows in reverence and fear, begs for forgiveness and pleads with the Deity to reveal himself in his original form of mildness. After beholding the Deity in his more human form again, Arjuna regains his composure.

Arjuna who has sought in more ways than one to come to an understanding with the Deity now inquires concerning different kinds of devotees of the Supreme Being and which are the best. He learns the characteristics of the true worshipper as that of one who hates no being, is friendly and compassionate, free from self-love, self-restrained and one to whom happiness and misery are both alike. The true devotee, as the Deity goes on to say, is full of devotion, feels neither joy nor sorrow, grieves not nor desires, is alike to both friend and foe and accepts both praise and blame. Such a devotee is dear to the Deity.

Real insight into the nature of being involves both the subject and object of knowledge, moral characteristics in the one and metaphysical forms in the other. The subject of knowledge attains to understanding negatively by the absence of vanity, of ostentation, of hurtfulness and self-love; positively by means of steadiness, purity, self-restraint and the like. When there is constancy in the relation of the individual self to the supreme object of knowledge, then there is indeed what may be called knowledge. The object of knowledge is characterized by its lack of beginning and end so that it cannot be said to be existent or non-existent. It is within all things and yet without them, movable and yet immovable, stands near and far and is both within all radiance and beyond all darkness. Hence when the devotee sees all entities as one he himself becomes one with Brahman.

Of all the entities in the world Krishna is the father, Brahman or Nature the womb in which he casts the seed. In Nature are found the three qualities, or *gunas,* of goodness, passion and darkness which bind the soul down and from which detachment should be sought. Darkness is ignorance, passion is action and both are so associated with goodness that one must be detached from all three that he may enter into the essence of the Divine Being. Those who adhere to goodness go up, the passionate remain in the middle while those who adhere to darkness go down. To transcend these qualities is to become immortal. He who thus transcends these mortal qualities is self-contained, to him pleasure and pain, a stone and a lump of gold, honor and dishonor, friend and foe are alike. Such an enlightened person comes to understand that Brahman is all and in all—light in the sun, nourishment in the herbs, life in the body, the meaning of the Veda and the like. He who knows Brahman in this way knows everything.

In the world there are two classes of beings, the godlike which have been described as devotees and the demoniac. Demoniac persons are ignorant of both action and inaction, declare that the universe is wanting in truth and fixed principle and that it was produced merely by the union of male and female. Such entertain insatiable desire, are full of vanity and adopt false ideas; their end is destruction. In a threefold way they proceed to hell; by lust, anger and avarice. Those who are released from these three ways proceed toward the highest goal with the sacred scriptures as their guide. Men, as Arjuna learns from Krishna, are what their faiths make them, or as the man so the faith. Those who have the quality of goodness worship the gods, those who have the quality of passion worship demons, while those whose quality is that of darkness worship departed spirits.

Finally Arjuna would have the Deity inform him concerning renunciation in its relation to action. True renunciation comes about, explains the Deity, when action from desires is rejected. One may cling to actions of sacrifice, gifts and penance but even such should be performed in a detached manner without regard for their fruits. In the matter of action, as well as in connection with knowledge, the agent of action, intelligence, courage and happiness, it is for Arjuna to realize the presence of the three qualities, or *gunas,* of the good, the passionate and the dark. Knowledge is of the good quality when one sees all things as a single entity; it is passionate when one beholds a variety of entities, and dark when it clings to some single thing. So action is good when it is devoid of attachment, passionate when one is filled with self-love, dark when it is all delusion. Similar distinctions apply to him who acts, to intelligence, courage and happiness.

Krishna has unfolded the mysteries of being for the sake of the young warrior prince who is so dear to him and now bids the youth come to him as to his sole refuge. Has delusion at last been destroyed in the mind of the young man who feared to enter the battle? Yes, the delusion has been destroyed, the young man has discovered the real essence of his being, is free from doubts and is ready to do the bidding of the incarnate god who appeared to him.

THAT A MAN OUGHT SOBERLY TO MEDDLE WITH JUDGING OF DIVINE LAWES

By

Michael Lord of Montaigne

Translated by JOHN FLORIO

MICHAEL EYQUEM DE MONTAIGNE (*1533–1592*) was a French essayist and moralist. After a lengthy college education in law he was appointed as a member of the Court of Aids and later became a city counselor at Bordeaux. When he was 38 he succeeded to his family estate and lived the life of a country gentleman, visiting various capitals of Europe for pleasure. In 1580 he published the first two volumes of his *Essais* which series gave him a front rank in all literary history. A third book containing some of his finest essays appeared in 1588. Some critics believe that now three centuries after his death the circle of his readers widens every year until he has almost as large a following as Shakespeare.

THINGS UNKNOWNE are the true scope of imposture and the subject of Legerdermaine; forasmuch as strangeness itselfe doth first give credit unto matters, and not being subject to our ordinarie, they deprives of meanes to withstand them. To this purpose, said Plato, it is an easie matter to please, speaking of the nature of the Gods, than of mens: for the Auditors ignorance lends a faire and large cariere, and free libertie, to the handling of secret hidden matters. Whence it followeth, that nothing is so firmly beleeved, as that which a man knoweth least; nor are there people more assured in their reports, than such as tell us fables, as Alchemists, Prognosticators, Fortune-tellers, Palmesters, Physitians, *id genus omne,* and such like. To which if I durst, I would joyne a rabble of men, that are ordinaire interpreters and controulers of Gods secret desseignes, presuming to finde out the causes of every accident, and to prie into the secret of Gods divine will, the incomprehensible motives of his works. And howbeit, the continuall verietie and discordance of events drive them from one corner to another, and from East to West, and they will not leave to follow their bowle, and with one small pensill drawe both white and blacke. There is this commendable observance in a certaine Indian nation, who if they chance to be discomfited in any skirmish or battle, they publikely beg pardon of the Sunne, who is their God, as for an unjust action, referring their good or ill fortune to divine reason, submitting their judgment and discourses unto it. It suffiseth a Christian to beleeve, that all things come from God, to receive them from his divine and inscrutable wisdome with thanksgiving, and in what manner soever they are sent him, to take them in good part. But I utterly disalow a common custome amongst us, which is to ground and establish our religion upon the prosperetie of our enterprises. Our beleefe hath other sufficient foundations, and need not be authorized by events. For the people accustomed to these plausible arguments, and agreeing with his tastes, when events sort contrarie and disadvantageous to their expectations, they are in hazard to waver in their faith: As in the civil warres, wherein we are now for religions sake, those which got the advantage, at the conflict of *Rochlebeille,* making great joy and bone-fires for that accident, and using that fortune, as an assured approbation of their faction: when afterward they came to excuse their disasters of *Montcontour* and *Jarnac,* which are scourges and fatherly chastisements: if they have not a people wholly at their mercy, they will easily make him perceive, what it is to take two kinds of corne out of one sacke: and from one and the same mouth to blow hot and cold. It were better to entertaine it with the true foundation of veritie. It was a notable Sea-battle, which was lately gained against the Turkes, under the conduct of *Don Juan* of Austria. But it hath pleased God to make us at other times both see and feele other such, to our no small losse and deteriment. To conclude, it is no easie matter to reduce divine things unto our ballance, so they suffer no impeachment: And he that would yeeld a reason, why

Arrius and *Leo* is Pope, chiefie Principals, and maine supportors of this heresie, died both at severall times, of so semblage and so strange deaths (for being forced through a violent bellyach to goe from their disputations to their close-stoole, both suddenly yeelded up their ghosts on them) and exaggerate that divine vengeance by the circumstance of the place, might also adde the death of *Heliogabalus* unto it, who likewise was slaine upon a privie. But what? *Ireneus* is found to be engaged in like fortune: Gods intent being to teach us, that the good have something else to hope for, and the wicked something else to feare, than the good or bad fortune of this world: He manageth and applieth them according to his secret disposition: and depriveth us of the meanes, thereby foolishly to make our profit. And those that, according to humane reason will thereby prevaile, doe but mocke themselves. They never give one touch of it, that they receive not two for it. *S. Augustine* giveth a notable triall of it upon his adversaries. It is a conflict, no more decided by the armes of memorie, than by the weapons of reason. A man should be satisfied with the light, which it pleaseth the Sunne to communicate unto us by vertue of his beames; and he that shall lift up his eies to take a greater within his body, let him not thinke it strange, if for a reward of his overweening and arrogancie he loseth his sight. *Quis hominum potest scire consilium Dei? aut quis poterit cogitare, quid velit dominus* (Wisd. ix. 13). *Who amongst men can know Gods counsell or who can thinke what God will doe?*

THAT THOU ART

(*Tat tvam asi*)

(From *The Upanishads*)

As THE BEES, my son, make honey by collecting the juices of distant trees, and reduce the juice into one form; and as these juices have no discrimination, as that they might say, I am the juice of this tree or that; in the same manner, my son, all these creatures, when they have become merged in the True (either in deep sleep or in death), know not that they are merged in the True.

Now that which is that subtle essence, in it all that exists has its self. It is the true. It is the Self, and that thou art.

If some one were to strike at the root of this large tree here, it would bleed but live. If he were to strike at its stem, it would bleed but live. Pervaded by the living Self that tree stands firm, drinking in its nourishment and rejoicing. But if the life (the living Self) leaves one of its branches, that branch withers; if it leaves a second, that branch withers; if it leaves a third, that branch withers. In exactly the same manner, my son, know this. Thus he spoke: This body indeed withers and dies when the living Self has left it; the living Self dies not.

That which is that subtle essence, in it all that exists has its self. It is the True. It is the Self and that thou art.

"Fetch me from thence a fruit of the Nyagrodha tree."

"Here is one, sir."

"Break it."

"It is broken, sir."

"What do you see there?"

"These seeds, almost infinitesimal."

"Break one of them."

"It is broken, sir."

"What do you see there?"

"Not anything, sir."

The father said: "My son, that subtle essence which you do not perceive there, of that very essence this great Nyagrodha tree exists."

That which is the subtle essence, in it all that exists has its self. It is the True. It is the Self, and that thou art.

Those who depart from hence without having discovered the Self and those true desires, for them there is no freedom in all the worlds. But those who depart from hence, after having discovered the Self and those true desires, for them there is freedom in all the worlds.

And he who desires the world of friends, by his mere will the friends come to receive him, and having obtained the world of the friends he is happy.

And he who desires the world of perfumes and garlands, by his mere will perfumes and garlands come to him, and having obtained the world of perfumes and garlands he is happy.

And he who desires the world of song, by his mere will song and music come to him, and having obtained the world of song and music he is happy.

And he who desires the world of women, by his mere will women come to receive him, and having obtained the world of women he is happy.

AUTHOR INDEX

AUTHOR INDEX

AUTHOR INDEX

1881